D1491133

Chemistry *and* Biochemistry *of* Plant Pigments

Chemistry *and*
Biochemistry *of*
Plant Pigments

Edited by

T. W. GOODWIN

University College of Wales
Aberystwyth, Wales

ACADEMIC PRESS · LONDON *and* NEW YORK · 1965

ACADEMIC PRESS INC. (LONDON) LTD
BERKELEY SQUARE HOUSE
LONDON, W.1

U.S. Edition published by

ACADEMIC PRESS INC.
111 FIFTH AVENUE
NEW YORK, NEW YORK 10003

Library of Congress Catalog Card Number: 64–24671

PRINTED IN GREAT BRITAIN BY
SPOTTISWOODE, BALLANTYNE & CO. LTD.
LONDON AND COLCHESTER

LIST OF CONTRIBUTORS

L. BOGORAD, *Department of Botany, The University of Chicago, Chicago 37, Illinois, U.S.A.*

H. A. BORTHWICK, *Agricultural Research Service, U.S. Department of Agriculture, Beltsville, Maryland, U.S.A.*

J. H. BURNETT, *Department of Botany, The University of Newcastle upon Tyne, England*

W. L. BUTLER, *Agricultural Marketing Service and Agricultural Research Service, U.S. Department of Agriculture, Beltsville, Maryland, U.S.A.*

C. O. CHICHESTER, *Department of Food Science and Technology, University of California, Davis, California, U.S.A.*

B. H. DAVIES, *Department of Biochemistry and Agricultural Biochemistry, University College of Wales, Aberystwyth, Wales*

T. W. GOODWIN, *Department of Biochemistry and Agricultural Biochemistry, University College of Wales, Aberystwyth, Wales*

H. GRISEBACH, *Chemisches Laboratorium der Universität Freiburg i.Br., Freiburg i.Br., Germany*

J. B. HARBORNE, *John Innes Institute, Hertford, England*

S. B. HENDRICKS, *Agricultural Marketing Service and Agricultural Research Service, U.S. Department of Agriculture, Beltsville, Maryland, U.S.A.*

MARGARET HOLDEN, *Department of Biochemistry, Rothamsted Experimental Station, Harpenden, Herts, England*

A. S. HOLT, *Division of Biosciences, National Research Council, Ottawa, Canada*

T. O. M. NAKAYAMA, *Department of Food Science and Technology, University of California, Davis, California, U.S.A.*

C. Ó HEOCHA, *Department of Biochemistry, University College, Galway, Ireland*

H. W. SIEGELMAN, *Agricultural Marketing Service and Agricultural Research Service, U.S. Department of Agriculture, Beltsville, Maryland, U.S.A.*

T. SWAIN, *Low Temperature Research Station, Cambridge, England*

R. H. THOMSON, *Department of Chemistry, University of Aberdeen, Scotland*

B. C. L. WEEDON, *Department of Chemistry, Queen Mary College, Mile End Road, London, England*

C. P. WHITTINGHAM, *Department of Botany, Queen Mary College, London, England*

PREFACE

In August 1962 a colloquium on the "Biochemistry of Plant Pigments" was held by the Biochemical Society in Aberystwyth. It was successful in bringing together interested scientists from a number of countries to discuss critically the latest developments in this field. However, it also clearly demonstrated the need for collecting in one volume the scattered information discussed, and by early 1963 the Editor had planned the book and persuaded the various authors to take part in the venture and to prepare their contributions by early 1964. The coverage of the colloquium was extended to include the chemistry of the plant pigments and an analytical section was also planned. All the contributors have international reputations and the fact that they all willingly agreed to undertake the work re-emphasizes the need for this volume. A few manuscripts inevitably failed to be produced on time, but apart from this the co-operation of the contributors with the Editor has been excellent, and no Editor could have had an easier assignment. Furthermore, the expertise of the Publishers in dealing with late manuscripts has resulted in only a minimum delay in the appearance of the book. Owing to unforeseen circumstances it has not been possible to include a projected Chapter on plant cytochromes.

The plan of the book is simple; it is divided into four main sections, the first dealing with the chemistry and biosynthesis of the various pigments; the second and third with their function and metabolism respectively; and the fourth with analytical procedures used in dealing with plant pigments. All the contributors are still actively concerned in research in the speciality on which they write and this has resulted in critically written, forward-looking chapters in which not only is the well-established information thoroughly reviewed but the gaps in our knowledge are clearly indicated, and sufficient suggestions for future investigations are made, either implicitly or explicitly, to keep an army of research workers busy for a long time. The detailed analytical chapters, considered in association with Parts I, II and III, should be of particular value.

Biochemical investigations on higher plants have been relatively few compared with those on animals and protista. During the past few years, however, more and more biochemists have become interested in this field and, in spite of the many difficulties in dealing with higher plants, the number of investigations reported in the Journals is increasing rapidly each year. This book should be of background value to those who are contemplating entry into the field of plant biochemistry via plant pigments; it should also be useful to senior undergraduate students in biochemistry who are finding that more and more plant biochemistry is appearing in their courses every year. Their instructors may also find useful suggestions for laboratory exercises in the analytical sections. Finally, the "Chemistry and Biochemistry of Plant Pigments" should appeal to the increasing number of botanists who are keen to specialize in the more biochemical aspects of plant physiology.

The final stages of the editing of this volume were carried out whilst the Editor was holder of a National Science Foundation Senior Foreign Scientist Fellowship at the University of California, Davis.

Dr. B. H. Davies kindly prepared the subject index.

T. W. Goodwin

Department of Biochemistry and Agricultural Biochemistry
University College of Wales
Aberystwyth

November, 1964

CONTENTS

PART II: FUNCTION

PART IV: ANALYTICAL METHODS

17. Chlorophylls

MARGARET HOLDEN

18. Analysis of Carotenoid Pigments

B. H. DAVIES

19. Analytical Methods for Flavonoids

T. SWAIN

PART I: NATURE, DISTRIBUTION AND BIOSYNTHESIS

Chapter I

NATURE, PROPERTIES AND DISTRIBUTION OF CHLOROPHYLLS *

A. S. HOLT

*Division of Biosciences, National Research Council,
Ottawa, Canada*

I. INTRODUCTION

Chlorophyll is the general name of green pigments in organisms capable of photosynthesis. It was first used by Pelletier and Caventou (1818) to describe the pigment complex responsible for the green colouration of leaves. Years later, it was shown by Stokes (1864) to be a mixture of yellow pigments plus two different green pigments. Sorby (1873) obtained the green pigments relatively pure and published their absorption spectra; he referred to them as blue and "yellow" chlorophylls.

* Issued as N.R.C. No. 7931.

Twsett (1906) separated them using column chromatography and called them chlorophylls α and β, which later became a and b. The distribution of the different chlorophylls known at present throughout the plant kingdom is given in Table I.

TABLE I

Distribution of Chlorophylls among Photosynthetic Organisms*

Organism	Pigment				
	Chlorophyll				
	a	b	c	d	e
Higher plants, ferns and mosses	+	+	−	−	−
Algae†					
Chlorophyta	+	+	−	−	−
Chrysophyta					
Xanthophyceae	+	−	−	−	+ ‡
Chrysophyceae	+	−	±	−	−
Bacillariophyceae	+	−	+	−	−
Euglenophyta	+	+	−	−	−
Pyrrophyta					
Cryptophyceae	+	−	+	−	−
Dinophyceae	+	−	+	−	−
Phaeophyta	+	−	+	−	−
Rhodophyta	+	−	−	+	−
Cyanophyta	+	−	−	−	−

Organism	Bacterio-chlorophyll		Chlorobium Chlorophylls	
	a	b	650	660
Bacteria				
Thio- and Athiorhodaceae	+ or	+	−	−
Chlorobacteriaceae	+	−	+ or	+

* See Fischer and Stern (1940), Strain (1958), Haxo and Fork (1959), Allen *et al.* (1960), Stanier and Smith (1960) and Eimhjellen *et al.* (1963).
† Taxonomic classification according to Prescott (1962).
‡ Chlorophyll *e* has been isolated from only one organism; it seems to resemble chlorophyllide *c* (Strain, 1951).

II. CHEMICAL PROPERTIES

A. STRUCTURE

Chlorophylls may be regarded as magnesium complexes of compounds derived from phorbin (Fig. 1), which, in turn, may be regarded as the dihydro derivative of porphin (Fig. 2), but with the addition of the isocyclic ring V. Individual pyrrole nuclei are numbered I–IV; the outer (β-pyrrole) positions of the nuclei are numbered 1–8; the methine bridge carbon atoms are designated α–δ.

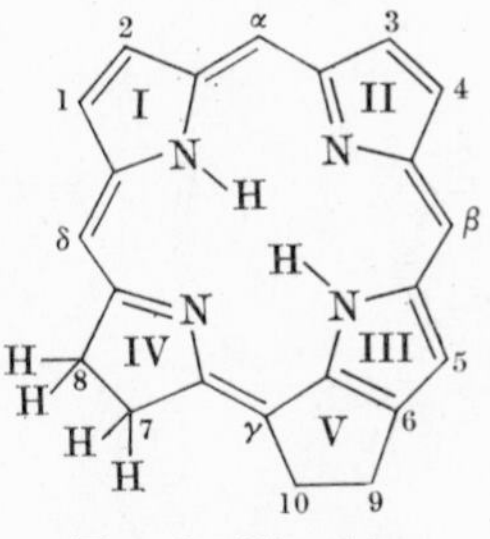

FIG. 1. Phorbin.

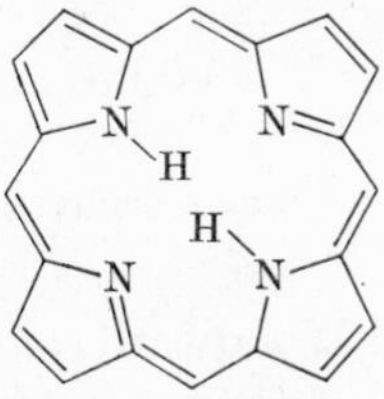

FIG. 2. Porphin.

Clarification of the structures of chlorophylls a and b (Fig. 3) involved the work of many investigators, among whom were Willstätter, Stoll, Conant and Hans Fischer. By 1940 the latter, after many years of synthetic, analytical and degradative investigations on both the blood pigments and chlorophylls, established the essential structures of chlorophylls a, b and bacteriochlorophyll a.

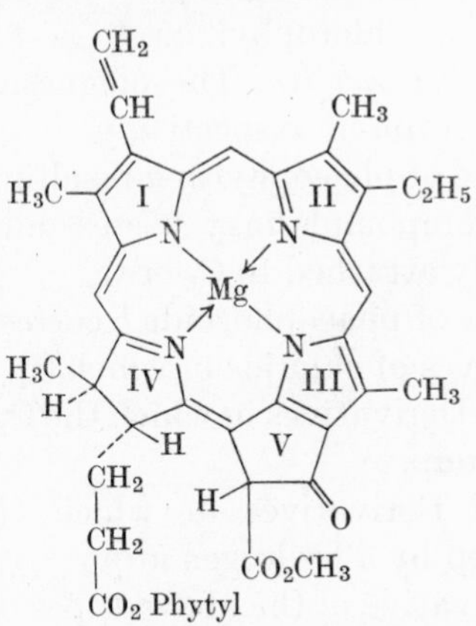

FIG. 3. Chlorophyll a. For chlorophyll b: replace —CH_3 at C_3 with —CHO. For chlorophyll d: replace —$CH=CH_2$ at C_2 with —CHO.

Confirmation of the structure of chlorophyll a by synthesis was advanced by Fischer $et\ al.$ (1940) to the stage of phaeoporphyrin a_5 (Fig. 4), a porphyrin isomeric with phaeophorbide a. Recently, Strell $et\ al.$ (1960)

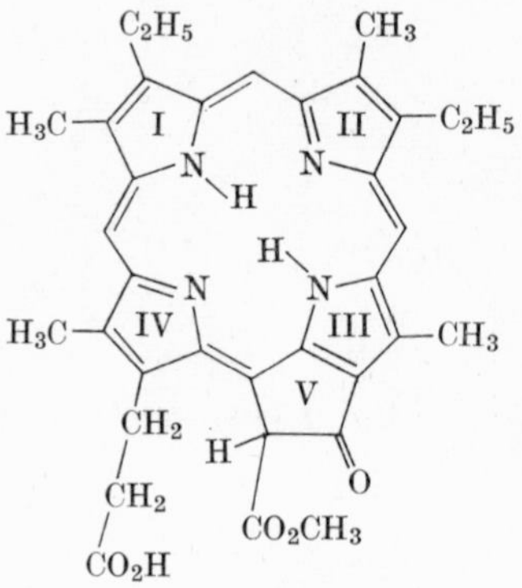

FIG. 4. Phaeoporphyrin a_5.

using Fischer's methods, and Woodward $et\ al.$ (1960) using an ingenious, novel synthesis, prepared derivatives readily convertible into phaeophorbide a, the conversion of which to chlorophyll a had previously been shown to be possible.

B. NOMENCLATURE

Terms used in chlorophyll chemistry include:

Chlorophyllide. The derivative resulting from removal of the alcohol esterified to the C_7 propionic acid group.

Phytyl chlorophyllide a. Chlorophyll a.

Phaeophorbide and Phaeophytin. The magnesium-free derivatives of chlorophyllide and chlorophyll, respectively.

Chlorins. Derivatives of phaeophytin a resulting from cleavage of the isocyclic ring; these compounds may possess all, some or none of the carbon atoms originally attached to C_6 or C_γ.

Rhodins. Derivatives of phaeophorbide b corresponding to chlorins.

Purpurins. Derivatives of chlorins in which C_{10} has been oxidized.

"Meso" compounds. Derivatives in which the C_2-vinyl group has been reduced to an ethyl group.

"Pyro" compounds. Derivatives in which the C_{10}-carbomethoxy group has been replaced by a hydrogen atom.

Porphyrin. Any derivative of the above types of compounds in which Ring IV has been oxidized by removal of the hydrogen atoms at C_7 and C_8, i.e. a substituted porphin. Porphyrins which possess a C_2-vinyl group in place of an ethyl group are referred to as vinyl porphyrins, e.g. vinyl phaeoporphyrin a_5 (protophaeophorbide a). The subscript refers to the number of oxygen atoms in the compound.

Porphyrinogen. A hexahydro porphyrin whose methine bridges have been reduced to methylene.

Phyllin. Any chlorophyll derivative containing magnesium.

Farnesol. 3,7,11-trimethyl-2,6,10-dodecatrien-1-ol; $C_{15}H_{25}OH$ (*trans, trans*; Rapoport and Hamlow, 1961).

Phytol. 3,7,11,15-tetramethyl-2-hexadocen-1-ol; $C_{20}H_{39}OH$ (*trans*; Burrell *et al.*, 1959).

Hydrochloric acid number. The per cent hydrochloric acid (w/w) which extracts two-thirds of a metal-free derivative from an equal volume of ether.

C. REACTIONS

Below are listed some of the many reactions which have proved useful for the characterization of chlorophylls. In the main, only references not included in Willstätter and Stoll (1913), Fischer and Stern (1940), Rothemund (1944) and Aronoff (1960) are given.

1. *Removal of Magnesium and the Preparation of other Metal Derivatives*

Addition of dilute, aqueous mineral acid to a miscible solvent containing a phyllin causes immediate removal of magnesium with a consequent change in the visible absorption spectrum. Magnesium can be reintroduced by a Grignard reagent or its alkoxy derivative. If the phyllin is to retain the capacity to give a positive Molisch phase test, the latter reaction must be carried out in the absence of oxygen, otherwise it will be "allomerized".

Tracer experiments with ^{28}Mg *in vivo* or in aqueous acetone solution have shown that the magnesium of chlorophyll is not exchangeable (Becker and Sheline, 1955; Aronoff, 1962).

Other metals, e.g. zinc, mercury, copper, silver, iron, are introduced from acetic acid solutions, or as chlorides or acetates from methanolic solutions containing a small amount of pyridine.

2. *Removal or Replacement of the C_7 esterifying alcohol*

This is removed enzymatically with chlorophyllase (see Chapter 17) or hydrolytically with acid or alkali. The product(s) is either a free acid, or an ester resulting from transesterification, depending upon the conditions used. Two alcohols have been identified: phytol from chlorophylls *a, b* and bacteriochlorophyll *a*, and farnesol from *Chlorobium* chlorophylls "650" and "660" (Rapoport and Hamlow, 1961; Holt *et al.*, 1963).

3. C_2-Vinyl Group

a. *Reduction.* Hydriodic acid (65°), hydrazine-hydrate in pyridine (Fischer and Gibian, 1941), and palladium-hydrogen in organic solvents reduce the vinyl group to an ethyl group.

b. *Oxidation.* Permanganate in acetone yields several products, the most readily identifiable of which, are the glycoyl, the formyl and the carboxyl derivatives (Fischer and Walter, 1941; Holt and Morley, 1959). Treatment of the glycoyl derivative with periodate yields the C_2-formyl derivative.

c. *Hydration.* Warm hydrogen bromide-acetic acid or warm aqueous hydrochloric acid yields the C_2-α-hydroxyethyl derivative, which in turn can be oxidized to the C_2-acetyl derivative or dehydrated back to the vinyl group.

d. *Oxo-reaction.* Dilute hydriodic acid in acetic acid at room temperature converts into a vinyl or α-hydroxy ethyl group into an acetyl group. At the same time phorbins, chlorins and purpurins are changed to porphyrins (see Section II, C, 6). This reaction helped to establish the presence of a vinyl group in chlorophyll a.

e. *Adduct formation.* Diazoacetic acid adds to a vinyl group to yield the cyclopropylcarboxylate derivative. Degradation with chromic acid yields the maleimide corresponding to Ring I; if the vinyl group is not protected Ring I is decomposed. This reaction also helped to establish the presence of the vinyl group in chlorophylls a and b.

4. Ring V

a. *Molisch phase test and allomerization.* The classical test for the presence of the cyclopentanone ring plus the C_{10}-hydrogen atom and carbomethoxy group involves generation of a reddish-brown intermediate when an alkali is added to a chlorophyll solution. In the presence of oxygen the original colour rapidly returns.

Chlorophyll preparations that fail to give the phase test are said to be "allomerized" (this term is not applicable to "pyro" compounds) and were first observed when pure chlorophylls a and b were stored in methanol or ethanol for long periods of time. It is now known that "allomerization" involves slow oxidation by oxygen of undetectable amounts of the intermediate generated by traces of alkali. Under appropriate conditions the intermediate of a phaeophytin can be kept indefinitely and its infrared and visible absorption spectra recorded (Weller, 1954; Holt, 1958, 1963). It is thought that the intermediate is either an enolate ion of the β-keto ester or a diradical arising from this ion (Weller, 1954).

The intermediate is also generated from chlorin e_6-trimethyl ester (and its analogues in other pigments) if conditions are adjusted to effect ring closure.

b. Cleavage. Hot, rapid saponification of phaeophytin *a* in strong alkali removes phytol and cleaves ring V to yield chlorin e_6 (C_6-COOH, C_γ-CH$_2$COOH). Under other conditions, e.g. boiling, dilute methanolic potassium hydroxide, methanolic hydrogen chloride, or diazomethane-methanol, chlorin e_6-trimethylester is produced. The quantitative cleavage by diazomethane-methanol has been asserted to be the most reliable test for determing the absence of allomerized pigment.

Ring V is also cleaved hydrolytically by amines to yield the C_6-acid amide of chlorin e_6-diester.

c. Decarboxylation. Refluxing in pyridine or heating to elevated temperatures removes the C_{10}-carbomethoxy group to yield "pyro" derivatives containing an unsubstituted cyclopentanone ring. They do not give a positive phase test. However, under the same conditions they are readily oxidized by oxygen to yield a ring diketone (H. J. Kende and A. S. Holt, unpublished).

5. *Carbonyl Groups*

These groups form oximes, semicarbazones, acetals and hemiacetals and undergo reduction to an alcohol with borohydride (Holt, 1959) or complete reduction with the Wolff-Kishner reaction. The spectral shifts accompanying reduction in the di- and tetrahydroporphyrin series help to indicate the particular pyrrole ring to which the group is attached.

The formyl group of phaeophytin *b* reacts also with cysteine (Tyray, 1944), and Girard's reagent "T" (Wetherell and Hendrickson, 1959). The latter reagent converts the *b* series into water-soluble derivatives and leaves the *a* series unreacted, thus permitting their separation.

6. *Porphyrin Formation*

Di- and tetrahydroporphyrins can be converted into porphyrins by several methods. A common procedure is to reduce the nucleus to a colourless porphyrinogen, followed by subsequent aerobic oxidation to a porphyrin. The reagents include hydriodic acid in acetic acid (65°) or other solvents, catalytic hydrogenation or powdered iron in formic acid. The latter method reduces vinyl groups to ethyl groups to a much lesser extent than do the previous two. Direct oxidation of Ring IV in simple chlorins can be effected by silver acetate-acetic acid, or by oxygen in acetic acid containing a catalytic amount of copper acetate.

Other methods include heating to elevated temperature in acid, basic or inert solutions, e.g. 1% hydrochloric acid in acetic acid (185°) in the absence of air, or 35% methanolic potassium hydroxide for up to 5 h at temperatures ranging from 130 to 200°. These methods frequently require that vinyl or hydroxyethyl groups be converted into ethyl groups to prevent their transformation. The latter method was used

1*

(Willstätter and Stoll, 1913) to prepare rhodo-, phyllo- and pyrropor-phyrin (Fig. 5).

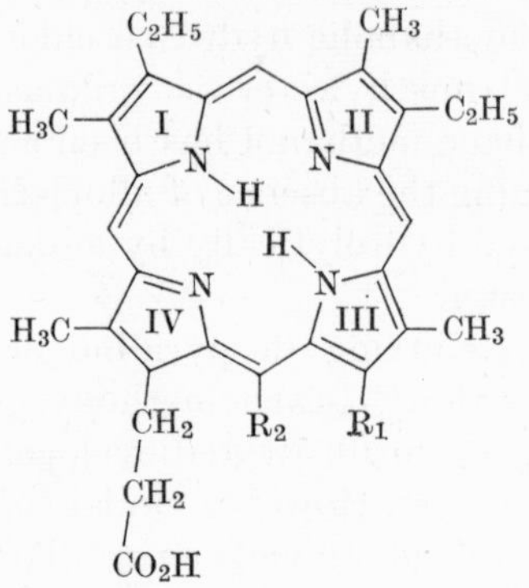

FIG. 5. Rhodoporphyrin (R_1 = COOH, R_2 = H); Phylloporphyrin (R_1 = H; R_2 = CH$_3$); Pyrroporphyrin (R_1 and R_2 = H).

7. *Reductive and Oxidative Degradation*

Drastic reduction by hydriodic acid in acetic acid, or oxidation by chromic acid in sulphuric acid breaks the aromatic nucleus into sub-stituted monocyclic compounds which correspond to the original pyrrole rings. Reduction complicates the analytical problem because each pyrrole ring can yield as many as four different pyrroles. Oxidation yields but one imide per pyrrole ring but has the disadvantage of de-composing those rings with unstable substituents, e.g. vinyl, carboxyl, formyl or hydroxyethyl groups.

The dihydrohaematinic acid imide obtained on oxidation of pyro-phaeophorbide *a* is identical with a synthetic product that probably has the *trans* configuration (Ficken *et al.*, 1956).

III. PHYSICAL PROPERTIES

A. SOLUBILITY

Chlorophylls are usually soluble in organic solvents such as ether, acetone, methanol, chloroform and pyridine, and insoluble (when pure) in hydrocarbons. Free acids are less soluble than esters. Phaeophytins and phaeophorbides are readily soluble in warm acetic and formic acids, and also in aqueous hydrochloric acid, depending on their acid number. This constant is lowest for a free acid, increasing with increasing chain length of the esterifying alcohol. Ring cleavage to yield chlorins or reduction of carbonyl groups to alcohols causes a marked drop in the acid number. Table II presents the acid numbers of some representative chlorophyll derivatives. By partition chromatography between ether

TABLE II

Hydrochloric Acid Numbers of Chlorophyll Derivatives

Compound	Acid number
Phaeophytin a	29
Methyl phaeophorbide a	16
Phaeophorbide a	15
Chlorin e_6-trimethyl ester	8
Phaeophytin b	35
Methyl phaeophorbide b	21
Phaeophorbide b	19·5
Rhodin g_7-trimethyl ester	12–13
Methyl phaeophorbide d	16·5
Bacteriophaeophytin a	> 36
Methyl bacteriophaeophorbide a	> 22
Bacterio(a)-chlorin e_6-trimethyl ester	16–17
Chlorobium phaeophytins "660"	18
Chlorobium phaeophorbides "660"	7–11
Chlorobium phaeophytins "650"	22
Chlorobium phaeophorbides "650"	9–13
Protophaeophorbide a (vinyl phaeoporphyrin a_5)	11–12
Phaeophorbide(s) c	12

and hydrochloric acid with Celite as a solid support, phaeophorbides differing by only one methylene group have been readily separated from each other (Hughes and Holt, 1962).

B. CRYSTALLIZATION

Willstätter and Stoll (1913) described chlorophyll precipitated by slow evaporation from ether-petroleum ether as microcystalline. Chlorophyll a formed thin, lancet-shaped leaflets which fused at 117–120°. Chlorophyll b sintered between 86 and 92°. Hanson (1939) found that such preparations did not show a sharp diffraction pattern. Jacobs *et al.* (1953, 1954) reported the first X-ray data on chlorophylls a, b and bacterio-chlorophyll a. These preparations were obtained by evaporating ether solutions of chromatographically pure samples in the presence of water. Such samples, when dispersed in pentane, had their "red" absorption peaks shifted 80–100 mμ to longer wavelengths from that in solution. This had been found earlier to be characteristic of dispersions of micro-crystals of ethyl chlorophyllides. Electron micrographs showed that the crystals occurred as extremely thin, triangular platelets. Donnay (1959) calculated 2·03 molecules per unit cell. Klesper *et al.* (1961) have found that X-ray diffraction distinguishes between closely related porphyrins, including isomers, when no differences can be detected from absorption spectra or melting points.

C. MELTING POINTS

Crystalline esters of chlorophyll derivatives melt at lower temperatures than do those of free acids, thereby reducing the possibility of decomposition. Mixed melting points are helpful in determining the identity of two compounds. Occasionally, in the porphyrin series, polymorphism is encountered which is often eliminated by converting the compound into its copper derivative.

D. ABSORPTION SPECTRA

1. *Visible Absorption Spectra*

Prior to the study of infrared and proton magnetic resonance spectra, the visible absorption spectra of chlorophylls and related compounds were the most used physical properties for determining the nature of substituents. For quantitative purposes either the molar (α_M) or the specific (α_{sp}) absorption coefficient can be plotted. These constants are defined by the following:

$$\frac{\alpha_M}{\text{Mol. Wt.}} = \alpha_{sp} = \frac{l}{Cl}\log_{10}\frac{I_0}{I}$$

where C = grams per litre and l = centimetres path length.

Neutral, metal-free porphyrins usually have four absorption bands between 500 and 700 mμ, plus a strong Soret at about 400 mμ. Stern and Wenderlein (1936) distinguished three types of porphyrin spectra (Fig. 6, A, B, C). Aetio spectra have absorption bands which increase regularly in intensity; rhodo spectra have Band III more intense than Bands II or IV; phyllo spectra have Band III less intense than Bands II or IV.

Aetio spectra are characteristic of porphyrins possessing non-chromophoric groups (methyl, ethyl, acetic acid, propionic acid) in place of the hydrogen atoms of porphin at positions 1–8. They also result if a β-chromophoric group (keto, formyl, carboxyl, vinyl) occurs under the following conditions: (1) with an alkyl methine bridge substituent, (2) with a second chromophore on an adjacent ring or adjacent methine bridge. Conversion of a β-carbonyl group to its oxime produces an aetio spectrum.

Rhodo spectra result from the presence of the C_9 keto group of Ring V and from β-carbonyl or carboxyl groups. In the absence of a β-carbonyl group retention of the rhodo spectrum by an oxime is a diagnostic criterion for Ring V and its C_9 keto group. Under certain conditions: (1) if the C_{10} carbomethoxy group is present or (2) a second chromophore is present on an opposite ring, Band II absorbs more intensely than Band IV. The resulting type of spectrum is called "oxo-rhodo". In the absence of the C_{10} carbomethoxy group, as in the case of phylloerythrin, Bands II and IV absorb equally.

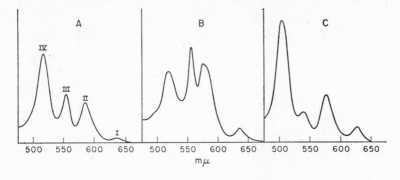

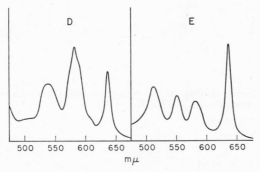

Fig. 6. Porphyrin Spectra. A = Aetio; B = Oxorhodo (Band II > Band IV); Rhodo (Band IV > Band II); D and E (see text).

Phyllo spectra are characteristic of substituted porphyrins without a chromophore but with alkyl methine bridge substituents.

In Fig. 6, two other unnamed types of spectra are presented. Curve D was obtained when Ring V of phylloerythrin was converted into a ring diketone; Curve E, when the C_9 keto group of the diketone was reduced to an alcohol.

Dihydroporphyrins are characterized by two types of spectra: (1) the "chlorin" type of phaeophytin a (Fig. 7) and (2) the "rhodin" type of phaeophytin b (Fig. 8). As a result of the reduction of Ring IV both have a strong "red" absorption maximum. Relative to that of a porphyrin they are shifted 20–25 mμ to longer wavelengths and absorb forty to fifty times more intensely.

Reduction of the C_3-formyl group of the b series converts the "rhodin" spectrum into a "chlorin" spectrum with an accompanying shift of the "red" maximum of 15 to 20 mμ to longer wavelengths. Reduction of the C_2-vinyl group of both series of compounds (or its oxidation to a glycol or hydroxyethyl group) causes the maximum to shift 8–10 mμ to shorter wavelengths. Oxidation to a carboxyl, acetyl or formyl group

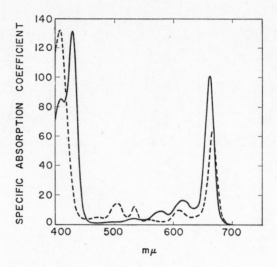

FIG. 7. Absorption spectra of chlorophyll *a* (solid line) and phaeophytin *a* (broken line) in ether. Smith and Benitez (1954, 1955).

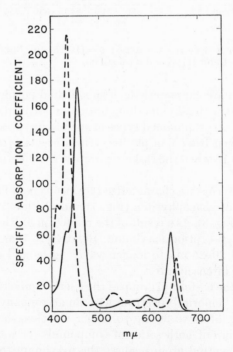

FIG. 8. Absorption spectra of chlorophyll *b* (solid line) and phaeophytin *b* (broken line) in ether. Smith and Benitez (1954, 1955).

causes increasing shifts to longer wavelengths. Cleavage of Ring V leaving hydrogen, methyl, carboxyl or carboxymethyl groups on C_γ and hydrogen or a carboxyl group on C_6 does not change the type of spectrum, or cause considerable spectral shift of the "red" maximum (except in the case of the phyllins whose maxima are shifted approximately 20 mμ to shorter wavelengths). Neither removal of the C_{10}-carbomethoxy group and its replacement by a hydrogen atom, nor replacement of the C_{10}-hydrogen atom by a hydroxy or alkoxy group has a significant effect on the spectrum. Reduction of the C_9-keto group causes a shift to shorter wavelengths. Oxidation of pyrophaeophorbide a to yield the ring diketone causes a shift to longer wavelengths; reduction of the C_9-keto group of the diketone causes the "red" maximum to return to its former wavelength.

Tetrahydroporphyrins, typified by bacteriochlorophyll a (Fig. 12, p. 20) also have strong "red" absorption maxima. As a result of the reduction of ring II this maximum is located in the near infrared portion of the spectrum, at approximately 800 mμ.

Introduction of magnesium into either di- or tetrahydroporphyrins causes no change in the type of spectrum as compared to the change observed on its introduction into porphyrins (compare Fig. 6B and Fig. 9).

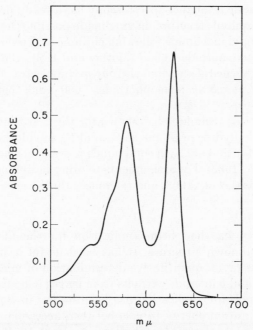

Fig. 9. Absorption spectrum of chlorophyllide c-dimethylester (Fraction 2) in ether (J. W. F. Wasley, J. W. Purdie and A. S. Holt, unpublished).

2. *Infrared and Proton Magnetic Resonance Spectra*

Formyl, acetyl, O-acetyl, ester, carboxyl and hydroxyl groups are detectable in the infrared spectra of chlorophylls and their derivatives. (Falk and Willis, 1951; Holt and Jacobs, 1955). Approximate frequencies of such groups are given in Table III.

TABLE III

Infrared Absorption Bands of Substituent Groups of Phaeophorbides

Group	cm^{-1}
Formyl (C_2)	1,675
Acetyl (C_2)	1,665–1,675
O-Acetyl (C_2)	1,725
Formyl (C_2)	1,675
Formyl (C_3)	1,665
Ester (C_7)	1,720–1,740
Carboxyl (C_7)	1,700
OH (C_2)	3,580
OH (C_{10})	3,580

Proton magnetic resonance spectroscopy has already proved useful in studies of chlorophyll structure, having made possible the identification of methyl n-propyl maleimide following chromic acid oxidation of crude *Chlorobium* phaeophorbide "660" (Morley and Holt, 1961) and having indicated the presence of an isobutyl group in the spectra of four fractions obtained from *Chlorobium* phaeophorbides "650" and "660" (Holt *et al.*, 1963).

In addition, this technique has shown for the first time the presence of exchangeable hydrogen atoms at C_γ and C_δ in chlorins (Woodward and Škarić, 1961), and at C_{10} in compounds possessing a cyclopentanone ring (Katz *et al.*, 1963). For assignments to other individual proton substituents see Closs *et al.* (1963) and references therein.

E. FLUORESCENCE

This property has had little application for the identification of pigments of unknown structure. It has been useful in other respects, among which is rapid, quantitative determination of micro amounts of chlorophylls *a* and *b* in crude extracts from leaves (Goodwin, 1947).

Its most important application has been its use in the study of the transfer of excitation energy *in vivo* between accessory pigments and chlorophylls *a* or bacteriochlorophyll *a* (Duysens, 1951, 1952; French and Young, 1952; Rabinowitch, 1945, 1951, 1956) and also its relation to the primary photochemical processes of photosynthesis (Duysens and Sweers, 1963).

Fluorescence spectra of the various chlorophylls have been given by French *et al.* (1956) and French (1960).

IV. PROPERTIES OF SPECIFIC CHLOROPHYLLS

A. CHLOROPHYLLS a AND b

The properties of these pigments have been outlined in the previous sections. Their molecular structures (Fig. 3) differ only by the C_3-formyl group of chlorophyll b. The presence of this group moves the red absorption maximum from 660 mμ to 643 mμ (Figs. 7 and 8, p. 14), and lowers the absorption coefficient.

One measure of the purity of chlorophylls is the ratio of the absorbancies of the "blue" and "red" maxima, which in the case of chlorophyll a is 1·31 to 1·32. Recent claims of higher purity indicated by a lower figure (Anderson and Calvin, 1962) have been refuted (Perkins and Roberts, 1963).

In vivo chlorophyll a absorbs maximally at three different wavelengths, namely 673, 683 and 694 mμ (French *et al.*, 1959). On extraction with organic solvent and chromatographic purification the chlorophyll a zone is homogeneous. A somewhat similar situation is also found in the case of bacteriochlorophyll a. The extent to which these different maxima are the result of association between individual molecules of chlorophyll a or the result of complex formation with different proteins is not yet known. *In vivo* chlorophyll b absorbs at 650 mμ.

B. CHLOROPHYLLIDE c (CHLOROFUCINE)

This pigment was discovered in extracts of "olive-coloured sea weeds" by Stokes (1864). Sorby (1873) named it "chlorofucine" and published its absorption spectrum as observed through a visual spectroscope. For many years it was believed to be an artifact (Willstätter and Page, 1914). Strain and Manning (1942) and Strain *et al.* (1943) showed beyond reasonable doubt that it is not. Since then its presence *in vivo* has been indicated by absorption at 640 mμ (French and Elliott, 1958).

In agreement with previous investigations (Strain and Manning, 1942; Smith and Benitez, 1954, 1955) it has been found (J. W. F. Wasley, J. W. Purdie and A. S. Holt, unpublished) that several fractions are obtainable. All occur as free acids. The wavelengths of their absorption maxima are essentially identical; however, the ratios of their absorbancies differ. A portion of the visible spectrum of one of the fractions is given in Fig. 9. The methoxyl contents of the mono and the dimethyl esters indicate that its molecular weight is between 550 and 600. Recently, Jeffrey (1963) calculated a molecular weight of more than 1,000.

Its magnesium-free derivative has an oxo-rhodo type spectrum (see Fig. 6B, p. 13), reminiscent of vinyl phaeoporphyrin a_5. It gives a positive phase test and yields an aetio spectrum on treatment with methanolic hydrogen chloride (Granick, 1949), showing the presence of the cyclopentanone ring and its usual C_{10} substituents. Chlorophyllide c and its derivatives are extremely insoluble in most solvents, except pyridine.

C. CHLOROPHYLL d

This pigment was discovered as a minor constituent accompanying chlorophyll a in extracts of various species of Rhodophyceae (Manning and Strain, 1943). Smith and Benitez (1954, 1955) prepared chromatographically pure samples of the phyllin and phaeophytin. Holt and Morley

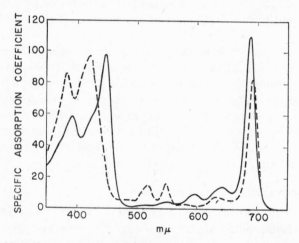

FIG. 10. Absorption spectra of chlorophyll d (solid line) and phaeophytin d (broken line) in ether (Smith and Benitez, 1954, 1955).

(1959) found that permanganate in acetone converted chlorophyll a into its 2-desvinyl-2-formyl derivative. The visible absorption spectra of the phyllin and the phaeophytin matched exactly those previously published (Fig. 10). Holt (1961) obtained chlorophyll d from three species of red algae and compared some of its chemical and chromatographic properties with those of the product obtained from chlorophyll a. It was concluded that the two samples were identical. It was not possible, however, to establish whether the pigment is an artifact of extraction or not.

Sagromsky (1960) found a spectral change from 667 to 695 mμ when a chlorophyll extract from red algae was exposed to 2% methanolic potassium hydroxide for some hours. However, the presence of a formyl group was not investigated and the product may well have been a purpurin resulting from allomerization (Holt, 1958).

The formyl group is readily converted into a dimethylacetal group (Holt and Morley, 1959), yielding a product previously referred to as an "iso" derivative (Manning and Strain, 1943).

D. BACTERIOCHLOROPHYLLS a AND b

Bacteriochlorophyll a (Fig. 11) was shown by Schneider (1934) to contain magnesium, to give a positive phase test, to yield a phaeophorbide which contained one methoxyl group and to be convertible

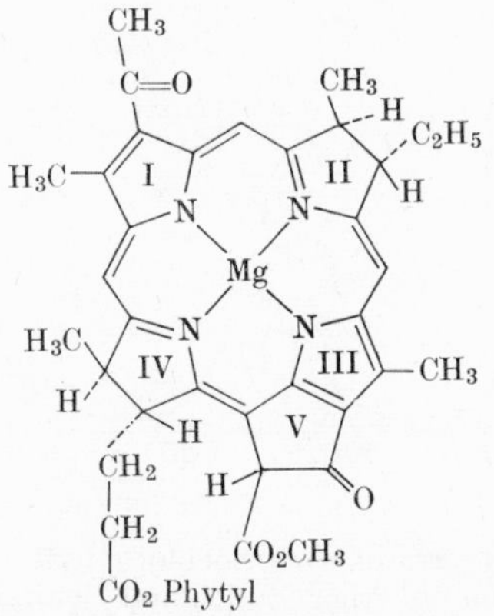

FIG. 11. Bacteriochlorophyll a.

into porphyrins. He also noted that oxidants or visible light converted it to a product with a strong absorption band near that of chlorophyll a.

The relationship between chlorophyll a and bacteriochlorophyll a was established by the fact that hydriodic acid (65°) converted bacteriophaeophorbide a into the same porphyrin (oxo-phaeoporphyrin a_5), as is formed by the same reagent at room temperature from phaeophorbide a (oxo-reaction). Phytol was shown to be the esterifying alcohol.

Elementary analysis showed that the bacteriochlorophyll a series contains four more hydrogen atoms than the corresponding porphyrins. It was deduced that they are at C_3 and C_4. Golden *et al.* (1958) confirmed this and showed that the configuration is probably *trans*, as it probably is in Ring IV.

Removal of the hydrogen atoms yields 2-desvinyl-2-acetyl chlorophyll a, the oxidation product observed by Schneider (1934).

Bacteriochlorophyll *a* also occurs in green sulphur bacteria together with the *Chlorobium* chlorophylls in a ratio of approximately 1:20. It was first observed as a minor peak in organic extracts (Katz and Wassink, 1939; Larsen, 1953), and isolated as a protein-pigment complex by Olson and Romano (1962). It was shown to contain phytol, to be oxidizable to 2-desvinyl-2-acetyl chlorophyll *a*, and to yield oxo-phylloerythrin, identical (m.p. and X-ray diffraction) with a sample obtained from pyrophaeophorbide *a* by the oxo-reaction (Holt *et al.*, 1963).

The visible absorption spectra of bacteriochlorophyll *a* and bacterio-phaeophytin *a* are given in Fig. 12.

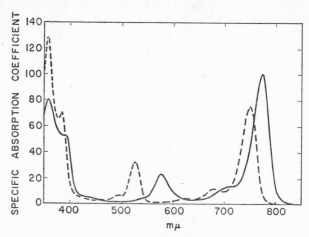

Fig. 12. Absorption spectra of bacteriochlorophyll *a* (solid line) and bacterio-phaeophytin *a* (broken line) in ether (Smith and Benitez, 1954, 1955).

Bacteriochlorophyll *b* has only recently been discovered and was obtained from a newly isolated bacterium tentatively identified as *Rhodopseudomonas* sp. (Eimhjellen *et al.*, 1963). Its absorption spectrum differs from that of bacteriochlorophyll *a* by having its maxima shifted 10 to 20 mμ to longer wavelengths. Otherwise, the spectra of both are very similar.

In vivo, bacteriochlorophyll *a* can have as many as three near infrared absorption maxima at 800, 850 and 890 mμ (Katz and Wassink, 1939).

E. *Chlorobium* CHLOROPHYLLS

Two classes of *Chlorobium* chlorophylls, obtained from two different strains of *Chlorobium thiosulfatophilum* exist. They are designated at the "650" and "660" series according to the wavelengths of their respective "red" absorption maxima in ether. Both have been shown to contain magnesium (Stanier and Smith, 1960; Holt and Morley, 1960a, b).

The visible absorption spectra of the "650" series (Figs. 13, 14) are typical of "meso" derivatives of chlorophyll a, while those of the "660" (Figs. 15, 16) differ considerably.

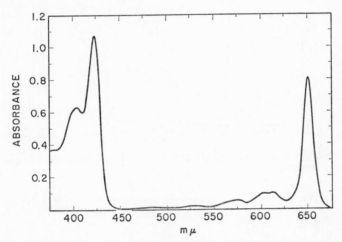

Fig. 13. Absorption spectrum of *Chlorobium* chlorophylls "650" in ether. (A. S. Holt and D. W. Hughes, unpublished). α_{sp} at $650 = 113 \cdot 5$ (Stanier and Smith, 1960).

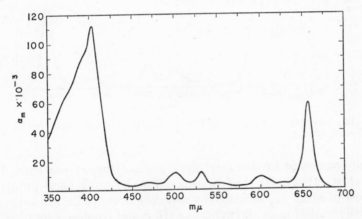

Fig. 14. Absorption spectrum of *Chlorobium* phaeophorbide "650" methylester (Fraction 2) in ether. (A. S. Holt and D. W. Hughes, unpublished).

The two classes differ from chlorophyll a by the following: (1) they lack the C_{10}-carbomethoxy group and are thus "pyro" compounds (Holt and Hughes, 1961; Holt et al., 1962); (2) they contain farnesol in place of phytol (Rapoport and Hamlow, 1961; Holt et al., 1963); (3) they exist as six different compounds (numbered fractions 1–6 in the order of their decreasing acid number), each compound differing from its next

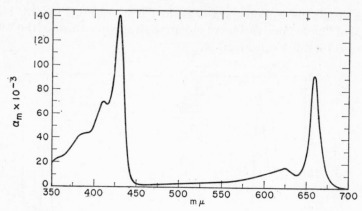

FIG. 15. Absorption spectrum of *Chlorobium* chlorophylls "660" in ether (Holt and Morley, 1960b).

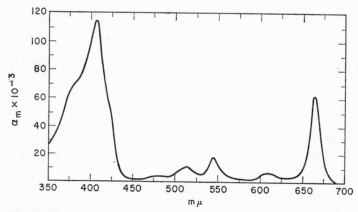

FIG. 16. Absorption spectrum of *Chlorobium* phaeophytins "660" in ether (Holt and Morley, 1960b).

related compound by one methylene group (Hughes and Holt, 1962; Holt *et al.*, 1963); (4) they possess a C_2-α-hydroxy alkyl group, the presence of which was indicated by acetylation, oxidation to a keto group and dehydration to an alkenyl group (Holt and Hughes, 1961).

After conversion into a porphyrin by hydriodic acid in acetic acid (65°) the "650" series gave a rhodo spectrum while the "660" series gave an aetio spectrum. The oxime of the "650" series retained sufficient rhodo type characteristics (Band III = Band IV) to indicate the presence of a cyclopentanone ring. That of the "660" series retained an aetio spectrum.

Oxidative degradation of the phaeophorbides of both series yielded the dihydrohaematinic acid imide identical to the synthetic *trans* product of Ficken *et al.* (1956). Methyl ethyl maleimide, methyl n-propyl maleimide and isobutyl maleimide were found depending on which fraction was oxidized. The imides were identified by comparison with synthetic compounds under various conditions of gas-liquid partition chromatography (Morley and Holt, 1961).

In the "650" series the nature of Ring I was determined by converting the hydroxyalkyl group into an alkyl group and oxidizing those fractions which had yielded only methyl n-propyl maleimide. Methyl ethyl maleimide was then also obtained. Fraction 6 was dehydrated to the C_2-vinyl derivative which was identical to pyropheophorbide a. This showed that the arrangement of the methyl substituents was the same as that in chlorophyll a. Synthetic 4-desethyl-4-n-propyldesoxophylloerythrin (Archibald et $al.$, 1963) was found to be identical to the

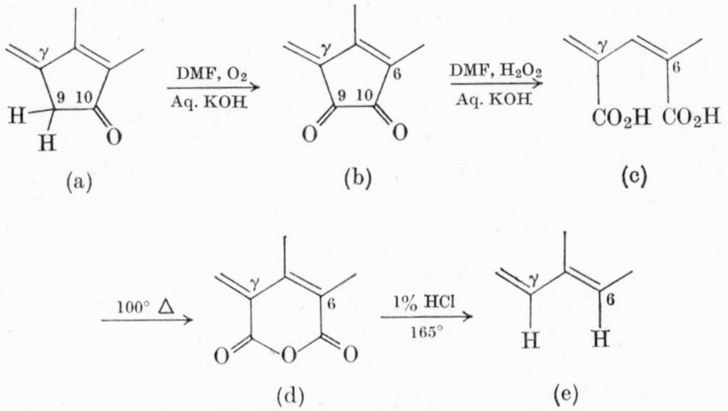

FIG. 17. Degradation of Ring V of $Chlorobium$ phaeophorbides "650" and "660" (DMF = dimethylformamide).

analytical product made from Fraction 5, establishing the presence of a C_5-methyl group and the order of the substituents.

The nature of the C_5 substituents of other fractions was found by chromic acid oxidations of the "pyrroporphyrins". These were obtained by the series of reactions outlined in Fig. 17. The cyclopentanone ring was oxidized to a diketone (b) in alkaline dimethyl formamide; the diketone was oxidized to the "chlorin p_6" derivative (c) by hydrogen peroxide. The latter, or its anhydride (d) ("purpurin 18") was decarboxylated and converted into the "pyrroporphyrin" (e) by hydrochloric acid (in the absence of air to prevent degradation). Chromic acid oxidation yielded ethyl maleimide from fractions 1, 2 and 4. Methyl ethyl maleimide was also obtained from fractions 1, 2 and 3.

In the "660" series similar results were obtained with the exception that the porphyrin obtained after heating the "chlorin p_6" derivative in hydrochloric acid had a phyllo spectrum, compared with the aetio of pyrroporphyrins. This showed the presence of an alkyl substituent at a methine bridge. It was concluded that this substituent must be at C_δ from comparison of the proton magnetic resonance spectra of the methyl esters of the "meso" derivative of fraction 5, δ-Cl-mesopyrophaeophorbide a and mesopyrophaeophorbide a. The signal assigned to the C_δ proton (Woodward and Škarić, 1961) was missing from the spectra of the fraction 5 and δ-Cl-mesopyrophaeophorbide. The assignment of the alkyl group to the δ position has been challenged (Mathewson *et al.*,

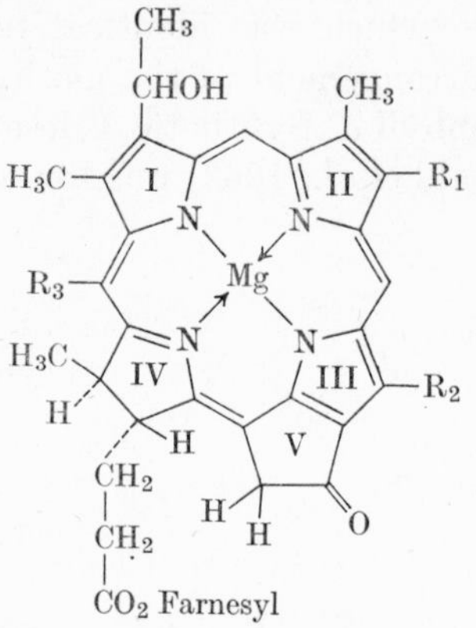

650 Series	R_1	R_2	R_3
Fraction 1	isobutyl	ethyl	H
2	n-propyl	ethyl	H
3	isobutyl	methyl	H
4	ethyl	ethyl	H
5	n-propyl	methyl	H
6	ethyl	methyl	H
660 Series	R_1	R_2	R_3
Fraction 1	isobutyl	ethyl	methyl
2	isobutyl	ethyl	ethyl
3	n-propyl	ethyl	methyl
4	n-propyl	ethyl	ethyl
5	ethyl	ethyl	methyl
6	ethyl	methyl	methyl

FIG. 18. Structures of Fractions 1–6 of *Chlorobium* chlorophylls "650" and "660".

1963). However, the phylloporphyrin derived from the "meso" derivative of fraction 5 has been shown to be identical with synthetic δ-methyl-5-desmethyl-5-ethyl-pyrroporphyrin (Archibald *et al.*, 1963).

The structures of the various fractions of the "650" and "660" series of *Chlorobium* chlorophylls, based on degradative and synthetic evidence plus their behaviour on the Celite partition columns are given in Fig. 18.

Jones (1963a) has obtained pigments with the absorption spectra of the "660" and "650" phaeophorbides from *Rhodopseudomonas spheroides* grown in the presence of 8-hydroxyquinoline. These differed from the *Chlorobium* pigments by giving a positive phase test.

In vivo, the "650" and "660" chlorophylls absorb at 725 and 746 mμ respectively (Stanier and Smith, 1960).

F. PROTOCHLOROPHYLL

The existence of a minor green pigment in leaves of etiolated plants has been known since the late nineteenth century. That it is a precursor of chlorophyll *a* has been clearly shown by Smith and Young (1956).

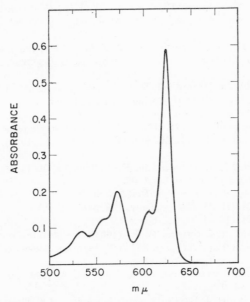

Fig. 19. Absorption spectrum of protochlorophyll *a* in ether.

Noack and Kiessling (1930) isolated a similar pigment from cucurbit seed coats and showed a close relation between it and a porphyrin obtained by treating methyl phaeophorbide *a* with powdered iron in formic acid. Following the elucidation of the structure of chlorophyll *a*, Fischer *et al.* (1939) showed that protochlorophyll was probably the magnesium complex of vinyl phaeoporphyrin a_5-phytyl ester (compare Fig. 4, p. 6).

Stanier and Smith (1959) have cast doubt on the identity of the etiolated leaf pigment with that obtained from the seed coat. They also obtained a protochlorophyll type pigment from a mutant of

Rhodopseudomonas spheroides whose spectrum more closely resembled that of the seed coat pigment. Jones (1963b) has also obtained a similar protochlorophyll-like pigment from the same organisms grown in the presence of 8-hydroxyquinoline. It was identified as Mg-2,3 divinyl-phaeophorphyrin a_5.

The absorption spectrum of Mg-vinyl phaeoporphyrin a_5 phytyl ester is given in Fig. 19. The magnesium-free derivative has an oxo-rhodo spectrum (compare Fig. 6B). *In vivo,* protochlorophyll (ide) absorbs at 638 mμ (Smith and Coomber, 1959).

REFERENCES

Allen, M. B., French, C. S., and Brown, J. S. (1960). *In* "Comparative Biochemistry of Photoreactive Systems" (M. B. Allen, ed.), pp. 33–52, Academic Press, New York.

Anderson, A. F. H., and Calvin, M. (1962). *Nature, Lond.* **194**, 285.

Archibald, J. L., MacDonald, S. F., and Shaw, K. B. (1963). *J. Amer. chem. Soc.* **85**, 644.

Aronoff, S. (1960). *In* "Handbuch Der Pflanzenphysiologie" (W. Ruhland, ed.), vol. V, part I, pp. 234–251, Springer-Verlag, Berlin.

Aronoff, S. (1962). *Biochim. biophys. Acta*, **60**, 193.

Becker, R. S. and Sheline, R. K. (1955). *Arch. Biochem. Biophys.* **54**, 259.

Burrell, J. W. K., Jackman, L. M., and Weedon, B. C. L. (1959). *Proc. chem. Soc.* 263.

Closs, G. L., Katz, J. J., Pennington, F. C., Thomas, M. R., and Strain, H. H. (1963). *J. Amer. chem. Soc.* **85**, 3809.

Donnay, G. (1959). *Arch. Biochem. Biophys.* **80**, 80.

Duysens, L. N. M. (1951). *Nature, Lond.* **168**, 548.

Duysens, L. N. M. (1952). Thesis, Utrecht.

Duysens, L. N. M., and Sweers, H. E. (1963). *In* "Studies on Microalgae and Photosynthetic Bacteria", pp. 353–372, Japanese Society of Plant Physiologists, The University of Tokyo Press.

Eimhjellen, K. E., Aasmundrud, O., and Jensen, A. (1963). *Biochem. Biophys. Res. Comm.* **10**, 232.

Falk, J. E., and Willis, J. B. (1951). *Aust. J. sci. Res. A* **4**, 579.

Ficken, G. E., Johns, R. B., and Linstead, R. P. (1956). *J. chem. Soc.* 2272.

Fischer, H., and Gibian, H. (1941). *Liebigs Ann.* **548**, 183.

Fischer, H., and Stern, A. (1940). "Die Chemie des Pyrrols", vol. II, 2, 478 pp. Akademische Verlagsgesellschaft, Leipzig.

Fischer, H., and Walter, H. (1941). *Liebigs Ann.* **549**, 44.

Fischer, H., Mittenzwei, H., and Oestreicher, A. (1939). *Hoppe-Seyl. Z.* **257**, IV–VII.

Fischer, H., Stier, E., and Kanngieser, W. (1940). *Liebigs Ann.* **543**, 258.

French, C. S. (1960). *In* "Handbuch Der Planzenphysiologie" (W. Ruhland, ed.), vol. V, part I, pp. 252–297, Springer-Verlag, Berlin.

French, C. S., and Elliott, R. F. (1958). *Yearb. Carneg. Instn.* **57**, 278.

French, C. S., and Young, V. M. K. (1952). *J. gen. Physiol.* **35**, 873.

French, C. S., Smith, J. H. C., Virgin, H. I., and Airth, R. L. (1956). *Plant Physiol.* **31**, 369.

French, C. S., Brown, J. S., Allen, M. B., and Elliott, R. F. (1959). *Yearb. Carneg. Instn.* **58**, 327.

Golden, J. H., Linstead, R. P., and Whitham, G. H. (1958). *J. chem. Soc.* 1725.

Goodwin, R. H. (1947). *Anal. Chem.* **19**, 789.

Granick, S. (1949). *J. biol. Chem.* **179**, 505.

Hanson, E. A. (1939). *Rec. Trav. botan. neérl.* **36**, 180.

Haxo, F. T., and Fork, D. C. (1959). *Nature, Lond.* **184**, 1051.

Holt, A. S. (1958). *Canad. J. Biochem. Physiol.* **36**, 439.

Holt, A. S. (1959). *Plant Physiol.* **34**, 310.

Holt, A. S. (1961). *Canad. J. Botany* **39**, 327.

Holt, A. S. (1963) *In* "Mechanism of Photosynthesis" (H. Tamiya, ed.), vol. VI, pp. 59–63, Pergamon Press, Oxford.

Holt, A. S., and Jacobs, E. E. (1955). *Plant Physiol.* **30**, 553.

Holt, A. S., and Hughes, D. W. (1961). *J. Amer. chem. Soc.* **83**, 499.

Holt, A. S., and Morley, H. V. (1959). *Canad. J. Chem.* **37**, 507.

Holt, A. S., and Morley, H. V. (1960a). *J. Amer. chem. Soc.* **82**, 500.

Holt, A. S., and Morley, H. V. (1960b). *In* "Comparative Biochemistry of Photo-reactive Systems" (M. B. Allen, ed.), pp. 169–179, Academic Press, New York.

Holt, A. S., Hughes, D. W., Kende, H. J., and Purdie, J. W. (1962). *J. Amer. chem. Soc.* **84**, 2835.

Holt, A. S., Hughes, D. W., Kende, H. J., and Purdie, J. W. (1963). *Plant and Cell Physiol.* **4**, 49.

Hughes, D. W., and Holt, A. S. (1962). *Canad. J. Chem.* **40**, 171.

Jacobs, E. E., Vatter, A. E., and Holt, A. S. (1953). *J. chem. Phys.* **21**, 2246.

Jacobs, E. E., Vatter, A. E., and Holt, A. S. (1954). *Arch. Biochem. Biophys.* **53**, 228.

Jeffrey, S. W. (1963). *Biochem. J.* **86**, 313.

Jones, O. T. G. (1963a). *Biochem. J.* **88**, 335.

Jones, O. T. G. (1963b). *Biochem. J.* **89**, 182.

Katz, E., and Wassink, E. C. (1939). *Enyzmologia* **7**, 97.

Katz, J. J., Dougherty, R. C., Pennington, F. C., Strain, H. H., and Closs, G. L. (1963). *J. Amer. chem. Soc.* **85**, 4049.

Klesper, E., Corwin, A. H., and Iber, P. K. (1961). *Anal. Chem.* **33**, 1091.

Larsen, H. (1953). *K. norske videnskab. Selsk.*, 1–205.

Manning, W. M., and Strain, H. H. (1943). *J. biol. Chem.* **151**, 1.

Mathewson, J. W., Richards, W. R., and Rapoport, H. (1963). *J. Amer. chem. Soc.* **85**, 364.

Morley, H. V., and Holt, A. S. (1961). *Canad. J. Chem.* **39**, 755.

Noack, K., and Kiessling, W. (1930). *Hoppe-Seyl. Z.* **193**, 97.

Olson, J. M., and Romano, C. A. (1962). *Biochim. Biophys. Acta* **59**, 726.

Pelletier, P. J., and Caventou, J. B. (1818). *Ann. chim. et phys.* **9**, 194.

Perkins, H. J., and Roberts, D. W. A. (1963). *Proc. Can. Soc. Plant Physiologists*, **4**, 29.

Prescott, G. W. (1962). "Algae of the Western Great Lakes Area," 997 pp., W. C. Brown Co., Dubuque, Iowa.

Rabinowitch, E. I. (1945, 1951, 1956). "Photosynthesis and Related Processes." **I**, 1–599; **II**, 1, 603–1208; **II**, 2, 1211–2088, Interscience, New York.

Rapoport, H., and Hamlow, H. P. (1961). *Biochem. Biophys. Res. Comm.* **6**, 134.

Rothemund, P. (1944). *In* "Medical Physics" (O. Glasser, ed.), pp. 154–180, Year Book Pub. Inc. Chicago.

Sagromsky, H. (1960). *Ber. dtsch. bot. Ges.* **73**, 3.

Schneider, E. (1934). *Hoppe-Seyl. Z.* **226**, 221.

Smith, J. H. C., and Benitez, A. (1954). *Yearb. Carneg. Instn.* **53**, 168.

Smith, J. H. C., and Benitez, A. (1955). *In* "Modern Methods of Plant Analysis" (K. Paech and M. V. Tracey, eds.), vol. IV, pp. 142–196, Springer-Verlag, Berlin.

Smith, J. H. C. and Coomber, J. (1959). *Yearb. Carneg. Instn.* **58**, 331.

Smith, J. H. C., and Young, V. M. K. (1956). *In* "Radiation Biology" (A. Hollaender, ed.), vol. III, pp. 393–442, McGraw-Hill, New York.

Sorby, H. C. (1873). *Proc. roy. Soc.* **21**, 442.

Stanier, R. Y. and Smith, J. H. C. (1959). *Yearb. Carneg. Instn.* **58**, 336.

Stanier, R. Y., and Smith, J. H. C. (1960). *Biochim. biophys. Acta* **41**, 478.

Stern, A., and Wenderlein, H. (1936). *Z. physik. Chem. A* **176**, 81.

Stokes, G. G. (1864). *Proc. roy. Soc.* **13**, 144.

Strain, H. H. (1951). *In* "Manual of Phycology" (G. M. Smith, ed.), pp. 243–262, Chronica Botanica Co., Waltham.

Strain, H. H. (1958). "Chloroplast Pigments and Chromatographic Analysis." Priestley Lectures No. 32, 180 pp., Pennsylvania State Univ., University Park, Pa.

Strain, H. H., and Manning, W. M. (1942). *J. biol. Chem.* **144**, 625.

Strain, H. H., Manning, W. M., and Hardin, G. (1943). *J. biol. Chem.* **148**, 655.

Strell, M., Kalagonoff, A., and Koller, H. (1960). *Angew. Chem.* **72**, 169.

Twsett, M. (1906). *Ber. dtsch. bot. Ges.* **24**, 384.

Tyray, E. (1944). *Liebigs Ann.* **556**, 171.

Weller, A. (1954). *J. Amer. chem. Soc.* **76**, 5819.

Wetherell, H. R., and Hendrickson, M. J. (1959). *J. org. Chem.* **24**, 710.

Willstätter, R., and Page, H. J. (1914). *Liebigs Ann.* **404**, 237.

Willstätter, R., and Stoll, A. (1913). "Untersuchungen über Chlorophyll," 424 pp., J. Springer, Berlin.

Woodward, R. B., Ayer, W. A., Beaton, J. M., Bickelhaupt, F., Bonnett, R., Buchschacher, P., Closs, G. L., Dutler, H., Hannah, J., Hauck, F. P., Itô, S., Langemann, A., LeGoff, E., Leimgruber, W., Lwowski, W., Sauer, J., Valenta, Z., and Volz, H. (1960). *J. Amer. chem. Soc.* **82**, 3800.

Woodward, R. B., and Škarić, V. (1961). *J. Amer. chem. Soc.* **83**, 4676.

Chapter 2

CHLOROPHYLL BIOSYNTHESIS*

Lawrence Bogorad†

*Department of Botany, The University of Chicago,
Chicago 37, Illinois, U.S.A.*

I. Introduction

The biosynthesis of porphyrins, including the chlorophylls, is discussed in this chapter. Evidence for the chemical structures of the chlorophylls and their natural distribution has been described in the preceding chapter; the role of the chlorophylls in photosynthesis is examined in a later chapter (Chapter 13).

It seems almost unnecessary to call the attention of any reader of this

* Preparation supported in part by grants from the National Science Foundation and from the National Institutes of Health, U.S.P.H.S.
† Research Career Awardee, National Institute of General Medical Sciences, U.S.P.H.S.

29

book to the ubiquity of chlorophylls among photosynthetic organisms or to the probably universal distribution of iron-porphyrin-proteins, hemoproteins, among organisms.

Most of the intermediates in the biosynthesis of chlorophyll a have been identified; this knowledge restricts speculations on the nature of some "missing" ones. In common with much of the rest of current biochemistry, understanding of the enzymatic mechanisms involved lags far behind what has quickly become descriptive biochemistry, but a great deal of work is starting to be done on the question of modes of control of porphyrin biogenesis.

The discussion of chlorophyll biosynthesis will be prefaced by a brief outline of pyrrole porphyrin chemistry, as a supplement to Dr. Holt's discussion in the previous chapter, and will be followed by considerations of demonstrated as well as imagined mechanisms by which biogenesis is controlled.

II. Pyrroles, Porphyrinogens, and Porphyrins

Porphyrins are cyclic tetrapyrroles. The fundamental pyrrole heterocycle is shown in Fig. 1. It is apparent that each of the four carbon atoms in the pyrrole ring is capable of forming a bond with another carbon

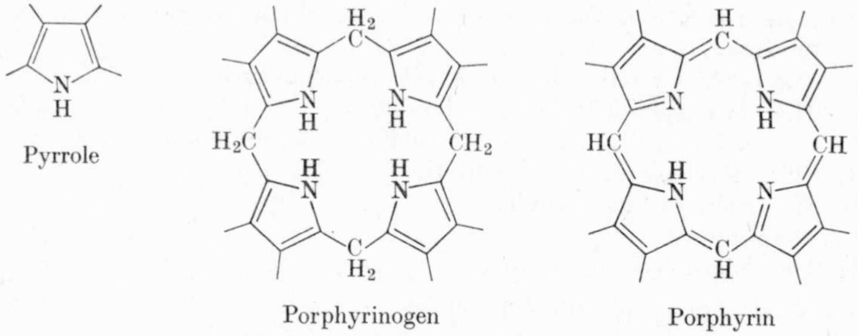

FIG. 1. Pyrrolic and cyclic tetrapyrrolic skeletons.

atom. The two ring carbon atoms adjacent to the nitrogen are designated α and the other two carbon atoms β.

Also shown in Fig. 1 is a porphyrinogen. This compound is formed when four pyrroles are joined to one another through their α carbon atoms by saturated carbon bridges. A porphyrinogen of the sort shown in Fig. 1 is readily oxidized by air, by iodine, or by other mild oxidizing agents to form a porphyrin. The porphyrin, unlike the porphyrinogen, is a planar molecule capable of chelating any number of metals. It is highly coloured. All these new properties are a consequence of the oxidation to this new state.

It is apparent that in the porphyrinogen and porphyrin shown in Fig. 1 the two β carbons of each pyrrole ring can be substituted. Porphyrins can be distinguished from one another by the nature of the substituents on these eight β-carbon atoms as well as by the absence or presence of a metal held in the centre of this cyclic tetrapyrrole. Only magnesium and iron have so far been found in biologically active porphyrins.

Much of the discussion of porphyrin biosynthesis dwells on modifications of side chains. Falk (1963) and Phillips (1963) have reviewed current information on chemical and physico-chemical properties of porphyrins.

III. THE BIOSYNTHESIS OF PORPHYRINS

The probable biosynthetic pathway for chlorophyll a and bacteriochlorophyll is shown in Fig. 2. The reactions can be grouped as follows:

(1) The diversion of carbon and nitrogen atoms from the general metabolism of the cell into porphyrin formation: Glycine + succinylcoenzyme A → δ-aminolevulinic acid (ALA).

(2) The formation of the precursor pyrrole: 2ALA → 1 porphobilinogen (PBG).

(3) The formation of a cyclic tetrapyrrole: 4PBG → uroporphyrinogen + 4 NH_3.

(4) The modifications of porphyrinogen side chains (i.e. substituents on β-carbon atoms):

    (a) Decarboxylation of acetate side chains: uroporphyrinogen → coproporphyrinogen + 4 CO_2.

    (b) Oxidative decarboxylation of propionic acid side chains on rings A and B: Coproporphyrinogen → protoporphyrinogen + 2 CO_2 + 4H.

(5) The oxidation of the macrocycle: Protoporphyrinogen → protoporphyrin + 6H.

(6) Incorporation of metal atoms:

    (a) Fe + protoporphyrin → protohaem → haemoglobin, catalase, peroxidase, cytochromes.

    (b) Mg + protoporphyrin → Mg protoporphyrin → chlorophylls.

(7) For the formation of chlorophylls: further alterations of side chains including esterifications and reductions, formation of a cyclopentanone ring, and the reduction of one (chlorophyll) or two pyrrole rings (bacteriochlorophyll).

Evidence for these reactions in chlorophyll formation as well as the

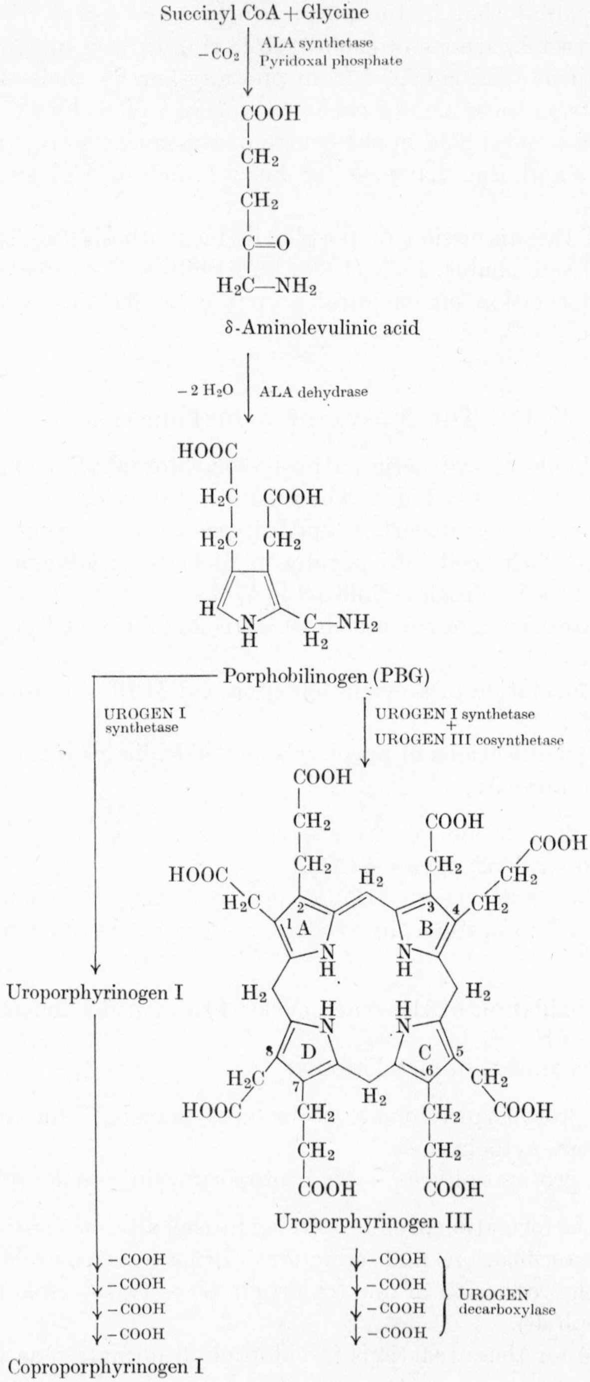
Succinyl CoA + Glycine
$-CO_2$
ALA synthetase
Pyridoxal phosphate
δ-Aminolevulinic acid
$-2\,H_2O$
ALA dehydrase
Porphobilinogen (PBG)
UROGEN I synthetase
UROGEN I synthetase + UROGEN III cosynthetase
Uroporphyrinogen I
Uroporphyrinogen III
UROGEN decarboxylase
Coproporphyrinogen I

FIG. 2.

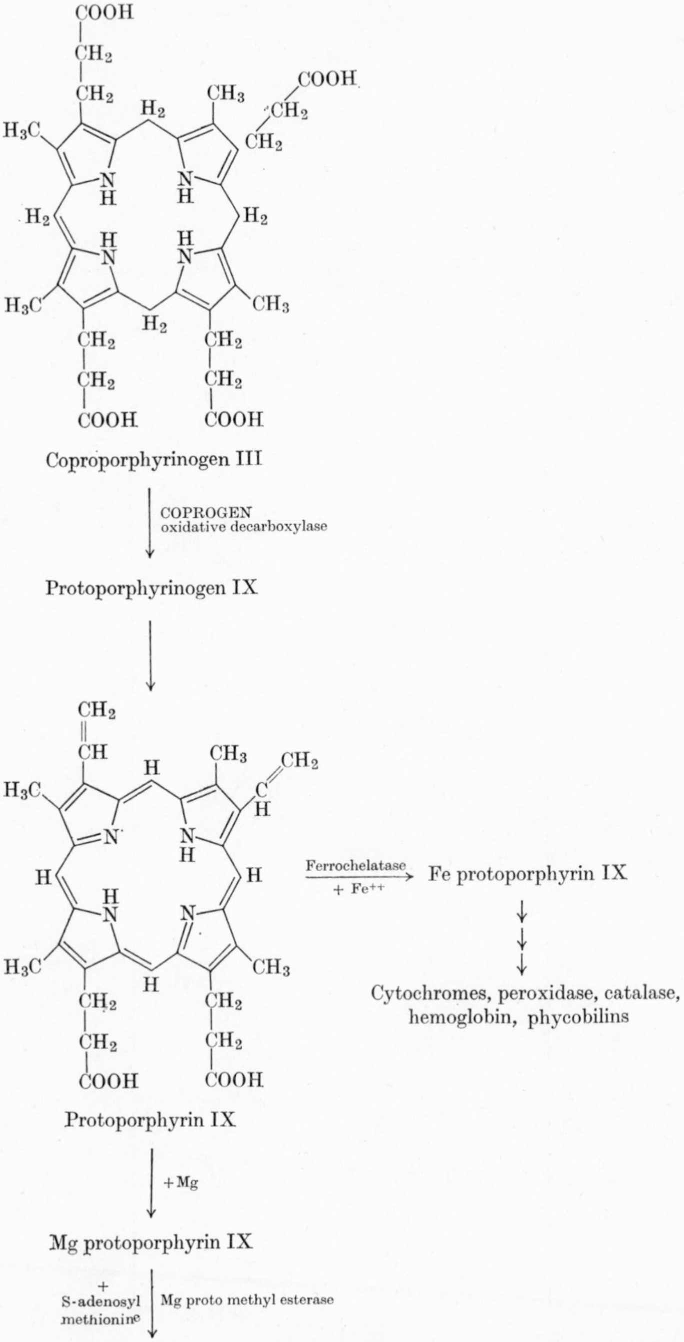

Coproporphyrinogen III

| COPROGEN
oxidative decarboxylase

Protoporphyrinogen IX

Ferrochelatase
+ Fe⁺⁺ ⟶ Fe protoporphyrin IX

Cytochromes, peroxidase, catalase,
hemoglobin, phycobilins

Protoporphyrin IX

| +Mg

Mg protoporphyrin IX

+
S-adenosyl | Mg proto methyl esterase
methionine

FIG. 2.—cont.

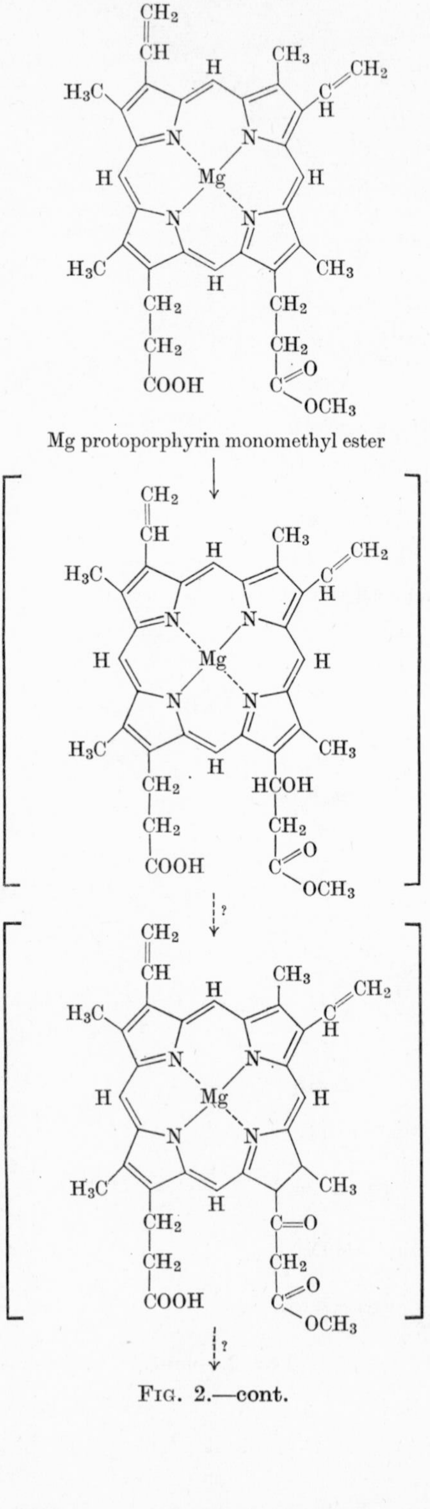

Mg protoporphyrin monomethyl ester

Fig. 2.—cont.

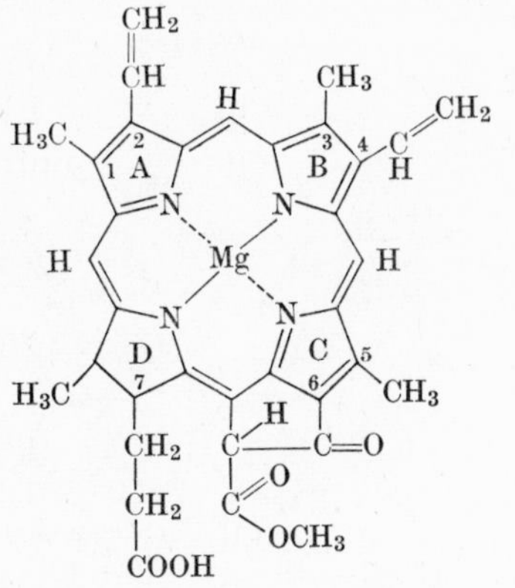

Mg 2,4—divinyl pheoporphyrin a_5

$+ 2H$ ↓

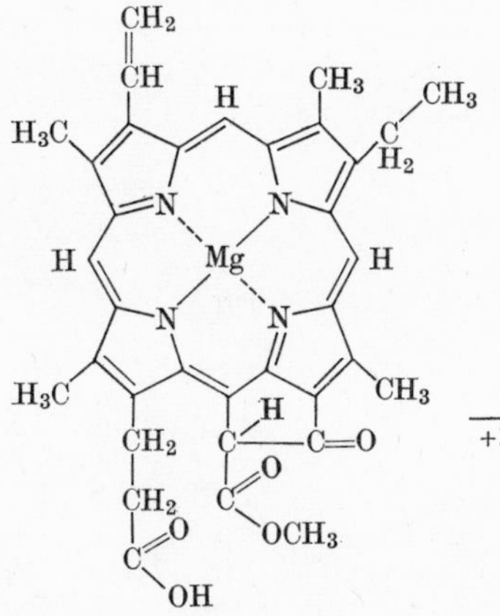

Protochlorophyllide a

$\xrightarrow{+ \text{Phytol}}$ Protochlorophyll a

$+ 2H$ ↓ [Transformation may be of protochlorophyllide-holochrome only.]

FIG. 2.—cont.

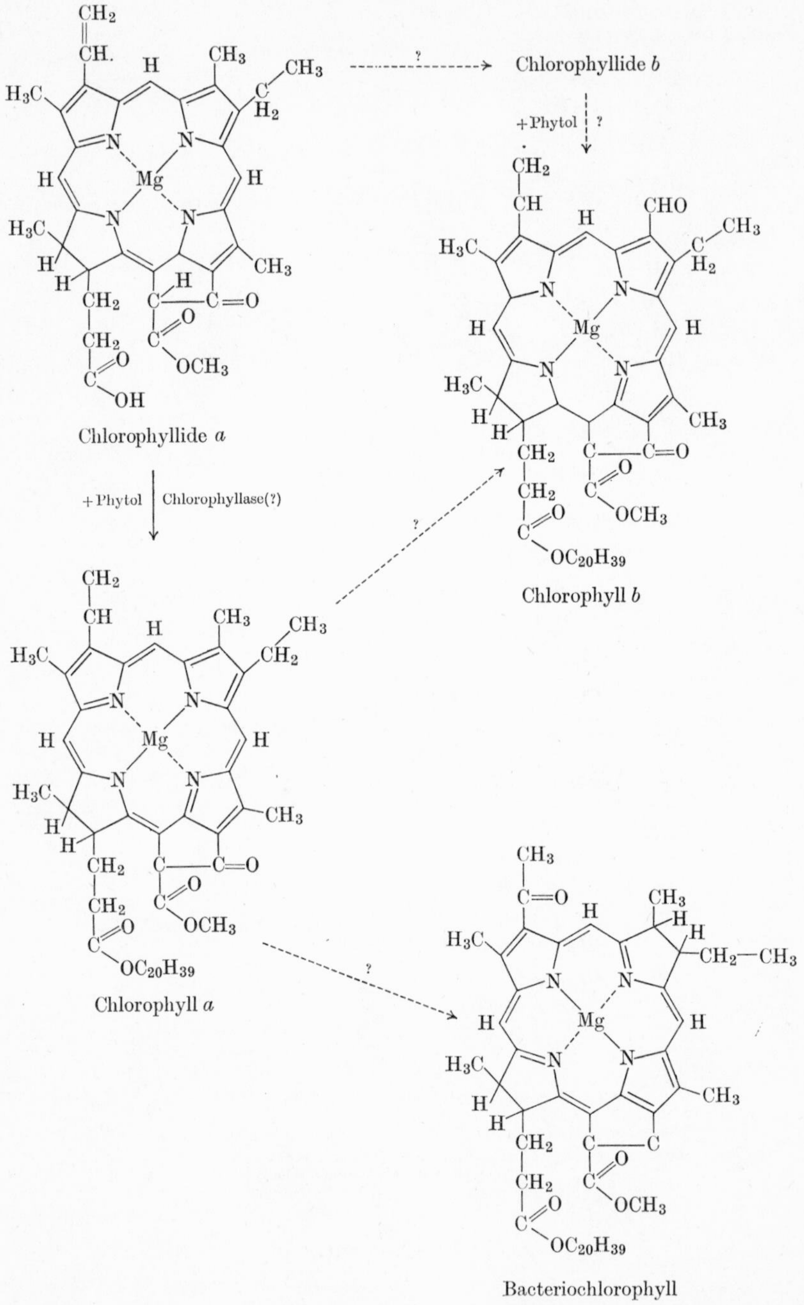

FIG. 2. A summary of demonstrated and hypothetical steps in porphyrin biosynthesis.

limits of current knowledge of them will be examined in the following section. Some of the most crucial data are available only from studies on animals or enzymes prepared from animal tissues. The biosynthetic path to haem appears to be identical in plant and animal systems although the control systems may differ sharply.

A. THE PATH OF CARBON AND NITROGEN ATOMS INTO PORPHYRINS. THE BIOSYNTHESIS OF δ-AMINOLEVULINIC ACID (ALA)

Experiments with labelled atoms revealed the α-carbon and nitrogen atoms of glycine and the carbon atoms of succinic acid to be fairly direct sources of all the carbon atoms used in the biosynthesis of haem (= protohaem = iron protoporphyrin) by avian erythrocytes. These now classical examples of the power of skilful degradative organic chemistry when coupled with tracer techniques, particularly the work of Wittenberg and Shemin, has been described in detail in many places (e.g. Kamen, 1957).

These early tracer experiments provided data which led to the following conclusions regarding the biosynthesis of protohaem:

(a) One carbon atom and the nitrogen atom of each pyrrole ring of protohaem is derived from the α-carbon atom and the associated nitrogen atom of glycine (Muir and Neuberger, 1949, 1950; Wittenberg and Shemin, 1949, 1950).

(b) Each of the four methene bridge carbon atoms of protohaem also originates from the α-carbon atom of glycine. (Wittenberg and Shemin, 1950; Muir and Neuberger, 1950.)

(c) The remaining carbon atoms of the pyrrole rings as well as of the side chains are derived from acetate (Shemin and Wittenberg, 1951) or, more directly, from succinate (Shemin and Kumin, 1952). This observation led Shemin to suggest that the carbon atoms of succinate might enter porphyrin metabolism as succinyl coenzyme A.

(d) Finally, contrary to some ideas current at that time (e.g. Lemberg and Legge, 1949), strong support was provided for the growing conviction that all four pyrroles rings of protohaem arise from a common precursor pyrrole.

Investigations of the course of utilization of succinate and the α-carbon plus nitrogen of glycine for protohaem biosynthesis were brought to a logical and highly satisfactory conclusion in Shemin's laboratory (Shemin and Russel, 1953). It was shown that δ-aminolevulinic acid (ALA) can serve as the sole source of all the carbon and nitrogen atoms for the synthesis of protohaem by suspensions of avian erythrocytes (Fig. 2). This discovery, which was quickly confirmed by Neuberger and Scott

(1953), immediately led to a search for enzymes which on the one hand catalyse the formation of δ-aminolevulinic acid (ALA) and on the other hand mediate the utilization of this compound for porphyrin formation.

The enzyme ALA synthetase, which catalyses the synthesis of ALA from succinyl coenzyme A and glycine, has been prepared as freeze-dried particles from chicken red cells (Gibson *et al.*, 1958) and in higher states of purity as fractionated cell-free extracts of *Rhodopseudomonas spheroides*. Kikuchi *et al.* (1958) obtained an eighty-fold and Burnham (1962) a twenty-fold purified preparation of ALA synthetase from this bacterium. The enzyme is undoubtedly present in plants but has not been purified from any alga or higher plant.

Lascelles (1957) found that *Tetrahymena vorax* deficient in panto-thenate and pyridoxal produced only 20–30% as much porphyrin as controls but that the ability of deficient cells to form tetrapyrroles from ALA was unimpaired. Experiments on porphyrin formation by prepara-tions of red cells from ducks deficient in vitamin B_6 and pantothenate also indicated the involvement of these cofactors in the formation of ALA (Schulman and Richert, 1957). The requirement of pantothenate was in agreement with Shemin's earlier suggestion that succinyl co-enzyme A is utilized in ALA formation (Shemin and Russel, 1953). The ALA synthetase preparations of Kikuchi *et al.* (1958) and Gibson *et al.* (1958) were found to require pyridoxal phosphate as a cofactor for the condensation of glycine and succinyl coenzyme A, the substrates necessary for ALA synthesis. Neuberger (1961) has discussed a possible mechanism for the condensation.

The expected product of the condensation of glycine and succinyl coenzyme A is δ-amino-β-ketoadipic acid (Shemin and Russel, 1953) but this compound has not been detected in reaction mixtures, probably because it is rapidly and spontaneously decarboxylated to δ-amino-levulinic acid (Laver *et al.*, 1959). The half-life of δ-amino-β-ketoadipic acid at pH 7 in aqueous solution is estimated to be less than one minute. The ALA synthetase reaction is inhibited by substances which complex with the aldehydic group of pyridoxal phosphate (e.g. l-cysteine, peni-cillamine, and cyanide) and also by aminomalonate (Gibson *et al.*, 1958, 1961).

At the time of the discovery of the role of δ-aminolevulinic acid in porphyrin metabolism Shemin and Russel (1953) proposed another possible metabolic role for the aminoketone. A modification of their succinate-glycine cycle, for which there is some evidence from studies with intact rats (Nemeth *et al.*, 1957) is shown in Fig. 3. Increasing attention is being paid to reactions involving aminoketones other than ALA. Mitochondria of guinea-pig liver contain an enzyme which seems to catalyse preferentially the formation of aminoketones other than

ALA: it catalyses the condensation of glycine with acetyl coenzyme A, malonyl coenzyme A, or propionyl coenzyme A; however, only traces of ALA were formed with succinyl coenzyme A (Urata and Granick, 1963). The reaction mechanism has been considered by Shemin and Kikuchi

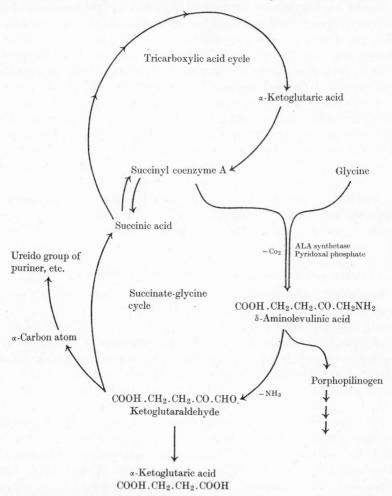

FIG. 3. The succinate-glycine cycle and its relationship to the tricarboxylic cycle (Shemin and Russel, 1953).

(1958) and by Neuberger (1961) who has also discussed the apparent lack of specificity of aminoketone synthetase systems examined in his laboratory. Gibson *et al.* (1961) have suggested the possibility that chlorophyll synthesis might be controlled by competition for glycine and for the aminoketone synthetase capacity of the organism by acyl coenzyme A's other than succinyl coenzyme A. If plant as well as animal cells possess specific aminoketone synthetases of the kinds described by Urata and Granick the value of the suggestion of Gibson *et al.* would be partly reduced and even now, as they point out, there is no evidence to support it.

Among photosynthetic organisms, evidence for the operation of the succinate-glycine cycle has thus far been obtained only in extracts of *Rhodopseudomonas spheroides* which catalyse the deamination of ALA (Gibson *et al.*, 1961) although the equilibrium for the reaction is reported to be in favour of the production of ALA. Marks (1963) reports that Neuberger and Turner have found L-alanine to be the specific donor of an amino group to γδ-dioxovaleric acid for the formation of ALA by the *R. spheroides* enzyme. If a biosynthetic route for γδ-dioxovaleric acid other than directly from ALA is found, this system might, at least in some organisms, provide an alternate path of ALA synthesis. It should be borne in mind that ALA synthetase has been studied in only a few organisms and that the utilization of glycine nitrogen is based entirely on studies of haem synthesis in animals. However, the similarity in substrate and cofactor requirements of ALA synthetase from chicken erythrocytes and photosynthetic bacteria encourages the unitary point of view on this question.

B. PYRROLE FORMATION. THE BIOSYNTHESIS OF PORPHOBILINOGEN

The isolation and crystallization of porphobilinogen (PBG) from the urine of acute porphyrin sufferers by Westall (1952); the characterization of this compound as a monopyrrole (Cookson and Rimington, 1953; Granick and Bogorad, 1953); and the demonstration of its utilization in the enzymatic synthesis of porphyrins (Bogorad and Granick, 1953b; Falk *et al.*, 1953) coincided with the experiments by Shemin and Russel (1953) which established the role of ALA in the biogenesis of protohaem.

ALA dehydrase catalyses the condensation of two molecules of ALA to form one of PBG; two molecules of water are eliminated. This enzyme has been purified to various extents from avian erythrocytes (Granick, 1954; Schmid and Shemin, 1955), rabbit reticulocytes (Granick and Mauzerall, 1958), and liver from various animals (Gibson *et al.*, 1955; Iodice *et al.*, 1958). Gibson *et al.* (1955) have purified the ox liver enzyme 270-fold—the most highly purified preparation yet reported. Changes in the level or activity of this enzyme with conditions of culture of *Rhodopseudomonas spheroides* has been the subject of experiments by Lascelles (1959) and by Gibson *et al.* (1962a). ALA dehydrase has not been purified from algae or higher plants but there is little doubt of its presence: Granick (1954) demonstrated the conversion of ALA into porphyrin by extracts of *Chlorella* and of spinach; etiolated barley accumulates protochlorophyllide when supplied with ALA (Granick,

1959, 1961); etiolated bean leaves behave similarly (Sisler and Klein, 1963; Klein and Bogorad, 1964).

In vitro ALA dehydrase is activated by sulfhydryl group containing compounds such as glutathione and cysteine and is inhibited by various heavy metals as well as by ethylenediaminetetraacetic acid (Gibson *et al.*, 1955; Granick and Mauzerall, 1958).

C. TETRAPYRROLE FORMATION

Uroporphyrinogen III (Urogen III) is the first cyclic tetrapyrrole on the biosynthetic path to chlorophylls and other biologically useful porphyrins. This compound is transformed via several intermediates into protoporphyrin IX, the porphyrin moiety of haemoglobin, catalase and peroxidases, and a precursor of chlorophylls, by broken cell preparations of *Chlorella* (Bogorad, 1955, 1957a, 1958c). It is also converted into protoporphyrin IX or a more immediate precursor of this porphyrin by haemolysed red cells (Neve *et al.*, 1956; Mauzerall and Granick, 1958).

The enzymatic synthesis *in vitro* of Urogen III from PBG can be shown to occur with ease but the mechanism of the reaction is unclear. It is obvious (Fig. 4) that the simplest tetrapyrrole which could be formed by the condensation of four molecules of PBG is not Urogen III but its completely symmetrical isomer I. These isomers differ from one another in the arrangement of the acetic and propionic acid side chains on ring D. Inspection of the structural formulae of Urogen III and Proto IX reveals their close relationship if it is recognized that: methyl side chains of Proto IX are derived from acetic acid side chains of Urogen; the vinyl side chains on rings A and B are derived from propionic acid substituents; and, of course, the propionic acid groups on rings C and D of Proto are as they exist in Urogen. It is also worthwhile, at this point, to compare the structural formula of a chlorophyll, e.g. chlorophyll *a*, with that of Proto IX. The propionic acid side chain on ring C of Proto IX becomes part of the cyclopentanone ring of chlorophyll *a*; the vinyl group on ring B of Proto IX is the ethyl group in the same position in chlorophyll *a*; the carboxyl groups of Proto IX are esterified in chlorophyll *a*. Thus chlorophyll *a* is a close structural relative of Proto IX which, in turn, is derived from Urogen III as has been shown experimentally. Proto IX is not formed when Urogen I is incubated in a broken cell preparation capable of synthesizing Proto IX from PBG.

Uroporphyrin I (Uro I), the compound formed by mild oxidation of Urogen I, is the only other one of the four possible isomers of Uro found in nature; it is best known as a constituent of the urine of human or other animals afflicted with certain hereditary or acquired diseases (for discussion and review of porphyria diseases see e.g. Schmid, 1960; Bogorad, 1963).

2*

A = —CH_2—COOH M = CH_3
P = —CH_2—CH_2—COOH
V = CH═CH_2
E = —CH_2—CH_3

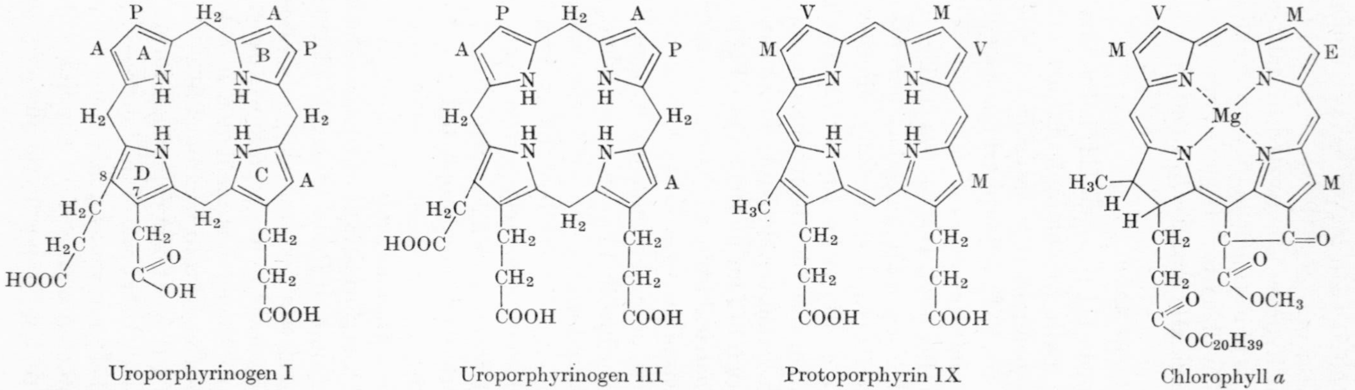

FIG. 4. Structural relationships among some cyclic tetrapyrroles. Compare the arrangement of substituents on positions 7 and 8 (Ring D).

Frozen and thawed preparations of the green alga *Chlorella* catalyse the consumption of PBG and the production of a number of porphyrins including Proto IX, Uro III, and Uro I. (Presumably some of the Urogen formed is oxidized during the incubation while some of the Urogen III is used for Proto IX synthesis; oxidized intermediates between Urogen III and Proto IX are also detected). If such preparations are heated at 55° for 30 min prior to incubation with substrate, their capacity to consume PBG is essentially unaltered quantitatively, i.e. the rate of utilization of PBG is unaffected, but only Uro I is made from PBG (Bogorad and Granick, 1953b). (Roughly similar observations have been made with haemolysed avian and human erythrocytes by Booij and Rimington (1957) and by Rimington and Booij (1957).)

These observations indicate that in the preparations studied an enzyme which plays a, or the, major role in the utilization of PBG for tetrapyrrole synthesis is relatively heat stable as compared with many, if not all, of the other enzymes present and required for the formation of Proto IX. The most striking effect of the heat treatment is the change in the nature of the tetrapyrrole isomer which is produced. One interpretation of these results is that two enzymes are required for the synthesis of Urogen III—the precursor of Proto IX—and that one of them is considerably more heat-labile than the other. Furthermore, the relatively heat-stable enzyme (it is destroyed at higher temperatures) when incubated alone with PBG catalyses the formation of Urogen I.

1. *Uroporphyrinogen I Synthetase*

Urogen I synthetase (formerly designated PBG deaminase) has been partially purified from spinach leaf tissue (Bogorad, 1955, 1958a) and from *Rhodopseudomonas spheroides* (Heath and Hoare, 1959; Hoare and Heath, 1959). The enzyme from spinach is only slightly affected by heating at 70° at pH 8·2 but is inactivated at 100° at this pH value and at lower temperature in more acid or alkaline solutions.

Since the product of the action of Urogen I synthetase on PBG is Urogen I in yields close to 100%, and this cyclic tetrapyrrole can be visualized as arising by the sequential addition of four PBG molecules to one another with the elimination of ammonia to form a linear tetrapyrrole which cyclizes, the simplest role to assign Urogen I synthetase is the catalysis of the condensation of PBG's to form first a dipyrrole, then a tripyrrole, and finally a linear tetrapyrrole. The last of these would have a very high probability of cyclizing to form Urogen I, perhaps non-enzymatically; it has been known since the work of Waldenström and Vahlquist in 1939, when PBG was known only by its products, that uroporphyrins are formed in the absence of enzymes upon heating aqueous solutions of PBG.

Three classes of inhibitors of Urogen I synthetase are known:

(1) Non-competitive inhibitors such as formaldehyde, p-chloromercuribenzoate, silver and mercuric ions (Bogorad, 1958a). Inhibition by the mercurials is reversed by sulfhydryl-containing compounds.

(2) Competitive inhibitors including PBG analogues such as opsopyrrole dicarboxylic acid (Bogorad, 1957b, 1960; Carpenter and Scott, 1959) and isoporphobilinogen (Carpenter and Scott, 1961).

(3) A group of inhibitors whose effect, unlike that of the two types already described, is not primarily on the rate of substrate consumption, although this is affected to some extent, but rather upon the nature of the reaction. In the presence of high enough concentrations of ammonium ions or hydroxylamine the rate of PBG consumption is not matched by that of Urogen I formation—compounds which appear to be linear polypyrroles accumulate in the reaction mixture. Under some conditions these accumulated compounds can form additional Urogen I, thus they are intermediates in Urogen I biosynthesis (Bogorad, 1961, 1963).

2. *Uroporphyrinogen III Cosynthetase*

The III rather than the I isomer of Urogen is the precursor of protohaem IX and of the chlorophylls. How is the III isomer formed? Some aspects of the phenomenon are known but the mechanism is not.

Urogen III is formed from PBG by crude enzyme preparations (e.g. preparations from: *Chlorella* (Bogorad and Granick, 1953b), haemolysed chicken erythrocytes (Falk *et al.*, 1953, 1956; Dresel and Falk, 1956), rabbit reticulocytes (Granick and Mauzerall, 1958), haemolysed chicken erythrocytes (Lockwood and Benson, 1960), *Rhodopseudomonas spheroides* (Heath and Hoare, 1959). It can also be synthesized enzymatically *in vitro* by the action of two enzymes: Urogen I synthetase and Urogen III cosynthetase (previously designated Uroporphyrinogen isomerase). The later enzyme has been partly purified from aqueous extracts of wheat germ (Bogorad, 1958b).

The best preparations of Urogen III cosynthetase do not catalyse the condensation of PBG molecules when the enzyme and pyrrole are incubated together. However, the same concentration of this enzyme when included in a reaction mixture with Urogen I synthetase and PBG brings about the formation of Urogen III. The cosynthetase does not convert Urogen I into Urogen III nor does it appear to alter PBG, e.g. to isomerize some molecules into iso-PBG. Preincubation of the very heat-labile Urogen III cosynthetase with PBG, destruction of the enzyme by mild heating, and addition of Urogen I synthetase results in the synthesis of only Urogen I (Bogorad, 1957a, 1958b). Granick and Mauzerall (1958) also observed, with a Urogen III synthesizing system from rabbit reticulocytes, that Urogen I was not converted into the III isomer.

In reaction mixtures of Urogen I synthetase, Urogen III cosynthetase, and PBG the rate of utilization of the monopyrrole is governed chiefly by the concentration of Urogen I synthetase, in accord with the earlier observations on the crude *Chlorella* system (Bogorad and Granick, 1953b). However, kinetic studies reveal that the maximum velocity of the reaction is higher in the presence of both Urogen III cosynthetase and Urogen I synthetase than when the former is omitted—despite its failure to catalyse any measurable consumption of PBG when alone (Bogorad, 1958b).

The mechanism of cooperation of the two enzymes must probably await recognition of the substrates of Urogen III cosynthetase. Current work on the isolation and characterization of polypyrrolic intermediates

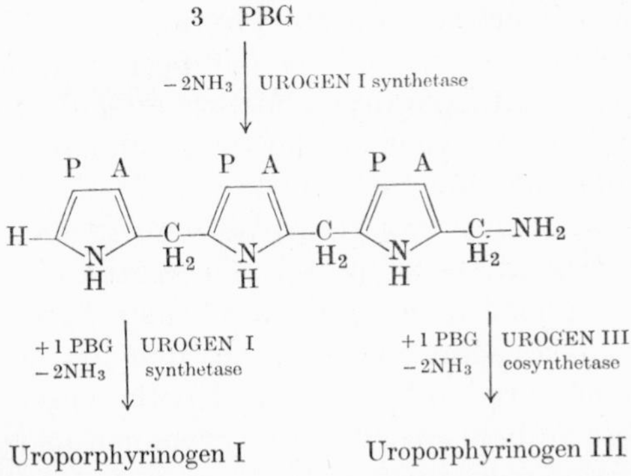

FIG. 5. A possible functional relationship between the enzymes Uroporphyrinogen I synthetase and Uroporphyrinogen III cosynthetase.

in Urogen I biosynthesis may be useful. One of a number of possibilities is that a linear tripyrrole formed from PBG by Urogen I synthetase is one substrate (Fig. 5). Many proposed schemes have been discussed extensively (Bogorad, 1960). A scheme based on the alteration by Urogen III cosynthetase of a linear tetrapyrrole formed from PBG by the action of Urogen I synthetase has been advanced more recently by Mathewson and Corwin (1961); a system with many similar features but involving the exchange of pyrrole residues between a pair of linear tetrapyrroles was proposed by Wittenberg (1959).

As noted above, PBG in aqueous solution condenses non-enzymatically. The Uro isomer (or isomers) produced is affected by the acidity or alkalinity of the solution (e.g. Cookson and Rimington, 1954; Mauzerall, 1960). Current biological practice appears to differ greatly from the mechanisms of non-enzymatic formation of Uro III but the latter is of considerable interest in speculations on the origin of life.

D. THE DECARBOXYLATION OF UROPORPHYRINOGENS. THE FORMATION OF COPROPORPHYRINOGENS

Mammals afflicted with hereditary or acquired porphyrias excrete varying amounts of uroporphyrins and coproporphyrins of the I and III isomeric series. How the biological occurrence of these porphyrins and of protoporphyrin IX could be rationalized was the subject of extensive speculation before the biogenetic relationships among these compounds became clear. Lemberg and Legge (1949) discussed some of the then current ideas about the interrelationships of coproporphyrin, uroporphyrins, and protoporphyrins. By the early 1950's most students of porphyrin biosynthesis had become convinced that uroporphyrin III and coproporphyrin III were closely related to protoporphyrin IX or precursors of it. At that time not only the tetracarboxylic coproporphyrins and the octacarboxylic uroporphyrins, but porphyrins with 7, 6, and 5 carboxyl groups per molecule had been identified in the urine of patients with congenital porphyria (McSwiney et al., 1950; Rimington and Miles, 1951); a somewhat similar array of porphyrins had been identified in a chlorophyll-less mutant strain of Chlorella (Bogorad and Granick, 1953a); and, most important, Wittenberg and Shemin's (1949, 1950) degradative analyses of protohaem synthesized from position labelled acetate supplied to cell preparations strongly suggested, first, that the methyl substituents on each of the four pyrrole rings of protohaem had a common origin and, second, that the vinyl substituents on rings A and B were probably derived from propionic acid residues formed initially by the same mechanism as those on rings C and D. Numerous attempts, generally not published, were made to demonstrate the conversion of uroporphyrin into coproporphyrin or protoporphyrin in biological systems shown to be capable of making protoporphyrin from ALA or PBG. Then, from a few experiments it became clear that uroporphyrinogens, the unoxidized precursors of uroporphyrins, were the substrates for the synthesis of coproporphyrinogens. In turn, Coprogen III rather than Copro III, was shown to be the precursor of Protogen IX (Bogorad, 1955, 1957a, 1958c; Neve et al., 1956; Mauzerall and Granick, 1958).

Urogen decarboxylase catalyses the removal of the carboxyl group from each of the four acetic acid side chains of Urogen; the methyl residues of the corresponding Coprogen isomers remain. The enzyme attacks not only the biologically occurring isomers, Urogens I and III, but also isomers II and IV. The reaction rate varies with the isomeric configuration of the substrate in the following order: Urogen III > IV > II > I. Porphyrins with 7, 6, or 5 carboxyl groups per molecule, i.e. with 4 propionic acid residues plus 3, 2, or 1 not yet decarboxylated acetic acid substituents, have been identified in oxidized reaction mixtures of urogen and its decarboxylase (Mauzerall and Granick, 1958). Although it is clear that this enzyme is present in tissues of higher plants and in broken cell preparations of *Chlorella* which can catalyse the synthesis of protoporphyrin from PBG or Urogen III and of Coprogen I from Urogen I (Bogorad and Granick, 1953b; Bogorad, 1958c) the most detailed investigations have been conducted on an enzyme prepared from rabbit red cells (Granick and Mauzerall, 1958; Mauzerall and Granick, 1958).

Conditions affecting the production of Coprogen by cultures of *Rhodopseudomonas capsulata* have been studied by Cooper (1963); Cohen-Bazire *et al.* (1957) have investigated this problem in *Rhodopseudomonas spheroides*. Heath and Hoare (1959) report the presence of a heat-stable factor for coproporphyrin formation in broken cell preparations of *R. spheroides*; this factor has not been identified further.

E. THE OXIDATIVE DECARBOXYLATION OF COPROPORPHYRINOGEN III. THE FORMATION OF PROTOPORPHYRINOGEN IX

The conversion of Coprogen III into Protogen IX requires the formation of vinyl groups from propionic acid groups on rings A and B. That this decarboxylation and dehydrogenation might require aerobic conditions was indicated by the observations of Bénard *et al.* (1951) that blood from anaemic rabbits formed protoporphyrin when incubated with glycine aerobically but predominantly coproporphyrin, when incubated under nitrogen. This observation of an oxygen requirement was extended by Falk *et al.* (1953) in studies on the formation of porphyrins from porphyrinogen by haemolysed chicken erythrocytes.

In work with partly purified Coprogen oxidative decarboxylase from guinea-pig liver mitochondria (Sano and Granick, 1961) or with acetone-dried powders of ox liver mitochondria (Porra and Falk, 1964) no oxidant other than O_2 was found to be used by the enzyme. Sano and Granick reported trying flavine mononucleotide, 1,4-naphthoquinone, and hydrogen peroxide without success. Porra and Falk found the product of the reaction to be Protogen IX.

The guinea-pig mitochondrial enzyme studied by Sano and Granick does not act on Copro, mesoporphyrinogen, hematoporphyrinogen, Urogen III, monopropionic monoacryllic deutero porphyrinogen, 2,4-diacryllic protoporphyrin or the corresponding porphyrinogen. Sano and Granick report that this enzyme is also inactive against Coprogen isomers other than III. However, Porra and Falk (1964) found the substrate specificity not to be absolute; in their experiments Coprogen IV was used by the enzyme they obtained from ox liver mitochondria. However, Sano and Granick indicate that some Proto IX was produced from Coprogen I; they believe that the Proto formed was derived from Urogen III which contaminated the sample of the isomer I they used. Small amounts of Proto IX were also detected upon incubation of Urogen I with broken *Chlorella* cells; it is not clear whether there was indeed porphyrin formation by the *Chlorella* enzyme from isomers other than those of the III series in these experiments (Bogorad, 1958c).

Granick and Sano (1961) followed the formation of Proto IX from coproporphyrinogen in the presence of T_2O. They conclude that the mechanism of oxidation is hydride–ion removal from the propionic acid– CH_2 group adjacent to the pyrrole ring occurring simultaneously with the decarboxylation to form the vinyl group.

F. METAL CHELATION. THE FORMATION OF IRON AND MAGNESIUM PROTO-PORPHYRINS

The intermediates in porphyrin biosynthesis to this point, i.e. the formation of Protogen, are all hexahydroporphyrins, that is, porphyrinogens; these reduced cyclic tetrapyrroles are not effective chelators of metal ions. However, biologically useful porphyrins are magnesium and iron derivatives. Thus the next step in porphyrin biosynthesis is the oxidation of Protogen to Proto IX. As pointed out much earlier in this chapter, porphyrinogens are relatively easily oxidized non-enzymatically to the corresponding porphyrins. There is some evidence, however, for the possible existence of systems, of undetermined specificity, which stimulate the oxidation of porphyrinogens. Sano and Granick (1961) have presented some evidence for a system which catalyses the oxidation of protoporphyrinogen and Bogorad (1958a) reported that preparations from spinach leaf tissue stimulate the oxidation of uroporphyrinogens.

Iron and magnesium metalloporphyrins are known in biological systems. Granick has pointed out that the nature of the metal inserted into protoporphyrin determines the use of that compound in either of two biosynthetic pathways, either as a component of haemoproteins or for further use in synthesis of chlorophylls.

Labbe and his co-workers have described an enzyme prepared from rat liver mitochondria which catalyses the chelation of iron by protoporphyrin. They find that it will catalyse the incorporation of ferrous or cobaltous ions but not ferric or stannous ions. The enzyme is inhibited by ions of Mg, Ca, Ni, Ca, Cd, Pb, Cu, Mn, An, and Hg. With regard to porphyrin specificity, the enzyme appears to catalyse the chelation of iron by Proto IX as well as by deuteroporphyrin, haematoporphyrin, mesoporphyrin, and 2,4 dibromodeuteroporphyrin, but not by Uro, Copro, 2,4-diacetyl-deuteroporphyrin, or 2,4-bis (2 carboxycyclopropyl) protoporphyrin. Porphyrins which were not active appeared to have no effect on the utilization by the enzyme of porphyrins such as Proto into which metals could be incorporated (Nishida and Labbe, 1959; Labbe, 1959; Labbe and Hubbard, 1960, 1961; Labbe et al., 1963). An enzyme with similar properties has been studied in preparations from duck erythrocytes (Oyama et al., 1961), chicken erythrocytes (Schwartz et al., 1959) and pig liver, as well as in extracts of a number of microorganisms such as baker's yeast, Escherichia coli, Thiobacillus X, and the photosynthetic bacteria Chromatium strain D (Porra and Jones, 1963a, b).

Porphyrin-iron chelating enzyme prepared from chicken erythrocytes has been separated into two heat-labile non-dialysable components by Schwartz et al. (1959).

Porra and Jones (1963b) have found that the specificity for porphyrins of the pig liver enzyme is in general similar to that of the enzyme from rat liver mitochondria studied by Labbe and Hubbard (1961). In addition, Porra and Jones report that the pig enzyme attacks neither porphyrin a nor porphyrin c (the porphyrin of cytochrome c). In studying the effect of pH on the formation of haem by the pig liver enzyme, Porra and Jones (1963a) observed that a plot of activity against pH gave either an asymmetric or a two peaked curve with maxima at pH 8 and pH 9. In addition Porra and Jones (1963b) found that freshly broken cells of Thiobacillus X catalysed the formation of corresponding haems from meso- and from monoformaldeutero-porphyrins while stored cells of the same micro-organism utilized only mesorphyrin as a substrate for this reaction. On the basis of these observations it was suggested that more than one ferrochelatase (their name for the porphyrin-iron chelating enzyme) might be present in the same organism. This might be pertinent to the synthesis of the various haems in an organism.

Except for the work with Chromatium described above there has been no work on the porphyrin-iron chelating enzyme in photosynthetic or other plant materials. However, Neuberger and Tait (1964) have investigated an enzyme they describe as zinc-protoporphyrin chelatase from chromatophores of Rhodopseudomonas spheroides. They also found this enzyme of undetermined utility in mitochondria from guinea-pig livers, and in rabbit liver, heart, and kidney. The enzyme from R. spheroides appears to be specific for Zn^{2+} while salts of Cu^{2+}, Co^{2+}, Mn^{2+}, and Ca^{2+} inhibit the reaction. Fe^{2+} ions competitively inhibit zinc protoporphyrin formation. On the other hand, when these preparations are incubated with ascorbate they show ferrochelatase activity. Neuberger and Tait suggest the possibility of two enzymes being present in their preparation (1) chelatase as described by other workers and (2) the zinc chelating enzyme. A zinc chelating enzyme from leaf-tissue has also been described by Little and Kelsey (1964). One of the problems in this area of work is the relatively rapid non-enzymatic uptake of metal ions like zinc and copper by porphyrins. This always makes for some uneasiness regarding the biological reality of the observations. Furthermore, the lack of knowledge about zinc porphyrins as biologically useful compounds is also disconcerting in view of these findings. It is conceivable of course that zinc protoporphyrin might be an intermediate in the formation of magnesium protoporphyrin. However, Phillips's (1963) data indicate that zinc porphyrin complexes are more stable than the corresponding magnesium ones.

Neither the iron nor the zinc protoporphyrin chelatase preparations are capable of catalysing the insertion of magnesium into protoporphyrin. That an enzyme for the incorporation of magnesium into protoporphyrin must exist is clear from the fact that magnesium is relatively difficult to inert into porphyrins chemically and so this is probably done enzymatically. Furthermore, magnesium protoporphyrin has been shown to be the substrate for the next reaction in the biosynthesis of chlorophyll.

G. THE ESTERIFICATION OF MAGNESIUM PROTOPORPHYRIN

In 1948 Granick reported on a series of mutants of *Chlorella* which formed no chlorophyll but accumulated large amounts of other porphyrins. One strain accumulated protoporphyrin IX, another magnesium protoporphyrin, and later (Granick, 1950) a third mutant was found which accumulated magnesium vinyl phaeoporphyrin a$_5$. These compounds, in the order listed, then appeared to establish a few landmarks along the path between protoporphyrin IX and chlorophyll (see Fig. 2).

The first step in the further utilization of magnesium protoporphyrin appears to be the esterification of the carboxyl group of the propionic acid residue on ring C with methanol to make magnesium protoporphyrin IX monomethyl ester. Such a compound has been isolated from *Chlorella vulgaris* mutant No. 60-A and from etiolated barley leaves supplied with δ-aminolevulinic acid and α,α'-dipyridyl (Granick, 1961); from cultures from *Rhodopseudomonas spheroides* (Jones, 1963a) and from cultures of *R. capsulata* (Cooper, 1963). Tait and Gibson (1961) found that chromatophores from *R. spheroides* when incubated with magnesium protoporphyrin and S-adenosyl methionine catalyse the formation of magnesium protoporphyrin monomethylester. They found that while protoporphyrin IX could be esterified by this enzyme the rate of this reaction was only about $\frac{1}{15}$ that of the esterification of magnesium protoporphyrin. This appears to support the contention that magnesium protoporphyrin methyl ester is derived from magnesium protoporphyrin which in turn is formed from protoporphyrin. Green *et al.* (1957) had found that when cultures of *Chlorella vulgaris* were incubated with [^{14}C]formate the labelled carbon atom appeared in the methyl ester group of chlorophyll *a* without contributing extensively to the biosynthesis of the tetrapyrrole skeleton. Also in accord with the findings of Tait and Gibson are experiments of Gibson *et al.* (1962b) which indicate that the effect of both ethionine and threonine in blocking bacteriochlorophyll formation by *R. spheroides* is reversed by the addition of methionine or homocysteine thiolactone.

H. THE FORMATION OF PROTOCHLOROPHYLLIDE *a*

Protochlorophyllide *a* differs from magnesium protoporphyrin IX monomethyl ester in the presence of an ethyl rather than a vinyl group on carbon 4 (ring B), and of the cyclopentanone ring formed from the esterified propionic acid residue on carbon 6 (ring C). Jones's (1963b) isolation of magnesium 2,4-divinyl pheoporphyrin a_5 monomethylester from cultures of *Rhodopseudomonas spheroides* grown in the presence of 8-hydroxyquinoline suggests that the cyclopentanone ring is formed before the reduction of the vinyl substituent at carbon 4 occurs. The course of formation of the cyclopentanone ring can only be speculated upon but must be considered to begin with the methylation which has just been discussed. The next step might be the oxidation of the β-carbon atom of this methylated propionic acid side chain, perhaps by way of an hydroxyl intermediate although neither this compound nor the carbonyl has been found. In any event, if the divinyl pheoporphyrin a_5 found by Jones is not an artefact, the sequence of events in the conversion of Mg Proto IX to protochlorophyllide *a* appears to be: (1) formation of the cyclopentanone ring, and (2) the reduction of the vinyl group at carbon atom 4 to an ethyl group.

I. CONVERSION OF PROTOCHLOROPHYLLIDE INTO CHLOROPHYLLIDE *a*

Many, though not all, algae and some higher plants can form chlorophylls in darkness. Other plants, including leaves of all flowering plants examined, form chlorophyll only upon illumination. Plants which have grown in total darkness from seed are etiolated; i.e. they are pale yellow in colour and are markedly different morphologically from light-grown plants of the same age. Etiolated dicotyledonous plants such as Red Kidney beans characteristically have unexpanded leaves and an elongated hypocotyl; etiolated monocots such as barley or maize bear long thin leaves. Yellow, etiolated plants form chlorophyll when illuminated. Much work on the final steps in the formation of chlorophylls has been done with illuminated leaves from etiolated plants.

Interest in the final steps in the formation of chlorophylls, including curiosity about the role of protochlorophyll, antedates most of the research already described in this chapter on other aspects of chlorophyll biosynthesis.

The discovery of protochlorophyll dates to Monteverde's (1893) discovery in an alcoholic extract of etiolated leaves of a compound with absorption properties closer to those of chlorophyll than anything then known. As might be expected, for a pigment which was found not only in etiolated leaves but also in inner seed coats of cucurbits such as squash and pumpkin, two opposing positions regarding the role of protochlorophyll were taken: Lubimenko's that protochlorophyll is a by-product of chlorophyll synthesis and, e.g. Noack and Kiessling's (1930) that protochlorophyll is the immediate precursor of chlorophyll. Protochlorophyll was shown to be 7,8 dehydrochlorophyll a by the work of Noack and Kiessling (1929) and of Fischer et al. (1939) and thus it became clear that if protochlorophyll were to be converted to chlorophyll a a reduction of pyrrole ring D would be required.

In 1946 Sylvia Frank reported that light of 445 and 645 mμ most effectively promoted the greening of oat seedlings. Minor maxima in the action spectrum occurred at 575 and 545 mμ. This action spectrum was in general accord with the absorption spectrum as then known for protochlorophyll dissolved in organic solvents. Not long afterwards J. H. C. Smith began a series of studies which established that protochlorophyll (or rather, as it later developed, the spectroscopically identical phytol-less close relative, Mg vinyl phaeoporphyrin a_5 or protochlorophyllide a) is the immediate precursor of chlorophyll a. Koski and Smith (1948) began by isolating sufficient quantities of protochlorophyll from etiolated barley to permit the accurate determination of the absolute absorption spectrum in ether solution. Then, since similar data were available for chlorophyll a, it was possible to estimate the concentration of both chlorophyll a and protochlorophyll a in extracts of leaves (see Smith and Benitez (1955) for discussion of procedures). The protochlorophyll present in an etiolated leaf is of the order of $\frac{1}{100}$ or $\frac{1}{200}$ to $\frac{1}{1000}$ of the maximum amount of chlorophyll which the same leaf may contain after prolonged illumination. As will be discussed in greater detail later, a small amount of chlorophyll is formed immediately upon illumination of an etiolated leaf; much larger amounts are produced later, sometimes after a lag of several hours. Smith (1948), in order to deal only or primarily with photochemical conversions, cooled etiolated barley leaves to 0 to 7° C, took samples for determination of chlorophyll and protochlorophyll, and then, still at lowered temperatures, illuminated the remaining leaves for various periods of time before harvest. He was able to demonstrate a mole for mole correspondence between the decrease in protochlorophyll and the increase in chlorophyll during the experiment. Similar results were obtained by Koski (1950) using dark-grown maize seedlings illuminated at room temperature but for short periods of time ranging from 10 sec to 16 min.

Koski *et al.* (1951) studied the action spectrum for chlorophyll formation by etiolated normal and albino maize seedlings exposed to short
periods of illumination. Since the albino strain was almost free from
carotenoids possible screening by these pigments in the blue region of
the spectrum was eliminated. In general agreement with Frank's data on
oats, action maxima at 445 and 650 mμ were observed for chlorophyll
formation by both albino and normal maize plants. However, while the
response to 650 mμ light was about equal in the two strains of maize,
445 mμ light was almost three times more effective in evoking chlorophyll
formation by albino than normal plants in accord with expectations of
the screening effect of carotenoids.

The data enumerated provided firm support for the proposal that
chlorophyll *a* is formed upon illumination of protochlorophyll *a* in seed
plants. However, the action spectrum maxima at 445 mμ and 650 mμ do
not precisely coincide with the absorption spectrum maxima for protochlorophyll dissolved in organic solvents [434 and 629 mμ in methanol;
432 and 623 mμ in diethyl ether (Koski *et al.*, 1951)]. The differences
between the action spectrum for chlorophyll formation and the absorption spectrum of protochlorophyllide *a* in organic solvents in a general
way resembled those between the absorption maxima of an extract of
chlorophyll *a* and *b* from a plant and the wavelengths of maximum
photosynthesis; the differences were attributed to the arrangement of
protochlorophyll molecules within the cell or their attachment to some
cell component. Shibata (1957), using his opal glass technique for studying absorption spectra of opaque, i.e. highly light scattering materials
such as leaves (for full discussion of this method, see Shibata, 1959) with
commercial spectrophotometers, followed spectroscopic changes in intact
etiolated leaves during greening. (Investigations of this sort have generally been confined to the red region of the spectrum because the
carotenoids do not absorb there). He observed that unilluminated
etiolated leaves absorb light of 650 mμ strongly, i.e. the absorption
maximum for protochlorophyll in the red region of the spectrum *in vivo*
is at 650 mμ, in excellent agreement with the maximum for effectiveness
of chlorophyll formation.

Shibata also observed that a complex series of spectral changes
follows illumination of an etiolated Pole bean or maize leaf. As the
absorption at 650 mμ declines a new absorption band appears immediately at 684 mμ; this spectral change presumably reflects the reduction
of ring D of protochlorophyll and the consequent formation of chlorophyll
a. Then, within about ten minutes, either in light or darkness, the 684 mμ
absorption band decreases in intensity while a new band with a maximum
at 671–673 mμ develops. Finally, after an additional two hours either in
darkness or light an absorption band whose maximum absorption is at

about 677 mμ replaces the one at 673 mμ. The significance of the absorption "shifts" is not yet clear.

In addition to the absorption maximum at 650 mμ which changes upon illumination, Shibata (1957) observed an absorption peak at 636 mμ which was present in young leaves but particularly prominent in old leaves. This absorption band was unaltered after illumination of the leaf; Shibata attributed the absorption at 636 mμ to an inactive, i.e. non-transformable, type of protochlorophyll a.

Granick (1950) isolated a mutant *Chlorella* which when grown in darkness forms no chlorophylls but accumulates Mg vinyl phaeoporphyrin a_5 (= protochlorophyllide = protochlorophyll not esterified with phytol). Protochlorophyllide was also found in the "protochlorophyll fraction" of etiolated leaves of angiosperms (Granick, 1950; Loeffler, 1955). Wolff and Price (1957) clearly demonstrated the significance of the presence of both protochlorophyllide a and its phytol ester in etiolated leaves.

Protochlorophyllide a and protochlorophyll a have identical absorption maxima but are considerably different in solubility in non-polar organic solvents such as light petroleum. The presence of the C-20 isoprenoid phytol side chain of protochlorophyll confers upon it solubility in light petroleum or iso-octane which protochlorophyllide a lacks. An analogous set of similarities in spectral property and differences in solubility mark the relationship between chlorophyllide a and chlorophyll a. Wolff and Price (1957) took advantage of the ability to separate easily "-phylls" from "-phyllides" in aqueous acetone extracts of etiolated or illuminated bean leaves. In etiolated leaves they found about 20%–25% protochlorophyll a; 75–80% protochlorophyllide a. After illumination for ten seconds the protochlorophyll a level was unchanged, i.e. the protochlorophyll a was not reduced, but the protochlorophyllide was converted to chlorophyllide a. The esterification of chlorophyllide a with phytol starts after illumination, following a sigmoid pattern with a lag phase extending from about 10 min to about 40 min from the termination of the irradiation, it is completed only after about 50 to 60 min; this can all occur in darkness. The period of phytolation covers almost the entire time span of the spectral shifts observed by Shibata (1957). This leads to the conjecture that the last of the spectral shifts—673 to 677 mμ—*may* coincide with the phytolation of chlorophyllide a; however, the data of Smith *et al.* (1959) on spectral shifts and phytolation in a group of maize mutants illustrates the difficulty in strongly supporting such a guess.

Godnev *et al.* (1963) have determined the amounts of protochlorophyll and protochlorophyllide in etiolated plants of seventeen species; they report the percentage of protochlorophyllide to range from twelve to ninety. Smith *et al.* (1959) have examined a number of maize mutants in this respect. Fischer and Rüdiger (1959) raised some doubts about whether "protochlorophyll" is esterified with phytol; they were unable to detect phytol upon hydrolysis of the pigment from etiolated barley. Godnev *et al.* (1963) were unable to confirm this finding.

Is the inactive protochlorophyll of Wolff and Price (1957) the same material as the inactive (636 mμ) pigment of Shibata? Virgin (1960) implies that they are, but this is not necessarily the case. Protochlorophyllide *a* which absorbs at about 636 mμ rather than 650 mμ *in vivo* is known in two instances: (1) dark-grown cells of *Chlorella vulgaris* mutant C-10 isolated by Bryan and Bogorad (1963) (which appears very similar or identical to Granick's (1950) protochlorophyllide *a* accumulating strain 31) contains protochlorophyllide *a* with an absorption maximum *in vivo* at 632 mμ but 647 mμ light rather than 632 mμ radiation is effective in promoting chlorophyll synthesis; (2) etiolated leaves supplied δ-amino-levulinic acid accumulate about ten times more protochlorophyllide *a* than originally present; this new protochlorophyllide, or at least the bulk of it, absorbs at about 632 mμ and not at 650 mμ (Granick, 1959). This 632 mμ absorbing protochlorophyllide *a* formed from exogenous δ-aminolevulinic acid is rapidly bleached upon illumination and also appears to bring about the photodestruction of 650 mμ absorbing compounds and their products (Klein and Bogorad, 1964). Protochlorophyllide *a* which absorbs *in vivo* at 650 mμ is assumed to be associated with a particular protein; the 632–636 mμ absorbing form (*in vivo*) is thought to lack such an association and thus to be incapable of being converted into chlorophyllide.

The arguments presented do not preclude the absorption *in vivo* at 632–636 mμ by any or all of the protochlorophyll present, but it is apparent that protochlorophyllide can also absorb there.

In green leaves which are steadily accumulating chlorophyll *a* the near terminal step is the photoreduction of a pigment with the fluorescence spectrum of protochlorophyll *a* or protochlorophyllide *a* (Litvin *et al.*, 1959). Shlyk *et al.* (1960) have shown that in green as well as etiolated leaves protochlorophyllide *a* is the pigment which is converted.

1. *Protochlorophyllide Holochrome*

Before Shibata had carried out his detailed studies of the spectral shifts which accompany the conversion of protochlorophyllide *a* into chlorophyllide *a in vivo*, the transformation had been observed in glycerol homogenates or buffered aqueous extracts of etiolated leaves. The unit of conversion *in vitro*, and presumably *in vivo* as well, is not protochlorophyllide alone but a protochlorophyllide–protein complex termed the "protochlorophyll holochrome" (now more appropriately the "protochlorophyllide holochrome") by Smith (1952). (Also see Smith and Young, 1956; and Smith, 1960.)

Smith (1952) found that the opalescent supernatant fluid from centrifuged glycerine homogenates of dark-grown barley leaves contained a complex of protochlorophyllide and protein which absorbed at about 650 mμ; upon illumination as the 650 mμ absorption maximum disappeared a new absorption band, presumably that of chlorophyllide holochrome, appeared at 680 mμ. Similar photo-transformable protochlorophyllide holochromes, sometimes with slightly different absorption maxima, can also be prepared from bean leaves and from squash cotyledons (Smith et al., 1957). The discovery by Krasnovsky and Kosobutskya (1952) that soluble photo-transformable protochlorophyllide holochrome could be prepared by grinding etiolated bean leaves in buffered aqueous solution opened the way for extensive purification of the holochrome.

Smith has summarized the findings of his laboratory on purified bean leaf protochlorophyll holochrome: it is estimated to have one protochlorophyllide molecule per protein of molecular weight about 0·5 to 1·4 × 10^6; a volume of 2·05 × 10^{-18} c.c; a density, as determined on a sucrose gradient, of 1·16; and in electron micrographs it appears as an oblate spheroid particle with axial diameters of 218, 193, and 93 Å (Smith, 1960; Smith and Coomber, 1961). Boardman (1962a) has obtained slightly different values from studies of the isolated protochlorophyllide protein particle: an average of one protochlorophyllide molecule per protein of molecular weight 600,000 ± 50,000; a sedimentation coefficient of 18 S; a density of 1·37. Boardman reports the complex to be a sphere of 100–110 Å diameter when viewed with the electron microscope; this is a major difference compared with reports from Smith's laboratory.

Based on studies of protochlorophyllide a conversion in situ in etiolated leaves and in vitro, as a component of the holochrome, the following conclusions have been reached: the quantum yield for the reaction is about 0·6 or about one quantum required per molecule being transformed; the reaction proceeds at −70° C but not at −195° C and the reaction rate is also directly proportional to light intensity, suggesting the possibility that the reaction has a bimolecular aspect; however the rate of conversion is independent of the initial concentration of complex and of the viscosity of the medium (Smith and Benitez, 1954; Smith, 1960; Boardman, 1962b). In agreement with work by Smith's group, Boardman (1962b) found that only the native protochlorophyllide complex is required for conversion; no evidence for the involvement of a dialysable cofactor could be obtained. Boardman's data lead him to "suggest that the transformation does not involve a collision process either between independent protein molecules or between a protein molecule and a hydrogen donor molecule" and he concludes that "the photo-transformation of protochlorophyll to chlorophyll a can be explained by a restricted collision process within the protochlorophyll-protein complex...".

2. *Chlorophyll Accumulation in Darkness*

Those algae and flowering plants which produce chlorophyll in total darkness apparently contain enzyme systems capable of reducing protochlorophyll (or protochlorophyllide). There are, however, numerous species or strains of algae which require light for chlorophyll formation; among these are: *Euglena gracilis*, which has been widely used in studies of chlorophyll formation and plastid development (e.g. Wolken, 1961); wild-type *Cyanidium caldarium* which requires light for the formation of chlorophyll a, phycocyanin, and allophycocyanin (Allen, 1959; Nichols and Bogorad, 1962); a strain of *Chlorella vulgaris* which requires light for growth and greening even on a nutrient medium containing 1% glucose (Finkle *et al.*, 1950); and *Chlorella vulgaris* mutants which grow and accumulate protochlorophyllide in darkness but when grown in the light closely resemble wild-type cells in chlorophyll production and content (Granick, 1950; Bryan and Bogorad, 1963). There is no evidence upon which to decide whether the substrate for enzymatic (dark) reduction is protochlorophyll or protochlorophyllide nor whether a protochlorophyll(ide)–holochrome is involved. However, as discussed earlier, a *Chlorella* mutant which accumulates protochlorophyllide which absorbs at 632 mμ when grown in darkness (Bryan and Bogorad, 1963) produces maximal amounts of chlorophyll when illuminated with light of 647 mμ the wavelength at which a protein-protochlorophyllide complex would be expected to absorb.

Traces of chlorophyll have been detected in dark-grown oats (Goodwin and Owens, 1947) and in a variety of angiosperms by Godnev *et al.* (1959). However, among higher plants, chlorophyll production in darkness by conifer seedlings is of particular interest (Schmidt, 1924; Bogorad, 1950; Schou, 1951; also see general discussion by Egle, 1960) because large amounts of chlorophyll are formed and two distinct tissues are involved. Besides the various seed coats, a conifer seed consists of a massive haploid megagametophyte tissue in which is embedded the sporophyte, a diploid embryo complete with a number of long thin cotyledons. During germination in a Petri dish the cotyledons elongate pushing the radicle out of the enveloping megagametophyte first. As the embryo enlarges the megagametophyte is digested away, but almost to its last remnant it remains in contact with the tips of the expanding cotyledons. Even in total darkness the cotyledons become green forming chlorophylls a and b at about the same rate as those of illuminated excised seedlings.

However, if embryos of *Pinus jeffreyi* are excised before germination and grown in darkness on a medium containing sugar, little (Schou, 1951) or no (Bogorad, 1950) chlorophyll is reported to be formed. On the other hand, if seedlings are separated from megagametophytes after germination and a few days growth in darkness they continue to produce some chlorophyll although at a lower rate than do intact seedlings; the rate of chlorophyll production by isolated seedlings depends in part on the duration of previous contact with megagametophyte tissue. It appears as though the megagametophyte may provide a specific compound which promotes greening without light, but the possibility of a general growth promoting effect of digested megagametophyte cannot be excluded.

Röbbelen (1956) has studied a mutant of *Arabidopsis thaliana*, a small flowering plant, which accumulates protochlorophyll (or protochlorophyllide?) but fails to make chlorophyll when illuminated unless an extract of etiolated wild-type *Arabidopsis* plants is administered. Some of Röbbelen's experiments suggest the involvement of reduced pyridine nucleotides in the reduction of protochlorophyll(ide) to chlorophyll(ide); unless this effect is quite indirect, it is difficult to reconcile with Smith's and Boardman's studies showing that no cofactors are required for the conversion of purified protochlorophyllide holochrome *in vitro*.

J. CHLOROPHYLLASE: AN ENZYME FOR THE PHYTOLATION OF CHLOROPHYLLIDE *a*?

From current data it seems likely that the final step in chlorophyll *a* synthesis is the esterification with phytol of the propionic acid residue at position 7 (Ring D) of chlorophyllide *a*. (The metabolism of isoprenoids such as phytol is discussed in Chapter 4.)

The hydrolysis of chlorophylls to chlorophyllides and phytol by the action of chlorophyllase has been known indirectly since the work of Borodin who, in 1881, found crystals of "chlorophyll" in and around alcohol-treated leaf sections. The "chlorophyll" crystals were later found to be ethyl chlorophyllide; the enzyme chlorophyllase which is present in the leaf apparently catalyses the hydrolytic removal of the phytol from chlorophyll and esterification of the resulting chlorophyllide with the ethanol in which the leaf is bathed. It is probably more appropriate (although less lyrical) to ascribe the discovery of the enzyme to Willstätter and his co-workers. Chapters on the "Action of chlorophyllase," the "Application of the enzyme to partial chlorophyll synthesis," and the "Applications of chlorophyllase for making preparations: the chlorophyllides" are included in an extensive summary of investigations on chlorophyll by Willstätter and Stoll published in 1913.

From the first reinterpretations of Borodin's experiments it was clear that chlorophyllase is an exceptional enzyme: although it is destroyed if the leaves are boiled in water the enzyme is active in the presence of high concentrations of alcohol or acetone.

Chlorophyllase is apparently normally intimately associated with lipids or, if it has a removable lipid segment, this portion is not essential for activity. Upon finding large amounts of the enzyme in their preparations of spinach chloroplastin, a chloroplast–lipoprotein complex obtained by digitonin treatment of chloroplasts, Ardao and Vennesland (1960) suggested that all the chlorophyllase of a mature spinach leaf may be present in a chlorophyll–lipoprotein complex. Klein and Vishniac (1961) prepared 500-fold purified chlorophyllase (or a sodium deoxycholate–chlorophyllase complex) by extracting isobutanol-treated etiolated rye seedlings with sodium deoxycholate. On the other hand, Holden (1961; 1963) obtained a 500–600-fold purified water-soluble enzyme preparation by cellulose ion-exchange chromatography of an alkaline buffer extract of sugar beet leaf acetone powder. Shimizu and Tamaki (1962) prepared soluble chlorophyllase from tobacco chloroplasts by treatment with n-butanol, heating, and acetone and ammonium sulphate fractionation.

There is strong but not obligatory dependence upon organic solvents for enzyme activity; the chlorophyllase in Ardao and Vennesland's chloroplastin did not act upon the chlorophyll of the complex until an organic solvent suitable for dissociating the pigment had been introduced but Klein and Visniac devised an active aqueous system in which the substrate was solubilized by the detergent Triton X-100. However, in a solution containing 0.2% of this detergent purified sugar beet chlorophyllase hydrolyses chlorophyll at about one-third the rate observed in 40% acetone (Holden, 1963).

Chlorophyllase acts upon chlorophylls including bacteriochlorophyll and *Chlorobium* chlorophyll "650" (chlorophyll → chlorophyllide + phytol) and their Mg-free derivative (summarized by Holden, 1963 (see also Chapter 17)), pheophytins (pheophytin → pheophorbide + phytol), but not protochlorophyll (Mayer, 1930; Sudyina, 1963). The activity of the enzyme is limited to porphyrins with a carboxymethyl group at carbon 10 and hydrogens at positions 7 and 8—i.e. cyclic tetrapyrroles with ring D reduced as in chlorophyll (Fischer and Stern, 1940). These interesting data leave unexplained the presence of protochlorophyll in etiolated tissues—perhaps the specificity of chlorophyllase is not absolute although other explanations could be concocted readily.

Chlorophyllase catalyses a reversible reaction; thus by manipulating the concentrations of reactants the net accumulation of either chlorophyll or chlorophyllide can be effected. But what is the normal role of the enzyme *in vivo*? Does it participate in chlorophyll synthesis? Knowledge of the specificity of the enzyme and the view that chlorophyll a synthesis proceeds via the sequence protochlorophyllide $a \rightarrow$ chlorophyllide $a \rightarrow$ chlorophyll a does not eliminate the possibility that chlorophyllase acts synthetically. Indeed, indirect evidence favours assigning chlorophyllase a synthetic and not a degradative role. Holden (1963) reports that etiolated tissues have considerably lower chlorophyllase activity than green leaves, that when etiolated leaves are transferred to the light chlorophyllase activity increases, and that this increase parallels the accumulation of chlorophyll. Furthermore, Sudyina (1963) found that chlorophyllase activity increased sharply during the first few minutes of illumination of etiolated plants, a more rapid response than observed by Holden. Finally, Shimizu and Tamaki (1962, 1963) studied longer term changes in chlorophyllase activity. They found that chlorophyllase activity in tobacco was highest in 51 day-old plants and began to decline even before the maximum chlorophyll content was reached after 91 days of growth.

Assuming that chlorophyllase does participate in the synthetic reaction, future work on this problem may reveal whether the substrate is newly formed chlorophyllide holochrome or may relate the action of this enzyme to final stages in situating chlorophyll at its functional site in the chloroplast, either indirectly, by conferring lipophilic properties upon it, or directly by the enzymes being situated in the lamellar system. (Chlorophyllase is treated in further detail in Chapter 17).

K. THE ORIGIN OF CHLOROPHYLL b

It might be simpler to understand the origin of chlorophyll b if Seybold and Egle's (1937) observations on the existence of two chromatographically separable protochlorophylls in pumpkin seed coats had been confirmed and extended to leaf tissue. There is, however, no assurance of the existence of a protochlorophyll(ide) b (Seybold, 1949; Egle, 1960) and other possible precursors of chlorophyll b must be considered.

Shlyk and Godnev (1958) have summarized some logical possible interrelationships between the biosynthesis of chlorophylls a and b: "1. Each pigment is formed as a result of a separate biosynthetic chain; 2. Both pigments are formed in parallel from a common precursor; 3. Chlorophyll b is produced from previously formed chlorophyll a...; 4. Chlorophyll a is produced from previously formed chlorophyll b..." The choice among these possibilities is made mainly by default.

Proposal 4 cannot be embraced warmly because many plants make chlorophyll a but no chlorophyll b. Among these are mutants of strains which normally make both chlorophyll a and b (e.g. Highkin, 1950; Allen, 1958). Besides this indirect evidence, the photoconversion *in vitro* of protochlorophyllide a holochrome into chlorophyllide a holochrome clearly identifies the precursor of the latter.

Propositions 1 and 2 are related, depending only upon whether the common precursor is taken to be glycine or protochlorophyllide a. The former seems extraordinarily unlikely; the latter is possible but not strongly supported by presently available data.

Much of the evidence which has accumulated, some of it contradictory, has been interpreted to support the concept that chlorophyll b is formed from a. The most direct experiment is that of Godnev et al. (1960, 1963) in which the tops were trimmed off onion leaves which were just starting to become green and [^{14}C]chlorophyll a dissolved in sunflower oil was introduced into the hollow centre of the remaining leaf. Two days later the leaves were extracted with acetone and, after purification of the extract, [^{14}C]chlorophyll b was found. No radioactivity was found in chlorophyll a from a leaf similarly exposed to chlorophyll b. Most other pertinent data are from experiments in which changes in the specific radioactivity of each chlorophyll was followed after the administration of a pulse or during continuous exposure to $^{14}CO_2$, or to [^{14}C]glycine, [^{14}C]acetate, [^{14}C]δ-aminolevulinic acid or some other appropriate precursor of chlorophyll of green leaves, a growing algal culture, or etiolated leaves subsequently illuminated.

Shlyk and Godnev (1958) found, for a number of plants, the specific radioactivity of chlorophyll a to be about 2·5 to 4·7 times higher than that of chlorophyll b in the same leaf. Perkins and Roberts (1960) obtained similar data with wheat leaves. In a 10-day-long experiment with *Ceratophyllum demersum* L. Shlyk and Godnev (1958) found that the ratio "specific activity chlorophyll a/specific activity chlorophyll b" rose to a maximum of 4·7 on the third day but then declined to 2·8 on the tenth day. However, there are further complexities: an effect of day-length on the ratio of specific activities of the two chlorophylls has been observed by Sironval et al. (1961). Furthermore, Duranton et al. (1958) found that chlorophyll a from tobacco supplied with [^{14}C]δ-amino-levulinic acid had at first three times the specific activity of the chlorophyll b but in the course of the experiment the activity of b remained constant while that of a declined.

The data from some studies of algal cultures, *Chlorella* (Blass et al., 1959; Becker and Sheline, 1955; Shlyk et al., 1963b; Michel-Wolwertz, 1963) and *Scenedesmus* (Blass et al., 1959) are similar to those from investigations on green leaves, i.e. the specific activity of chlorophyll a remains 2·5 to 3 times higher than that of b. On the other hand, under different conditions the two chlorophylls can become equally radioactive in *Chlorella* (Della Rosa et al., 1953; Shlyk et al., 1963a) and in one case chlorophyll b of specific radioactivity more than 1·6 times that of chlorophyll a was isolated from *Chlorella vulgaris* cells which had been incubated with [2-^{14}C]glycine for 6 h (Brzeski and Rucker, 1960). Michel-Wolwertz's (1963) observations on the effect of light intensity upon the relative specific activities of the two chlorophylls in *Chlorella* may help explain such variations: "The specific activity of chlorophyll b increases progressively with the light intensity and very rapidly with the strongest intensities. On the other hand, chlorophyll a, so long as there is light, reveals a fairly constant specific activity..." All these observations may not argue very strongly for the conversion of chlorophyll a into b but they do not preclude the possibility of such a transformation. The complexities of interpretation of changes in relative specific activities are also apparent; they are undoubtedly compounded by any chlorophyll turnover which may occur.

Much more satisfactory are labelling studies with etiolated plants which convert their protochlorophyllide a to chlorophyll α immediately upon illumination, later produce additional "new" chlorophyll a, and sometimes at about the same time (e.g., maize: Koski, 1950), sometimes considerably later (oats: Goodwin and Owens, 1947), begin to make chlorophyll b (also see Seybold and Egle, 1938). Michel-Wolwertz (1963) supplied [^{14}C]δ-aminolevulinic acid to etiolated barley leaves and later illuminated them. After 4 and 6 h of illumination the chlorophylls were extracted and their specific activities were determined to be equal. According to Michel-Wolwertz this finding argues for a sequential synthesis of chlorophyll b from a; Smith and French (1963) point out that it could equally support the concept of the production of the two pigments from a close common precursor.

In another type of experiment Shlyk *et al.* (1963a) supplied illuminated green barley plants with $^{14}CO_2$ for 20–30 min, transferred the plants to darkness, and over the next 8 days periodically took samples and determined the specific activities of chlorophylls a and b. During this interval the specific activity of the chlorophyll b rose, that of a dropped. Shlyk is an outspoken champion of the origin of chlorophyll b from a.

It is not known whether there is normally a light-requiring step specific for chlorophyll b synthesis but Allen (1958) has isolated a *Chlorella* mutant which forms only chlorophyll a in darkness but both chlorophylls a and b when illuminated. Such an organism might be useful in studies of possible chlorophyll interconversions.

The acceptance and accommodation of conflicting data from tracer experiments is complicated by the great difficulty of bringing chlorophylls to radio-purity; a problem recognized at some time in the writing of almost every worker in this area. The complications introduced by differences in the rate of labelling with carbon of the tetrapyrrole nucleus and the esterifying groups of chlorophylls are fairly generally recognized if not always taken into account.

Smith (1960) has argued that chlorophylls a and b might arise from a common precursor (chlorophyllide a?) because the rates of formation of a and b are equal once chlorophyll b production has begun in greening etiolated barley. He also cites the experiments of Della Rosa $et\ al.$ (1953) and Duranton $et\ al.$ (1958) as evidence $against$ the formation of chlorophyll b from a.

In trying to interpret the effects of light intensity on the relative radioactivity of chlorophylls a and b in $Chlorella$ supplied with [^{14}C] acetate Michel-Wolwertz (1963) suggest that two kinds of chlorophyll a molecules might be recognized, old ones which are more readily photooxidized than young ones, the latter remaining more available for transformation to chlorophyll b. This could account for some of the observations, but it does bring up other important issues. Where might chlorophyllide a fit in this biosynthetic scheme (chlorophyllase can act on chlorophyllide b as well as a)? Where is the enzyme for the oxidation of the methyl group at position 3? Is it in the lamellar structure? And the major question: When and how are the chlorophylls set into their functional places?

To summarize: The two most likely possible immediate precursors of chlorophyll b are (1) chlorophyll a or (2) a compound which can be transformed into either chlorophyll a or b.

L. CHLOROPHYLLS c AND d

The structure of chlorophyll c is not known but it resembles protochlorophyllide a; it is not esterified with phytol and ring D is not reduced. Granick (1949) has suggested that it may be derived from protochlorophyllide a.

Chlorophyll d, 2-desvinyl, 2-formyl chlorophyll a, (Holt, 1960), could arise by oxidation of chlorophyll a although its precursor has not been identified.

M. THE CHLOROPHYLLS OF BACTERIA

The large amount of work on porphyrin biosynthesis in which $Athiorhodaceae$ have been used supports the view that early steps in the formation of chlorophyll a and of bacteriochlorophyll are similar. From a "tan" mutant of $R.\ spheroides$, Stanier and Smith (see Smith, 1960) isolated a pigment which closely resembles protochlorophyll spectroscopically. Griffiths (1962) also found a pigment which spectroscopically resembles protochlorophyll a, or protochlorophyllide a, as well as one similar to chlorophyll a in mutants of $R.\ spheroides$ which lack bacteriochlorophyll. In addition Sistrom *et al.* (1956) observed a mutant *R. spheroides* which excretes pheophorbide *a*.

If the identifications of the pigments are all correct and these compounds are not "mistakes" of the organism, it seems appropriate to conclude that bacteriochlorophyll is derived from chlorophyll or chlorophyllide *a*. The mechanism of the reduction of ring B is not known. There is no information on the possible requirement for light, the necessity for a holochrome, or whether the reduction follows or precedes the oxidation of the substituent at position 2 (Ring A) of chlorophyll(ide) *a*.

The hydroxyethyl (—CHOH—CH$_3$) group at position 2 of *Chlorobium* chlorophylls 650 and 660 could reflect the course of oxidation of the vinyl of chlorophyll *a* to the —CO—CH$_3$ of bacteriochlorophyll.

IV. The Control of Porphyrin Metabolism

When etiolated leaves are illuminated their protochlorophyllide *a* is converted to chlorophyllide *a*. If such leaves are returned to darkness after the brief exposure to light required for the conversion of the pigment they accumulate protochlorophyllide again. Madsen (1963) reports that 12 to 15 min after being returned to darkness etiolated wheat and barley leaves contain as much protochlorophyllide as before they were illuminated; from about this point protochlorophyllide production continues at a constantly decreasing rate and finally ceases after a total of about 1 h in darkness. While new protochlorophyllide is being formed, the chlorophyllide produced during illumination is being esterified with phytol. By repeatedly illuminating leaves with light flashes as short as $\frac{1}{1000}$ sec, a considerable amount of chlorophyll can be accumulated if adequate (10–15 min) dark periods are interposed (Madsen, 1963).

The situation is more complex in leaves under continuous light. The production of additional protochlorophyllide *a* apparently occurs just as in darkness (as has already been discussed); the protochlorophyllide *a* is converted into chlorophyllide *a*; and finally chlorophyll is formed. However, the rate of chlorophyll production generally increases drastically during illumination.

Early during illumination new chlorophyll is formed in continuously illuminated leaves at about the same rate as protochlorophyllide accumulates in leaves returned to darkness (Virgin, 1955). This is termed the "lag phase" because soon afterward the rate of chlorophyll synthesis increases sharply and continues at a constant rapid rate until net chlorophyll synthesis ceases in the fully-greened leaf. For example, 12 day-old etiolated bean leaves illuminated with 30 μW/cm^2 of red

(600–700 mμ) light formed less than 50 μg of chlorophyll per leaf during the 2-h long lag period but about 400 μg per leaf during the next hour, i.e. the first hour of the period of rapid greening (Sisler and Klein, 1963). Thus when etiolated leaves are illuminated continuously, the protochlorophyllide present is rapidly converted to chlorophyllide, new protochlorophyllide is formed (and converted to chlorophyllide) first slowly and then, accelerating to a constant rapid level, as much as ten times more rapidly than during the "lag phase" until the leaf is completely green. Phytolation and the development of lamellae in the chloroplast occur during greening (Virgin *et al.*, 1963).

The lag phase varies from being imperceptible to lasting five or so hours depending upon the age of the leaf, the species or variety of plant, light intensity, temperature, and some other conditions (Virgin, 1955; Sisler and Klein, 1963). Two-, three-, or four-day-old etiolated beans formed chlorophyll at a constant slow rate throughout the 3-h period of illumination studied by Sisler and Klein (1963); i.e. a period of rapid greening never developed or, according to their view, there was no lag phase. However, in leaves of the 5-day-old etiolated Black Valentine bean plants chlorophyll formed rapidly from the very beginning of illumination. Leaves from 7-, 12-, and 21-day-old plants exhibited lag phases of 1·5 to 2 h duration.

Why does a lag phase in chlorophyll production occur? Why does the rate of synthesis increase after the lag phase? How is the rate of chlorophyll formation controlled? Why is the rate different in illuminated and unilluminated plants? What determines the maximum content of protochlorophyllide or of chlorophyll in an etiolated or a green leaf?

Most attempts to answer these questions will evoke considerable speculation.

It is important to recognize that while there are quantitative variations except in a few mutants the biosynthetic chain of chlorophyll generally is qualitatively either on or off—intermediates do not accumulate. This marks the functioning of δ-aminolevulinic acid synthetase as an important control point. The importance of this step in controlling porphyrin metabolism is emphasized by the observation that etiolated leaves accumulate large amounts of protochlorophyllide when incubated with δ-aminolevulinic acid in darkness (Granick, 1959). Quantitative comparisons of the activity of enzymes "beyond" ALA synthetase in illuminated and unilluminated leaves are not available but it is clear that the enzymes for converting ALA into protochlorophyllide *a* are active in etiolated leaves when ALA is supplied. Thus the problem *appears* to be narrowed to the regulation of ALA synthetase activity which could be accomplished by controlling: (1) the concentration of the enzyme; (2) the concentration of pyridoxal phosphate, which is a cofactor for the

3

enzymatic reaction *in vitro*; (3) the availability of its substrates succinyl coenzyme A and glycine; or (4) the concentration of an inhibitor.

With regard to the possible control of porphyrin metabolism by inhibitors, protoporphyrin and various metalloporphyrins reduce the activity of ALA synthetase prepared from *Rhodopseudomonas spheroides*. At a final concentration of 20 μM protoporphyrin inhibited 25%, iron protoporphyrin IX (haemin) 53%, magnesium protoporphyrin IX 40%, and other metalloporphyrins from 40 to 58% (Burnham and Lascelles, 1963; see also Gibson *et al.*, 1961; Burnham, 1962). On the basis of these data plus the observation by Lascelles (1956) that iron suppresses porphyrin formation in *R. spheroides*, Burnham and Lascelles (1963) suggest that feedback inhibition of ALA synthetase by haemin might be one means of controlling porphyrin formation. ALA dehydrase was found to be only slightly inhibited by haemin.

R. spheroides forms bacteriochlorophyll when grown anaerobically in light of moderate intensity but only traces of the pigment are found in thoroughly aerated cultures maintained in darkness (van Niel, 1944; Cohen-Bazire *et al.*, 1957); small amounts of pigment are accumulated by unilluminated cells grown under reduced oxygen tension (Cohen-Bazire *et al.*, 1957; Lascelles, 1959). Lascelles (1959) found that ALA synthetase and ALA dehydrase are five times more active in organisms grown photosynthetically, i.e. anaerobically in the light, than in aerated dark-grown cells which are bacteriochlorophyll-poor. In general, the level of bacteriochlorophyll parallels, and is presumably at least in part regulated by, the activity of one of these enzymes.

Chlorophyll which would normally form upon the illumination of dark-grown *Euglena gracilis* or leaves or upon the reduction of oxygen tension in a *R. spheroides* culture fails to accumulate if protein or nucleic acid synthesis is blocked by any one of a number of agents. For example: protein synthesis: *R. spheroides*—inhibitors: DL-*p*-fluorophenylalanine, chloramphenicol (Sistrom, 1962; Bull and Lascelles, 1963); etiolated bean leaves—inhibitor: chloramphenicol (Margulies, 1962); nucleic acid synthesis: *R. spheroides*—inhibitor: 5-fluorouracil (Bull and Lascelles, 1963); *Euglena*—inhibitor: 5-fluorouracil (Smillie, 1963); Etiolated bean and corn leaves—inhibitor: actinomycin D (Bogorad and Jacobson, 1964).

There is good evidence (Lascelles, 1960a; Bull and Lascelles, 1963) that ALA synthetase is one of the proteins formed by *R. spheroides* preparing to make bacteriochlorophyll in response to reduced oxygen tension or illumination of anaerobically-grown cells. Mego and Jagendorf (1961) observed that chloroplasts of etiolated leaves contained more total protein after illumination.

How is chlorophyll formation regulated by changes in oxygen tension and illumination? Obviously effects which are exercised through nucleic acid synthesis could be specific, i.e. by initiating the activity of the group of genes which control the formation of enzymes of chlorophyll and bacteriochlorophyll biosynthesis as well as other proteins of the photosynthetic machinery. In a more general way, these environmental factors might indiscriminately stimulate all genes concerned with chloroplast development. The stimulation could be of nuclear genes, to whatever extent in a particular strain the chloroplast might be dependent upon nuclear activity, but recent evidence for chloroplast DNA (Chun et al., 1963; Leff et al., 1963; Sager and Ishida, 1963; Ris and Plaut, 1962; Kislev et al., 1964) opens the possibility of environmental effects upon the chloroplast genome exclusive of the nuclear genes. There is no evidence for compartmentalization of "chromatophore" DNA in R. spheroides.

The "specific" system would require light, for example, to bring about the formation or transport into the chloroplast of a specific inducer or de-repressor for each gene to be activated. On the other hand, control by the "general" system, by way of example, could be merely via a photochemical step in the synthesis of a purine or a pyrimidine, the phosphorylation of a nucleoside, the stimulation of an energy source, or any one of a number of easily imagined mechanisms for relieving "RNA starvation".

Evidence available now on the parallel development of photosynthetic pigments and enzymes would not eliminate consideration of the "general" system; particularly if differences in the effect of light on the stimulation of chloroplast and cytoplasmic (or nuclear-cytoplasmic) systems are granted—even if not understood. But the "general" system brings a few problems and peculiarities. Why, and how, does chlorophyll synthesis stop rapidly when a "greening" leaf is placed in darkness or when a "pigmenting" culture of R. spheroides is aerated vigorously? A rapid feed-back control could work but a separate blocking agent would be required for every enzyme. Besides, it is quite clear that protein synthesis and not just enzyme action is arrested; for example, Lascelles (1960b) found that the accumulation of ribulose $1:5$-diphosphate carboxylase by R. spheroides stopped abruptly upon vigorous aeration of an illuminated culture and resumed upon flushing with N_2—CO_2. "General" control over the rate of protein synthesis in the chloroplast (or photosynthetic area of R. spheroides?) coupled with differences in the rate of enzyme turnover seems attractive (negative feed-back control could, of course, complement the synthesis-turnover system). Now, suppose ALA synthetase turns over at an extremely rapid rate. Then, since the concentration of an enzyme at any time is the difference between the rates of its formation and inactivation, when the rate of protein synthesis (e.g. in the chloroplast) is very low the functional level of the enzyme could be zero even though it is being synthesized constantly. The extension of this argument is apparent: at every level of protein synthesis the relative concentration of enzymes in the system will be determined by differences among them in turnover rates.

As described above, etiolated leaves form large amounts of protochlorophyllide a when they are supplied with ALA in darkness. However, this protochlorophyllide a absorbs *in vivo* at about 632 mμ rather than at 650 mμ and is not convertible into chlorophyllide a; it is thought that the protochlorophyllide a formed from exogenously supplied ALA is not associated with protein while the normal pigment is. Thus while the chloroplast has made more pigment under these circumstances it is not making appreciably more protein. Although the enzyme for making ALA is obviously not functioning (according to this argument it is absent because its rate of decay is essentially equal to its rate of synthesis) other enzymes in the chain will work because they are more stable, but certainly not indestructible. In fact, it should be expected that if the rate of protein synthesis were reduced further a new block at another place in the chain might develop. This kind of interpretation would also fit the data of Margulies (1962) who found differences in sensitivity to chloramphenicol of pigment synthesis and the development of photosynthetic activity in bean leaves.

From an evolutionary point of view, one attractive feature of this type of mechanism is that both qualitative and step-less quantitative control of a whole biosynthetic chain could be developed by selecting for instability in a single protein which serves as the enzyme for the step which joins this biosynthetic path with the general metabolism of the cell. In the case of porphyrin biosynthesis there are particularly important reasons for providing a close integration with protein synthesis. In animals (e.g. Schmid, 1960) as in plants (e.g. Klein and Bogorad, 1964) free porphyrins can seriously damage the organism in the light.

The preceding argument that qualitative as well as quantitative changes in cellular activity *might* be effected by a "synthesis-turnover" mechanism could not possibly eliminate the mass of data on specific control systems. The discussion is not intended to do so but rather to suggest the possibility of alternative or complementary systems.

The participation of light in promoting the rapid phase of chlorophyll formation has been delimited to participation by the phytochrome system (see Chapter 15). Withrow *et al.* (1956) found that the lag phase in greening was of the same duration whether etiolated leaves were irradiated with a short flash of light and then returned to darkness or maintained under continuous illumination. The action spectrum for the light-induced "elimination" of the lag phase has a maximum at about

660 mμ; blue light is relatively ineffective (Virgin, 1961). The effect of 660 mμ light can be reversed by far-red light (Mitrakos, 1961; Price and Klein, 1961).

Deficiencies in any one of a number of mineral nutrients bring about chlorosis in plants. Iron deficiency chlorosis is of particular interest partly because of its easy reversibility. Perur et al. (1961) found that while chloroplast protein was 82% below normal in leaves of iron deficient maize other leaf protein fractions were essentially unaffected. Unfortunately, however, one of the serious problems in the fractionation of sub-cellular organelles in an aqueous medium is the tendency for leakage or adsorption. In these experiments tissues were frozen, thawed, and ground in water. The differences between iron-deficient and control fractions were great but arguments of permeability differences, etc. would be difficult to refute. Marsh et al. (1963a) found that chlorotic leaves from iron-deficient cowpea plants formed protoporphyrin when incubated with ALA in darkness indicating that porphyrin biosynthesis in these leaves was blocked by their failure to synthesize ALA and to incorporate magnesium into protoporphyrin. They found, however, that illuminated chlorotic leaf discs can incorporate radioactivity from [^{14}C]ALA into chlorophyll at the same rate as normal tissues (Marsh et al., 1963b). Differences in the effect of iron deficiency in darkness and light has also been observed in a Chlorella mutant (Bryan and Bogorad, 1963).

Depending upon the degree of chlorosis, discs from iron-deficient leaves of Swiss chard accumulate either protoporphyrin or proto-chlorophyllide when incubated with ALA in darkness (Treffry and Bogorad, unpublished data).

It is not unlikely that iron-deficiency chlorosis reflects some general-ized reduction in protein and/or nucleic acid synthesis. Van Noort and Wallace (1963) report that chlorophyll formation was severely inhibited in iron-deficient bush beans supplied 5-fluorouracil or 5-fluorodeoxyuri-dine in addition to iron. They conclude from their experiments that DNA synthesis may be required for recovery from iron-deficiency chlorosis in beans.

Many genes for chlorophyll formation are transmitted in a Mendelian, i.e. nuclear, manner (Rhoades, 1955). In some cases these genetic lesions have been circumvented, for example phenocopies of the yellow-stripe-1 (ys$_1$) mutant of maize can be produced by growing plants on low iron; conversely double recessive ys$_1$ plants can be "cured" by supplying them with particular chelates of iron or by withholding phosphorous (Bell et al., 1958, 1962). Chlorophyll deficient barley mutants xantha-23 and albina-7 form chlorophyll when fed leucine and aspartic acid respectively (Eriksson et al., 1961). Albina-7 plants become autotrophic upon greening after being fed aspartic acid. A tomato strain which normally bleaches and dies will grow if supplied thiamine (Langridge and Brock, 1961). Thiamine also permits normal growth in an ordinarily chlorophyll-less mutant of *Arabadopsis* (Langridge, 1958). In all of these cases, since the blocks are inherited via nuclear genes, interference with chlorophyll formation appears to be indirect: nutrients required for chloroplast development which are normally made available by nuclear activity are lacking. Considering the length of time during which chloroplastic-nuclear *systems* have been evolving, many different degrees of nutritional dependence of plastids upon nuclei probably occur.

REFERENCES

Allen, M. B. (1958). *Brookhaven Symp. Biol.* **11**, 339.
Allen, M. B. (1959). *Arch. Mikrobiol.* **32**, 270.
Ardao, C., and Vennesland, B. (1960). *Plant Physiol.* **35**, 368.
Becker, R. S., and Sheline, R. K. (1955). *Arch. Biochem. Biophys.* **54**, 259.
Bell, W. D., Bogorad, L., and McIlrath, W. J. (1958). *Bot. Gaz.* **120**, 36.
Bell, W. D., Bogorad, L., and McIlrath, W. J. (1962). *Bot. Gaz.* **124**, 1.
Bénard, H., Gadjos, A., and Gadjos-Török, M. (1951). *C. R. Soc. Biol.* **145**, 538.
Blass, U., Anderson, J. M., and Calvin, M. (1959). *Plant Physiol.* **34**, 329.
Boardman, N. K. (1962a). *Biochim. biophys. Acta* **62**, 63.
Boardman, N. K. (1962b). *Biochim. biophys. Acta* **64**, 279.
Bogorad, L. (1950). *Bot. Gaz.* **111**, 221.
Bogorad, L. (1955). *Science* **121**, 878.
Bogorad, L. (1957a). *In* "Research in Photosynthesis" (H. Gaffron, ed.), p. 475, Interscience, New York.
Bogorad, L. (1957b). *Plant Physiol.* **32**, xli.
Bogorad, L. (1958a). *J. biol. Chem.* **233**, 501.
Bogorad, L. (1958b). *J. biol. Chem.* **233**, 510.
Bogorad, L. (1958c). *J. biol. Chem.* **233**, 516.
Bogorad, L. (1960). *In* "Comparative Biochemistry of Photoreactive Systems" (M. B. Allen, ed.), p. 227, Academic Press, New York.
Bogorad, L. (1961). Fifth Intl. Cong. Biochem., Moscow, p. 158. Pergamon Press, Inc.
Bogorad, L. (1963). *Ann. N.Y. Acad. Sci.* **104**, 676.
Bogorad, L., and Granick, S. (1953a). *J. biol. Chem.* **202**, 793.
Bogorad, L., and Granick, S. (1953b). *Proc. nat. Acad. Sci., Wash.* **39**, 1176.
Bogorad, L., and Jacobson, A. B. (1964). *Biochem. Biophys. Res. Comm.* **14**, 113.
Booij, H. L., and Rimington, C. (1957). *Biochem. J.* **65**, 4P.
Bryan, G. W., and Bogorad, L. (1963). "Microalgae and Photosynthetic Bacteria" (A special supplement to *Plant and Cell Physiol.*), p. 399.
Bezeski, W., and Rucker, W. (1960). *Nature, Lond.* **185**, 922.
Bull, M. J., and Lascelles, J. (1963). *Biochem. J.* **87**, 15.
Burnham, B. F. (1962). *Biochem. Biophys. Res. Comm.* **7**, 351.
Burnham, B. F., and Lascelles, J. (1963). *Biochem. J.* **87**, 462.
Carpenter, A. T., and Scott, J. J. (1959). *Biochem. J.* **71**, 325.
Carpenter, A. T., and Scott, J. J. (1961). *Biochim. biophys. Acta* **52**, 195.
Chun, E. H. L., Vaughn, M. H., and Rich, A. (1963). *J. mol. Biol.* **7**, 130.
Cohen-Bazire, G., Sistrom, W. R., and Stanier, R. Y. (1957). *J. cell. comp. Physiol.* **49**, 25.

Cookson, G. H., and Rimington, C. (1953). *Nature, Lond.* **171**, 875.

Cookson, G. H., and Rimington, C. (1954). *Biochem. J.* **57**, 476.

Cooper, R. (1963). *Biochem. J.* **89**, 100.

Della, Rosa, Rocco, J., Altman, K. I., and Saloman, K. (1953). *J. biol. Chem.* **202**, 771.

Dresel, E. I. B., and Falk, J. E. (1956). *Biochem. J.* **63**, 80.

Duranton, J., Galmiche, J. M., and Roux, E. (1958). *C. R. Acad. Sci., Paris* **246**, 992.

Egle, K. (1960). *In* "Encyclopedia of Plant Physiology" (W. Ruhland, ed.), vol. V/1, p. 323, Springer Verlag, Berlin.

Eriksson, G., Kahn, A., Walles, B., and von Wettstein, D. (1961). *Ber. dtsch. bot. Ges.* **74**, 221.

Falk, J. E. (1963). *In* "Comprehensive Biochemistry" (M. Florkin and E. H. Stotz, eds.), vol. 9, p. 3, Elsevier Publ. Co., Amsterdam.

Falk, J. E., Dresel, E. I. B., and Rimington, C. (1953). *Nature, Lond.* **172**, 292.

Falk, J. E., Dresel, E. I. B., Benson, A., and Knight, B. C. (1956). *Biochem. J.* **63**, 87.

Finkle, B. J., Appleman, D., and Fleischer, F. K. (1950). *Science* **111**, 309.

Fischer, F. G., and Rüdiger, W. (1959). *Liebigs Ann.* **27**, 1, 35.

Fischer, H., and Stern, A. (1940). "Die Chemie des Pyrrols," vol. II, part 2, 478 pp., Akademische Verlagsgesell-Schaft M. B. H., Leipzig.

Fischer, H., Mittenzwei, H., and Oestreicher, A. (1939). *Hoppe-Seyl. Z.* **257**, IV–VII.

Frank, S. R. (1946). *J. gen. Physiol.* **29**, 157.

Gibson, K. D., Neuberger, A., and Scott, J. J. (1955). *Biochem. J.* **61**, 618.

Gibson, K., Laver, W., and Neuberger, A. (1958). *Biochem. J.* **70**, 71.

Gibson, K. D., Matthew, M., Neuberger, A., and Tait, G. H. (1961). *Nature, Lond.* **192**, 204.

Gibson, K. D., Neuberger, A., and Tait, G. H. (1962a). *Biochem. J.* **83**, 539.

Gibson, K. D., Neuberger, A., and Tait, G. H. (1962b). *Biochem. J.* **83**, 550.

Godnev, T. N., Shlyk, A. A., and Rotfarb, R. M. (1959). *Fiziol. Rastenii* **6**, 36. (Eng. Trans: Plant Physiol U.S.S.R., 33–38.)

Godnev, T. N., Rotfarb, R. M., and Shlyk, A. A. (1960). *C. R. Acad. Sci., U.R.S.S.* **130**, 663.

Godnev, T. N., Rotfarb, R. M., and Akulovich, N. K. (1963). *Photochem. Photobiol.* **2**, 119.

Goodwin, R. H., and Owens, O. H. (1947). *Plant Physiol.* **22**, 197.

Granick, S. (1948a). *J. biol. Chem.* **172**, 717.

Granick, S. (1948b). *J. biol. Chem.* **175**, 333.

Granick, S. (1949). *J. biol. Chem.* **179**, 505.

Granick, S. (1950). *J. biol. Chem.* **183**, 713.

Granick, S. (1954). *Science* **120**, 1105.

Granick, S. (1959). *Plant Physiol.* **34**, xviii.

Granick, S. (1961). *J. biol. Chem.* **236**, 1168.

Granick, S., and Bogorad, L. (1953). *J. Amer. chem. Soc.* **75**, 3610.

Granick, S., and Mauzerall, D. (1958). *J. biol. Chem.* **232**, 1119.

Granick, S., and Sano, S. (1961). *Fed. Proc.* **20**, 376.

Green, M., Altman, K. I., Richmond, J. E., and Salomon, K. (1957). *Nature, Lond.* **179**, 375.

Griffiths, M. (1962). *J. gen. Microbiol.* **27**, 427.

Heath, H., and Hoare, D. S. (1959). *Biochem. J.* **72**, 14.

Highkin, H. R. (1950). *Plant Physiol.* **25**, 294.

Hoare, D. S., and Heath, H. (1959). *Biochem. J.* **73**, 679.

Holden, M. (1961). *Biochem. J.* **78**, 359.

Holden, M. (1963). *Photochem. Photobiol.* **2**, 175.

Holt, A. S. (1960). *In* "Comparative Biochemistry of Photoreactive Systems" (M. B. Allen, ed.), p. 169, Academic Press, New York.

Iodice, A. A., Richert, D. A., and Schulman, M. P. (1958). *Fed. Proc.* **17**, 248.

Jones, O. T. G. (1963a). *Biochem. J.* **86**, 429.

Jones, O. T. G. (1963b). *Biochem. J.* **89**, 182.

Kamen, M. (1957). "Isotopic Tracers in Biology," 478 pp., Academic Press, New York.

Kikuchi, G., Kumer, A., Talmadge, P., and Shemin, D. (1958). *J. biol. Chem.* **233**, 1214.

Kislev, N., Swift, H., and Bogorad, L. (1964). *J. Cell. Biol.* (In press.)

Klein, A., and Vishniac, W. (1961). *J. biol. Chem.* **236**, 2544.

Klein, S., and Bogorad, L. (1964). *J. Cell Biol.* (In press.)

Koski, V. M. (1950). *Arch. Biochem. Biophys.* **29**, 339.

Koski, V. M., and Smith, J. H. C. (1948). *J. Amer. chem. Soc.* **70**, 3558.

Koski, Violet M., French, C. S., and Smith, J. H. C. (1951). *Arch. Biochem. Biophys.* **31**, 1.

Krasnovsky, A. A., and Kosobutskaya, L. M. (1952). *C.R. Acad. Sci., U.R.S.S.* **85**, 177.

Labbe, R. F. (1959). *Biochim. biophys. Acta* **31**, 589.

Labbe, R. F., and Hubbard, N. (1960). *Biochim. biophys. Acta* **41**, 185.

Labbe, R. F., and Hubbard, N. (1961). *Fed. Proc.* **20**, 376.

Labbe, R. F., Hubbard, N., and Caughey, W. (1963). *Biochem.* **2**, 372.

Langridge, J. (1958). *Austral. J. biol. Sci.* **11**, 58.

Langridge, J., and Brock, R. D. (1961). *Austral. J. biol. Sci.* **14**, 66.

Lascelles, J. (1956). *Biochem. J.* **62**, 78.

Lascelles, J. (1957). *Biochem. J.* **66**, 65.

Lascelles, J. (1959). *Biochem. J.* **72**, 508.

Lascelles, J. (1960a). *J. gen. Microbiol.* **23**, 487.

Lascelles, J. (1960b). *J. gen. Microbiol.* **23**, 499.

Laver, W. G., Neuberger, A., and Scott, J. J. (1959). *J. chem. Soc.* 1483.

Leff, J., Mandel, M., Epstein, H. T., and Schiff, J. A. (1963). *Biochem. Biophys. Res. Comm.* **13**, 126.

Lemberg, R., and Legge, J. W. (1949). "Haematin Compounds and Bile Pigments," 749 pp., Interscience, New York.

Little, H. N., and Kelsey, M. I. (1964). *Fed. Proc.* **23**, 223.

Litvin, F. F., Krasnovsky, A. A., and Rikhireva, G. T. (1959). *C.R. Acad. Sci., U.R.S.S.* **127**, 699.

Lockwood, W. H., and Benson, A. (1960). *Biochem. J.* **75**, 372.

Loeffler, J. E. (1955). *Yearb. Carneg. Instn.* **54**, 159.

Madsen, A. (1963). *Photochem. Photobiol.* **2**, 93.

Margulies, M. M. (1962). *Plant Physiol.* **37**, 473.

Marks, G. S. (1963). *Ann. Rep. chem. Soc.* **59**, 385.

Marsh, H. V. Jr., Evans, H. J., and Matrone, G. (1963a). *Plant Physiol.* **38**, 632.

Marsh, H. V. Jr., Evans, H. J., and Matrone, G. (1963b). *Plant Physiol.* **38**, 638.

Mathewson, J. A., and Corwin, A. H. (1961). *J. Amer. chem. Soc.* **83**, 135.

Mauzerall, D. (1960). *J. Amer. chem. Soc.* **82**, 2605.

Mauzerall, D., and Granick, S. (1958). *J. biol. Chem.* **232**, 1141.

Mayer, H. (1930). *Planta* **11**, 294.

McSwiney, R. R., Nicholas, R. E. H., and Prunty, F. T. G. (1950). *Biochem. J.* **46**, 147.

Mego, J. L., and Jagendorf, A. T. (1961). *Biochim. biophys. Acta* **53**, 237.

Michel-Wolwertz, M. R. (1963). *Photochem. Photobiol.* **2**, 149.

Mitrakos, K. (1961). *Physiol. Plantarum* **14**, 497.

Monteverde, N. A. (1893–4). *Acta Hort. Petropolitani* **13**, 201.

Muir, H. M., and Neuberger, A. (1949). *Biochem. J.* **45**, 163.

Muir, H. M., and Neuberger, A. (1950). *Biochem. J.* **47**, 97.

Nemeth, A. M., Russel, C. S., and Shemin, D. (1957). *J. biol. Chem.* **229**, 415.

Neuberger, A. (1961). *Biochem. J.* **78**, 1.

Neuberger, A., and Scott, J. J. (1953). *Nature, Lond.* **172**, 1093.

Neuberger, A., and Tait, G. (1964). *Biochem. J.* **90**, 607.

Neve, R. A., Labbe, R. F., and Aldrich, R. A. (1956). *J. Amer. chem. Soc.* **78**, 691.

Nichols, K. E., and Bogorad, L. (1962). *Bot. Gaz.* **124**, 85.

Nishida, G., and Labbe, R. F. (1959). *Biochim. biophys. Acta* **31**, 519.

Noack, K., and Kiessling, W. (1929). *Hoppe-Seyl. Z.* **182**, 13.

Noack, K., and Kiessling, W. (1930). *Hoppe-Seyl. Z.* **193**, 97.

Oyama, H., Sugita, Y., Yoneyama, Y., and Yoshikaya, H. (1961). *Biochim. biophys. Acta* **47**, 413.

Perkins, H. J., and Roberts, D. W. A. (1960). *Biochim. biophys. Acta* **45**, 613.

Perur, N. G., Smith, R. L., and Wiebe, H. H. (1961). *Plant Physiol.* **36**, 736.

Phillips, J. N. (1963). *In* "Comprehensive Biochemistry" (M. Florkin and E. H. Stotz, eds.), vol. 9, p. 34, Elsevier Publ. Co., Amsterdam.

Porra, R. J., and Falk, J. E. (1964). *Biochem. J.* **90**, 69.

Porra, R. J., and Jones, O. T. G. (1963a). *Biochem. J.* **87**, 181.

Porra, R. J., and Jones, O. T. G. (1963b). *Biochem. J.* **87**, 186.

Price, L., and Klein, W. H. (1961). *Plant Physiol.* **36**, 733.

Rhoades, M. M. (1955). *In* "Encyclopedia of Plant Physiology" (W. Ruhland, ed.), vol. I, p. 19, Springer Verlag, Berlin.

Rimington, C., and Booij, H. L. (1957). *Biochem. J.* **65**, 3P.

Rimington, C., and Miles, P. A. (1951). *Biochem. J.* **50**, 202.

Ris, H., and Plaut, W. (1962). *J. Cell Biol.* **13**, 383.

Röbbelen, G. (1956). *Planta* **47**, 532.

Sager, R., and Ishida, M. R. (1963). *Proc. nat. Acad. Sci., Wash.* **50**, 725.

Sano, S., and Granick, S. (1961). *J. Biol. Chem.* **236**, 1173.

Schmid, R. (1960). *In* "The Metabolic Basis of Inherited Diseases" (J. B. Stanbury, ed.), p. 939. McGraw-Hill, New York.

Schmid, R., and Shemin, D. (1955). *J. Amer. chem. Soc.* **77**, 506.

Schmidt, A. (1924). *Bot. Arch.* **5**, 260.

Schou, L. (1951). *Physiol. Plantarum* **4**, 617.

Schulman, M. P., and Richert, D. A. (1957). *J. biol. Chem.* **226**, 181.

Schwartz, H. C., Hill, R. L., Cartwright, G. E., and Wintrobe, M. M. (1959). *Fed. Proc.* **18**, 545.

Seybold, A. (1949). *Planta* **36**, 371.

Seybold, A., and Egle, K. (1937). *Planta* **26**, 491.

Seybold, A., and Egle, K. (1938). *Planta* **28**, 87.

Shemin, D., and Kikuchi, G. (1958). *Ann. N.Y. Acad. Sci.* **75**, 122.

Shemin, D., and Kumin, S. (1952). *J. biol. Chem.* **198**, 827.

Shemin, D., and Russel, C. S. (1953). *J. Amer. chem. Soc.* **76**, 4873.

Shemin, D., and Wittenberg, J. (1951). *J. biol. Chem.* **192**, 315.

Shibata, K. (1957). *J. Biochem., Tokyo* **44**, 147.

Shibata, K. (1959). *In* "Methods of Biochemical Analysis" (D. Glick, ed.), vol. 7, p. 77, Interscience, New York.

Shimizu, S., and Tamaki, E. (1962). *Bot. Mag., Tokyo* **75**, 462.

Shimizu, S., and Tamaki, E. (1963). *Arch. Biochem. Biophys.* **102**, 152.

Shlyk, A. A., and Godnev, T. N. (1958). *In* "First International Conference on Radioisotopes in Scientific Research," vol. IV, p. 479, Pergamon Press, London.

Shlyk, A. A., Kaler, V. L., and Podchufarova, G. M. (1960). *C.R. Acad. Sci.*, *U.R.S.S.* **133**, 1472.

Shlyk, A. A., Kaler, V. L., Vlasenok, L. I., and Gaponenko, V. I. (1963a). *Photochem. Photobiol.* **2**, 129.

Shlyk, A. A., Mikhailova, S. A., Gaponenko, V. I., and Kukhtenko, T. V. (1963b). *Fiziol. Rastenii* **10**, 275. (Engl. trans: *Soviet Plant Physiology* **10**, 227.)

Sironval, C., Verly, W. G., and Marcelle, R. (1961). *Physiol. Plantarum* **14**, 303.

Sisler, E. G., and Klein, W. H. (1963). *Physiol. Plantarum* **16**, 315.

Sistrom, W. R. (1962). *J. gen. Microbiol.* **28**, 599.

Sistrom, W. R., Griffiths, M., and Stanier, R. Y. (1956). *J. cell. comp. Physiol.* **48**, 459.

Smillie, R. M. (1963). *Canad. J. Bot.* **41**, 123.

Smith, J. H. C. (1948). *Arch. Biochem. Biophys.* **19**, 449.

Smith, J. H. C. (1952). *Yearb. Carneg. Inst.* **51**, 151.

Smith, J. H. C. (1960). *In* "Comparative Biochemistry of Photoreactive Systems" (M. B. Allen, ed.), p. 257, Academic Press, New York.

Smith, J. H. C., and Benitez, A. (1954). *Plant Physiol.* **29**, 135.

Smith, J. H. C., and Benitez, A. (1955). *In* "Modern Methods of Plant Analysis" (K. Paech and M. V. Tracey, eds.), vol. IV, p. 142, Springer Verlag, Berlin.

Smith, J. H. C., and Coomber, J. C. (1961). *Yearb. Carneg. Instn.* **60**, 371.

Smith, J. H. C., and French, C. S. (1963). *Annu. Rev. Pl. Physiol.* **14**, 181.

Smith, J. H. C., and Young, V. M. K. (1956). *In* "Radiation Biology" (A. Hollaender, ed.), vol. III, p. 393, McGraw-Hill, New York.

Smith, J. H. C., Kupke, D. W., Loeffler, J. E., Benitez, A., Ahrue, I., and Giese, A. T. (1957). *In* "Research in Photosynthesis" (H. Gaffron *et al.*, eds.), p. 464, Interscience, New York.

Smith, J. H. C., Durham, L. J., and Wurster, C. F. (1959). *Plant Physiol.* **34**, 340.

Sudyina, E. G. (1963). *Photochem. Photobiol.* **2**, 181.

Tait, G. H., and Gibson, K. D. (1961). *Biochim. Biophys. Acta* **52**, 614.

Urata, G., and Granick, S. (1963). *J. biol. Chem.* **238**, 811.

van Niel, C. B. (1944). *Bact. Rev.* **8**, 1.

van Noort, D., and Wallace, A. (1963). *Biochem. Biophys. Res. Comm.* **10**, 109.

Virgin, H. I. (1955). *Physiol. Plantarum* **8**, 630.

Virgin, H. I. (1960). *Physiol. Plantarum* **13**, 155.

Virgin, H. I. (1961). *Physiol. Plantarum* **14**, 439.

Virgin, H. I., Kahn, A., and von Wettstein, D. (1963). *Photochem. Photobiol.* **2**, 83.

Waldenström, J., and Vahlquist, B. (1939). *Hoppe-Seyl. Z.* **260**, 189.

Westall, R. G. (1952). *Nature, Lond.* **170**, 614.

Willstätter, R., and Stoll, A. (1913). "Investigations on Chlorophyll," English translation: (1928) by F. M. Schertz and G. R. Mertz, 385 pp., Science Press, Lancaster, Penna.

Withrow, R. B., Wolff, J. B., and Price, L. (1956). *Plant Physiol.* **31**, xiii.

Wittenberg, J. (1959). *Nature, Lond.* **184**, 876.

Wittenberg, J., and Shemin, D. (1949). *J. biol. Chem.* **178**, 47.

Wittenberg, J., and Shemin, D. (1950). *J. biol. Chem.* **185**, 103.

Wolff, J. B., and Price, L. (1957). *Arch. Biochem. Biophys.* **72**, 293.

Wolken, J. J. (1961). "Euglena; an Experimental Organism for Biochemical and Biophysical Studies," 173 pp., Institute of Microbiology, Rutgers, New Brunswick, New Jersey.

Chapter 3

CHEMISTRY OF THE CAROTENOIDS

B. C. L. WEEDON

Queen Mary College, Mile End Road, London, England

I. INTRODUCTION

Although the occurrence in Nature of red and yellow pigments, now known to be carotenoids, has been reported for well over a century, the chemistry of these substances can, for most practical purposes, be regarded as starting in the late 1920's. In the succeeding decade the structures of some of the more readily available representatives were determined, largely through the classical work of the Karrer school, and other important studies were undertaken by Kuhn, Zechmeister, Heilbron, and their respective collaborators.

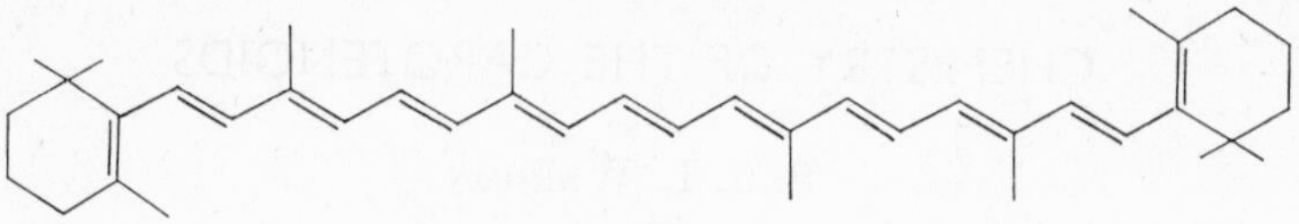

(I)

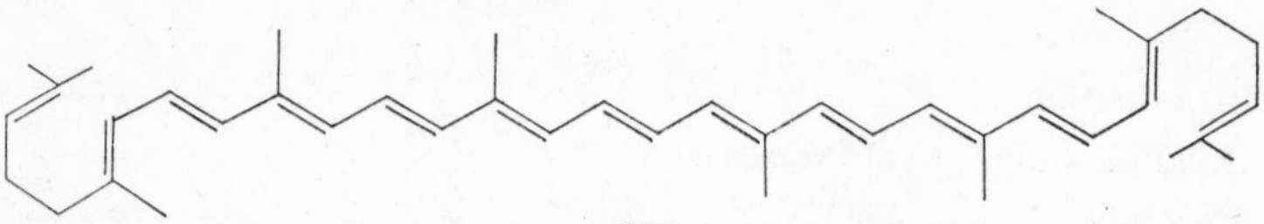

(II)

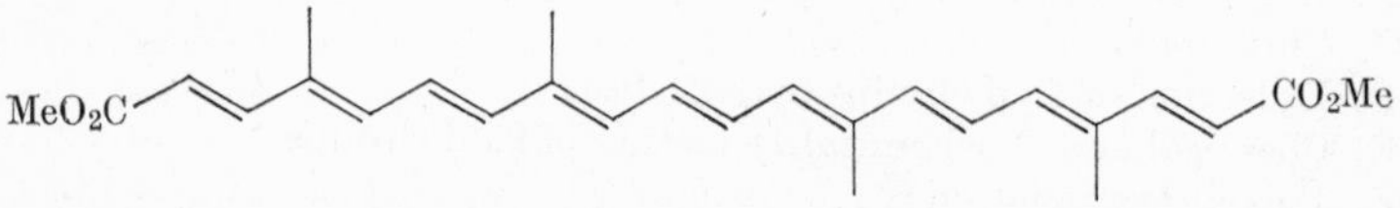

MeO₂C ⋯⋯⋯⋯⋯ CO₂Me

(III)

Much effort has also been devoted to the synthesis of carotenoids and related polyenes. A crude product which apparently contained traces of β-carotene (I) was prepared from vitamin A (IV) by Karrer and Schwyzer in 1948, but the unambiguous total synthesis of carotenoids in isolatable amounts was first achieved with the hydrocarbons β-carotene (I) and lycopene (II) in 1950 (Karrer and Eugster, a; Inhoffen et al., b, c, d; Milas et al.) and with the oxygenated carotenoid all-trans-methylbixin (III) in 1952 (Ahmad and Weedon), all by the same basic approach which was developed independently in several laboratories. Following these initial successes, the range of synthetic methods in the carotenoid field has been greatly extended, principally by the groups of Karrer, Inhoffen, Weedon, Isler, and Pommer (cf. Isler and Schudel, 1963). As a result, a wide variety of natural carotenoids have now been synthesized, some even on an industrial scale.

Latterly attention has been directed to the intriguing question of the way in which carotenoids are formed in Nature, and already the main biosynthetic outlines are emerging as the result of work by Goodwin, Grob, Davies, Porter, Stanier, Chichester, Quackenbush, and others (see Chapter 5). Although at different periods different interests, such as isolation, structure, properties, and synthesis, have predominated, these have always tended to overlap. Thus the last few years have seen not only important advances on the biosynthetic front, but also the isolation of several new carotenoids, the detection of new structural types, and success in tackling some of the outstanding problems in synthesis. This broad interest is scarcely surprising in view of the growing realization of the importance and variety of these widespread natural pigments.

It is perhaps worth recalling at this stage that studies on carotenoids and related compounds have also had important repercussions on other branches of chemistry. The original discovery of chromatography by Tswett, using extracts of leaves, passed largely unnoticed until the technique was re-introduced to separate mixtures of carotenoids. The pioneer work by Kuhn *et al.* with model polyenes (cf. Kuhn, 1938) made significant contributions to theories on the correlation of colour and constitution, at a time when colour was commonly held to be associated with the presence of chromophores containing nitrogen or other hetero-atoms. The carotenoids themselves also provide a unique series of compounds for spectral studies, the examination of the influence of steric factors on light absorption properties, and for checking the results of theoretical calculations of light absorption maxima. Moreover, such standard analytical procedures as microhydrogenation (see Section III, B), and the Kuhn-Roth C-methyl determination (see Section III, H), were first developed specifically to deal with natural carotenoids.

II. ISOLATION AND GENERAL PROPERTIES

With the exception of crocin, the digentiobioside of crocetin, (48–48)* and some protein complexes, such as the astaxanthin (8–8) derivative ovoverdin, the carotenoids are fat-soluble pigments which can be isolated by extraction with a suitable solvent, e.g. benzene, petrol, (peroxide-free) ether, carbon disulphide, ethanol, methanol, or (acid-free) chloroform. Evaporation of the extract then gives a crude material which occasionally need only be crystallized to yield the desired product

---

* *Formulae*—For brevity most structures are represented by symbols such as (1–1), for lycopene, and (6–7), for lutein. The figures refer to the end groups listed in Table I, and which are attached to the central C_{18}-unit (IX). Synthetic compounds possessing the central C_{18}-unit (X) are shown as, for example, (12:12) for 15,15′-dehydroastacin.

End groups attached to the central C_{18}-unit (XI), in compounds with chromophores of the "retro-type", are listed in Table II and are indicated with numbers prefixed by "R". Thus the structure of rhodoxanthin is given as (R3–R3).

The conventional numbering of the positions in carotenoid formulae is indicated below for β-carotene.

directly (e.g. in the isolation of lycopene from tomatoes). Usually, however, it is necessary to carry out a preliminary purification. This is often best done after treatment with 10% methanolic potassium hydroxide to hydrolyse any lipids or esters of hydroxylated carotenoids. (In some isolations the destruction of lipids is most conveniently achieved by reaction with lithium aluminium hydride.) A rough separation can then be obtained by partitioning the crude mixture between two immiscible solvents. Petrol and 90% methanol are commonly used, the former dissolving the non-hydroxylated carotenoids ("epiphasic fraction") and the latter the carotenoids with two or more hydroxyl groups ("hypophasic fraction"); the mono-hydroxy carotenoids tend to be distributed between both phases. This simple partition procedure can, of course, be greatly improved by the use of a Craig machine (Curl, 1960; cf. Krinsky, 1963).

Despite the procedures mentioned above, the great success which has been achieved in isolating carotenoids, and in separating the complex mixtures of these pigments which are frequently encountered in Nature, would have been impossible but for the technique of chromatography. This is well illustrated by the fact that "carotene" was known as a crystalline product, and believed to be homogeneous, for nearly 100 years before it was separated chromatographically into the three hydrocarbons α-, β-, and γ-carotene (2–3, 2–2, and 1–2 respectively). Paper chromatography (Jensen, 1963) and thin-layer chromatography (Stahl et al., 1963) provide, on an analytical scale, a more efficient, and much more rapid, means of separation, and these techniques are now widely used to monitor the more conventional (liquid–solid) chromatograms, or the course of a reaction.*

Although many carotenoids appear to have sharp melting points, these may vary greatly with the rate of heating (decomposition, stereomutation?), and the way in which the determination is made (Kofler block, evacuated capillary, open tube). Some compounds may also exhibit polymorphism. In practice visible and infra-red light absorption spectra, and N.M.R. spectra, afford the best means of characterization, and a mixed chromatogram with an authentic specimen (preferably using thin-layer or paper chromatography) provides a far more reliable proof of identity than the classical mixed melting point. Nevertheless it should always be remembered that, by itself, failure to observe a separation in a mixed chromatogram constitutes premissive, and not conclusive, evidence of identity. In the past there has been considerable confusion owing to the similarity in chromatographic behaviour of rhodopin (1–37) and lycoxanthin (1–5) (Goodwin and Land, 1956b; cf. Jensen, 1959b), of cryptoxanthin (2–6) and a reduction product

* For further details see Chapter 18.

(2–18) of echinenone (2–4) (Goodwin, 1956), of chlorobactene (1–32) and γ-carotene (1–2) (Goodwin and Land, 1956a; cf. Jensen *et al.*, 1964), and of neurosporene (1–9) and a synthetic nonaene of different structure (Eugster *et al.*, 1956; cf. Davis *et al.*, 1961). However, the failure to carry out a mixed chromatogram probably led to the incorrect identification of an oxidation product of spirilloxanthin (39–39) as bixindial (46–46) (Karrer and Koenig, 1940; cf. M. S. Barber and B. C. L. Weedon, unpublished results). A micro-method for the comparison of carotenoids, based on mixed chromatograms and stereomutation studies, has been developed by Jensen (1962), and is particularly valuable when the supplies of pigment are inadequate for full spectral studies.

Some carotenoids, notably the various epoxides such as violaxanthin (24–24) and antheraxanthin (6–24), are sensitive to acids, even to the trace amounts of hydrogen chloride in "aged" chloroform, whilst fucoxanthin* is also remarkably labile to dilute alkalis.

A few carotenoids (e.g. bixin (44–45) and crocetindial (50–50)) are surprisingly stable to air, and others (e.g. β-carotene (I) and astacin (12–12)) reasonably stable provided that they are pure and well crystallized. Lycopene (II) is noticeably less stable than β-carotene (I), and ζ-carotene (XV), a tetrahydro-lycopene, is notoriously unstable in air. However, phytoene (XIII), an octahydro-lycopene, is comparatively stable. Compounds of the spirilloxanthin series, lacking the 1,2-double bond, but containing an additional double bond in the 3,4-position, are considerably less stable than lycopene. Compounds containing an additional conjugated double bond in the cyclic end group also seem to possess lowered stability. Thus vitamin A_2 (VII) is noticeably less stable than vitamin A_1 (IV), and bis-dehydro-β-carotene (34–34) than β-carotene. Astaxanthin (8–8), a bis-acyloin, is rapidly oxidized in alkaline solution by air to the bis-diosphenol, astacin (12–12) (Kuhn and Sörensen, 1938).

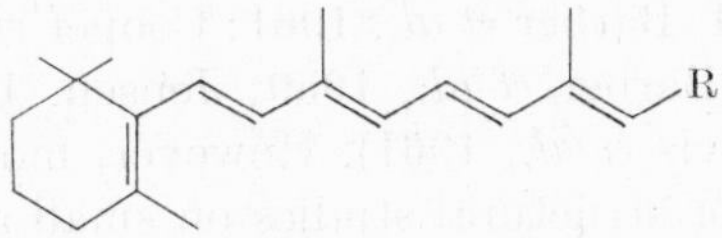

(IV) R = CH₂OH

(V) R = CHO

(VI) R = CO₂H

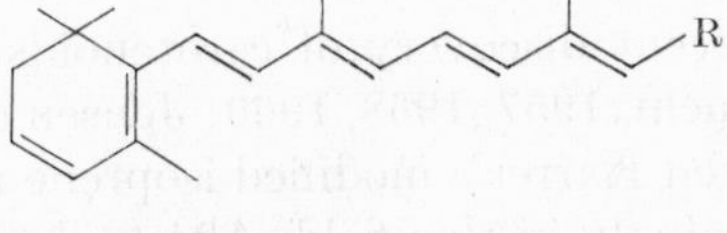

(VII) R = CH₂OH

(VIII) R = CHO

Because of the instability of many carotenoids, and their tendency to undergo stereomutation (see Section V), all operations involving these

* Published structures are unacceptable.

compounds should, whenever possible, be carried out in an inert atmosphere (e.g. nitrogen), solvents should be freshly purified, and solutions should not be heated more than necessary nor exposed to bright light.

III. STRUCTURE

In the years just before and after 1930 a big effort was made, largely by the schools of Karrer and Kuhn, to elucidate the structures of some of the more readily available carotenoids, in particular lycopene (1–1), β-carotene (2–2) and bixin (44–45), and much inter-connecting evidence was obtained. After invoking the isoprene rule, modified by Karrer's bold postulate that the isoprene units were joined head to head at the centre of the molecule so as to give a symmetrical carbon skeleton, plausible structures were advanced (cf. Karrer and Jucker, 1948). Further support for these proposals was subsequently obtained in a variety of ways. Thus a particularly elegant series of partial oxidations by Kuhn and others provided strong evidence in favour of Karrer's structure of β-carotene (see Section III, F). Finally, after an interval of about twenty years, the formulae proposed in the early 1930's for the three carotenoids mentioned above, were confirmed by synthesis (cf. Isler and Schudel, 1963).

No other carotenoid has been subjected to such detailed structural studies as β-carotene. With some other compounds it has been assumed that the carbon skeleton will be identical with that of either lycopene or β-carotene, and work has been directed very largely to providing a clue from which to postulate a structural difference between the compound in question and a closely related carotenoid of known structure. This approach has obvious attractions when dealing with rare substances, and has proved successful on many occasions, but it is unlikely to reveal readily a completely novel structural feature. It is mainly for this reason that incorrect formulae were entertained until recently for capsanthin (6–28), capsorubin (28–28) (cf. Barber et al., 1961; Cooper et al., 1962), spirilloxanthin* (39–39) (cf. Barber et al., 1959; Jensen, 1959a), and spheroidenone (9–40) (cf. Davis et al., 1961). However, more rigorous methods are now available for structural studies on small amounts of material.

With the comparatively recent discovery of carotenoids possessing aromatic end groups (Yamaguchi, 1957, 1958, 1960; Jensen et al., 1964; Jensen and Weedon, 1964) even Karrer's modified isoprene rule can no longer be accepted unquestioningly in this field. Although there seems little doubt that these aromatic compounds are transformation products of more conventional carotenoids it is to be hoped that their biosynthesis

* Also known as rhodoviolascin.

will receive attention before long. There is ample precedent for the formation of the 2,3,6-trimethylphenyl end group found in isorenieratene (32–32)*, and at one end of renieratene (32–33), but the presence of the 2,3,4-trimethylphenyl end group in renierapurpurin (33–33), and at the "other" end of renieratene, is most unexpected (cf. Cooper *et al.*, 1963).

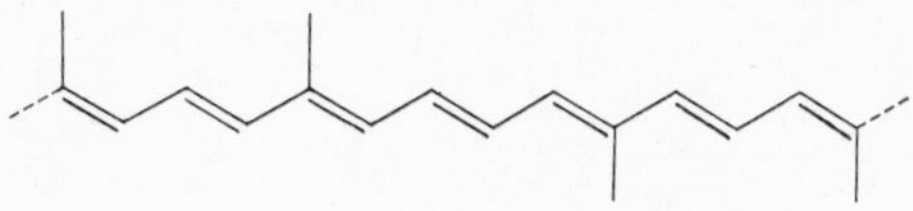

(IX)

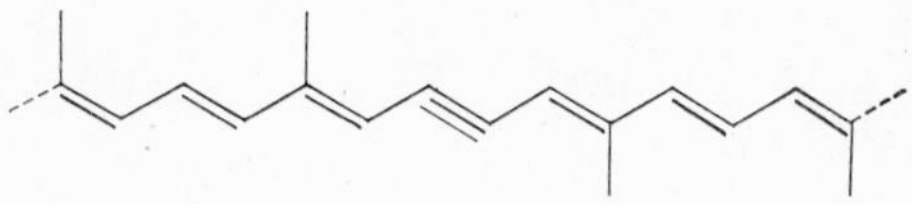

(X)

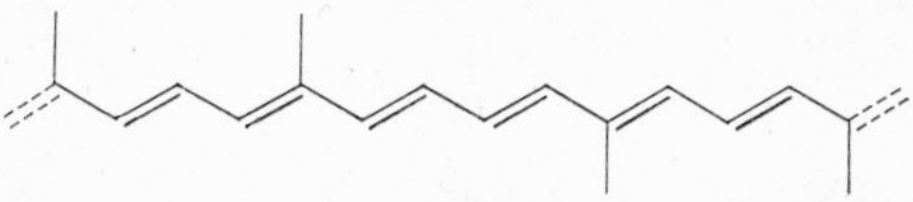

(XI)

The majority of carotenoids have a C_{40} carbon skeleton, and most possess a C_{18} central unit (IX) consisting of seven conjugated double bonds and four side chain methyl groups. The two end groups attached to this unit may be the same, as in lycopene (1–1), β-carotene (2–2), and zeaxanthin (6–6), or different, as in α-carotene (2–3), lutein (6–7), and echinenone (2–4). The end groups in those carotenoids (and some related polyenes) whose structures seem well established are listed in Table I.

The polyene systems in compounds of the types mentioned above are said to be "normal". Rhodoxanthin (R3–R3), eschscholtzxanthin (R4–R4), and a few related pigments, possess "retro" systems in which the positions of the single and double bonds in the polyene chain are reversed compared with the "normal" chromophores. Most of these retro-compounds contain the C_{18} central unit (XI), and the end groups which may be attached to it are given in Table II.

Carotenoids are also known whose carbon skeletons possess fewer than forty carbon atoms: (C_{30}-) β-citraurin (6–50), (C_{27}-) azafrin (XII), (C_{24}-) bixin (44–45), and (C_{20}-) crocetin (48–48). It seems possible that these compounds are natural degradation products of various C_{40}-

* Isorenieratene is now known to be identical with leprotene (Jensen and Weedon, 1964).

TABLE I

End Groups in Carotenoids, and Related Polyenes, with "normal" Chromophores[a]

TABLE I—*Continued*

TABLE I—*Continued*

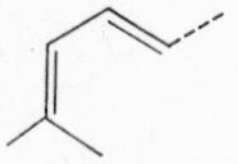

43 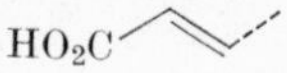   44    45

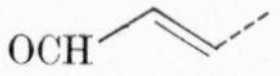

46 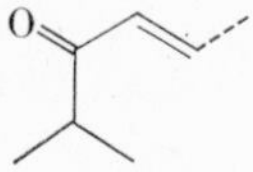   47 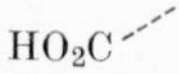   48

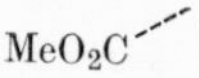

49 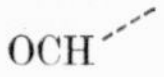   50

^a Dotted lines show the positions of attachment of the end groups to the central units (IX) or (X). The formulae should not be taken as indicating the preferred conformation about bonds corresponding to the 6,7 bond in β-carotene (cf. Section V, B). Moreover, the coiling of acyclic end groups is purely a conventional way of emphasizing the similarity of the carbon skeleton with that in β-carotene. Thus the formulae are not intended to imply either preferred conformations, or *cis* configurations about 3,4-double bonds in end groups such as 35, 36, 38–40; it is probable that such double bonds are *trans*.

End groups 10, 11, 13–19, 21, 22, 27, 29–31, 43, 46 and 47 have not been encountered in natural carotenoids.

TABLE II

End Groups in Carotenoids, and Related Polyenes, with "retro" Chromophores^a

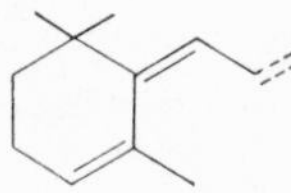

R1 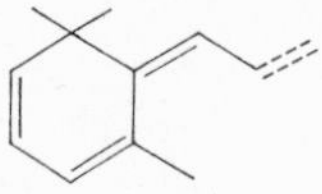   R2 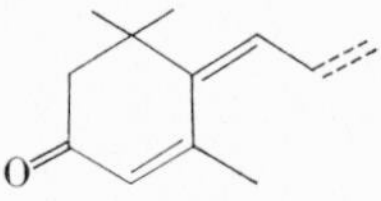   R3

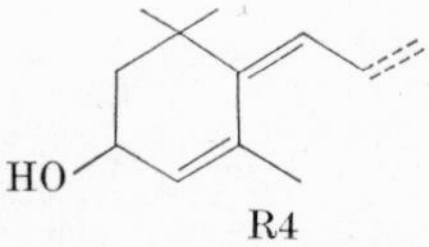

R4 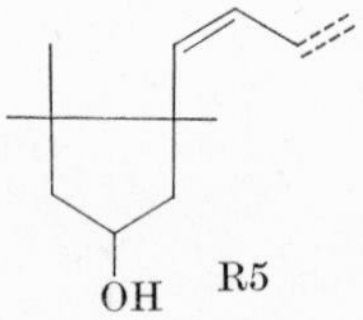   R5

^a Dotted lines show the position of the double bond connecting the end group to the C₁₈ central unit (XI).

carotenoids. There is, of course, strong evidence for the conversion in mammals of β-carotene, and some other carotenoids, into (C₂₀-) retinene (V) and vitamin A (IV). In the past, structural studies on the latter substance have materially assisted those on β-carotene.

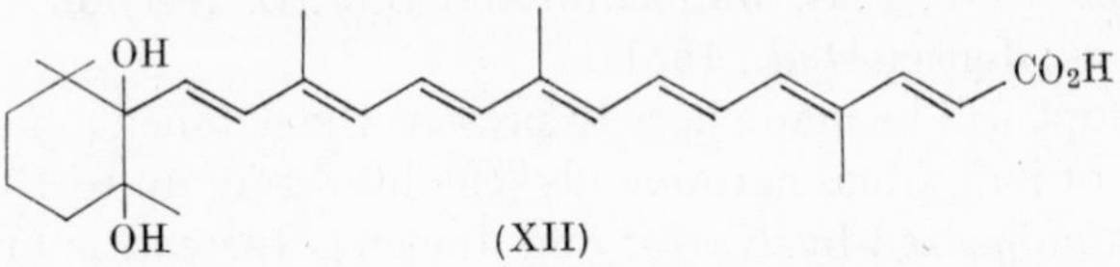

(XII)

It is now believed that the naturally occurring polyenes, phytoene (XIII), phytofluene (XIV), ζ-carotene (XV), and neurosporene (XVI), are key intermediates in the biosynthesis of carotenoids (see Chapter 5). Structural studies on these "precursors" have shown that they constitute a series of hydrolycopenes, each member of which has two fewer hydrogen atoms than its predecessor, and a chromophore extended by two double bonds (Davis *et al.*, 1961). A number of carotenoids, namely chloroxanthin (9–37), spheroidene (9–39), spheroidenone (9–40), α-zeacarotene (3–9), and β-zeacarotene (2–9), are now known to have the 7,8-dihydro system characteristic of neurosporene, and are probably derived from the latter by biosynthetic routes not involving lycopene

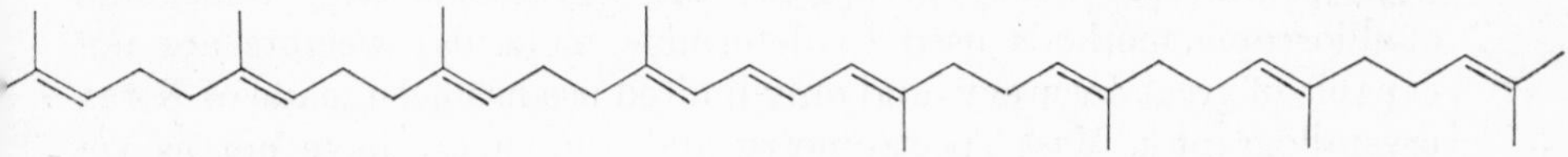

(XIII)

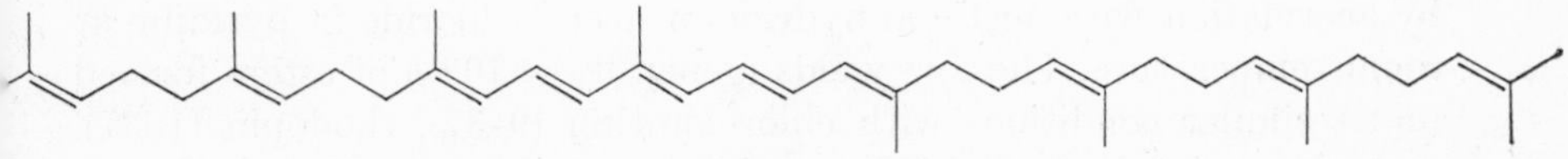

(XIV)

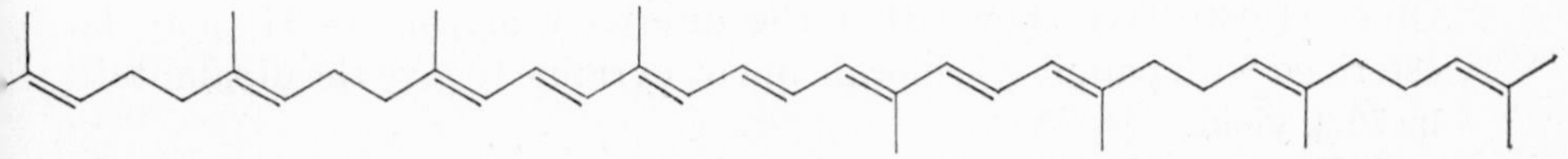

(XV)

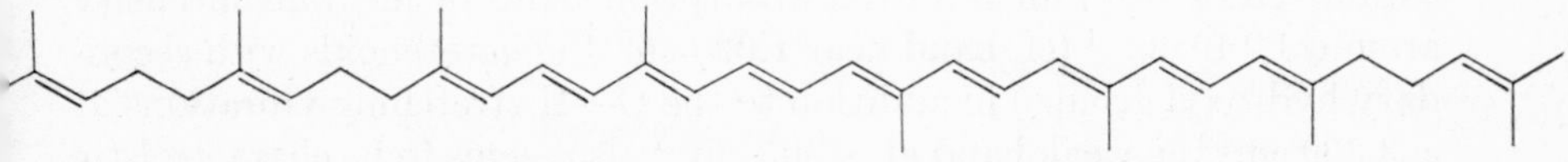

(XVI)

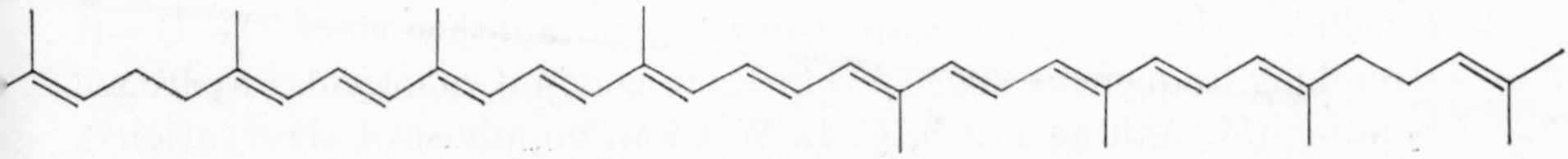

(II)

(Davis *et al.*, 1961; P. S. Manchand and B. C. L. Weedon, unpublished observations; Jensen *et al.*, 1961).

No attempt will be made here to present the detailed evidence for the structures of individual carotenoids (the literature up to 1948 has been expertly summarized by Karrer and Jucker). Instead a brief account is given below of the scope and limitations of the methods by which this information has been obtained.

A. MOLECULAR FORMULA AND OXYGEN FUNCTIONS

The instability of some carotenoids, and the tendency of others to solvate or occlude solvent, often complicates the task of obtaining correct analytical data. Even when these difficulties can be cirumvented, the limitations of conventional microanalytical techniques are such that it is not always possible to specify precisely the number of hydrogen atoms present. [Cholnoky *et al.* (1957) carried out thirty-seven microanalyses on capsanthin (6–28) and its derivatives before concluding, correctly, that the molecular formula of the carotenoid is $C_{40}H_{56}O_3$, and not $C_{40}H_{58}O_3$ as previously accepted.] The cryoscopic (e.g. Rast) and ebullioscopic methods used to determine molecular weights are not capable of great accuracy, and only limited use has been made of X-ray crystallography. Mass spectrometry and osmometry have not as yet received the attention which they deserve in this field.

Primary and secondary hydroxyl groups in carotenoids can be detected by acetylation with acetic anhydride or acetyl chloride in pyridine at room temperature. The low yields (generally $< 10\%$) of esters formed under similar conditions with chloroxanthin (9–37), rhodopin (1–37), and α-bacterioruberin (38–38), reveal the tertiary nature of the hydroxyl groups in these carotenoids (cf. Jensen, 1962). Recently Surmatis and Ofner (1963) have shown that the ditertiary glycol (37–37) may be esterified with palmitoyl chloride in hot pyridine to give the dipalmitate in 70% yield.

A distinction between tertiary and other types of hydroxy groups can also be made spectroscopically. Tertiary hydroxyl groups invariably exhibit (KBr disc) an infra-red absorption band of medium intensity around $1,140$ cm^{-1} (cf. band near $1,030$ cm^{-1} in carotenoids with secondary hydroxyl groups) in addition to the O—H stretching vibrations at $c.$ $3,300$ cm^{-1}; a weak band at ~ 905 cm^{-1} also seems to be characteristic (Jensen, 1962). The infra-red light absorption of azafrin (XII) methyl ester provides direct evidence for the hydroxyl groups; it has been concluded that the latter are *trans* to one another since the O—H stretching frequencies suggest that there is no intramolecular hydrogen bonding (M. Akhtar and B. C. L. Weedon, unpublished observations).

A band at $c.$ $1,078$ cm^{-1} in some bacterial carotenoids is believed to be associated with methoxyl groups (Jensen, 1962), but these substituents are most conveniently detected by means of their characteristic nuclear magnetic resonance (cf. Section III, D).

Aldehyde, ketone, acid, and ester groups are detected easily by means of their C=O stretching frequencies in the infra-red light absorption spectrum (cf. Section III, C).

The number of hydroxyl substituents may be estimated by the Zerewitinoff method, but misleading results have been obtained with highly oxygenated compounds, and with some ketones (cf. Karrer and Jucker, 1948). The usual Zeisel method has been used successfully to estimate methoxyl groups in spirilloxanthin (39–39) and some other bacterial carotenoids.

Carboxyl groups may be determined by titration of the carotenoid or, preferably, its perhydro-derivative.

B. DEGREE OF UNSATURATION

Microhydrogenation of a solution, or suspension, of a carotenoid over a platinum or palladium catalyst has been developed into a standard analytical procedure (Kuhn and Möller, 1934). Excellent results are normally obtained, though difficulties have been reported with some of the unstable hydrolycopenes found in nature. In interpreting the results it should be borne in mind that aromatic rings (Yamaguchi, 1957, 1958; Jansen and Weedon, 1964), epoxy groups (Karrer and Jucker, 1945), and (at least partially) carbonyl groups (Barber *et al.*, 1961b) are reduced as well as carbon-carbon double bonds under the experimental conditions used. Some hydrogenolysis of allylic hydroxyls, or their esters, is also to be expected.

Attempts to estimate the total number of double bonds by treatment with halogens or peracids have been made, but reaction is often incomplete (cf. Karrer and Jucker, 1948).

C. CHROMOPHORE

The ultra-violet or visible light absorption properties of a polyene provide the best indication of the chromophoric system present. The wavelengths of the light absorption maxima increase with the number of conjugated double bonds, but the actual positions of the maxima are dependent on various structural features and on the solvent used (cf. Table IV). The principal light absorption maxima of some standard polyenes in the carotenoid series are given in Table III and Fig. 1. The wavelengths of the maxima are longer than those observed with the corresponding polyenes devoid of methyl side chains (cf. Dale, 1954, 1957). A comparison of β-carotene with 13,13′-bisdesmethyl-β-carotene (Inhoffen *et al.*, 1950a), and of crocetin dimethyl ester (49–49) with less highly methylated analogues (Mildner and Weedon, 1953), suggests that each methyl substituent on the polyene chain produces a bathochromic shift comparable to that (c. 5 mμ) observed in simple dienes (cf. Braude, 1945).

TABLE III

Visible Light Absorption Properties of Some Isoprenoid Polyene Hydrocarbons (Acylic Chromophore)*

Polyene	Number of conjugated double bonds	Principal light absorption maxima (mμ)			Reference
Phytoene (XIII)	3	298	286	276	a
Photofluene (XIV)	5	366	347	331	a
ζ-Carotene (XV)	7	425	401	380	a
7,8,7′,8′-tetrahydro-β-carotene (10–10)	7	426	401	380	b
α-Zeacarotene (3–9)	8	449	421	398	b
Neurosporene (XVI)	9	470	440	416	a
ε-Carotene (3–3)	9	471	440	418	c
δ-Carotene (1–3)	10	487	456	431	c
Lycopene (II)	11	504	472	443	d
3′,4′-dehydro-δ-carotene (3–35)	12	515	481	456	e
3,4-dehydrolycopene (1–35)	13	535	500	468	f
(C₅₀-) decapreno-ε-carotene	13	528	495	468	g
3,4,3′,4′-bisdehydrolycopene (35–35)	15	540	510	480	h
(C₅₀-) decaprenolycopene	15	547	513	486	b

[a] Davis et al., 1961.
[b] P. S. Manchand, P. T. Siddons, and B. C. L. Weedon (unpublished).
[c] Manchand et al., 1964.
[d] Karrer and Jucker, 1948.
[e] Kargl and Quackenbush, 1960.
[f] Winterstein et al., 1960.
[g] Karrer et al., 1951.
[h] Surmatis and Ofner, 1963.

Many carotenoids exhibit light-absorption properties which do not correspond exactly with the data given in Fig. 1. These departures, which are often of great help in making structural assignments, are due to the presence of cyclic end groups of the type found in β-carotene, to conjugation of the polyene system with another chromophore (—CHO, —CO₂H, —CO₂Me, >C=O, aryl), or to the fact that one or more double bonds in the polyene chain has the cis-configuration. The first two of these causes for deviation will be discussed briefly here, and the third deferred to Section V.

Although lycopene (1–1), γ-carotene (1–2), and β-carotene (2–2)

* Determined on dilute solutions of the all-trans-isomers in light petroleum or hexane. For further spectral data see Chapter 18.

TABLE IV

Visible Light Absorption Properties of Some Carotenoid Hydrocarbons

Carotenoid	Structure	Wavelengths (mμ) of principal absorption bands, and solvents[a]											
		Light petroleum			Benzene			Chloroform			Carbon disulphide		
Lycopene	(1-1)	506	475·5	447	522	487	455	517	480	453	548	507·5	477
γ-Carotene	(1-2)	495	462	431	510	477	447	508·5	475	446	533·5	496	463
β-Carotene	(2-2)	482	451	430	500	467	442	497	466	—	520	485	450
[b] α-Carotene	(2-3)	475	444	423	495	462	436	485	454	—	509	477	—
ε-Carotene	(3-3)	471	440	418	487	452	434	483	452	433	501·5	470	449
δ-Carotene	(1-3)	487	456	431	501	467	445	499	466	443	523	487	460

[a] Compiled from Karrer and Jucker, 1948; Manchand et al., 1964; and unpublished data.
[b] Cf. Isler and Schudel, 1963.

formally possess the same chromophore, the positions of their light absorption maxima differ significantly (Table IV). A study of molecular models reveals that the presence of the cyclic end groups leads to steric

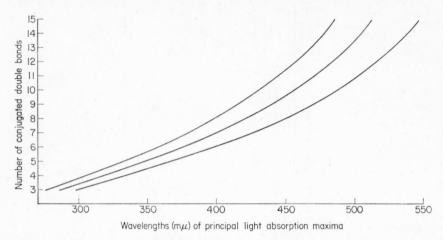

FIG. 1. Positions of principal light absorption maxima of polyenes in the carotenoid series with acyclic chromophores (plotted from data given in Table III).

hindrance between the ring methyls and the polyene side chain. The resulting lack of planarity in the molecule limits overlap of the π-orbitals associated with the ring double bond and the polyene chain, and produces

TABLE V

Wavelength of Maximal Light Absorption of
β-Carotene and its Keto-derivatives[a]

Polyene	λ_{max} ($m\mu$)
β-Carotene (2–2)	466
Echinenone (2–4)	480
Canthaxanthin (4–4)	486·5
3-Keto-echinenone (2–12)	490·5
3-Keto-canthaxanthin (4–12)	494·5
Astacin (12–12)	499·5

[a] Determined on chloroform solutions; C. W. Price and B. C. L. Weedon, unpublished results.

the observed shift of the light absorption maxima to shorter wavelengths (c. 12 $m\mu$ for each end which has been cyclized) together with a partial loss of fine structure. Similar changes are also observed in the spectra of some of the aryl carotenoids (Yamaguchi, 1958; Cooper et al., 1963).

Despite the "incomplete conjugation" of the double bond in β-end groups, the difference between the light absorption maxima of β-carotene (2–2), α-carotene (2–3), and ϵ-carotene (3–3) indicates the progressive shortening of the chromophore (Table IV). Many other pairs of isomers, differing only in the presence of end groups of the "α-" or "β-type", exhibit the same effect (e.g. lutein (6–7) and zeaxanthin (6–6); γ-carotene (1–2) and δ-carotene (1–3)).

The conjugation of the polyene chain with another chromophore will, of course, result in a shift of the light absorption maxima to longer wavelengths (cf. Table V), and this shift is also frequently accompanied by some loss of fine structure. The classical chemical methods for the detection of aldehydes and ketones are of very limited application in this field. Thus bixindial (46–46) is stated to be stable to silver oxide (Kuhn and Grundman, 1932), whilst crocetindial (50–50) gives crocetin (48–48) in only poor yield ($< 20\%$) (M. S. Barber and B. C. L. Weedon, unpublished observations). Again, though most polyene aldehydes react normally with carbonyl reagents, some conjugated ketones do not (e.g. capsanthin (6–28), capsorubin (28–28), fucoxanthin). Fortunately, however, the presence of "additional" chromophores can easily be detected by their characteristic infra-red light-absorption properties. Aryl groups may be recognized by the C—H out-of-plane deformations near 800 cm^{-1} (12·5 μ) (Yamaguchi, 1957, 1958) which are clearly differentiated from the strong absorption close to 970 cm^{-1} (10·3 μ) (due to C—H out-of-plane deformations of $trans$-CH=CH) present in the spectra of all carotenoids (Lunde and Zechmeister, 1955). Conjugated esters have a carbonyl stretching frequency near 1,690 cm^{-1} (5·9 μ) (cf. Lunde and Zechmeister, 1955), and conjugated aldehydes and ketones have corresponding bands in the range 1,650–1,670 cm^{-1} (c. 6·0 μ) (cf. Warren and Weedon, 1958; Liaaen and Sørensen, 1956). The carbonyl band in astacin (12–12) occurs at exceptionally low frequency (1,610 cm^{-1}), doubtless owing to hydrogen bonding with the enolic hydroxyl. In all cases conjugation with a carbonyl group results in a noticeable intensification of the bands near 1,600 cm^{-1} (6·25 μ), which are attributable to carbon-carbon double bond stretching vibrations.

The intensity of the carbonyl band in the infra-red light absorption spectra of conjugated aldehydes ($\epsilon = 750$–1,200) is greater than that in the spectra of conjugated ketones ($\epsilon = 175$–500) (M. S. Barber and B. C. L. Weedon, unpublished observations). The marked variation in the intensity of the carbonyl band with different conjugated ketones may be roughly correlated with molecular environment, and ascribed to differences in the preferred conformations about the carbon-carbon single bond joining the carbonyl group to the polyene chain (Warren and Weedon, 1958). A further distinction between conjugated aldehydes and ketones is provided by the C—H stretching frequency of aldehydes near $2,700$ cm^{-1} ($3 \cdot 7$ μ). However, with complicated molecules this band may be difficult to observe, and it is far safer to rely on the characteristic nuclear magnetic resonance absorption of aldehydic protons.

If only trace amounts of the material are available, or if a distinction between polyene aldehyde, dialdehyde, or keto-aldehyde is desired, it is possible to subject the material to an aldol condensation with acetone or pinacolone, and observe the changes in light absorption; most conjugated aldehydes and dialdehydes react readily, extending the chromophore by one and two carbon-carbon double bonds respectively (cf. Warren and Weedon, 1958; Akhtar and Weedon, 1959). By these means a permanganate oxidation product of fucoxanthin was characterized as a pentaenedial (chromatographically indistinguishable from (XVII)) (R. Bonnett, J. L. Tee and B. C. L. Weedon, unpublished observations), and a fission product from lagosin as a methylpentaenedial (Dhar *et al.*, 1964).

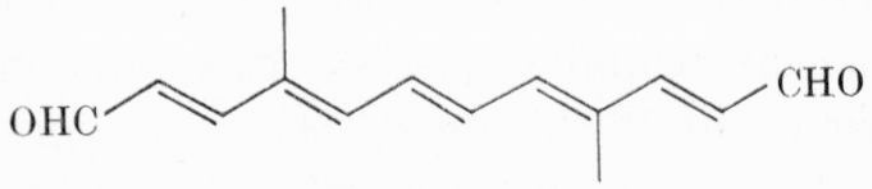

(XVII)

Another commonly used method of detecting carbonyl groups conjugated with the polyene chain is to treat the compound with a selective reducing agent (LiAlH$_4$, KBH$_4$). A shift of 20–30 mμ in the light-absorption maxima to shorter wavelengths provides good evidence that the original chromophore contained a carbonyl group. The magnitude of the shift may also indicate whether one or two conjugated carbonyl groups were originally present. With aldehydes and ketones, oxidation of the resulting allylic alcohol with a selective oxidizing agent (MnO$_2$, quinone, chloranil) sometimes regenerates the original carotenoid, e.g. capsanthin (6–28), capsorubin (28–28), echinenone (2–4), (cf. Warren and Weedon, 1958; Ganguly *et al.*, 1956).

D. DETECTION OF END GROUPS BY N.M.R.

A new approach to the study of carotenoids, based on nuclear magnetic resonance spectroscopy (N.M.R.), was introduced by Weedon, Jackman, and their collaborators, in 1959 (Barber *et al.*, 1960). It has already played a major role in establishing the novel structures of several bacterial carotenoids (e.g. spirilloxanthin (39–39), spheroidene (9–39), spheroidenone (9–40), chlorobactene (1–32)), and of the paprika pigments (capsanthin (6–28), capsorubin (28–28), and kryptocapsin (2–28)), and in settling the structures of some hydrolycopenes believed to be natural precursors of the carotenoids (phytoene (XIII), phytofluene (XIV), ζ-carotene (XV), and neurosporene (XVI)) (Barber *et al.*, 1959, 1961b; Davis *et al.*, 1961; Jackman and Jensen, 1961; Cholnoky *et al.*, 1963; Jensen *et al.*, 1964). By providing information about parts of the molecule outside the main chromophore it is, to a large extent, complimentary to the spectroscopic techniques discussed earlier, but, like these, is non-destructive so that the sample used may subsequently be recovered for other studies. At the present time *c.* 10 mg of a carotenoid is normally required to obtain a satisfactory spectrum, but it is probable that considerably less will be needed with the instruments now coming into use.

All natural carotenoids of known structure have methyl groups attached either to oxygen atoms or to fully substituted carbon atoms. There is therefore no spin–spin coupling of the methyl protons with protons on adjacent atoms, and the different methyl groups give rise to single peaks which are readily distinguished from absorption due to methylene groups, if any; the latter generally give broad bands as the result of complex spin–spin coupling. So far attention has been confined mainly to the methyl bands.

The typical N.M.R. absorptions associated with most carotenoid end groups have now been determined, and the positions of the more important bands are indicated in Table VI. It will be noticed that the characteristic end groups of lycopene (1–1), β-carotene (2–2), ε-carotene (3–3), capsorubin (28–28), astacin (12–12), spirilloxanthin (39–39), the di-epoxide (23–23), aurochrome (25–25), isorenieratene (32–32), and renierapurpurin (33–33), can all be readily distinguished (Barber *et al.*, 1960; Davis and Weedon, 1960; Cooper *et al.*, 1963). Slight differences can also be discerned between the end groups of zeaxanthin (6–6) and canthaxanthin (4–4), and those of β-carotene (2–2). The differences are, however, too small to be of much diagnostic value in the investigation of an unknown carotenoid, unless supported by other evidence.

Methyl groups attached to oxygen, as in the esters methylbixin (45–45) and torularhodin methyl ester (2–36), or in methoxylated carotenoids such as spirilloxanthin (39–39) and spheroidenone (9–40), are strongly deshielded and give rise to bands at lower fields than those of the C-methyls (Barber *et al.*, 1960).

The N.M.R. spectra of all carotenoids show strong absorption in the region 7·95–8·15 due to the "in-chain" methyls (i.e. the methyl groups attached to the non-terminal double bonds of the polyene chain). Since the number of these methyls is usually known from oxidation studies (see Section III, H), this N.M.R. band affords a convenient internal standard for estimating the number of methyls represented by the other bands.

More than one band is observed in the region 7·95–8·15 when an acetate grouping is also present, or when the "in-chain" methyls are not

TABLE VI

N.M.R. Bands Associated with Different Types of Carotenoids[1]

End group	Example	C-methyl groups[2]				Other bands	Reference
		C-1	C-5	C-9	C-13		
1	Lycopene	8·38	8·18	8·03	8·03	—	*a*
2	β-Carotene	8·97	8·28	8·03	8·03	—	*a*
3	ε-Carotene	9·17	8·40	8·10	8·03	—	*b*
4	Canthaxanthin	8·81	8·14	8·04	8·04	—	*a, c*
6	Zeaxanthin	8·92	8·26	8·05	8·05	—	*a*
7	Lutein (6–7)[3]	9·15	8·36	8·02	8·02	—	*a*
9	ζ-Carotene	8·42	8·42	8·20	8·09	—	*d*
9	Phytoene	8·42	8·42	8·42	8·26	—	*d*
10	Tetrahydro-β-carotene	8·99	8·39	8·17	8·07	—	*e*
12	Astacin	8·70	7·90[4]	7·98[4]	7·98[4]	—	*f*
13	Astacin acetate	8·65	≈7·96	≈7·96	≈7·96	7·71 (MeCOO—)	*f*
14	Bisphenazine astacin	8·79	7·61	7·94	7·94	—	*f*
18	Isozeaxanthin	8·98	8·18	8·03	8·03	—	*c*
19	Dimethyl isozeaxanthin	8·98	8·22	8·05	8·05	6·65 (OMe)	*c*
20	Azafrin (XII), methyl ester	9·16	8·81[5]	8·01	8·01	8·07 (C-13′ Me), 6·25 (OMe)	*a*
23	β-Carotene diepoxide	9·06	8·87[5]	8·08	8·08	—	*a*
25	Aurochrome	8·89[6], 8·74[6]	8·58	8·27	8·07	4·84 (C-7 and C-8 H)	*a*
28	Capsorubin	9·16	8·63	8·03	8·03	—	*g*
29	E/epi-capsorubin	9·03	8·85	8·00	8·00	—	*g*
30	Capsanthone (6–30)[3]	9·02	8·65	8·03	8·03	—	*g*
32	Isorenieratene	7·73[7]	7·73[7]	7·93	8·02	—	*h*
33	Renierapurpurin[8]	7·72[7]	7·72[7]	7·96	8·03	—	*h*
34	3,4,3′,4′,15,15′-Trisdehydro-β-carotene (34:34)	8·96	8·14	8·02	7·90	—	*c*
35	3,4,3′,4′-Bisdehydrolycopene[10]	(8·18)	(8·04)	(8·04)	(8·04)	—	*a*
36	Torularhodin methyl ester (2–36)[3]	—	8·06	8·06	8·06	6·28 (OMe)	*a*

No.	Compound						
37	Rhodopin (1-37)[3]	8·79	8·79	8·19	8·03	8·03	—	i
39	Spirilloxanthin	8·83	8·83	8·02	8·02	8·02	7·70 ($J = 6·8$) (CH_2)	a
40	Spheroidenone (9-40)[3]	8·65	8·65	8·02	8·02	8·02	6·78 (OMe)	d
41	(41-41) (Synthetic)	8·44	8·33	8·89 ($J = 7·0$)	8·04	8·04	6·79 (OMe)	a
45	Methyl bixin	—	—	—	8·03	8·03	6·24 (OMe)	a
46	Bixindial	—	—	—	8·00	8·00	—	j
47	(47-47) (Synthetic)[11]	—	—	8·84(×2) ($J = 6·5$)	8·02	8·02	—	a
49	Crocetin dimethyl ester	—	—	—	7·99	7·99	6·23 (OMe)	a
50	Crocetindial	—	—	—	8·10	7·97	0·55 (CHO)	a
R1	Retro-dehydrocarotene[12]	(8·70)	(8·70)	(8·10)	(8·03)	(8·03)	—	a

a Barber et al., 1960.
b Manchand et al., 1964.
c C. W. Price and B. C. L. Weedon, unpublished results.
d Cf. Davis et al., 1961.
e P. S. Manchand and B. C. L. Weedon, unpublished results.
f Davis and Weedon, 1960.

g Barber et al., 1959, 1961b; Cooper et al., 1962.
h R. D. G. Cooper, J. B. Davis, C. W. Price and B. C. L. Weedon, unpublished observations.
i Bonnett et al., 1964.
j M. S. Barber and B. C. L. Weedon, unpublished results.

1 Spectra determined on dilute solutions (2–5%) in carbon tetrachloride, or deuterochloroform, using tetramethylsilane as an internal reference. The positions of the bands are given in τ-values, as defined by Tiers (1958).
2 Positions to which methyls are attached are indicated by the numbers of the corresponding positions in β-carotene.
3 With unsymmetrical carotenoids the bands cited refer to that half of the molecule which contains the end group indicated.
4 Of the bands marked 4, the assignment of the one at lowest field to the C-5 methyl is arbitrary.
5 One of each pair of bands marked 5 must be due to a C-1 methyl; the assignment of the band at higher fields to this group is arbitrary.
6 Relative intensities c. 6:5:1; the synthetic sample used was probably a mixture of epimers.
7 Assignment of aryl methyl bands to particular positions is arbitrary.
8 Bands quoted refer to the appropriate half of unsymmetrical molecules with the 2,6,6-trimethylcyclohexenyl ring (2) at the other end.
9 The C-13 methyls in the synthetic 15,15'-dehydro-analogues of carotenoids lie in regions above the triple bond where the induced field is paramagnetic; their N.M.R. bands are therefore shifted to lower fields.
10 Estimated from synthetic C_{30}-analogue (43–43).
11 Pyridine solution.
12 Estimated from simple C_{19}-analogues.

all subject to similar shielding (e.g. in astacin (12–12), azafrin (XII), the aryl carotenoids, and the (C_{25}) α- and β-apocarotenals (XVIII and XIX), (Barber *et al.*, 1960; Davis and Weedon, 1960; Cooper *et al.*, 1963; P. S. Manchand and B. C. L. Weedon, unpublished observations). Particularly strong deshielding is observed with an "olefinic" methyl group which is on the β-carbon atom to a carbonyl group (e.g. retinene (V)) (cf. Planta *et al.*, 1962).

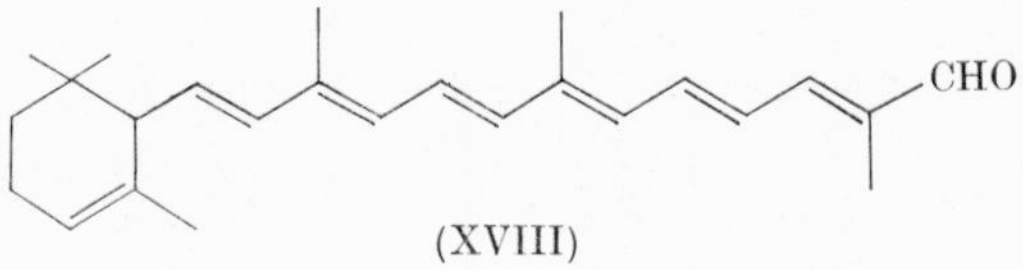

(XVIII)

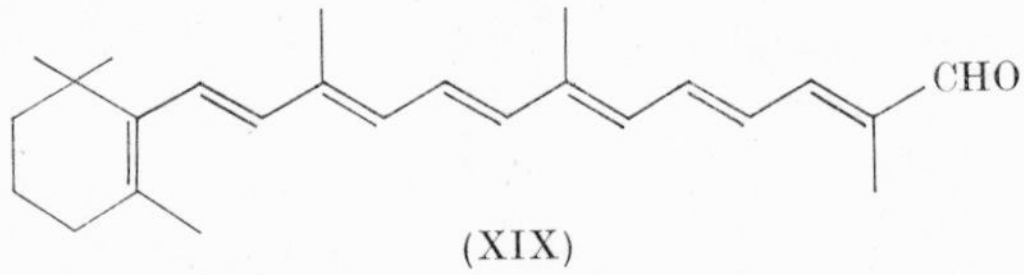

(XIX)

The olefinic protons in carotenoids give rise to absorption in the region 2·0–4·5; the bands are usually complex owing to spin–spin coupling.

Aldehydic protons are uniquely deshielded and, in conjugated polyene aldehydes, give rise to a band at 0·45–0·60. This occurs as a singlet in the α-methyl aldehydes (e.g. crocetindial (50–50)), but is split into a doublet ($J \sim 8$) when the nearest methyl group is on the β- (e.g. retinene (V)) or γ-carbon atom (e.g. XVII). (Barber *et al.*, 1960; Planta *et al.*, 1962). A consideration of the aldehydic proton and methyl proton absorptions therefore enables α-, β-, and γ-methyl polyene aldehydes to be distinguished.

For a fuller discussion of the N.M.R. properties of carotenoids and related polyenes the reader is referred to the original literature.

E. CHEMICAL AND BIOCHEMICAL DETECTION OF END GROUPS

Isopropylidene end groups ($Me_2C=C$) give acetone on ozonolysis (Kuhn and Roth, 1932). This test must be carried out quantitatively since low yields (*c.* 0·3–0·4 mol.) of acetone have been obtained with compounds which have no isopropylidene group (α-terpineol, vitamin A_2 (VII), spirilloxanthin (39–39), capsanthin (6–28) (Karrer and Schneider, 1950; Cholnoky *et al.*, 1957; Karrer and Solmssen, 1936; cf. Jensen, 1962). Under standard conditions (oxidation with ozone, followed by permanganate, and iodometric titration of the acetone produced) lycopene and γ-carotene give 1·6 and 0·85 mol. of acetone respectively. (The presence or absence of an isopropylidene group is, as a rule, readily confirmed by N.M.R.).

Ozonolysis of lycopene (1–1) and the natural hydrolycopenes gives laevulic aldehyde (XX) as well as acetone:

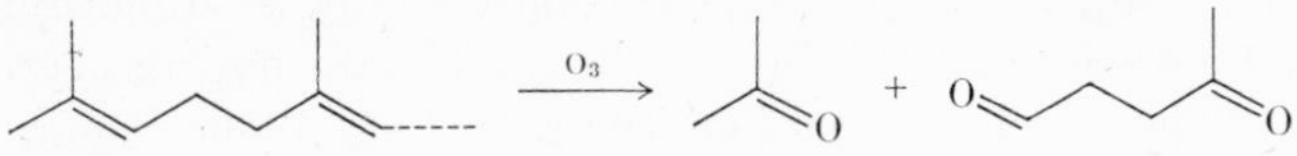

(XX)

The yield of the former product (XX) affords a rough measure of the number of $=CH.CH_2.CH_2.CMe=$ units present in the molecule (Strain, 1933; Rabourn and Quackenbush, 1956).

Ozonolysis of a carotenoid containing the 2,2,6-trimethylcyclohexenyl (or "β") end group of β-carotene (2–2) gives geronic acid (XXI) together with further reaction products. Comparison of the yield of geronic acid with that obtained from β-ionone provided the first evidence for the presence in β-carotene of two β-end groups. Under similar conditions the isomeric (or "α") end group found in α-carotene gives isogeronic acid (XXII) (Karrer *et al.*, 1930, 1933), though Kargl and Quackenbush (1960) were unable to identify this product after ozonolysis of δ-carotene (1–3).

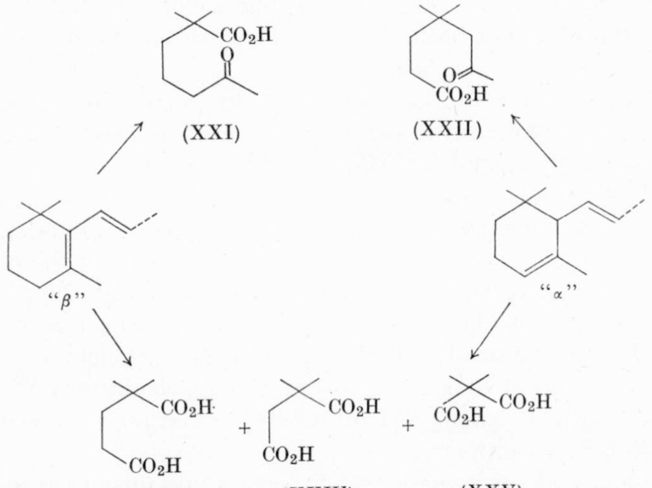

(XXI) (XXII) (XXIII) (XXIV) (XXV)

Oxidation of α- and β-end groups with an excess of alkaline potassium permanganate gives αα-dimethylglutaric acid (XXIII) and, by further degradation, αα-dimethylsuccinic (XXIV) and αα-dimethylmalonic acid (XXV) (rather surprisingly no ββ-dimethyladipic or ββ-dimethylglutaric acid have been reported from the α-end group).

Oxidation with permanganate or ozone of oxygenated carotenoids gives information regarding the position of attachment of oxygen substituents to any α- and β-end groups present. Thus, the detection of αα-dimethylmalonic and αα-dimethylsuccinic acid on oxidation of zeaxanthin (6–6), and the failure to observe any αα-dimethylglutaric acid or geronic acid, leads to the conclusion that the hydroxyl groups are attached to the 3- and 3'-positions (Karrer et al., 1930). Again, astacin (12–12) gives only αα-dimethylmalonic acid, whereas its bisphenazine derivative (14–14) gives dimethylsuccinic acid as well, in good agreement with the structures proposed (Karrer and Loewe, 1934). Formerly the dicarboxylic acids from these degradations had to be separated by fractional crystallization, and at least 0·5 g of the carotenoid had to be oxidized before much reliance could be placed on the failure to observe certain acids. The detection of the products by paper chromatography (Torto and Weedon, 1955; Grob and Bütler, 1956), or, after esterification, by gas–liquid chromatography (R. Bonnett, J. L. Tee and B. C. L. Weedon, unpublished observations) permits far greater precision, and the degradation can now be carried out on as little as 5 mg.

In passing, it is interesting to note that the positions of the hydroxyl substituents in kryptoxanthin (2–6), lycophyll (5–5), and lycoxanthin (1–5) were assigned "by analogy" at a time when oxygenation of the 1 and 4 positions had not been observed. The structures of lycophyll and lycoxanthin have yet to be confirmed.

Oppenauer oxidation of capsanthin (6–28), capsorubin (28–28), and kryptocapsin (2–28) leads to oxidation of the 3-hydroxyl substituents attached to the five membered rings (Barber et al., 1961b; Entschel and Karrer, 1960; Cholnoky et al., 1963). Recognition of the capsanthin product as a cyclopentanone (6–30) by means of its characteristic infrared light absorption properties provided the first clue to the existence of a new class of carotenoids with a five-membered ring (the possibility that the five-membered ring was formed during the oxidation was excluded by further studies (Barber et al., 1961b)). Under similar conditions zeaxanthin (6–6) is not attacked, though the latter gives rhodoxanthin (R3–R3) in poor yield on drastic oxidation with manganese dioxide (Entschel and Karrer, 1959).

β-Carotene, and carotenoids which possess one unsubstituted β-end group, are converted in mammals into vitamin A (IV). The detection of strong growth-promoting properties in feeding tests with vitamin A-deficient rats has been used on a number of occasions to show that one-half of the molecule in an unknown carotenoid is identical with that of β-carotene. An apparent exception to the above generalization is provided by the diepoxide (23–23) of β-carotene, but the activity of this compound is probably due to the ease with which epoxy end groups are converted into β-end groups *in vivo* (Karrer and Jucker, 1948). Reports that astaxanthin (8–8), and some of its esters, exhibit growth-promoting properties of the vitamin A type require careful re-investigation (Grangaud *et al.*, 1957; Massonet, 1956).

F. PARTIAL DEGRADATION

By carefully controlled chromic acid oxidation of β-carotene (2–2) Kuhn and Brockmann (1935) succeeded in isolating a whole series of partial oxidation products, which not only forged a link between β-carotene and azafrin (XII) (see Scheme 1), but also provided valuable confirmation of the structures assigned to these two carotenoids. Similar, though less detailed, studies have also been carried out with α-carotene (2–3), capsanthin (6–28), physalien (the dipalmitate of zeaxanthin (6–6)), and lycopene (1–1). The latter yielded, among other products, bixin dialdehyde (46–46), which was transformed via the dioxime and dinitrile into nor-bixin (44–44) (Kuhn and Grundmann, 1932; cf. Karrer and Jucker, 1948).

By partial permanganate oxidation of α-carotene, β-carotene, azafrin, and lycopene, Karrer *et al.* obtained polyene aldehydes which were different from those reported from the chromic acid oxidations; thus β-carotene gave the apocarotenals (2–50) and (XIX) (Karrer and Solmssen, 1937), and lycopene the apolycopenal (1–50) (Karrer and Jaffé, 1939). With the cyclic carotenoids, permanganate degrades the polyene chain leaving one ring intact. With chromic acid, however, degradation of the chain seems to follow the initial formation of an acyclic structure.

It is noteworthy that in both permanganate and chromic acid oxidations, α-carotene degrades from the β-end to yield products isomeric with those obtained from β-carotene. The same difference is observed in the permanganate oxidation of lutein (6–7) and zeaxanthin (6–6) which give mainly α-citraurin (7–50) and β-citraurin (6–50) respectively (cf. Karrer and Jucker, 1948).

Partial oxidation of bixin (44–45) (to aldehyde esters with 6, 7, and 8 conjugated C:C) (Karrer and Solmssen, 1937), of spirilloxanthin (39–39) (to dialdehydes containing 7, 9, and 11 conjugated C:C) (Karrer and Koenig, 1940; M. S. Barber and B. C. L. Weedon, unpublished observations), of renieratene (32–33) and isorenieratene (32–32) (to a heptaenedial and aryloctaenals) (Yamaguchi, 1957, 1958), and of fucoxanthin (to a 14-keto-hexaenal and a pentaenedial) (R. Bonnett, J. L. Tee and B. C. L. Weedon, unpublished observations) have provided most helpful information concerning the structures of these compounds.

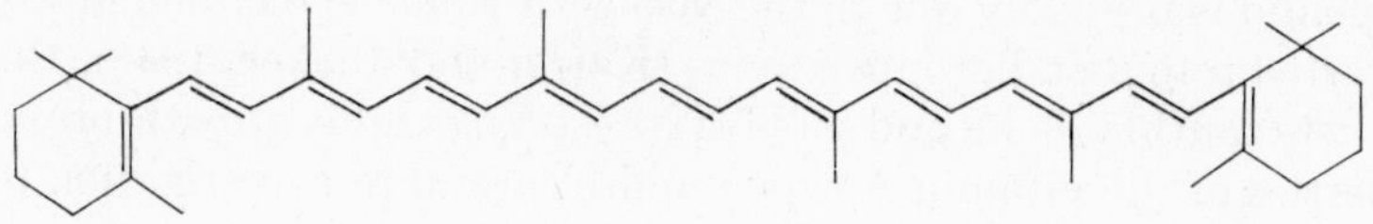

β-Carotene (I)

↓ 1

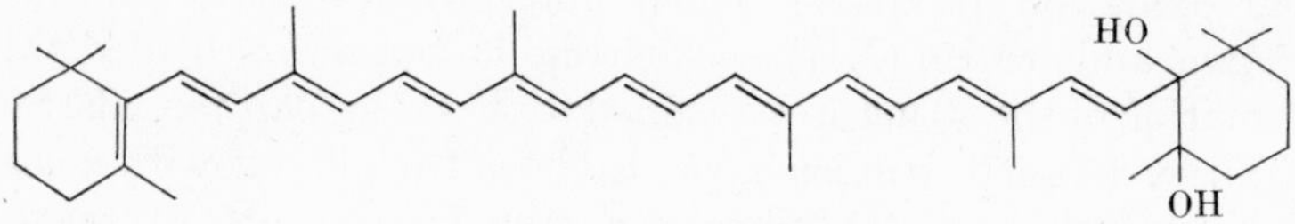

↓ 1 or 2

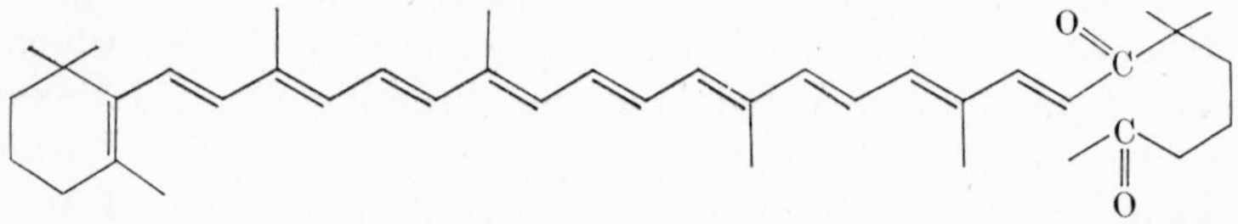

Semi-β-carotenone

↓ 1

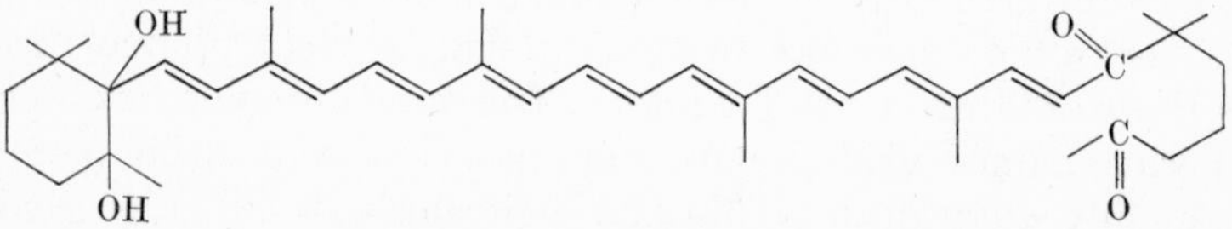

↓ 1 or 2

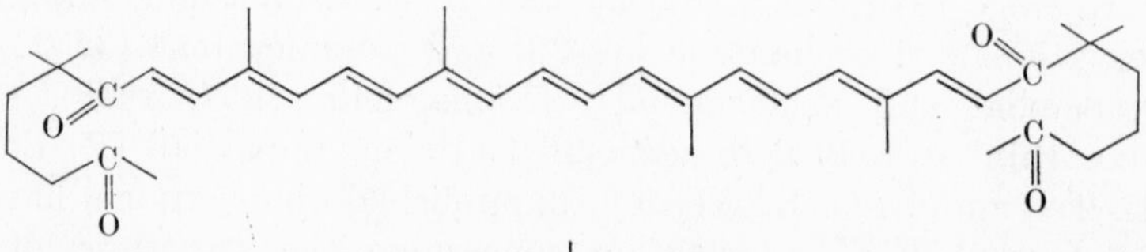

β-Carotenone

↓ 1

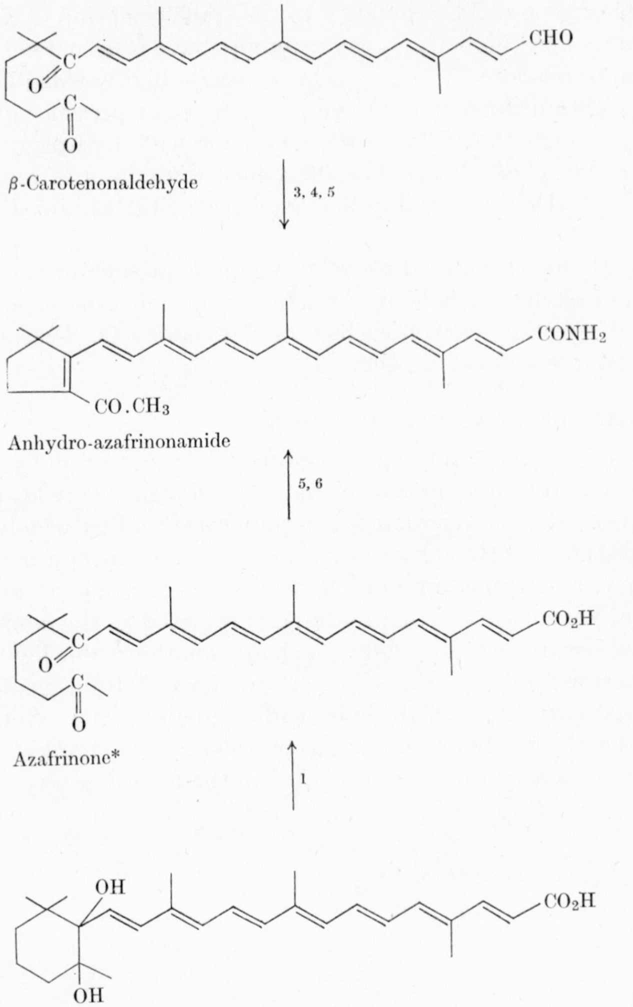
CHO
β-Carotenonaldehyde
3, 4, 5
CONH2
CO.CH3
Anhydro-azafrinonamide
5, 6
CO2H
Azafrinone*
1
OH
CO2H
OH
Azafrin (XII)

Reagents: 1. Chromic acid 2. $Pb(OAc)_4$ 3. NH_2OH
4. Ac_2O 5. KOH 6. CH_2N_2

* Synthesized by chromic acid oxidation of C_{27}-β-apo-carotenoic acid methyl ester (M. Akhtar and B. C. L. Weedon unpublished observations)

SCHEME 1.

Because of its possible similarity to the transformation of β-carotene into vitamin A in the body, many attempts have been made to oxidize β-carotene to retinene (V) *in vitro*. Surprisingly high yields (30%) were ultimately obtained using hydrogen peroxide in the presence of osmium tetroxide, though the yields were very poor with hydrogen peroxide alone (Wendler *et al.*, 1950). The subsequent reduction of retinene (V) to vitamin A (IV) was readily accomplished with lithium aluminium hydride.

In view of the widespread use of manganese dioxide for the selective oxidation of allylic alcohols, it is worth noting that this reagent is also capable of splitting carbon-carbon double bonds in β-carotene and lycopene (Winterstein *et al.*, 1960).

G. DEHYDRATION OF ALLYLIC ALCOHOLS

Most allylic alcohols in the polyene series dehydrate rapidly on treatment with chloroformic hydrogen chloride. Though the yields obtained are very variable, the reaction forms the basis of a test widely used in structural studies both on hydroxy compounds and, after a preliminary reduction with lithium aluminium hydride or similar reagent, on ketones and esters. Very little starting material is required as the course of the reaction can easily be followed by the changes in the visible light absorption properties. Allylic ethers, which are formed from many allylic alcohols by treatment with alcoholic acids, undergo similar eliminations, but rather more slowly (cf. Zechmeister, 1958). In its simplest form the dehydration reaction can be represented in the following way:

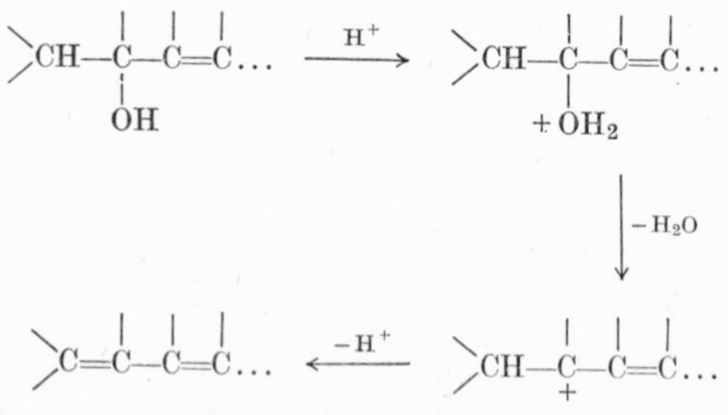

$$
\begin{array}{l}
\text{>CH--C--C=C...} \xrightarrow{\;H^+\;} \text{>CH--C--C=C...} \\
\quad\quad\;\;\overset{|}{O}H \quad\quad\quad\quad\quad\quad\quad\;\; +\overset{|}{O}H_2 \\[1em]
\quad\quad\quad\quad\quad\quad\quad\quad\quad\quad\quad\quad \Big\downarrow{\scriptstyle -H_2O} \\[1em]
\text{>C=C--C=C...} \xleftarrow{\;-H^+\;} \text{>CH--C--C=C...} \\
\quad\quad\quad\quad\quad\quad\quad\quad\quad\quad\quad\quad\;\; +
\end{array}
$$

Thus eschscholtzxanthin (R4–R4) gives the bis-anhydroderivative (R2–R2) (Karrer and Leumann, 1951). Frequently, however, dehydration involves loss of a proton not from the adjacent carbon atom, but from the vinylogous position at the other end of the polyene chain. Thus kryptocapsol (2–31), prepared by reduction of kryptocapsin (2–28) with lithium aluminium hydride, gives the anhydro-compound (R1–R5) (Cholnoky *et al.*, 1963) and the reduction product (2–18) from echinenone (2–4) gives the anhydro-compound (R1–R1) (Petracek and Zech-meister, 1956a). These reactions are obviously analogous to the formation of anhydro-vitamin A (XXVI) on treatment of vitamin A with alcoholic hydrogen chloride (Shantz et al., 1943).

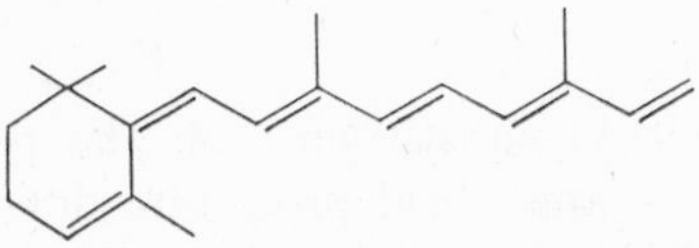

(XXVI)

Limitations to the chloroformic hydrogen chloride reaction are known. The substitution pattern present in capsorubinol (31–31), the reduction product of capsorubin (28–28), precludes dehydration (Cholnoky and Szabolcs, 1957). Furthermore, the glycol from (41–41) gives only trace amounts of lycopene. This failure is probably due to interaction of the carbonium ions first formed with the 1,2 and 1′,2′ double bonds since the reduction products of (42–42) and (47–47) react normally (M. S. Barber and B. C. L. Weedon, unpublished observations).

The elimination of an allylic function may produce another allylic system, which then reacts further. Thus capsanthol (6–31), prepared from capsanthin (6–28), yields the bis-anhydro derivative (R2–R5) (Cholnoky and Szabolcs, 1957), and the reduction product of spheroide-none (9–40) gives 3,4-dehydrolycopene (1–35) (Goodwin et al., 1956), the chromophores being lengthened by two and three double bonds res-pectively.

Isozeaxanthin (18–18), formed on reduction of canthaxanthin (4–4), exhibits an unexpected reaction on treatment with chloroformic hydrogen chloride. In addition to a mixture of hydrocarbons, some of which seem to have chromophores of the retro-type, 3′,4′-dehydro-echinenone (4–34) is produced (Petracek and Zechmeister, 1956a; C. W. Price and B. C. Weedon, unpublished results; cf. Bodea and Tamas, 1961). The nature of this reaction, which leads to dehydration at one end of the molecule, and oxidation at the other, is still obscure. It is, however, of interest that 15,15′-dehydroisozeaxanthin (18:18) reacts normally to give (34:34). The isomeric glycol (2:16) yields, among other products, the ketone (2:17) which may be converted into kryptoxanthin (2–6); similar transformations with the tetrol (16:16) derived from 15,15′-dehydroastacene (12:12) lead to a formal synthesis of zeaxanthin (6–6) (C. W. Price and B. C. L. Weedon, unpublished observations).

The limiting number of double bonds necessary in the polyene chain to promote the above reactions of allylic systems has not been determined. As would be expected, the reagent normally used (c. 0·01 M hydrogen chloride in chloroform) attacks the homoallylic systems present in, for example, zeaxanthin (6–6) and spirilloxanthin (39–39), comparatively slowly, or not at all (Jensen, 1959a; Grob and Pflugshaupt, 1962).

H. SIDE CHAIN METHYL GROUPS

The number of methyl substituents on the polyene chain can be estimated using a microanalytical procedure developed by Kuhn and Roth (1933). This consists of oxidizing the carotenoid with chromic acid and measuring the amount of acetic acid produced from the methyl groups and the carbon atoms to which they are attached. Both "in-chain" (XXVII) and "end-of-chain" methyls (XXVIII) give acetic acid

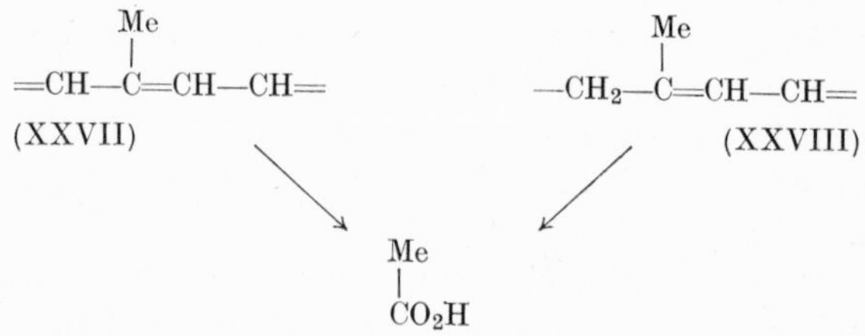

under these conditions. With alkaline potassium permanganate as the oxidizing agent, methyls of the former type are readily oxidized to acetic acid, but there is little, if any, acetic acid formed from methyls in more saturated environments (cf. Karrer and Jucker, 1948; Grob and Bütler, 1954).

Some evidence for the 1,5 and 1,6 arrangements of the side chain methyl groups was obtained in early studies on carotenoids by pyrolysis. Bixin (44–45) and capsanthin (6–28) gave m-xylene, azafrin (XII) gave in addition toluene and m-toluic acid, and a number of other carotenoids yielded 2,6-dimethylnaphthalene (cf. Karrer and Jucker, 1948). However, the significance of these results is doubtful since the yields were poor, and the possibility of rearrangement under the drastic conditions used cannot be excluded.

I. CARBON SKELETON

That lycopene (1–1), bixin (44–45) and crocetin (48–48) had the carbon skeletons assigned to them in the early 1930's was first confirmed by synthesis of their perhydro-derivatives (cf. Karrer and Jucker, 1948). The synthesis of perhydro-vitamin A also served indirectly to confirm the carbon skeleton of β-carotene (2–2) in view of the connection that had already been established between this carotenoid and vitamin A (IV) (cf. Heilbron and Weedon, 1958). It is fortunate that these syntheses, and the catalytic reductions of the natural polyenes, seem to have given similar mixtures of diasteroisomers of the perhydro compounds. However, the methods of comparison then available were hardly likely to have revealed small isomeric differences in the products. More reliable has been the work to establish the carbon skeletons of the natural hydrolycopenes (Rabourn and Quackenbush, 1956). The latter, and lycopene itself, were reduced under similar conditions and the products identified by comparison of their infra-red light absorption spectra. The carbon skeleton of δ-carotene (1–3) was shown to be identical with that of γ-carotene (1–2) in the same way (Kargl and Quackenbush, 1960). Studies on the hydro-lycopenes are now facilitated by the fact that perhydrolycopene can be quickly detected by means of gas–liquid chromatography (Anderson and Porter, 1962).

J. SYNTHESIS

The elucidation of the structures of some carotenoids has been achieved, sometimes accidentally, by partial synthesis. Thus the structures of the natural epoxides and furanoid oxides such as violaxanthin (24–24) and auroxanthin (26–26) were only revealed when a number of these compounds were identified with products prepared from known carotenoids (Karrer, 1948; Karrer and Jucker, 1948; cf. Section IV, C), and the fortuitous preparation of a diketone believed to be 4,4'-dioxo-β-carotene provided the essential clue to the structure of canthaxanthin (4–4) (Petracek and Zechmeister, 1956c; cf. Section IV, E).

The final confirmation of the structures of many carotenoids has now been provided by unambiguous total synthesis. A great deal of effort has been devoted to developing good synthetic routes in this field and a recent review by Isler and Schudel (1963) provides an excellent summary of the success that has been achieved. It will suffice here to point out that these synthetic methods have now been developed to the stage when synthesis can be used as an integral tool in structural studies, and not just to confirm a structure for which there is already ample evidence. This thesis is exemplified by recent work on the natural hydrolycopenes (XIII–XVI) (Davis et al., 1961), the α- and β-zeacarotenes (3–9 and 2–9) (Rüegg et al., 1961; P. S. Manchand and B. C. L. Weedon, unpublished observations), δ-carotene (1–3), ε-carotene (3–3) (Manchand et al., 1964; Karrer and Eugster, 1950b; Chapman and Haxo, 1963), kryptocapsin (2–28) (Cholnoky et al., 1963), rhodopin (1–37), chlorobactene (1–32), and "HO-chlorobactene" (32–37) (Bonnett et al., 1964). Synthesis has also established the correct structures of torulene (2–35) (Rüegg et al.,

4*

1961), and torularhodin (2–36) (Isler *et al.*, 1959), and shown the need for a revision of the structure (2–12) previously assigned to euglenanone (R. D. G. Cooper, J. B. Davis, C. W. Price and B. C. L. Weedon, unpublished observations).

IV. INTERCONVERSION AND OTHER TRANSFORMATIONS

Studies on the reactions of carotenoids have furnished a wealth of interesting information, some of which has provided new insight into the structures of carotenoids, or valuable confirmation of the structures suggested on the basis of degradative evidence (Zechmeister, 1958). Attention has already been drawn to the connections established chemically between β-carotene and vitamin A, between lycopene and norbixin, between zeaxanthin and β-citraurin, and between spheroidenone and 3,4-dehydrolycopene. Further examples of the inter-conversion of different carotenoids are given in this section, together with brief notes on other reactions of special interest.

A. ISOMERIZATION OF α- INTO β-END GROUPS

On treatment with sodium alkoxide α-carotene (2–3) and lutein (6–7) undergo prototropic rearrangement to give the fully conjugated isomers β-carotene (2–2) and zeaxanthin (6–6) respectively (Scheme 2) (Karrer and Jucker, 1947). δ-Carotene (1–3) similarly yields γ-carotene (1–2) (Kargl and Quackenbush, 1960).

R = H or OH

SCHEME 2.

B. INTERCONVERSION OF RHODOXANTHIN AND ZEAXANTHIN

Reduction of rhodoxanthin (R3–R3) with zinc and acetic acid in pyridine gives a dihydro derivative (17–17). Further reduction of the latter by the Ponndorf method gives (±)-zeaxanthin (6–6) (Kuhn and Brockmann, 1933; Karrer and Solmssen, 1935). Vigorous oxidation of zeaxanthin with manganese dioxide gives rhodoxanthin (Scheme 3) (Entschel and Karrer, 1959). The latter is also formed when a solution of dihydrorhodoxanthin in piperidine or pyridine, containing some alcoholic alkali, is exposed to air (Kuhn and Brockmann, 1933). (The dihydro-derivatives of methylbixin (45–45) and crocetin dimethyl ester (49–49) similarly regenerate the parent carotenoids.)

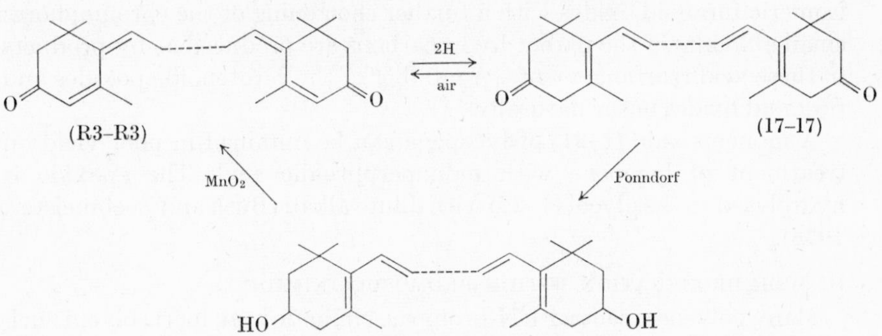

SCHEME 3.

C. FORMATION AND REARRANGEMENT OF EPOXIDES

Controlled oxidation of β-carotene and zeaxanthin with mono-perphthalic acid gives, depending on the conditions, the mono- or di-epoxy derivative in which one or both cyclic double bonds have been

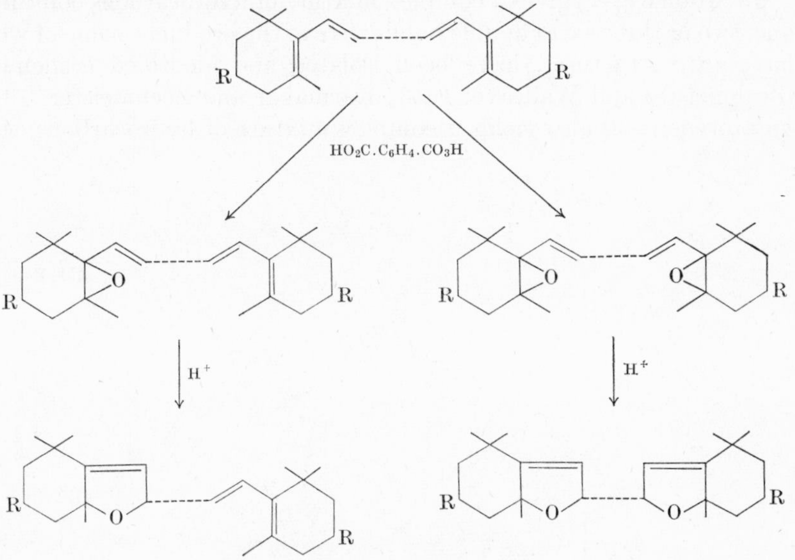

R = H or OH

SCHEME 4.

epoxidized (Scheme 4). The β-end groups, and their 3-hydroxy deriva-tives, present in some other carotenoids may be oxidized similarly (Karrer, 1948; Karrer and Jucker, 1948).

In the presence of mineral acids (aged chloroform contains sufficient free hydrochloric acid!) the epoxides are rapidly converted into the isomeric furanoid oxides with a further shortening of the chromophore; small amounts of the parent hydrocarbons are produced as by-products in these acid rearrangements. A number of the carotenoid epoxides and furanoid oxides occur naturally.

A monoepoxide (1–21) of lycopene can be obtained in poor yield on treatment of lycopene with monoperphthalic acid. The epoxide is hydrolysed to the glycol (1–22) with dilute alkali (Bush and Zechmeister, 1958).

D. DEHYDROGENATION WITH N-BROMOSUCCINIMIDE

Many polyenes react with N-bromosuccinimide in an inert solvent such as carbon tetrachloride to give allylic bromides which lose hydrogen bromide, either spontaneously or on treatment with a base. The overall process is therefore one of dehydrogenation.

Lycopene (1–1) gives 3,4,3',4'-bisdehydrolycopene (35–35) and, under appropriate conditions, 3,4-dehydrolycopene (1–35); both substances have been found in Nature (Karrer and Rutschmann, 1945; Winterstein et al., 1960).

β-Carotene (2–2) gives a complex mixture of hydrocarbons containing one, two or three extra double bonds; five of the products, some of which have *retro* structures, have been isolated and identified (Scheme 5) (Zechmeister and Wallcave, 1953; Karmakar and Zechmeister, 1955). α-Carotene (2–3) also yields a complex mixture of hydrocarbons, some

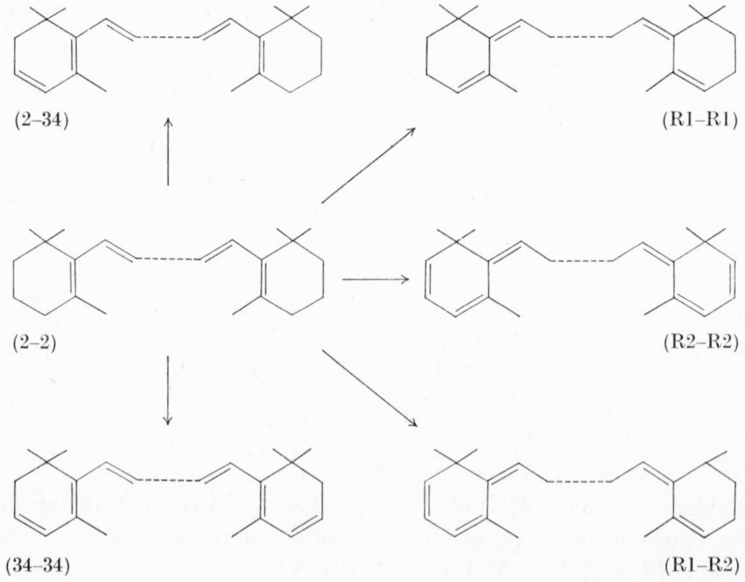

(2–34) (R1–R1)

(2–2) (R2–R2)

(34–34) (R1–R2)

β-series *retro*-series

SCHEME 5.

of which are identical with those obtained from β-carotene. A mixture of hydrocarbons is again obtained from kryptoxanthin (2–6), dehydration presumably accompanying dehydrogenation (Karmakar and Zechmeister, 1955). Under similar conditions some compounds of the vitamin A_1 series, with β-end groups, are converted into their analogues of the vitamin A_2 series, with 3,4-dehydro end groups (Farrar *et al.*, 1952; Henbest *et al.*, 1955). Depending on the experimental conditions used, β-ionone yields 3,4-dehydro-β-ionone (Henbest, 1951) or the aromatic compound (XXIX) with a ring system of the type found in isorenieratene (leprotene) (32–32) and chlorobactene (1–32) (Karrer and Ochsner, 1948; Büchi *et al.*, 1949).

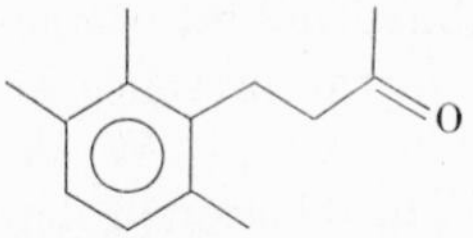

(XXIX)

Physalien, the natural dipalmitate of zeaxanthin (6–6), gives eschscholtzxanthin (R4–R4) dipalmitate on treatment with N-bromosuccinimide in commercial chloroform containing 1% of alcohol (Entschel and Karrer, 1957). The α- and β-zeacarotenes (3–9 and 2–9) are reported to give δ- and γ-carotene ((1–3) and (1–2)) respectively (Petzold *et al.*, 1959). The natural hydro-lycopenes (XIII–XVI) are dehydrogenated on treatment with N-bromosuccinimide. In each case a fraction can be isolated which is chromatographically indistinguishable from the next more highly unsaturated member of the series (Zechmeister and Koe, 1954). However, it seems possible that some of these products may be mixtures of isomers differing in the location of the chromophore.

E. OXYGENATION WITH N-BROMOSUCCINIMIDE

When β-carotene in chloroform containing 1% alcohol is reacted with N-bromosuccinimide and the crude product is treated with base, a mixture of hydrocarbons and oxygenated compounds is obtained. These have been identified and include two naturally occurring carotenoids: echinenone (2–4) and canthaxanthin (4–4) (Petracek and Zechmeister, 1956a). The mechanism of the reaction leading to ketones has not yet been fully elucidated, but transformations of the type shown in Scheme 6 are probably involved:

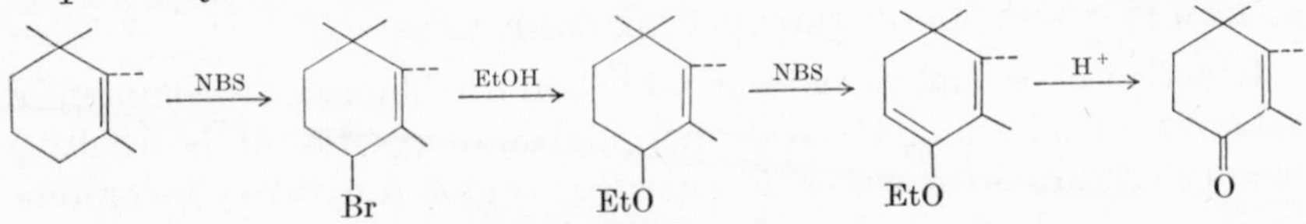

SCHEME 6.

Treatment of β-carotene with N-bromosuccinimide in the presence of glacial acetic acid gives, after hydrolysis of the crude product, 4,4'-dihydroxy-β-carotene (18–18) in high yield (Entschel and Karrer, 1958). This "isozeaxanthin" has not as yet been found in Nature, but can be oxidized to canthaxanthin (4–4) (Petracek and Zechmeister, 1956a; cf. Zeller *et al.*, 1959).

N-Bromosuccinimide is capable of oxidizing allylic alcohols to ketones, but other reagents, e.g. quinones, are usually superior (Petracek and Zechmeister, 1956a; Warren and Weedon, 1958).

F. AUTOXIDATION OF KETO-CAROTENOIDS

Canthaxanthin (4–4) is converted into astacin (12–12) in *c.* 90% yield when shaken with oxygen in the presence of potassium *t*-butoxide in *t*-butanol (Davis and Weedon, 1960; C. W. Price and B. C. L. Weedon, unpublished observations). The reaction probably proceeds by autoxidation of the enolate of the starting material, and decomposition of the resulting hydroperoxide (Scheme 7).

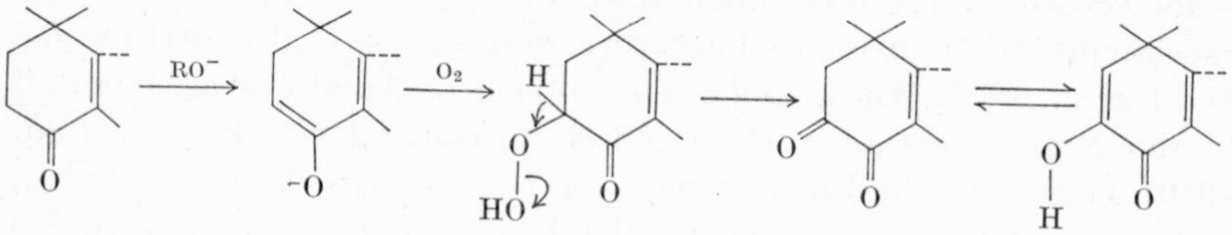

SCHEME 7.

The product (4–12) resulting from autoxidation at one end of the molecule only can be isolated under appropriate conditions. Autoxidation of astacin (12–12) slowly gives a substance believed to be (12–15), and decomposition products. Similar autoxidation of echinenone (2–4) yields the diosphenol (2–12). This structure has been proposed for euglenanone (Krinsky and Goldsmith, 1960), but a chromatographic comparison with the synthetic compound shows that the two are not identical (R. G. D. Cooper, J. B. Davis, C. W. Price and B. C. L. Weedon, unpublished observations).

Reference has been made previously to the facile dehydrogenation of dihydrorhodoxanthin (17–17) with air.

G. REACTIONS OF BORON TRIFLUORIDE COMPLEXES

Reaction of α- and β-carotene with boron trifluoride in commercial chloroform (containing 1% of alcohol), and decomposition of the resulting blue complexes with water, is reported to give 4-hydroxy-α-carotene (3–18) and 4-hydroxy-β-carotene (2–18) respectively (Petracek and Zechmeister, 1956b; Bush and Zechmeister, 1958). There is reason to believe that the boron trifluoride acts first as a dehydrogenating reagent; when the complex from β-carotene is decomposed with dry ammonia instead of water *retro*-dehydro-β-carotene (R1–R1) is obtained, and it is known that this compound yields (2–18) on treatment with boron trifluoride and hydrolysis of the complex thus produced.

The main product resulting from the formation and hydrolysis of the boron trifluoride complex of lycopene is formulated as the glycol (1–22). γ-Carotene (1–2) appears to react preferentially at the cyclic end to give 4-hydroxy-γ-carotene (1–18), but the yield is poor (Bush and Zechmeister, 1958).

H. TRANSFORMATIONS OF TERTIARY ALCOHOLS

Methylation of α-bacterioruberin (38–38) with methyl iodide and silver oxide in dimethylformamide gives both "mono-demethylated spirilloxanthin" (38–39) and spirilloxanthin (39–39). Although the yields are low these results provide valuable confirmation of the structures assigned to the two hydroxylated pigments (Jensen, 1962).

Recently it has been shown that the di-tertiary glycol (37–37) is smoothly dehydrated to lycopene on treatment with phosphorous oxychloride in pyridine (Surmatis and Ofner, 1963). In the same way Jensen *et al.* (1964) have converted rhodopin (1–37) into lycopene (1–1) and "HO-chlorobactene" (32–37) into chlorobactene (1–32).

V. STEREOCHEMISTRY

A. GEOMETRICAL ISOMERISM

The transformation of bixin (44–45) into a higher melting form provided the first example of *cis-trans* isomerism in a natural polyene (Herzig and Faltis, 1923; Karrer *et al.*, 1929). Later a *cis* form of crocetin (48–48) was reported (Kuhn and Winterstein, 1933), but it was the pioneer observations of Gillam, and the subsequent extensive studies of Zechmeister and his collaborators, that revealed the full extent and importance of geometrical isomerism in the carotenoid field (cf. Zechmeister, 1962). It was shown that all carotenoids may be converted into mixtures of stereoisomers under appropriate conditions. A number of *cis* and poly-*cis* isomers of carotenoids have also been isolated from natural sources, though a few of the compounds containing one or two *cis* bonds may conceivably be artefacts formed by stereomutation of the more familiar *trans* forms during isolation. Phytoene (XIII), which is believed to be a natural precursor of the carotenoids, is now known to have a *cis* configuration. The natural occurrence of these *cis* compounds, and the realization that the *cis-trans* isomerism of retinene plays an all-important role in the chemistry of the visual process, emphasizes the need for careful consideration to be given to the stereochemical aspects of the problem when considering the biosynthesis and functions of carotenoids.

A detailed review of the *cis-trans* isomerism of carotenoids, vitamins A, and related polyenes, has recently been published (Zechmeister, 1962). The account given below is therefore confined to the more important general aspects of the subject, and to recent developments.

1. *Number and Types of* cis-*Carotenoids*

By methods outlined below, any carotenoid can be converted into a quasi-equilibrium mixture of *cis-trans* isomers. Once this had been appreciated, calculation of the numbers of isomers theoretically possible gave some rather startling figures. For a conjugated system with n non-cyclic double bonds, the number of stereoisomers N is given by the expressions:

$$N = 2^n \qquad \text{for unsymmetrical systems}$$
$$N = 2^{(n-1)/2} \cdot (2^{(n-1)/2} + 1) \quad \text{for symmetrical systems, } n \text{ odd}$$
$$N = 2^{(n/2)-1} \cdot (2^{n/2} + 1) \quad \text{for symmetrical systems, } n \text{ even.}$$

Thus lycopene, with a symmetrical carbon skeleton and eleven conjugated double bonds, should be capable of existing in 1,056 different forms! Of these only about forty have so far been encountered.

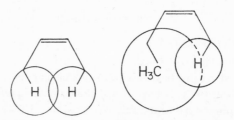

FIG. 2. Overlapping of hydrogen atoms in —CH—CH=CH—CH—, and of hydrogen and methyl in —CH—CH=CH—CMe— with *cis* configuration; according to Pauling. [From *Fortschr. Chem. Organ. Naturstoffe.* **3**, 203 (1939).]

Fortunately the situation is not, in practice, as complex as has just been implied. As was first pointed out by Pauling (1939), the double bonds in the polyene chain of carotenoids are of two types: those for which the adoption of a *cis* configuration involves very little steric hindrance (between two hydrogen atoms), and those for which a *cis* configuration leads to a serious clash between a methyl group and a hydrogen atom (cf. Fig. 2). The methyl substituted double bonds come into the first category, as do the 15,15'- double bonds corresponding to the centre of the carbon skeleton in most carotenoids. All other disubstituted double bonds are adjacent to a methyl side chain, and therefore fall into the second category. This classification is helpful in indicating the double bonds about which stereomutation is most likely to take place. A further calculation reveals that the number of "sterically unhindered" isomers of lycopene is only 72. It must not, however, be concluded, as was widely done at one time, that carotenoids with a *cis* configuration about a double bond of the second category are incapable of existence. A number of these "sterically hindered" isomers have been prepared indirectly from acetylenic analogues (cf. Section V, A, 3), moreover, it is now known that retinene undergoes stereomutation about the 11,12- double bond before it combines with opsin in the visual cycle (cf. Heilbron and Weedon, 1958; Zechmeister, 1962). However, in practice, relatively few isomers constitute the bulk of the mixtures produced by stereomutation, as would be expected on purely statistical grounds (Zechmeister, 1962).

2. *Stereomutation*

Stereomutation of a carotenoid occurs under a variety of conditions, but the rate of reaction depends greatly on the structure and configuration of the starting material. Moreover, different mixtures of products may be formed using different procedures. Normally the most stable isomer of a carotenoid is the all-*trans* form. The 15,15'-*cis*, and "hindered" *cis* isomers are particularly labile. Phytoene seems to provide an exception to this generalization; although it is believed to have a central-*cis* structure, it has not yet been converted into the all-*trans* form which has been synthesized (Rabourn *et al.*, 1954; Davis *et al.*, 1961).

The principal methods of isomerizing carotenoids are given below.*

a. Thermal methods. Stereomutation of a carotenoid begins immediately on solution. The process is usually slow at room temperature. Thus in benzene or light petroleum solution, in diffuse daylight, only *c*. 1–2% of α-, β-, and γ-carotene undergo stereomutation in 24 h. However, with all-*trans* lycopene under similar conditions the proportion is 10%, with spirilloxanthin (39–39) 23%, and with α-bacterioruberin (38–38) as much as 42% (Zechmeister, 1962; Jensen, 1962).

Stereomutation is more rapid at elevated temperatures, and with all-*trans* carotenoids in boiling benzene or hexane a quasi-equilibrium mixture of geometrical isomers is produced within 10–60 min. Since many of these mixtures contain several isomers, it is obvious that heating or storage of carotenoid solutions should be avoided as far as possible.

Most *cis* isomers of carotenoids exhibit marked thermal lability, but some poly-*cis* carotenoids are as stable as the corresponding all-*trans*

* See also Chapter 18.

forms (Zechmeister, 1962), and (*cis*) methylbixin yields a di-*cis* isomer as the main product (Barber *et al.*, 1961a).

As would be expected, stereomutation also occurs when a carotenoid is melted.

b. Photochemical methods (without catalyst). All carotenoids undergo *cis-trans* isomerization on irradiation in solution, light of wavelengths corresponding to the main absorption band being most effective. A similar process probably operates in nature in the conversion of *cis* and poly-*cis* isomers into the more familiar all-*trans* forms, and reference has already been made to the formation of a "hindered" *cis* isomer on irradiation of (all-*trans*) retinene.

c. Iodine catalysis, in light. The most commonly used method of stereomutation is to expose a solution of the carotenoid, containing catalytic amounts of iodine, to light. The quasi-equilibrium mixture of isomers, containing as a rule one-third to one-half of the pigment in *cis* configurations, is formed rapidly. Each isomer when isolated and submitted again to rearrangement yields a mixture of approximately the same composition.

3. *Synthesis of* cis *Isomers*

Many total syntheses of carotenoids involve the partial reduction of an acetylenic analogue over a palladium or nickel catalyst. Such hydrogenations occur by *cis* addition, and under appropriate conditions the *cis* carotenoids formed initially may be isolated before rearrangement to the all-*trans* forms. In this way several central (15,15'-) *cis* isomers have been prepared, and a few compounds with "hindered" *cis*-configurations (cf. Isler and Schudel, 1963; Zechmeister, 1962).

The synthesis of these and other polyene isomers of known configuration has necessitated revision of the structures tentatively assigned to some stereomutation products, but has confirmed many of the general principles used in drawing structural conclusions from spectral properties (cf. Zechmeister, 1962; Akhtar *et al.*, 1959).

Extensive studies have been made on the controlled synthesis of *cis* isomers in the vitamin A_1, and vitamin A_2 series; all "unhindered" forms, and some "hindered" forms of the vitamins and the related retinenes are now available (cf. Heilbron and Weedon, 1958; Isler and Schudel, 1963).

4. *Differences between* cis-trans *Isomers*

a. General properties. The carotenoids so far studied conform to the general principle that the all-*trans* compound is the isomer of lowest solubility and highest melting point. Because of stereomutation on fusion, some *cis* isomers exhibit the phenomenon of a double melting point.

The *cis*-forms of optically active carotenoids exhibit rotation which may differ markedly from that of the all-*trans* isomer, both in size and sometimes even in sign. (Most recorded rotations of carotenoids are for the cadmium line; little use has yet been made in this field of optical rotatory dispersion.)

The geometrical configuration of a carotenoid has a profound influence on its adsorption affinity. This means that even complex mixtures of isomers can usually be separated by chromatography. However, some *cis* isomers are more, and others less, strongly adsorbed than the corresponding all-*trans* compound.

b. Visible and ultra-violet light absorption. All *cis* forms of carotenoids so far examined exhibit light absorption at lower wavelengths, and of lower intensity, than the corresponding all-*trans* isomer. The same is true for the vitamins A and the retinenes, except that neo a vitamin A_1 and the corresponding vitamin A_2, both of which have the 13-*cis* configuration, have maximal absorption at a wavelength which is 2–3 mμ longer than that of the all-*trans* vitamin. It has been suggested that the bathochromic shift in the neo a vitamins A may be associated with the *cis* configuration at the end of the chromophore, and this is consistent with the absence of such an effect in the corresponding retinenes, since the chromophore is extended by a carbonyl group (Hubbard, 1956). Unfortunately, there is no authentic example of a carotenoid with a terminal *cis* bond. (It is of interest that "all-*cis*" deca-2,4,6,8-tetraene also shows longer wavelength maxima than the all-*trans* form (Holme *et al.*, 1956).)

In the carotenoid series most isomers with one "unhindered" *cis* double bond absorb at wavelengths which are 2–5 mμ shorter than those of the corresponding all-*trans* compounds. As would be expected on theoretical grounds, the central-*cis* isomer has less intense absorption than the other mono- ("unhindered") *cis* forms. With di-"unhindered" *cis* isomers the "λ shift" seems to be c. 10 mμ.

The poly-*cis* carotenoids, such as the natural prolycopene and pro-neurosporene, exhibit light absorption at much shorter wavelengths, and of much lower intensity, than either the all-*trans* or the mono-"un-hindered"-*cis* forms. Their spectra also show little fine structure. In many respects these spectra resemble the "degraded" spectra seen with mono-*cis* isomers if the *cis* bond is of the "hindered" type. With both classes of carotenoids there is a spectacular change in light absorption properties on iodine catalysed isomerization (Fig. 3).

One of the most noticeable features of the spectra of mono-*cis* carotenoids is the appearance of a subsidiary peak in the near ultra-violet region (Fig. 4). The wavelength difference between the "*cis* peak" and the longest wavelength maximum of the all-*trans* compound is practically a constant (142 ± 2 mμ for C_{40}-carotenoids possessing 10–11 conjugated double bonds). Although the evidence is not conclusive, mono-"hindered"-*cis* isomers also seem to exhibit *cis* peaks, but the band appears to be masked with the *cis* forms of carotenoids possessing chromophores of the *retro* type (Zechmeister, 1962).

On theoretical grounds, it has been predicted that the intensity of the *cis* peak should be roughly proportional to the square of the distance

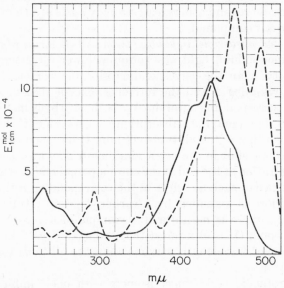

FIG. 3. Molecular extinction curves of prolycopene, in hexane: ——, fresh solution; and - - -, mixture of stereoisomers after catalysis by iodine; according to Zechmeister and Pinckard. [From *Prog. Chem. Org. Nat. Prod.* **18**, 284 (1960).]

between the centre of the conjugated system and the mid point of a straight line joining its two ends (i.e. zero in the case of the all-*trans* isomer) (Zechmeister *et al.*, 1943). In agreement with this prediction the central-*cis* isomers which have been prepared in a number of series by unambiguous total synthesis have more intense *cis* peaks than any of the other isomers that have been observed. Since the intensity of the *cis* peak seems to depend primarily on the overall shape of the chromophore, it is scarcely surprising that neither the poly-*cis*, nor the authentic di-*cis*, isomers exhibit significant absorption in this region; in both instances the molecules approximate to the linear shape of the all-*trans* form.

c. Infra-red light absorption. The central *cis* carotenoids can readily be recognized by a band near 780 cm^{-1} (12·84 μ) which may be ascribed to the C—H out-of-plane deformations of the *cis*-bond. Absorption in this region is the main justification for assigning a 15,15'-*cis* structure to phytoene (XIII) (Rabourn *et al.*, 1954). Few authentic "hindered" *cis* isomers have been examined, but the synthetic 11,11'-di*cis*-β-carotene has bands at 762 and 741 cm^{-1} (13·13 and 13·50 μ) (Isler *et al.*, 1957).

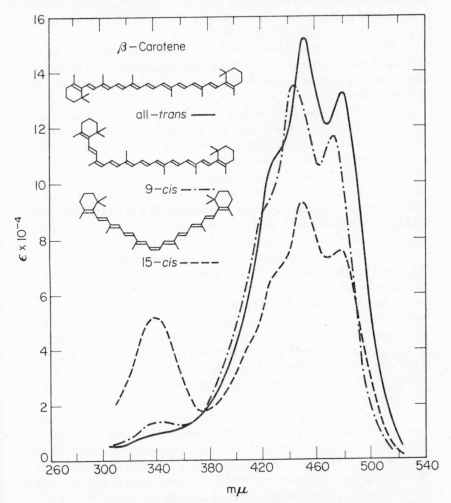

FIG. 4. Light absorption spectra of three stereoisomeric β-carotenes. [From "Theory and Applications of Ultraviolet Spectroscopy" (p. 233) by H. H. Jaffé and M. Orchin, Wiley, New York, 1962).]

The 11,13-di*cis* isomer of vitamin A$_2$ also exhibits absorption in this region, but, rather surprisingly, the 11-*cis* form does not (Planta *et al.*, 1962). Further studies on authentic "hindered" *cis* isomers are obviously needed.

Several of the carotenoids which possess a *cis* configuration about one of the methyl substituted double bonds of the polyene chain have a band at 1,380 cm^{-1} (7·25 μ), ascribable to the C—H in-plane deformation of the *cis* bond (Lunde and Zechmeister, 1955). However, this band is not always easily resolved, and is absent from the spectrum of methyl natural bixin though this pigment is now known to have a *cis* bond of the type in question (Barber *et al.*, 1961a).

In the spectra of some *cis* isomers, the characteristic band at about 966 cm^{-1} (10·35 μ), due to C—H out-plane-deformations of the *trans*-disubstituted double bonds, is split into a doublet (Lunde and Zechmeister, 1955).

d. N.M.R. spectra. Methyl groups which form part of unconjugated, trisubstituted, double bonds give rise to bands at positions which differ slightly according to whether the methyl group is *cis* or *trans* to the olefinic hydrogen atom (8·34 and 8·40 respectively) (Davis *et al.*, 1961; Bates and Gale, 1960). This difference, no doubt due to C—C long range shielding, has been used to assign *trans* configurations to the non-terminal, non-conjugated, double bonds in phytoene (XIII), phytofluene (XIV), ζ-carotene (XV), and neurosporene (XVI) (these assignments were later confirmed synthetically) (Davis *et al.*, 1961).

Differences are also observed between *cis* and *trans* isomers in the β-methyl bands of allylic systems; these are particularly marked when the functional substituent contains a carbonyl group (e.g. —CHO, —CO.Me, —CO$_2$Me) (Burrell *et al.*, 1959). Thus the C-13 methyl in all-*trans* vitamin A$_1$ acid methyl ester, and in the A$_2$ analogue, gives a band (7·84 and 7·58 respectively) at lower fields than the corresponding group in the 13-*cis* isomers (8·12 and 7·86 respectively) (Planta *et al.*, 1962). Such effects are attributed to the greater deshielding of the β-methyl protons in the *trans* isomers owing to the proximity of the carbonyl and β-methyl groups. Smaller differences also exist between the C-13 methyl bands of vitamin A$_1$ and A$_2$ (Planta *et al.*, 1962), and between the corresponding bands of *cis* and *trans* isomers of other β-methyl allylic alcohols, e.g. geraniol, farnesol, and phytol (Bates *et al.*, 1963; E. Oskay and B. C. L. Weedon, unpublished observations). No significant differences in the "in-chain" methyl bands have been observed (at 60 Mc) in the N.M.R. spectra of geometrical isomers.

The use of the olefinic proton bands to determine the stereochemistry of bixin is discussed later.

5. *Assignment of Geometrical Configuration*

It will be evident from the account given above that a consideration of the light absorption properties, and of the way in which these change on iodine catalysed isomerization, frequently allows a conclusion to be drawn regarding the configuration of a particular carotenoid.

If the visible light absorption maxima are at wavelengths not more than 15 mμ shorter than those of the all-*trans* form (prepared if necessary by chromatography of the mixture produced by iodine isomerization), and the fine structure is comparable, a poly-*cis* or "hindered"-*cis* structure is clearly unlikely. The magnitude of the λ shift then provides a good indication of the number of ("unhindered") *cis* bonds present, and the infra-red light absorption spectrum can be used to ascertain whether the disubstituted double bond corresponding to the central position of β-carotene and most carotenoids is *cis* or *trans*. If the results of the above investigations indicate a mono-*cis* structure involving one of the methylated bonds, the size of the *cis* peak before and after iodine-catalysed isomerization can often be used to deduce which of these bonds is most likely to have undergone isomerization. (Although there is a good theoretical basis for these latter predictions, few have yet been confirmed by independent means.)

Difficulty could conceivably arise in differentiating between a mono-"hindered"-*cis* and a poly-"unhindered"-*cis* structure, since both give similar "degraded" spectra. However, the former alternative would probably be associated with a *cis* peak in the near ultra-violet range, and possibly with infra-red absorption bands near 13 μ. Moreover, on partial isomerization (i.e. under conditions which leave most of the starting material unchanged), a mono-"hindered"-*cis* structure would be expected to give substantial amounts of the all-*trans* compound, whereas the poly-"unhindered"-*cis* structure should give a complex mixture of isomers containing (initially) little, if any, of the all-*trans* form (Zechmeister, 1962). It is of interest to note that proneurosporene appears to have a poly-"unhindered"-*cis* structure, and prolycopene a configuration which contains both methylated, "unhindered", *cis* bonds and un-methylated, possibly "hindered" *cis* bonds (Zechmeister, 1962). Methods have not yet been developed for studying such poly-*cis* structures.

At the present time bixin (44–45) is the only naturally occurring *cis* carotenoid whose configuration has been established unambiguously (notable success has, of course, also been achieved in the vitamin A and retinene series). Karrer and Solmssen (1937) first attempted to solve the problem by degrading (*cis*) bixin and all-*trans* bixin with permanganate to a series of apo-norbixinal methyl esters, and seeing at what stage a stereochemical difference ceased to exist. However, practical difficulties intervened and the conclusions drawn are now known to have been incorrect. From a consideration of ultra-violet and visible light absorption properties Zechmeister and Escue (1944) concluded that the dimethyl ester obtained by esterification of bixin had a *cis* configuration about one of the (methylated) $\gamma\delta$-double bonds. Later Lunde and Zechmeister

(1955) proposed an $\alpha\beta$-*cis* configuration on the basis of infra-red light absorption studies. A solution to the problem was finally provided by Barber *et al.* (1961a), using N.M.R. techniques. Their reasoning is summarized below.

The olefinic protons generally give rise to a complex absorption band in the N.M.R. spectrum of a carotenoid owing to spin-spin coupling. However, in all-*trans* methylbixin the two α- and the two β-protons can be observed separately since these constitute two identical AB systems and give rise to two doublets ($J = 15\cdot8$), one at $4\cdot12$ due to the α-protons and one at $2\cdot61$ due to the β-protons. The N.M.R. spectrum of methyl natural bixin reveals that the two α-protons are identical (doublet at $4\cdot12$, $J = 15\cdot8$), but that the two β-protons experience different fields (two doublets, of half the intensity, at $2\cdot63$ and $2\cdot07$). Since the coupling constant ($J = 15\cdot8$) remains unchanged, this cannot be ascribed to a *cis* configuration about one of the $\alpha\beta$-double bonds. The result is, however, readily explicable if one of the $\gamma\delta$-methylated double bonds has a *cis* configuration as this would bring the adjacent β-proton into a region where it is deshielded by the third double bond from the end of the polyene chain. Examination and analysis of the spectra of suitable models confirms the validity of this interpretation. Rather surprisingly, the N.M.R. spectrum of Karrer and Solmssen's *cis*-apo-1-norbixinal methyl ester (45–50) shows the bands characteristic of the *cis* end of methyl natural bixin. Contrary to all earlier suggestions bixin must therefore have the structure (XXX).

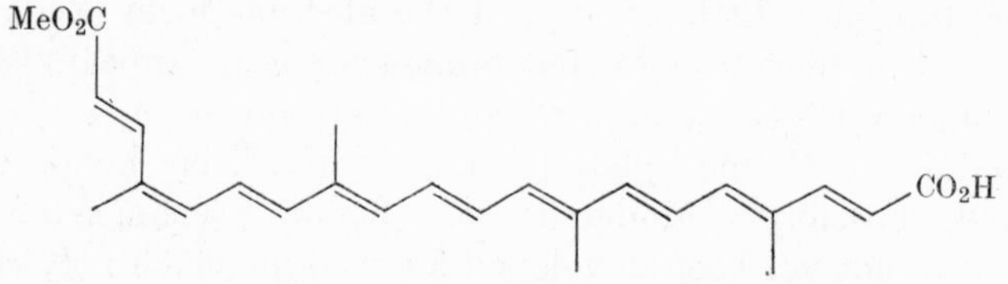

MeO$_2$C

(XXX)

As mentioned previously, N.M.R. also provides a convenient means of determining the configuration of unconjugated trisubstituted double bonds, and of β-methyl-$\alpha\beta$-unsaturated aldehydes and esters.

B. CONFORMATION

Although there seems little doubt that an *s-trans* conformation is preferred for all single bonds in the acyclic polyene system of carotenoids, the situation has never been clear with regard to the 6,7- single bond joining the acyclic polyene chain to cyclic end groups of the type found in β-carotene. Examination of models suggests steric hindrance between the ring methyls and the side chain in both the *s-cis* and *s-trans* conformations about this bond. Some information on this question has been supplied by recent X-ray crystallographic studies. These show that in *trans-β*-ionylidene crotonic acid (**XXXI**) the double bond in the ring is a continuation of the zigzag of the side chain, and is approximately in the same plane with it (Eichhorn and MacGillavry, 1959). However, in *trans*-vitamin A acid (**VI**) the ring is rotated from this position by an angle of about 145°, and the conformation about the 6,7- bond is therefore much closer to *s-cis* than *s-trans* (Stam and MacGillavry, 1963). A similar conformation is found in 9-*cis-β*-ionylidene crotonic acid (**XXXII**) (Eichhorn and MacGillavry, 1959), and in 15,15′-dehydro-β-carotene (2:2) (Sly, 1955, 1960). There is obviously no simple answer to the question of the preferred conformation about the 6,7- bond. Moreover, it should be clearly borne in mind that such information as is available at present relates to molecules in the crystal lattice where the conformation may be dictated by the packing of the molecules. The situation may be quite different with molecules in solution.

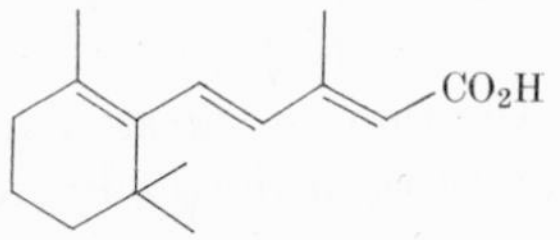

(**XXXI**)

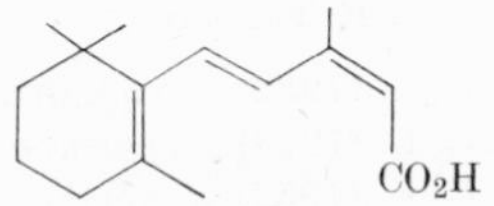

(**XXXII**)

Differences in the infra-red light absorption properties of polyene ketones related to capsorubin (28–28) and capsanthin (6–28) may be due to differences in the preferred conformation about the single bonds joining the carbonyl groups to the polyene chain (Warren and Weedon, 1958).

C. ABSOLUTE CONFIGURATION

Many natural carotenoids are optically active, but nothing was known about absolute configuration in this field until recently. Faigle and Karrer (1961) succeeded in determining the asymmetry of the C-5 positions in the five-membered rings of capsanthin and capsorubin by degrading both these pigments to a derivative of natural camphor, viz. (−)-camphoronic acid. Subsequently, Cooper *et al.* (1962) proved that the hydroxyls in these end groups are *trans* to the carbonyl substituents. Capsorubin must therefore have the absolute configuration shown by (**XXXIII**). Assuming that no change has occurred in the configuration

of the hydroxy groups during the biosynthesis of capsanthin and capsorubin from zeaxanthin, these results also reveal the complete stereochemistry of capsanthin (6–28) and zeaxanthin (6–6). Since the conversion in nature of kryptoxanthin (2–6) into kryptocapsin (2–28) is exactly
analogous to the conversion of zeaxanthin into capsanthin, there is little
doubt that the absolute configuration of kryptoxanthin is the same as
that of zeaxanthin (Cholnoky *et al.*, 1963).

(XXXlll)

There is as yet no information on the stereochemistry of the natural
epoxides and furanoid oxides, or of the α-end groups found, for example,
in α-carotene and lutein.

REFERENCES

Ahmad, R., and Weedon, B. C. L. (1952). *Chem. and Ind.* 882.
Ahmad, R., and Weedon, B. C. L. (1953). *J. chem. Soc.* 3286.
Akhtar, M., and Weedon, B. C. L. (1959). *J. chem. Soc.* 4058.
Akhtar, M., Richards, T. A., and Weedon, B. C. L. (1959). *J. chem. Soc.* 933.
Anderson, D. G., and Porter, J. W. (1962). *Arch. Biochem. Biophys.* **97**, 509.
Barber, M. S., Jackman, L. M., and Weedon, B. C. L. (1959). *Proc. chem. Soc.* 96.
Barber, M. S., Davis, J. B., Jackman, L. M., and Weedon, B. C. L. (1960). *J. chem. Soc.* 2870.
Barber, M. S., Hardisson, A., Jackman, L. M., and Weedon, B. C. L. (1961a). *J. chem. Soc.* 1625.
Barber, M. S., Jackman, L. M., Warren, C. K., and Weedon, B. C. L. (1961b). *J. chem. Soc.* 4019.
Bates, R. B., and Gale, D. M. (1960). *J. Amer. chem. Soc.* **82**, 5749.
Bates, R. B., Gale, D. M., and Gruner, B. J. (1963). *J. org. Chem.* **28**, 1086.
Bodea, C., and Tamas, V. (1961). *Angew. Chem.* **73**, 532.
Bonnett, R., Spark, A. A., and Weedon, B. C. L. (1964). *Acta chem. scand.* (In the press.)
Braude, E. A. (1945). *Rep. Progr. Chem.* **42**, 105.
Büchi, G., Seitz, K., and Jeger, O. (1949). *Helv. chim. acta* **32**, 39.
Burrell, J. W. K., Jackman, L. M., and Weedon, B. C. L. (1959). *Proc. chem. Soc.* 263.
Bush, W. V., and Zechmeister, L. (1958). *J. Amer. chem. Soc.* **80**, 2991.
Chapman, D. J., and Haxo, F. T. (1963). *Plant and Cell Physiol.* **4**, 57.
Cholnoky, L., and Szabolcs, J. (1957). *Naturwissenschaften* **19**, 513.

Cholnoky, L., Szabo, D., and Szabolcs, J. (1957). *Liebigs Ann.* **606**, 194.

Cholnoky, L., Szabolcs, J., Cooper, R. D. G., and Weedon, B. C. L. (1963). *Tetrahedron Letters* **19**, 1257.

Cooper, R. D. G., Jackman, L. M., and Weedon, B. C. L. (1962). *Proc. chem. Soc.* 215.

Cooper, R. D. G., Davis, J. B., and Weedon, B. C. L. (1963). *J. chem. Soc.* 5637.

Curl, A. L. (1960). *J. Agr. Food Chem.* **8**, 356.

Dale, J. (1954). *Acta chem. scand.* **8**, 1235.

Dale, J. (1957). *Acta chem. scand.* **11**, 265.

Davis, J. B., and Weedon, B. C. L. (1960). *Proc. chem. Soc.* 182.

Davis, J. B., Jackman, L. M., Siddons, P. T., and Weedon, B. C. L. (1961). *Proc. chem. Soc.* 261.

Dhar, M. L., Thaller, V., and Whiting, M. C. (1964). *J. chem. Soc.* 842.

Eichhorn, E. L., and MacGillavry, C. H. (1959). *Acta Crystallographica* **12**, 872.

Entschel, R., and Karrer, P. (1957). *Helv. chim. acta* **40**, 1809.

Entschel, R., and Karrer, P. (1958). *Helv. chim. acta* **41**, 402.

Entschel, R., and Karrer, P. (1959). *Helv. chim. acta* **42**, 466.

Entschel, R., and Karrer, P. (1960). *Helv. chim. acta* **43**, 89.

Eugster, C. H., Linner, E., Trivedi, A. H., and Karrer, P. (1956). *Helv. chim. acta* **39**, 690.

Faigle, H., and Karrer, P. (1961). *Helv. chim. acta* **44**, 1904.

Farrar, K. R., Hamlet, J. C., Henbest, H. B., and Jones, E. R. H. (1952). *J. chem. Soc.* 2657.

Ganguly, J., Krinsky, N. I., and Pinckard, J. H. (1956). *Arch. Biochem. Biophys.* **60**, 345.

Goodwin, T. W. (1956). *Biochem. J.* **63**, 481.

Goodwin, T. W., and Land, D. G. (1956a). *Biochem. J.* **62**, 553.

Goodwin, T. W., and Land, D. G. (1956b). *Arch. Mikrobiol.* **24**, 305.

Goodwin, T. W., Land, D. G., and Sissins, M. E. (1956). *Biochem. J.* **64**, 486.

Grangaud, R., Vignais, P., Massonet, R., and Moatti, J. P. (1957). *Bull. Soc. Chim. biol.* **39**, 1271.

Grob, E. C., and Bütler, R. (1954). *Helv. chim. acta* **37**, 1908.

Grob, E. C., and Bütler, R. (1956). *Helv. chim. acta* **39**, 1975.

Grob, E. C., and Pflugshaupt, R. P. (1962). *Helv. chim. acta* **45**, 1592.

Heilbron, I. M., and Weedon, B. C. L. (1958). *Bull. Soc. chim.* **1**, 83.

Henbest, H. B. (1951). *J. chem. Soc.* 1074.

Henbest, H. B., Jones, E. R. H., and Owen, T. C. (1955). *J. chem. Soc.* 2765.

Herzig, J., and Faltis, F. (1923). *Liebigs Ann.* **431**, 40.

Holme, D., Jones, E. R. H., and Whiting, M. C. (1956). *Chem. and Ind.* 928.

Hubbard, R. (1956). *J. Amer. chem. Soc.* **78**, 4662.

Inhoffen, H. H., Bohlmann, F., and Rummert, G. (1950a). *Liebigs Ann.* **569**, 226.

Inhoffen, H. H., Pommer, H., and Bohlmann, F. (1950b). *Liebigs Ann.* **569**, 237.

Inhoffen, H. H., Pommer, H., and Bohlmann, F. (1950c). *Chem-Ztg.* **74**, 309.

Inhoffen, H. H., Pommer, H., and Westphal, F. (1950d). *Liebigs Ann.* **570**, 69.

Isler, O., and Schudel, P. (1963). *Adv. org. Chem.* **4**, 115, Interscience, New York.

Isler, O., Chopard-dit-Jean, L. H., Montavon, M., Rüegg, R., and Zeller, P. (1957). *Helv. chim. acta* **40**, 1256.

Isler, O., Guex, W., Rüegg, R., Ryser, G., Saucy, G., Schwieter, U., Walter, M., and Winterstein, A. (1959). *Helv. chim. acta* **42**, 865.

Jackman, L. M., and Jensen, S. L. (1961). *Acta chem. scand.* **15**, 2058.

Jensen, A. (1963). "Carotine und Carotinoide," paper 5, Dietrich Steinkopff Verlag, Darmstadt.

Jensen, S. L. (1959a). *Acta chem. scand.* **13**, 381.

Jensen, S. L. (1959b). *Acta chem. scand.* **13**, 842, 2142.

Jensen, S. L. (1962). *Norske Videnskab. Selskabs Skrifter*, No. 8.

Jensen, S. L., and Weedon, B. C. L. (1964). *Naturwissenschaften* (In press.)

Jensen, S. L., Cohen-Bazire, G., and Stanier, R. Y. (1961). *Nature, Lond.* **192**, 1168.

Jensen, S. L., Hegge, E., and Jackman, L. M. (1964). *Acta chem. scand.* (in the press).

Kargl, T. E., and Quackenbush, F. W. (1960). *Arch. Biochem. Biophys.* **88**, 59.

Karmakar, G., and Zechmeister, L. (1955). *J. Amer. chem. Soc.* **77**, 55.

Karrer, P. (1948). *Fortschr. Chem. org. Naturst.* **5**, 1.

Karrer, P., and Eugster, C. H. (1950a). *Helv. chim. acta* **33**, 1172.

Karrer, P., and Eugster, C. H. (1950b). *Helv. chim. acta* **33**, 1433.

Karrer, P., and Jaffé, W. (1939). *Helv. chim. acta* **22**, 69.

Karrer, P., and Jucker, E. (1945). *Helv. chim. acta* **28**, 300.

Karrer, P., and Jucker, E. (1947). *Helv. chim. acta* **30**, 266.

Karrer, P., and Jucker, E. (1948). "Carotinoide," Birkhäuser, Basle. English translation by Braude, E. A. (1950). Elsevier, New York.

Karrer, P., and Koenig, H. (1940). *Helv. chim. acta* **23**, 460.

Karrer, P., and Leumann, E. (1951. *Helv. chim. acta* **34**, 445.

Karrer, P., and Loewe, L. (1934). *Helv. chim. acta* **17**, 745.

Karrer, P., and Ochsner, P. (1948). *Helv. chim. acta* **31**, 2093.

Karrer, P., and Rutschmann, J. (1945). *Helv. chim. acta* **28**, 793.

Karrer, P., and Schneider, P. (1950). *Helv. chim. acta* **33**, 38.

Karrer, P., and Schwyzer, R. (1948). *Helv. chim. acta* **31**, 1055.

Karrer, P., and Solmssen, U. (1935). *Helv. chim. acta* **18**, 477.

Karrer, P., and Solmssen, U. (1936). *Helv. chim. acta* **19**, 1019.

Karrer, P., and Solmssen, U. (1937). *Helv. chim. acta* **20**, 1396.

Karrer, P., Helfenstein, A., Widmer, R., and van Itallie, Th. B. (1929). *Helv. chim. acta* **12**, 741.

Karrer, P., Helfenstein, A., Wehrli, H., and Wettstein, A. (1930). *Helv. chim. acta* **13**, 1084.

Karrer, P., Morf, R., and Walker, O. (1933). *Helv. chim. acta* **16**, 975.

Karrer, P., Solmssen, U., and Gugelmann, W. (1937). *Helv. chim. acta* **20**, 1020.

Karrer, P., Eugster, C. H., and Tobler, E. (1950). *Helv. chim. acta* **33**, 1349.

Karrer, P., Eugster, C. H., and Faust, M. (1951). *Helv. chim. acta* **34**, 823.

Krinsky, N. I. (1963). *Anal. Biochem.* **6**, 293.

Krinsky, N. I., and Goldsmith, T. H. (1960). *Arch. Biochem. Biophys.* **91**, 271.

Kuhn, R. (1938). *J. chem. Soc.* 605.

Kuhn, R., and Brockmann, H. (1933). *Ber. dtshc. chem. Ges.* **66**, 828.

Kuhn, R., and Brockmann, H. (1935). *Liebigs Ann.* **516**, 95.

Kuhn, R., and Grundmann, C. (1932). *Ber. dtsch. chem. Ges.* **65**, 898, 1880.

Kuhn, R., and Möller, E. F. (1934). *Angew. Chem.* **47**, 145.

Kuhn, R., and Roth, H. (1932). *Ber. dtsch. chem. Ges.* **65**, 1285.

Kuhn, R., and Roth, H. (1933). *Ber. dtsch. chem. Ges.* **66**, 1274.

Kuhn, R., and Sörensen, N. A. (1938). *Ber. dtsch. chem. Ges.* **71**, 1879.

Kuhn, R., and Winterstein, A. (1933). *Ber. dtsch. chem. Ges.* **66**, 209.

Liaaen, S., and Sörensen, N. A. (1956). "Second International Seaweed Symposium," p. 25, Pergamon, London.

Lunde, K., and Zechmeister, L. (1955). *J. Amer. chem. Soc.* **77**, 1647.

Manchand, P. S., Rüegg, R., Schwieter, U., and Weedon, B. C. L. (1964). *J. chem. Soc.* (In the press.)

Massonet, R. (1956). *C. R. Soc. biol., Paris* **150**, 529.

Milas, N. A., Davis, P., Belič, I., and Fleš, D. (1950). *J. Amer. chem. Soc.* **72**, 4844.

Mildner, P., and Weedon, B. C. L. (1953). *J. chem. Soc.* 3294.

Pauling, L. (1939). *Fortschr. Chem. org. Naturst.* **3**, 203.

Petracek, F. J., and Zechmeister, L. (1956a). *J. Amer. chem. Soc.* **78**, 1427.

Petracek, F. J., and Zechmeister, L. (1956b). *J. Amer. chem. Soc.* **78**, 3188.

Petracek, F. J., and Zechmeister, L. (1956c). *Arch. Biochem. Biophys.* **61**, 137.

Petzold, E N., Quackenbush, F. W., and McQuistan, M. (1959). *Arch. Biochem. Biophys.* **82**, 117.

Planta, C. V., Schwieter, U., Chopard-dit-Jean, L. H., Rüegg, R., Kofler, M., and Isler, O. (1962). *Helv. chim. acta* **45**, 548.

Rabourn, W. J., and Quackenbush, F. W. (1956). *Arch. Biochem. Biophys.* **61**, 111.

Rabourn, W. J., Quackenbush, F. W., and Porter, J. W. (1954). *Arch. Biochem. Biophys.* **48**, 267.

Rüegg, R., Schwieter, U., Ryser, G., Schudel, P., and Isler, O. (1961). *Helv. chim. acta* **44**, 994.

Shantz, E. M., Cawley, J. D., and Embree, N. D. (1943). *J. Amer. chem. Soc.* **65**, 901.

Sly, W. G. (1955). *Acta cryst., Camb.* **8**, 115.

Sly, W. G. (1960). Quoted by Stam and MacGillavry (1963).

Stahl, E., Bolliger, H. R., and Lehnert, L. (1963). "Carotine und Carotinoide," paper 6, Dietrich Steinkopff Verlag, Darmstadt.

Stam, C. H., and MacGillavry, C. H. (1963). *Acta cryst., Camb.* **16**, 62.

Strain, H. H. (1933). *J. biol. Chem.* **102**, 137.

Surmatis, J. D., and Ofner, A. (1963). *J. org. Chem.* **28**, 2735.

Tiers, G. V. D. (1958). *J. phys. Chem.* **62**, 1151.

Torto, F. G., and Weedon, B. C. L. (1955). *Chem. and Ind.* 1219.

Warren, C. K., and Weedon, B. C. L. (1958). *J. chem. Soc.* 3972.

Wendler, N. L., Rosenblum, C., and Tishler, M. (1950). *J. Amer. chem. Soc.* **72**, 234.

Winterstein, A., Studer, A., and Rüegg, R. (1960). *Chem. Ber.* **93**, 2951.

Yamaguchi, M. (1957). *Bull. chem. Soc. Japan* **30**, 111, 979.

Yamaguchi, M. (1958). *Bull. chem. Soc. Japan* **31**, 51, 739.

Yamaguchi, M. (1960). *Bull. chem. Soc. Japan* **33**, 1560.

Zechmeister, L. (1958). *Prog. Chem. Org. Nat. Prod.* **15**, 31.

Zechmeister, L. (1962). "*Cis-Trans* Isomeric Carotenoids, Vitamins A, and Arylpolyenes." Springer-Verlag, Vienna.

Zechmeister, L., and Escue, R. B. (1944). *J. Amer. chem. Soc.* **66**, 322.

Zechmeister, L., and Koe, B. K. (1954). *J. Amer. chem. Soc.* **76**, 2923.

Zechmeister, L., and Wallcave, L. (1953). *J. Amer. chem. Soc.* **75**, 4493.

Zechmeister, L., LeRosen, A. L., Schroeder, W. A., Polgár, A., and Pauling, L. (1943). *J. Amer. chem. Soc.* **65**, 1940.

Zeller, P., Bader, F., Lindlar, H., Montavon, M., Müller, P., Rüegg, R., Ryser, G., Saucy, G., Schaeren, S. F., Schwieter, U., Stricker, K., Tamm, R., Zürcher, P., and Isler, O. (1959). *Helv. chim. acta* **42**, 841.

Chapter 4

DISTRIBUTION OF CAROTENOIDS

T. W. Goodwin

University College of Wales, Aberystwyth, Wales

I. Introduction

The distribution of carotenoids in plants has been discussed in detail in the proceedings of three recent symposia (Goodwin, 1961, 1963, a, b, c). The main object of this chapter will, therefore, be to summarize the basic information for the sake of completeness of the present volume, and to emphasize some recent observations. For details the reader is referred to the proceedings of the symposia; older references can be found in "The Comparative Biochemistry of Carotenoids" (Goodwin, 1952). Specific information regarding algal pigments can be found in a recent review by Nakayama (1963).

II. Photosynthetic Tissues

A. Higher Plants

The leaves of all green plants contain the same major carotenoids, β-carotene, lutein, violaxanthin and neoxanthin; β-carotene can be accompanied by α-carotene, and cryptoxanthin and zeaxanthin are occasionally found as minor components of the xanthophyll fraction. The xanthophylls are always unesterified in leaves, in contrast to the situation in fruit (see p. 90). Traces of *cis*-isomers probably exist in leaves, but claims of their occurrence must always be considered critically because isomerization can take place artifactually during extraction. Although the xanthophyll epoxides, e.g. violaxanthin, are always present in relatively large amounts in green leaves, β-carotene epoxides occur only in small amounts, if at all, in fresh tissues. They quickly appear in excised leaves, especially in those kept in the dark (Glover and Redfearn, 1953).

The carotenoids are all specifically located in the grana of the chloroplast in the form of chromoproteins. A crystalline β-carotene chromoprotein reported some years ago (Nishimura and Takamatsa, 1957) appears now to be an artefact (Thirkell, 1964). The relative amounts of each pigment present varies from species to species, but xanthophylls always predominate over the carotenes. A full quantitative analysis of leaf pigments has not been carried out on many species; a typical set of results is given in Table I. Table II records representative values for the

TABLE I

Quantitative Distribution of Xanthophylls
in Lucerne (Bickoff *et al.* 1954)

Pigment	Percentage of total xanthophylls present
Cryptoxanthin	4
Lutein	40
Zeaxanthin	2
Violaxanthin	34
Neoxanthin	19

α- and β-carotene and total carotenoid concentrations in green leaves of a number of trees in Poland (Wierzchowski *et al.*, 1962). Very similar values were obtained with shrubby plants.

The colourless polyenes phytoene and phytofluene occur in traces in many green tissues (Rabourn and Quackenbush, 1953; Zechmeister and Karmakar, 1953), but the concentration is only about one hundredth that of β-carotene; in tares (*Vicia sativa*) for example, the concentrations of phytoene and phytofluene were 28 and 15 μg/100 g fresh weight, respectively (Mercer *et al.*, 1963). One tomato phenotype (ghost, *gh*) accumulates phytoene in its leaves (Mackinney *et al.*, 1956). The intracellular localization of phytoene and phytofluene is unknown.

The changes which carotenoids undergo in senescent leaves are discussed in Chapter 16 but one unique report can be emphasized here. The bronze winter needles of *Cryptomeria* are said to contain rhodoxanthin, and this pigment is also found in the pondweed *Potamogeton* under conditions of high illumination (see Goodwin, 1959a).

TABLE II

Carotenoid Content of Leaves of Various Traces (Wierzchowski *et al.*, 1962)

	(Concentration mg/100 g dry wt.)		Carotenes as percentage of total carotenoids
	α-Carotene	β-Carotene	
Abies cephalonica	4·0	6·4	35·4
Acer campestre	6·8	20·3	22·9
Aesculus carnea	9·8	37·5	20·3
Alnus glutinosa	4·4	22·8	14·6
Bougainvillea glabra	18·8	39·2	30·8
Calycanthus occidentalis	12·1	33·9	25·8
Fagus engleriana	9·5	40·0	18·9
Ficus elastica	3·8	12·4	22·4
Fraxinus excelsiur	12·5	26·5	30·6
Gleditschia tricanthos	1·7	24·6	6·4
Hedera helix	10·1	33·6	25·4
Juglans nigra	5·0	31·1	14·0
Liriodendron tulipifera	1·9	27·4	6·0
Magnolia acuminata	10·6	21·7	32·4
Metasequium glyptostroboides	4·7	23·4	22·8
Picea breweriana	5·3	11·2	32·5
Pinus jeffreyi	5·4	11·1	31·8
Platanus occidentalis	2·1	24·4	7·7
Populus alba	1·6	25·0	5·9
Quercus borealis	2·1	30·3	6·6
Rhus typhina	5·3	33·8	13·5
Rosa centifolia	9·6	28·8	21·5
Syringa vulgaris	7·4	40·1	15·2
Taxodium distichum	10·0	15·6	38·4

Etiolated leaves of seedlings generally contain small amounts of "plastid" xanthophylls with only traces of β-carotene (see Goodwin, 1962). On the other hand, cotyledons (e.g. from runner beans) accumulate as their main carotenoids a preponderance of more highly oxidized pigments such as auroxanthin and chrysanthemaxanthin (Goodwin and Phagpolngarm, 1960). Similarly, small amounts of auroxanthin and neoxanthin are synthesized by plant tissue cultures of meristem from Paul's Scarlet Rose (Goodwin and Williams, 1962).

B. BRYOPHYTES AND PTERIDOPHYTES

The limited information available suggests that the distribution is similar to that in green leaves, although two, *Equisetum* and *Selaginella*, are reported to contain rhodoxanthin (see Goodwin, 1955).

C. LICHENS

Lichens would be expected to contain carotenoids characteristic of their algal symbionts and possibly, but not necessarily, carotenoids from their fungal components. The one lichen so far examined in detail, *Ramelia reticulata* has a distribution similar to that in green leaves (Strain, 1951).

D. ALGAE

The general distribution of the major carotenoids in the photosynthetic regions of the various divisions and classes of algae is summarized in Table III. The major differences between classes are found in the xanthophyll fractions. Typical quantitative values for unicellular algae grown under defined conditions are given in Table IV.

1. *Chlorophyceae*

Most of the unicellular green algae have the same major carotenoids as the green leaves of the higher plants. This is also true for the colonial Chlorophyceae except the Siphonales in which α-carotene is the major carotene and siphonaxanthin the main xanthophyll (Strain, 1951). Apart from being a carotenoid of unique structure siphonaxanthin is an esterified xanthophyll. The unesterified pigment is termed siphonein.

Of particular interest are two exceptions to the generalization just made, the marine *Bryopsis corticulans* and *Cyanidium caldarium*. In the carotene fraction of *B. corticulans* the α- isomer predominates over β-carotene and is accompanied by ϵ-carotene (Strain, 1951), which is now known to be identical with ϵ_1-carotene (Chapman and Haxo, 1963), a pigment with two α-ionone residues first synthesized by Karrer and Eugster (1950). Morphologically *Cyanidium caldarium* is classed as a green alga although biochemically it appears closely related to the blue-green algae because it synthesizes phycocyanins (Chapter 6) and fails to synthesize chlorophyll *b* (Chapter 2). However, a detailed examination of the carotenoids revealed that they were characteristic of neither the Chlorophyceae nor the Cyanophyceae (Allen *et al.*, 1960). The high proportion of β-carotene (over 50% of the total carotenoids) is characteristic of the Cyanophyceae (Goodwin, 1958) but the fact that the main xanthophyll is zeaxanthin, suggests that it might be more closely related to the Cryptophyceae, which tend to synthesize

Major Carotenoid Distribution in Various Algal Classes[a,b]

(+ = present; − = absent; ? possibly present in traces)

	Chlorophyta		Phaeophyta				Rhodophyta	Pyrrophyta	Euglenophyta	Archephyta	Cryptophyta
	Charophyceae	Chlorophyceae	Xanthophyceae (Heterokontae)	Bacillariophyceae (Diatomophyceae)	Chrysophyceae	Phaeophyceae	(Rhodophyceae)	(Dinophyceae)	(Euglenineae)	(Cyanophyceae)	(Cryptophyceae)
Carotenes											
α-Carotene	−	+	−	−	−	−	+	−	−	−	+
β-Carotene	+	+	+	+	+	+	+	+	+	+	−
γ-Carotene	+	+[d]	−	+	−	−	−	−	−	−	−
ε-Carotene	−	?[e]	−	+	−	−	−	−	−	+	−
Flavacene	−	−	−	−	−	−	−	−	−	+	−
Xanthophylls											
Echinenone	−	−	−	−	−	?	−	−	+	+	−
Lutein	+	+	−	−	−	+?	+	−	−	?	−
Zeaxanthin	+	+	+[h]	−	−	+?	+	−	+	+	+[j]
Violaxanthin	+	+	+?	−	−	+	+?	−	−	−	−
Flavoxanthin	−	−	−	−	−	?	−	−	−	−	−
Neoxanthin	+	+	+?	−	−	−	?	−	+	−	−
Anthera-xanthin	−	−	−	−	−	+?	−	−	+	−	−
Fucoxanthin	−	−	−	+	+	+	−	−	−	−	+
Diatoxanthin	−	−	−	+	+	?	−	−	−	−	−
Diadino-xanthin	−	−	−	+	+	−	−	+	−	−	−
Dinoxanthin	−	−	−	−	−	−	−	+	−	−	−
Peridin	−	−	−	−	−	−	−	+	−	−	−
Myxoxan-thophyll	−	−	−	−	−	−	−	−	−	+	−
Siphona-xanthin	−	+[f]	−	−	−	−	−	−	−	−	−
Astaxanthin	−	+[g]	−	−	−	−	−	−	+[i]	−	−
Oscilla-xanthin	−	−	−	−	−	−	−	−	−	+[i]	−

[a] Occasional variations from this general picture are discussed in the text.
[b] No information exists on the carotenoids of the Chloromonadophyta (Chloromonadineae).
[c] Only one species (*Chara fragilis*) studied; lycopene also reported present.
[d] Present in traces in some species.
[e] Present in one marine species.

[f] The main pigments of the Siphonales.
[g] The main extra-plastidic pigment (haematochrome) of some encysted flagellates.
[h] Unknown xanthophylls possibly related to zeaxanthin present in most species.
[i] Not present in every species.
[j] The pigment present may be diatoxanthin.

TABLE IV

Quantitative Distribution of Major Carotenoids in Representative Algae from Different Divisions and Classes

Concentration mg/g dry wt.

Pigment	CHLOROPHYTA Chlorophyceae Chlorella pyrenoidosa[a]	PHAEOPHYTA Heterokonatae Vischeria sp.[c]	PHAEOPHYTA Bacillariophyceae Phaeodactylum tricornutum[e]	PHAEOPHYTA Chrysophyceae Ochromonas danica[a]	PHAEOPHYTA Phaeophyceae Fucus vesiculosus[a]	RHODOPHYTA Bangioideae Rhodosorus marinus[c]	RHODOPHYTA Florideae Nemalion multifidum[c]	PYRROPHYTA Gymnodinum sp.[e]	EUGLENOPHYTA Euglena gracilis v. bacillaris[j]	ARCHEPHYTA Anabaena variabilis[k,l,m]	CRYPTOPHYTA Cryptomonas sp.[c]
α-Carotene	0·09	—	?	—	?	—	0·02	—	—	—	0·28
β-Carotene	0·33	3·27	0·31[f]	0·73	0·14[f]	0·09	0·10	0·10[f]	0·79	1·90	—
Echinenone	—[b]	—	—	—	—	—	—	—	—	1·56	—
Lutein	1·11	—	—	—	—	0·03	0·40	—	—	—	—
Antheraxanthin	—	—	—	—	—	—	—	—	5·86	—	—
Zeaxanthin	—	—	—	—	—	0·29	—	—	—	0·22	—
Violaxanthin	0·22	—	—	—	—	—	—	—	—	—	—
Neoxanthin	0·21	—	—	—	—	—	—	—	0·52	—	—
Fucoxanthin	—	—	5·35[g]	3·16	0·59	—	(?)0·05	—	—	—	—
Diatoxanthin	—	—	0·22	—	—	—	—	—	—	—	1·08
Diadinoxanthin	—	—	—	—	—	—	—	0·19[h]	—	—	—
Peridinin	—	—	—	—	—	—	—	0·52[i]	—	—	—
Myxoxanthophyll	—	—	—	—	—	—	—	—	—	1·90	—
Unknown pigments	0·25	1·74[d]	—	0·40	0·14	—	0·05	—	trace	—	0·25
TOTAL	2·21	5·01	5·88	4·29	0·87	0·41	0·62	0·81	7·15	5·58	1·61

[a] Allen et al. (1960).
[b] Dashes indicate absence of pigments.
[c] Allen et al. (1964).
[d] A mixture of at least four xanthophylls.
[e] Jeffrey (1961).
[f] Total carotenes.
[g] Including neofucoxanthins A and B.
[h] Dinoxanthin also present.
[i] Includes neoperidinin.
[j] Goodwin and Jamikorn (1954a).
[k] Goodwin (1959b).
[l] Glover and Shah (1957).
[m] Relative amounts can vary considerably with cultural conditions.

zeaxanthin or a closely related compound, diatoxanthin, as their main pigment (p. 134).

The carotenoid distribution in *C. caldarium* would support the view that it is a transitional form between the cryptomonads and the green algae.

2. *Phaeophyta*

Three main classes of the division Phaeophyta all characteristically synthesize fucoxanthin. This is well known for the Phaeophyceae (brown algae) and Bacillariophyceae (diatoms) (see Goodwin, 1952) but has only recently been demonstrated in pure cultures of members of the Chrysophyceae (golden-brown algae) (Allen *et al.*, 1960; Dales, 1960; Jeffrey, 1961; Allen *et al.*, 1964). The fourth class, the Heterokontae (Xanthophyceae do not synthesize fucoxanthin, but instead three or four compounds which appear to be hydroxylated derivatives of zeaxanthin (Strain, 1959; Allen *et al.*, 1964). If it is assumed that fucoxanthin is a derivative of zeaxanthin then the xanthophylls found in the heterokonts may represent biosynthetic intermediates between zeaxanthin and fucoxanthin. Most diatoms and golden-brown algae also synthesize diatoxanthin, a compound spectroscopically similar to but, on careful chromatography, separable from zeaxanthin (Strain *et al.*, 1944). Diadinoxanthin which is present in traces in some diatoms (Strain *et al.*, 1944) and possibly in some chrysophytes (Dales, 1960), appears to bear the same relationship to lutein as diatoxanthin does to zeaxanthin. Dinoxanthin, a characteristic pigment of the Pyrrophyta (see below) has been reported once in the Phaeophyta, in a species of *Sphaleromantis* (Chrysophyceae) (Jeffrey, 1961).

ε-Carotene, occurs as a minor component of the carotene fraction of diatoms (Strain *et al.*, 1944); it is also present in a Cryptophyte and a green marine alga (p. 130).

3. *Rhodophyta*

It is clear from the large number of red algae which have now been examined from both the classes Bangioideae and Florideae, that α- and β-carotene and their derivatives (especially lutein and zeaxanthin) are widely distributed. The distribution appears to be unconnected with the orders to which the algae belong (Strain, 1959; Allen *et al.*, 1964). The main qualitative differences observed are the presence or absence of α-carotene and the presence or absence of zeaxanthin.

4. *Pyrrophyta* (Dinophyceae)

The main characteristic pigment of this class is peridinin a pigment of unknown structure probably identical with sulcatoxanthin first isolated from the sea anemone *Anemonia sulcata* (Karrer and Jucker, 1950).

5. *Euglenophyta*

The significant aspect of the plastid carotenoids of the Euglenineae is that apart from the main xanthophyll they are the same as those in the green algae (Goodwin and Jamikorn, 1954a); the main xanthophyll is now known to be antheraxanthin and not lutein (Krinsky and Goldsmith, 1960). Trace amounts of echinenone, 3-hydroxyechinenone and euglenanone are also present (Krinsky and Goldsmith, 1960). It is possible that these ketonic pigments are located in the eye spots of the *Euglena* spp. and not in the plastids, because chlorotic sub-strains of *E. gracilis* in which the chloroplasts but not the eye spots have degenerated still contain echinenone but very little if any of the plastid components (Goodwin and Gross, 1958). Astaxanthin, once thought to be the eye-spot pigment, has never been detected in recent investigations on *Euglena* spp.*

6. *Archephyta* (Cyanophyceae)

The main xanthophyll of these algae is echinenone (Goodwin, 1958); apart from its existence in traces in the Euglenineae (see above) its distribution in plants is, according to present knowledge, confined to the blue-green algae.

7. *Cryptophyta*

The fascinating aspect of carotenoid distribution in the two Cryptomonas spp. so far examined is that α-carotene and not β-carotene is the major carotene present (Haxo and Fork, 1959; Allen *et al.*, 1964). α-Carotene is also present in *C. ovata* (Haxo and Fork, 1959). Furthermore, the xanthophyll distribution is unique in that the major pigment is either zeaxanthin or diatoxanthin in *C. ovata* (Haxo and Fork, 1959) and diatoxanthin in *Cryptomonas* sp. and *Hemiselmis virescens* (Allen *et al.*, 1964).

8. *Chloromonadophyta*

No information is available on the carotenoids of this class.

9. *Extraplastidic Algal Carotenoids*

Many algal flagellates in the resting state encyst and this change is often accompanied by a change in colour from green to bright orange or red. The pigments responsible are extraplastidic carotenoids; β-carotene in *Trentepholia aurea* (Heilbron, 1942) and *Dunaliella salina* (Fox and Sargent, 1938), astaxanthin in *Haematococcus pluvialis* (Goodwin and Jamikorn, 1954b) and *Brachiomonas simplex* (see Goodwin, 1952) and a pigment similar to astaxanthin in *Protosiphon botryoides* (Strain, 1951).

Carotenoids often accumulate in the specialized reproductive areas of

*Lutein has recently been reported as the main eye spot pigment (Batra and Tollin, 1964).

colonial algae. For example, the bright orange of the male gametes (antherozoids) in *Fucus* spp. and *Ascophyllum nodosum* is due entirely to β-carotene, whilst the olive-green of the egg cells is due to a mixture of chlorophylls and fucoxanthin (Carter *et al.*, 1948). γ-Carotene accumulates in relatively large amounts in both male and females gametes of *Ulva lactuca* although it is only present, in traces, if at all, in the photosynthetic areas (see Goodwin, 1963a).

It has already been mentioned (p. 134) that the eye spots of *Euglena* spp. probably contain carotenoids.

10. *Evolution of Algae*

Goodwin (1963a, b, c; 1964) has proposed a pattern of evolution of algae based on a consideration of the distribution of carotenoids amongst the various classes. It is in turn based on the views of Dougherty and Allen (1960) on the evolution of protista in general. The pattern is outlined in Fig. 1. The bases for the pattern have already been discussed

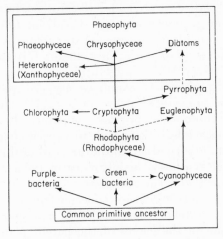

Fig. 1. Possible pattern of protistan evolution based on carotenoid studies.

in the references quoted but the following summarizing points should be emphasized:

(i) The Blue-green Algae produce only β-carotene derivatives; (ii) the Red Algae are more complex than the Blue-green Algae in producing both α- and β-carotene derivatives; (iii) carotenoid studies on the Cryptophyta, Rhodophyta and Phaeophyta support the conclusion, based on morphological considerations, that the Cryptophyta are intermediates between the other two; their xanthophylls appear to be in a higher state of oxidation than those of the Rhodophyta and in a lower state than in those of the Phaeophyta (Allen *et al.*, 1964); (iv) the Chrysophyceae synthesize fucoxanthin, which is a characteristic pigment of all Phaeophyta except the Heterokonts (Strain, 1959; Allen *et al.*, 1964); (v) a linkage between the Pyrrophyta and Bacillariophyceae is suggested by the common synthesis of diadinoxanthin, although the specific synthesis of peridinin and fucoxanthin, respectively, as the predominating xanthophyll emphasizes their separation; (vi) the carotenoids of the Euglenophyta (β-carotene derivatives—including the 4-substituted compounds such as echinenone) clearly ally them more closely with the Archephyta than with the Chlorophyta (α- and β-carotene derivatives and 3-substituted compounds, such as lutein).

III. Non-photosynthetic Tissues of Higher Plants

A. FRUIT

Not all fruit synthesize carotenoids but those that do can be divided into five main groups (Goodwin, 1959b); (i) those which contain traces of chlorophyll and "plastid carotenoids" (β-carotene, lutein, violaxanthin and neoxanthin) (e.g. *Sambucus nigra* (Goodwin, 1956)); (ii) those in which acyclic carotenoids (e.g. lycopene) are rapidly synthesized during ripening; the typical example is the tomato; (iii) those in which β-carotene or its derivatives, cryptoxanthin or zeaxanthin are rapidly synthesized during ripening; examples are red palm (β-carotene), honeysuckle (*Lonicera japonica*) (cryptoxanthin) and yellow maize (zeaxanthin); (iv) those which produce comparatively large amounts of carotenoids which are relatively specific to a species (e.g. rubixanthin in rose hips (Goodwin, 1956) and capsanthin and capsorubin in red peppers), and (v) those which synthesize mainly *cis* carotenoids, e.g. prolycopenes in *Pyracantha angustifolia*. The colourless polyenes phytoene and phyto-fluene are often encountered in carotenogenic fruit.

In general, the carotenoid distribution in carotenogenic fruit is far more complex than in the leaves of the parent plant. For example, Table V gives the quantitative and qualitative distribution in orange peel and pulp. The red flecks in commercial blood oranges are due to anthocyanins, but lycopene is the pink pigment in Sarah, a pink sport of the Jaffa orange (Monselise and Halevy, 1961).

Interspecies variation in constituent pigments can be considerable or slight. For example, berries from *Pyracantha coccinea* (Karrer and Rutschmann, 1945) and *P. rogersiana* (Goodwin, 1956) produce only traces of carotenoids; *P. flava* produces a complex mixture of xantho-phylls together with β-carotene (Goodwin, 1956) whilst *P. angustifolia* produces prolycopenes and phytofluene in addition to β-carotene (Zech-meister and Sandoval, 1945). On the other hand, sixteen species of

Berberis show very little qualitative variations, although the concentration of total carotenoids can vary from 15·0 $\mu g/g$ dry wt. to 0·8 $\mu g/g$ dry wt. (Bubicz and Wierzchowski, 1960).

TABLE V

The Quantitative and Qualitative Distribution of Carotenoids in Orange Pulp Peel (Curl and Bailey, 1956)

Carotenoid	Percentage of total pigments[a]	
Phytoene	4·0	3·1
Phytofluene	1·3	6·1
α-Carotene	0·5	0·1
β-Carotene	1·1	0·3
δ-Carotene	5·4	3·5
OH-α-Carotene-like	1·5	0·3
Cryptoxanthin epoxide-like	—	0·4
Cryptoxanthin	5·3	1·2
Cryptoflavin-like	0·5	1·2
Cryptochrome-like	—	0·8
Lutein	2·9	1·2
Zeaxanthin	4·5	0·8
Capsanthin-like	—	0·3
Antheraxanthin	5·8	6·3
Mutatoxanthins	6·2	1·7
Violaxanthins	7·4	44·0
Luteoxanthins	17·0	16·0
Auroxanthins	12·0	2·3
Valenciaxanthin	2·8	2·2
Sinensiaxanthin	2·0	3·5
Trollixanthin-like	2·9	0·5
Valencia-chrome	1·0	0·7
Sinensiachrome-like	—	0·2
Trollichrome-like	3·0	0·8

[a] Specific extinction values are assumed to be the same for all components.

Fruit carotenoids are present in chromoplasts, probably attached to proteins. The xanthophylls appear to be invariably esterified (Goodwin, 1962); for example, physalein (zeaxanthin dipalmitate) was first isolated from the berries of *Physalis alkekengi* (Karrer *et al.*, 1948).

B. FLOWERS

Carotenoids in flowers are characterized by (i) highly oxidized xanthophylls, especially the 5,8-epoxides, such as auroxanthin, flavoxanthin; (ii) species-specific pigments, e.g. eschscholtzanthin in *Eschscholtzia canadensis* and (iii) occasionally by the presence of comparatively large amounts of carotenes. Almost all yellow and lemon-yellow flowers contain large amounts of xanthophylls and only traces of carotenes, whilst deep orange flowers are often characterized by the presence of large amounts of β-carotene, as in the deep orange fringes of *Narcissus majalis* (Booth, 1957) and in *Mimulus cupreus* (v. Red Emperor) (Goodwin and Thomas, 1964), or lycopene in *Calendula officinalis* (Goodwin, 1954). Colourless polyenes are often encountered (Goodwin, 1954). In some flowers the rate of carotenoid synthesis can reach very high values. For example, the maximum rate of β-carotene formation during the formation of the red fringe of the corona of *N. majalis* is 70 μg/mg dry matter/day. This is over 10,000 times the rate observed in carrot roots (Booth, 1963).

The carotenoids in flower petals are concentrated in the chromoplasts and are probably attached to proteins.

A thorough study of carotenoids in different parts of the flowers of *Delonix regia* demonstrates the complexity of the pigment composition in flowers and also the differential distribution in the petals, sepals, filaments and anthers (Table VI) (Jungalwala and Cama, 1962). The anthers of this flower are characterized by a very high concentration of zeaxanthin, which is unique. The pollens and anthers examined by earlier workers (see Goodwin, 1952) contained mainly antheraxanthin or lutein esters together with traces of carotenes.

C. ROOTS

Few roots contain significant amounts of carotenoids, but in those that do carotenes generally preponderate (e.g. in carrots and sweet potatoes, see Goodwin, 1962). In species which can synthesize only small amounts of carotenoids (e.g. yellow-fleshed potatoes and wild carrots) xanthophylls generally predominate (see Goodwin, 1952) although occasionally (e.g. in swedes and turnips) *poly* and *cis-* carotenes are present (Joyce, 1954).

Green strains of carrot root cambial tissue cultures synthesize α- and β-carotene and lutein as well as chlorophylls; orange strains synthesize the same carotenoids in larger amounts but no chlorophylls (Naef and Turian, 1963). Cultures of carrot root tips, on the other hand, fail to synthesize carotenoids (Goodwin, 1955).

IV. FUNGI

Not all fungi synthesize carotenoids, but certain statements which appear to be reasonably general can be made regarding their distribution in fungi: (i) β-carotene is not universally present, although it is well distributed in the Mucorales (Hesseltine, 1961); (ii) the presence of the major characteristic xanthophylls of higher plants has never been

TABLE VI

Carotenoid Distribution in Petals, Sepals, Filaments and Anthers of *Delonix regia*
(Jungalwala and Cama, 1962)

	Percentage by wt. of total carotenoids present			
	in petals	in sepals	in filaments	in anthers
Carotene hydrocarbons				
Phytoene	7·66	36·64	11·79	—
Phytofluene	2·48	7·59	1·35	—
α-Carotene	—	0·54	—	—
Neo-β-carotene	—	—	1·49	0·12
β-Carotene	34·05	32·85	12·55	1·73
Pigment X	0·88	—	—	—
ζ-Carotene	1·49	1·34	1·61	—
δ-Carotene	1·65	—	—	—
γ-Carotene	11·21	1·64	3·03	—
Prolycopene	4·61	0·76	—	—
Neolycopene	2·07	1·65	1·6	—
Lycopene	4·27	1·42	2·0	—
Monohydroxy xanthophylls and epoxides of carotene hydrocarbons and of monohydroxy xanthophylls				
5,6-Monoepoxy-β-carotene	0·27	—	0·11	—
Mutatochrome	1·0 —	—	0·5	0·15
5,6-Diepoxy-β-carotene	0·17	—	1·16	—
Cryptoxanthin	0·07	1·21	5·7	2·21
Unidentified-428	0·19	0·45	0·9	—
Unidentified-420	0·8	—	—	—
Unidentified-425	1·13	—	—	—
Unidentified-430	—	—	—	0·05
Unidentified-435	—	—	—	0·22
cis-Rubixanthin	5·02	—	—	—
Rubixanthin	10·05	—	—	—
Unidentified-425a	1·60	—	—	—
Di- and poly-hydroxy xanthophylls and their epoxides				
Lutein	2·48	3·36	21·7	—
Zeaxanthin	1·82	2·59	15·2	89·82
5,6-Monoepoxylutein	0·82	—	3·7	—
Chrysanthemaxanthin + flavoxanthin	1·5	2·77	3·95	—
Antheraxanthin	0·44	0·55	6·15	5·24
Violaxanthin	0·85	1·77	4·43	0·29
cis-Auroxanthin	0·28	—	—	—
Auroxanthin	0·94	2·47	1·08	0·18
Neoxanthin	0·2	0·4	—	—

unequivocally established and such minor components as zeaxanthin and cryptoxanthin occur only very occasionally; (iii) characteristic fungal carotenoids are frequently acidic, for example, torularhodin (Rüegg *et al.*, 1958) and neurosporaxanthin (Zalokar, 1957).

The pigments can sometimes vary with the age of culture; for example, lycopene is the main pigment in young *Rhizophlyctis rosea* whilst lycopene and γ-carotene are present in mature cultures (Davies, 1961a, b; Goodwin, 1963d).

Differential distribution can occur in the two sexual forms of certain Phycomycetes, for example, the asexual and female plants of the aquatic fungus *Allomyces* synthesize no carotenoids, whilst the male forms accumulate γ-carotene in the cytoplasm of the gametangia (Emerson and Fox, 1940). The + and − forms of certain Mucorales, e.g. *Choanephora conjuncta* and *Blakeslea trispora*, synthesize different small amounts of β-carotene, but when grown in mixed culture synthesize up to fifteen to twenty times as much as do cultures of either mating type alone (Barnett *et al.*, 1956; Anderson *et al.*, 1958). This observation has been used as the basis for the industrial production of β-carotene microbiologically. Under optimum conditions, concentrations of β-carotene up to 8 mg/g dry wt. can be obtained (Ciegler *et al.*, 1959).

It is claimed that in some slime moulds (e.g. *Mycoplasma laidlawii*) the xanthophylls present occur in the form of β-glucosides; the carotene was always neurosporene (Smith, 1963).

Recent work has shown that in certain genera which were originally thought not to synthesize carotenoids (see Goodwin, 1952), species have been found which are carotenogenic. For example, carotenoids are present in *Penicillium sclerotiorium* (Mase *et al.*, 1957) and in *Fusarium aquaeductum* (Rau and Zehender, 1959).

Carotenoids have recently been identified in *Protomyces inundatus* (α,β-γ-carotenes) (Valadon, 1963) and *Arthrobotrys oligospora* (β,-γ-carotenes, torulene, neurosporaxanthin (Valadon and Cooke, 1963).

REFERENCES

Allen, M. B., Goodwin, T. W., and Phagpolngarm, S. (1960). *J. gen. Microbiol.* **23**, 93.
Allen, M. B., Fries, L., Goodwin, T. W., and Thomas, D. M. (1964). *J. gen. Microbiol.* **34**, 259.
Anderson, R. F., Arnold, M., Nelson, G. E. N., and Ciegler, A. (1958). *Agric. Food Chem.* **6**, 543.
Barnett, H. L., Lilly, V. G., and Krause, R. F. (1956). *Science* **123**, 141.
Batra, P. P., and Tollin, G. (1964). *Biochim. biophys. Acta*, **79**, 371.
Bickoff, E. M., Livingston, A. L., Bailey, G. F., and Thompson, C. R. (1954). *Agric. Food Chem.* **2**, 563.
Booth, V. H. (1957). *Biochem. J.* **65**, 660.
Booth, V. H. (1963). *Biochem. J.* **87**, 238.

Bubicz, M., and Wierzchowski, Z. (1960). *Bull. Acad. polon. Sci.* **8**, 323.

Carter, P. W., Cross, L. C., Heilbron, I. M., and Jones, E. R. H. (1948). *Biochem. J.* **43**, 349.

Chapman, D. J., and Haxo, F. T. (1963). *Plant and Cell Physiol.* **4**, 57.

Ciegler, A., Arnold, M., and Anderson, R. F. (1959). *Appl. Microbiol.* **7**, 94, 98.

Curl, A. L., and Bailey, G. F. (1956). *Agric. Food Chem.* **4**, 156.

Dales, R. P. (1960). *J. Mar. biol. Ass. U.K.* **39**, 693.

Davies, B. H. (1961a). *Biochem. J.* **80**, 48P.

Davies, B. H. (1961b). *Phytochemistry* **1**, 25.

Dougherty, E., and Allen, M. B. (1960). *In* "Comparative Biochemistry of Photoactive Pigments" (M. B. Allen, ed.), Academic Press, New York.

Emerson, R., and Fox, D. L. (1940). *Proc. roy. Soc.* **128** *B*, 275.

Fox, D. L., and Sargent, M. C. (1938). *Chem. & Ind.* **57**, 1111.

Glover, J., and Redfearn, E. R. (1953). *Biochem. J.* **54**, viii.

Glover, J., and Shah, P. P. (1957). *Biochem. J.* **67**, 15P.

Goodwin, T. W. (1952). "The Comparative Biochemistry of Carotenoids," Chapman and Hall, London.

Goodwin, T. W. (1954). *Biochem. J.* **58**, 90.

Goodwin, T. W. (1955). *Ann. Rev. Biochem.* **24**, 497.

Goodwin, T. W. (1956). *Biochem. J.* **62**, 346.

Goodwin, T. W. (1958). *J. gen. Microbiol.* **17**, 467.

Goodwin, T. W. (1959a). *In* "Encyclopaedia of Plant Physiology" (W. Ruhland, ed.), vol. 5, Springer, Heidelberg.

Goodwin, T. W. (1959b). *Advanc. Enzymol.* **21**, 295.

Goodwin, T. W. (1961). *In* "Comparative Biochemistry of Photoreactive Systems" (M. B. Allen, ed.), Academic Press, New York.

Goodwin, T. W. (1963a). *In* "Comparative Biochemistry" (M. Florkin and H. S. Mason, eds.), vol. 4, Academic Press, New York.

Goodwin, T. W. (1963b). *In* "Carotine and Carotinoide" (K. Lang, ed.), Steinkopf, Darmstadt.

Goodwin, T. W. (1963c). "Proc. Symp. 5th Int. Cong. Biochem. Moscow," Pergamon Press, Oxford.

Goodwin, T. W. (1963d). *In* "Biochemistry of Industrial Microorganisms" (C. Rainbow and A. H. Rose, eds.), Academic Press, London.

Goodwin, T. W. (1964). *In* "Advances in Protozoology" (S. H. Hunter, ed.), Academic Press, New York.

Goodwin, T. W., and Gross, J. A. (1958). *J. Protozool.* **5**, 292.

Goodwin, T. W., and Jamikorn, M. (1954a). *J. Protozool.* **1**, 216.

Goodwin, T. W., and Jamikorn, M. (1954b). *Biochem. J.* **57**, 376.

Goodwin, T. W., and Phagpolngarm, S. (1960). *Biochem. J.* **76**, 197.

Goodwin, T. W., and Thomas, D. M. (1964). *Phytochemistry* **3**, 47.

Goodwin, T. W., and Williams, B. L. (1962). *Biochem. J.* **85**, 12P.

Haxo, F. T., and Fork, D. C. (1959). *Nature, Lond.* **184**, 1047.

Heilbron, I. M. (1942). *J. chem. Soc.* 79.

Hesseltine, C. W. (1961). *Tech. Bull. U.S. Dep. Agric.* No. 1245, Washington, U.S. Printing Office.

Jeffrey, S. W. (1961). *Biochem. J.* **80**, 336.

Joyce, A. E. (1954). *Nature, Lond.* **173**, 311.

Jungalwala, F. B., and Cama, H. R. (1962). *Biochem. J.* **85**, 1.

Karrer, P., and Eugster, C. H. (1950). *Helv. chim. acta* **33**, 1433.

Karrer, P., and Jucker, E. (1950). "Carotinoide," Birkhauser, Basel.

Karrer, P., and Rutschmann, J. (1945). *Helv. chim. acta* **13**, 1104.

Karrer, P., Jucker, E., and Steinlin, K. (1948). *Helv. chim. acta* **31**, 113.

Krinsky, N. I., and Goldsmith, T. H. (1960). *Arch. Biochem. Biophys.* **91**, 271.

Mackinney, G., Rick, C. M., and Jenkins, J. A. (1956). *Proc. nat. Acad. Sci., Wash.* **42**, 404.

Mase, Y., Rabourn, W. J., and Quackenbush, F. W. (1957). *Arch. Biochem. Biophys.* **68**, 150.

Mercer, E. I., Davies, B. H., and Goodwin, T. W. (1963). *Biochem. J.* **87**, 317.

Monselise, S. P., and Halevy, A. H. (1961). *Science* **133**, 1478.

Naef, J., and Turian, G. (1963). *Phytochemistry* **2**, 173.

Nakayama, T. O. M. (1963). *In* "Physiology and Biochemistry of the Algae" (J. Myers, ed.), Academic Press, New York.

Nishimura, M., and Takamatsu, K. (1957). *Nature, Lond.* **180**, 699.

Rabourn, W. J., and Quackenbush, F. W. (1953). *Arch. Biochem. Biophys.* **44**, 159.

Rau, W., and Zehender, C. (1959). *Arch. Mikrobiol.* **32**, 423.

Rüegg, R., Guex, W., Montavon, M., Schwieter, U., Saucy, G., and Isler, O. (1958). *Chimia* **12**, 327.

Smith, P. F. (1963). *J. gen. Microbiol.* **32**, 307.

Strain, H. H. (1951). *In* "Manual of Physiology" (G. M. Smith, ed.), Waltham.

Strain, H. H. (1959). "Chloroplast Pigments and Chromatographic Analysis," Penn. State University.

Strain, H. H., Manning, W. M., and Hardin, G. (1944). *Biol. Bull.* **86**, 169.

Thirkell, D. (1964). *Phytochemistry* **3**, 301.

Valadon, L. R. G. (1963). *Phytochemistry* **2**, 71.

Valadon, L. R. G., and Cooke, R. C. (1963). *Phytochemistry* **2**, 103.

Wierzchowski, Z., Leonowicz, A., Sapiecha, K., and Sykut, A. (1962). *Roczn. Nauk. roln.* **81** *B*, 87.

Zalokar, M. (1957). *Arch. Biochem. Biophys.* **70**, 568.

Zechmeister, L., and Karmakar, G. (1953). *Arch. Biochem. Biophys.* **47**, 160.

Zechmeister, L., and Sandoval, A. (1945). *Arch. Biochem.* **8**, 425.

Chapter 5

THE BIOSYNTHESIS OF CAROTENOIDS

T. W. Goodwin

University College of Wales, Aberystwyth, Wales

I. Introduction

Biosynthetic investigations during the past ten years have consistently demonstrated that terpenoids are synthesized from a basic 5-carbon unit, a view held for some years previously by Ruzicka (see Ruzicka *et al.*, 1953) and generalized in his "isoprene rule". However, the elucidation of various structures which would not easily fit the isoprene rule (e.g. lanosterol) led to the development of the "biogenetic isoprene rule" (Ruzicka, 1959) which states that terpenes are formed from aliphatic compounds such as geraniol (C-10) (I), farnesol (C-15) (II), geranylgeraniol (C-20) (III) and other related compounds, and that they can be derived from these by theoretically acceptable cyclizations and rearrangements. Biochemical investigations which were going on during this period also strongly pointed to the same conclusions. These conclusions require the existence of a universal "biological isoprene unit", and this requirement was satisfied with the discovery of isopentenyl pyrophosphate (IPP, IV).

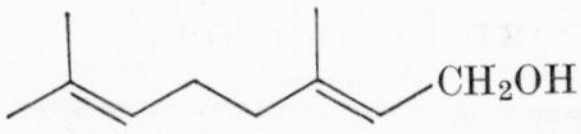

(I) 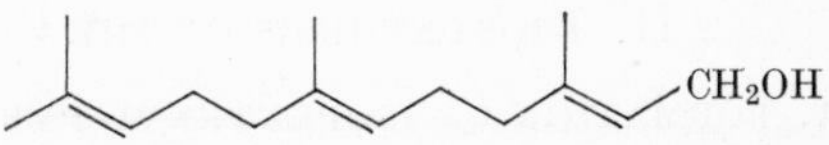   (II)

(III)

(IV)

A generalized scheme of terpenoid biosynthesis can now be produced with some confidence (Fig. 1), although gaps in our knowledge still exist (see Goodwin, 1964a).

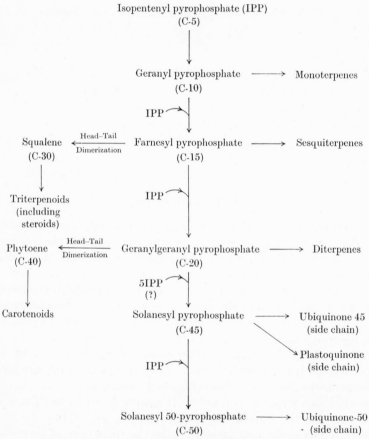

Fig. 1. Generalized scheme for biosynthesis of terpenoids.

II. Biosynthesis of the C-40 Carotenoid Precursor

A. Formation of Isopentenyl Pyrophosphate

The main building unit from which isopentenyl pyrophosphate IPP is synthesized is acetyl-CoA and the steps involved are indicated in Fig. 2.

The only way in which acetyl-CoA can be by-passed is in organisms which can metabolize the amino acid leucine to β-hydroxy-β-methyl-CoA (HMG-CoA) (reaction D, Fig. 2) (see p. 146). The reactions which lead from acetate to HMG-CoA (A, A_1, A_2, B, C, Fig. 2) are not specific to terpenoid biosynthesis. The first step which is specific is the formation of mevalonic acid (MVA) which represents the "point of no return" because it has no metabolic future other than being converted into

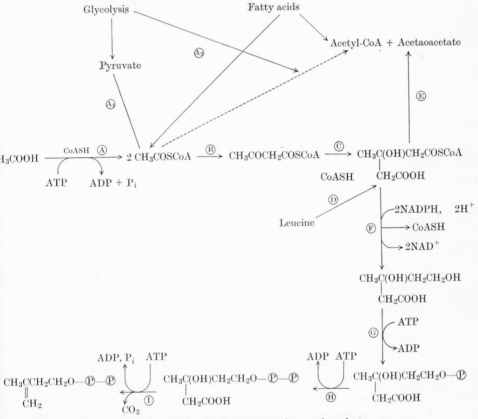

FIG. 2. The biosynthesis of isopentenyl pyrophosphate.

terpenoids (Popják and Cornforth, 1960). HMG-CoA on the other hand can be irreversibly cleaved to acetyl-CoA and acetoacetate (reaction E, Fig. 2). The formation of each key intermediate will be discussed first, and that will be followed by the evidence for its participation in carotenoid biosynthesis.

1. HMG-CoA

Apart from the usual biosynthetic route from acetyl-CoA it can also arise from the catabolism of leucine. The pathway (Fig. 3) was elucidated by Coon *et al.* (1959) and involves a CO_2-fixing step which is biotin-dependent. Some years ago Goodwin and Lijinsky (1952) discovered that

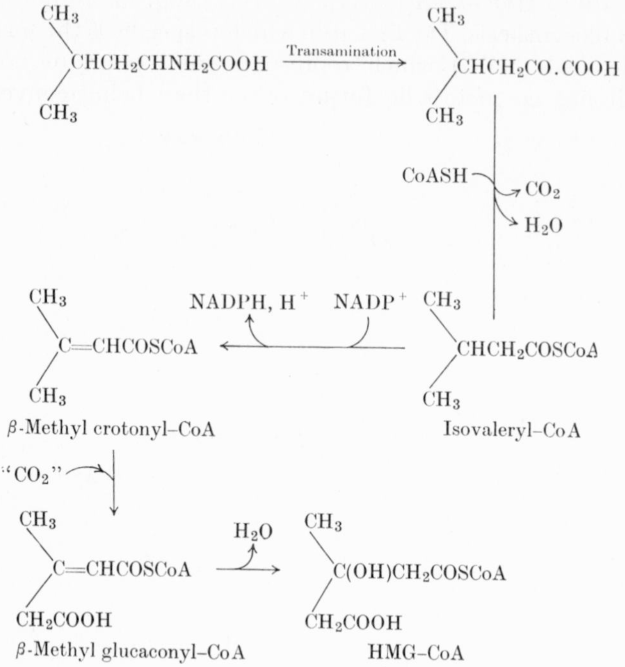

FIG. 3. The formation of HMG-CoA from leucine.

leucine greatly stimulated carotenogenesis in *Phycomyces blakesleeanus*. Later investigations have demonstrated that the pathway of Coon is probably being followed in this organism. The label from both [1-^{14}C]- and [2-^{14}C]leucine is not incorporated into β-carotene by *P. blakesleeanus* (Chichester *et al.*, 1955), but the incorporation of the remaining atoms (Chichester *et al.*, 1959; Wuhrmann *et al.*, 1957; Yokoyama *et al.*, 1957; Varma *et al.*, 1959) is consistent with the pathway outlined in Fig. 3. Furthermore, $^{14}CO_2$ is fixed into β-carotene by *P. blakesleeanus* only in the presence of leucine (Goodwin, 1959b; Braithwaite and Goodwin, 1960; Chichester *et al.*, 1959). However, the scheme in Fig. 3 leads to the fixation of CO_2 into C-5 of HMG-CoA and thus into C-1 of MVA and this is lost on conversion into IPP (Fig. 2). Randomization of C-1 and C-5 of HMG-CoA can, however, occur according to the known reactions indicated in Scheme 1 (the carbon arising from CO_2 is starred).

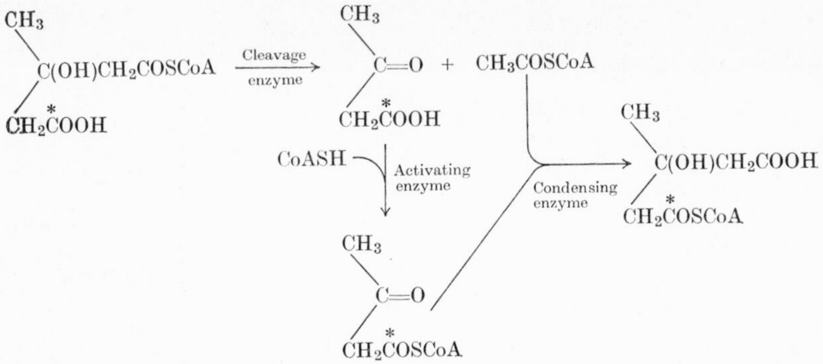

$$
\begin{array}{c}
CH_3 \\
\diagdown \\
\quad C(OH)CH_2COSCoA \\
\diagup \overset{*}{} \\
\overset{*}{C}H_2COOH
\end{array}
\xrightarrow[\text{enzyme}]{\text{Cleavage}}
\begin{array}{c}
CH_3 \\
\diagdown \\
\quad C{=}O \;+\; CH_3COSCoA \\
\diagup \overset{*}{} \\
\overset{*}{C}H_2COOH
\end{array}
$$

Reaction scheme (1)

2. *Mevalonic Acid*

MVA was discovered as the acetate-replacing factor for an acetate-requiring mutant of *Lactobacillus acidophilus* (Folkers *et al.*, 1959). Its structural resemblance to HMG prompted an experiment which demonstrated that racemic $[2\text{-}^{14}C]$MVA was converted into cholesterol by liver homogenates with an efficiency of 43%. As it was later shown that only one enantiomorph was biologically active the conversion was almost quantitative. Similar results were obtained with carotenoids (Braithwaite and Goodwin, 1960).

The conversion of HMG-CoA into MVA (Reaction F, Fig. 2) is essentially irreversible and is catalysed by the enzyme HMG-CoA reductase without the appearance of free mevaldic acid (V) (Ferguson *et al.*, 1959; Lynen *et al.*, 1959). It is the carbonyl group which carries the Coenzyme A residue which is reduced to the primary alcohol grouping of MVA. Popják and Cornforth (1960) have proposed reaction scheme (2) to explain the known facts. The first step (A) is the binding of the substrate as a thiol ester with the liberation of Coenzyme A. Reduction of one mole of NADPH (step B) yields a hemithioacetal which on further reduction with a second mole of NADPH yields an enzyme-MVA complex (step C). This in turn irreversibly dissociates (step D) to liberate unbound MVA together with the free enzyme which is then ready for further reaction. The enzymatic reduction of HMG-CoA is stereospecific (Ferguson *et al.*, 1959) as is the utilization of MVA (Tchen, 1958). Eberle and Arigoni (1960) have established the absolute configuration of biosynthetic MVA as (VI) and it follows that biologically active HMG-CoA is (VII).

It is clear that the active form of HMG is its Coenzyme A ester. This has not been tested for activity as a precursor of carotenoids but HMG itself is said to be active in *P. blakesleeanus* (Chichester *et al.* 1959; Chichester and Nakayama, 1963). This implies the presence of an HMG-activating enzyme in this mould. Such an enzyme does not exist in liver and yeast neither of which will incorporate HMG into sterols (Tavormina *et al.*, 1956; Dituri *et al.*, 1957).

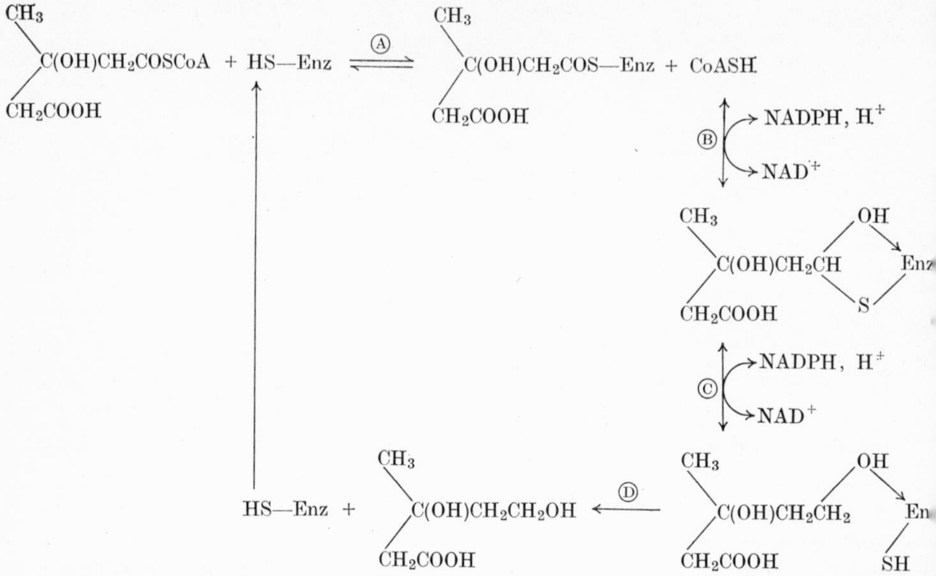

$$CH_3 \diagdown C(OH)CH_2COSCoA + HS\text{—Enz} \xrightarrow{\enspace \textcircled{A}\enspace} CH_3 \diagdown C(OH)CH_2COS\text{—Enz} + CoASH$$
$$CH_2COOH \qquad\qquad\qquad\qquad\qquad CH_2COOH$$

$$\textcircled{B} \quad\begin{array}{c} \nearrow NADPH,\ H^+ \\ \searrow NAD^+ \end{array}$$

$$CH_3 \diagdown C(OH)CH_2CH \diagup^{OH}_{\diagdown\ S}\ Enz$$
$$CH_2COOH$$

$$\textcircled{C} \quad\begin{array}{c} \nearrow NADPH,\ H^+ \\ \searrow NAD^+ \end{array}$$

$$HS\text{—Enz} + \quad CH_3 \diagdown C(OH)CH_2CH_2OH \xleftarrow{\enspace\textcircled{D}\enspace} CH_3 \diagdown C(OH)CH_2CH_2 \diagup^{OH}_{\diagdown\ SH}\ En$$
$$CH_2COOH \qquad\qquad\qquad\qquad CH_2COOH$$

[2-^{14}C]MVA was incorporated into β-carotene in the moulds *Phycomyces blakesleeanus* (Braithwaite and Goodwin, 1957, 1960; Yokoyama *et al.*, 1960; Mackinney *et al.*, 1958), *Mucor hiemalis* (Grob, 1959), *Blakeslea trispora* (Anderson *et al.*, 1960), *Neurospora crassa* Krzeminski

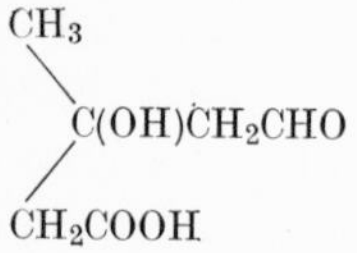

$$CH_3 \diagdown C(OH)CH_2CHO$$
$$CH_2COOH$$
$$(V)$$

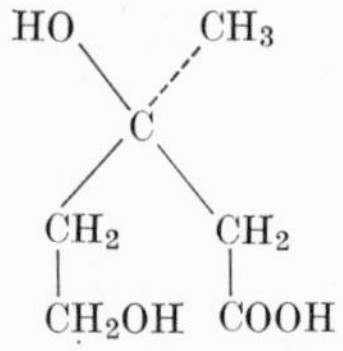

$$HO \diagdown C \diagup CH_3$$
$$CH_2 \quad CH_2$$
$$CH_2OH \quad COOH$$
$$(VI)$$

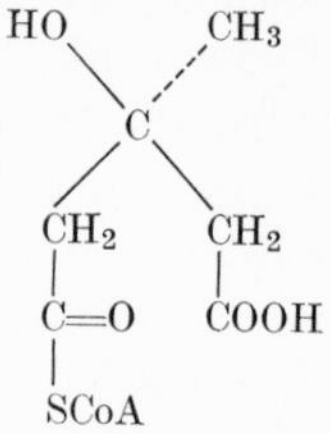

$$HO \diagdown C \diagup CH_3$$
$$CH_2 \quad CH_2$$
$$C{=}O \quad COOH$$
$$SCoA$$
$$(VII)$$

and Quackenbush, 1960), in carrot root preparations (Braithwaite and Goodwin, 1960; Modi and Patwa, 1961) and preparations from a mutant of *Staphylococcus aureus* (Suzue, 1960); it is also incorporated into lycopene in ripening tomatoes (Goodwin, 1959a; Braithwaite and Goodwin, 1960; Shneour and Zabin, 1958; Purcell *et al.*, 1959). Occasionally one finds that mevalonate is incorporated only insignificantly e.g. *E. gracilis* v. *bacillaris* (Steele and Gurin, 1960) or not at all, e.g. *Chlorella pyrenoidosa* (Anderson *et al.*, 1960), *E. gracilis* strain Z (D. R. Threlfall, 1963, unpublished observations) and etiolated seedlings of various species (Goodwin, 1958; Goodwin and Mercer, 1963; Treharne *et al.*, 1964). This problem is discussed later (p. 168).

Degradation of β-carotene synthesized by *Mucor hiemalis* (Grob and Bütler, 1954, 1955, 1956), *Phycomyces blakesleeanus* (Braithwaite and Goodwin, 1960; Lotspeich *et al.*, 1959, 1961) and *Euglena gracilis* (Steele and Gurin, 1960) in the presence of [1-^{14}C]- and [2-^{14}C]acetate revealed the labelling pattern expected if reaction C (Fig. 2) were operating (Fig. 4). Degradation of β-carotene produced by *P. blakesleeanus* (Braithwaite and Goodwin, 1960) and *E. gracilis* (Steele and Gurin, 1960)

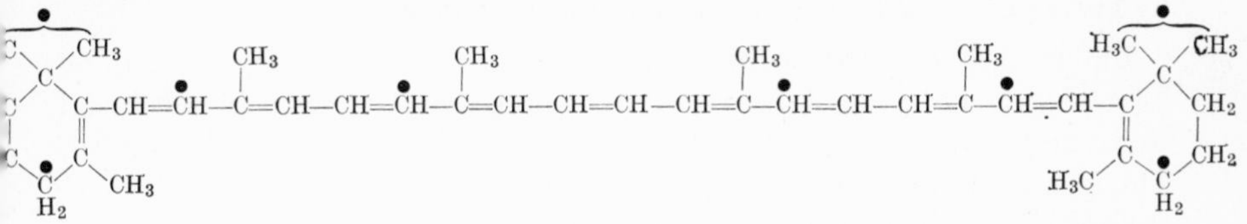

FIG. 4. The distribution of the label from [2-^{14}C]mevalonate in β-carotene.

demonstrated that, as with other terpenoids, C-2 of mevalonate retained its individuality and appeared only in the "backbone" of the molecule (Fig. 4).

3. *Isopentenyl Pyrophosphate*

The steps in terpenoid biosynthesis up to MVA are electrophilic reactions in which Coenzyme A acts by increasing the electron deficit at the carbonyl carbon to which it is attached. In the steps leading from MVA to IPP Coenzyme A is no longer required and phosphate esters are intermediates. MVA is "activated" by its stepwise conversion into MVA-5-pyrophosphate via MVA-5-phosphate (Reactions G and H) (Fig. 2). The enzymes concerned are mevalonic kinase (Tchen 1957; Witting *et al.*, 1959; Levy and Popják, 1960; Bataille and Loomis, 1961) and phosphomevalonic kinase (Bloch *et al.*, 1959; Henning *et al.*, 1959). The final step (reaction I, Fig. 2), catalysed by 5-pyrophosphomevalonic anhydrodecarboxylase requires ATP and Mn^{2+} as co-factors (de Waard *et al.*, 1959; Hellig and Popják, 1961) and probably takes place according to scheme 3. This scheme accounts for the fact that D$^+$ is not incorporated

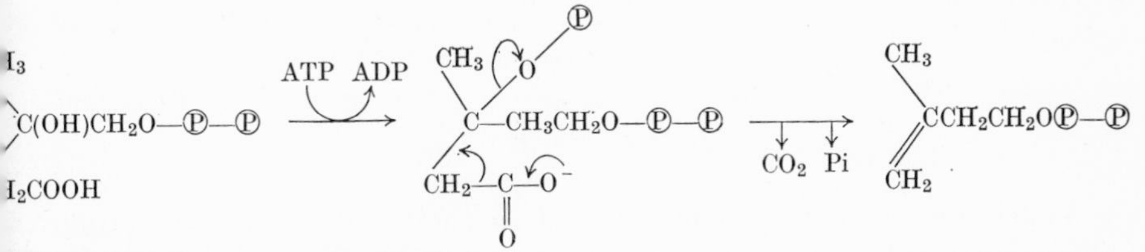

into the terminal methylene group when the reaction is carried out in the presence of D$_2$O. The postulated intermediate, 5-pyrophospho-3-phosphomevalonate has not yet been isolated but experiments with

[^{18}O]-MVA have indicated the formation of an ester link with the tertiary hydroxy group of MVA during the course of the reaction (Lindberg *et al.*, 1962).

The incorporation of [1-^{14}C]isopentenyl pyrophosphate into β-carotene in fungal extracts and into lycopene by tomato extracts has been reported by Varma and Chichester (1962); in both cases the relative incorporation was greater than that of mevalonate.

B. FORMATION OF DIMETHYLALLYL PYROPHOSPHATE

Before a C-10 terpene and subsequent higher homologues can be formed, one molecule of dimethylallyl pyrophosphate must be produced by isomerization of IPP in order to act as starter for chain elongation. The isomerase which catalyses the reaction has been purified from yeast (Lynen *et al.*, 1959); it has been shown to have an active SH group and is inhibited by iodoacetate. This is the only enzyme in the terpenoid sequence which is sensitive to this reagent. Because of the existence of the active SH group Lynen *et al.* have proposed a mechanism for the

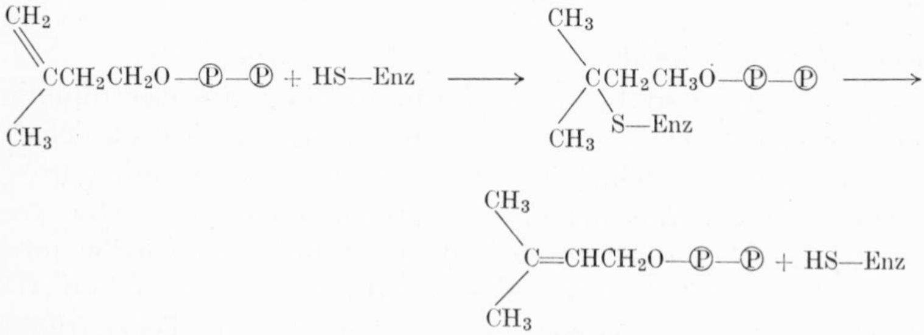

$$\begin{array}{c}\text{CH}_2\\\|\\\diagdown\\\diagup\text{CCH}_2\text{CH}_2\text{O}-\textcircled{P}-\textcircled{P} + \text{HS}-\text{Enz} \longrightarrow\\\text{CH}_3\end{array}\qquad\begin{array}{c}\text{CH}_3\\\diagdown\\\diagup\text{CCH}_2\text{CH}_3\text{O}-\textcircled{P}-\textcircled{P} \longrightarrow\\\text{CH}_3\ \ \text{S}-\text{Enz}\end{array}$$

$$\begin{array}{c}\text{CH}_3\\\diagdown\\\diagup\text{C}{=}\text{CHCH}_2\text{O}-\textcircled{P}-\textcircled{P} + \text{HS}-\text{Enz}\\\text{CH}_3\end{array}\qquad(4)$$

reaction outlined in scheme (4); Popják and Cornforth (1960), on the other hand, prefer the mechanism given in scheme (5).

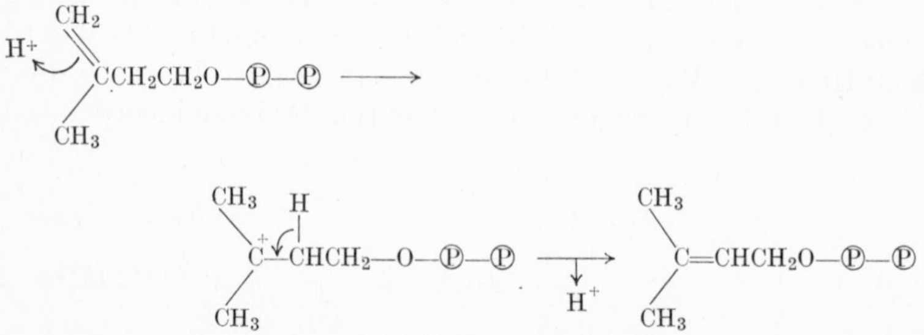

$$\text{H}^+\ \begin{array}{c}\text{CH}_2\\\|\\\diagdown\\\diagup\text{CCH}_2\text{CH}_2\text{O}-\textcircled{P}-\textcircled{P} \longrightarrow\\\text{CH}_3\end{array}$$

$$\begin{array}{c}\text{CH}_3\ \ \text{H}\\\diagdown\ \ |\\\overset{+}{\text{C}}{-}\text{CHCH}_2-\text{O}-\textcircled{P}-\textcircled{P} \xrightarrow[\text{H}^+]{}\\\text{CH}_3\end{array}\qquad\begin{array}{c}\text{CH}_3\\\diagdown\\\diagup\text{C}{=}\text{CHCH}_2\text{O}-\textcircled{P}-\textcircled{P}\\\text{CH}_3\end{array}\qquad(5)$$

Yokoyama *et al.* (1962) found that in their cell-free system from *Phycomyces* iodoacetamide inhibited the incorporation of MVA into carotenoids; this is circumstantial evidence for dimethylallyl pyrophosphate being an obligatory intermediate in carotenoid synthesis as it is for other terpenoids.

C. FORMATION OF GERANYLGERANYL PYROPHOSPHATE

Geranyl pyrophosphate (C-10) is formed by the condensation of IPP with dimethylallyl pyrophosphate in the presence of the enzyme farnesyl pyrophosphate synthetase (scheme 6) (Agranoff *et al.*, 1959). This enzyme will also add on two further IPP molecules, stepwise, to geranyl pyrophosphate to form farnesyl pyrophosphate (C-15) (Lynen *et al.*, 1958; Popják and Cornforth, 1960) and geranylgeranyl pyrophosphate (C-20) (Grob *et al.*, 1961). A direct demonstration of the formation of geranylgeranyl pyrophosphate by carrot and pig liver enzymes has recently been reported (Wells *et al.*, 1964).

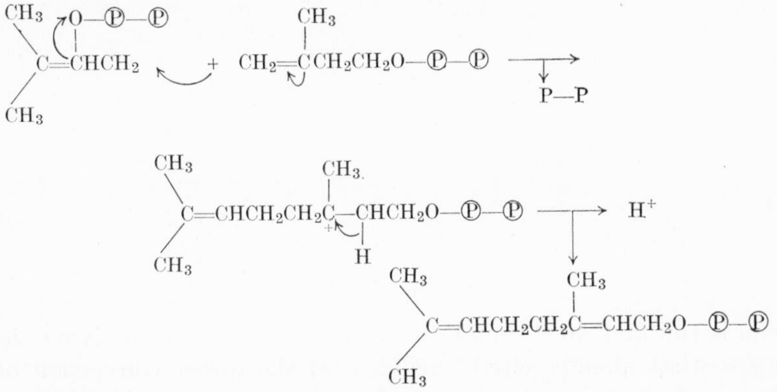

Geranyl pyrophosphate has not yet been shown to be an intermediate in carotenoid biosynthesis, but [^{14}C]farnesyl pyrophosphate is incorporated into β-carotene and other polyenes in a *P. blakesleeanus* cell-free system (Yokoyama *et al.*, 1961) and in a carrot plastid system (Anderson and Porter, 1962). As this incorporation was stimulated by the addition of MVA (Yokoyama *et al.*, 1961) it was reasonable to assume that geranylgeranyl pyrophosphate is formed as an intermediate in carotenogenesis.

D. FORMATION OF PHYTOENE (C-40)

The basic C-30 precursor of triterpenoids is squalene (VIII); which is formed by the dimerization of farnesyl pyrophosphate (see Goodwin, 1964); an analogous reaction with geranylgeranyl pyrophosphate would yield lycopersene (IX). Grob *et al.* (1961) claim to have obtained a particulate enzyme from *Neurospora crassa*, which would carry out this reaction, and Grob and Boschetti (1962) reported the presence of lycopersene in the mycelia of *N. crassa*. Other investigators have not been able to detect lycopersene in various carotenogenic systems (Davies *et al.*, 1963a; Mercer *et al.*, 1963; Pennock *et al.*, 1962) and it is not formed

in a system of carrot plastids which were capable of synthesizing
phytoene (X) (15,15'-dehydrolycopersene) from terpenyl pyrophosphates (Anderson and Porter, 1962). It is now the general view that

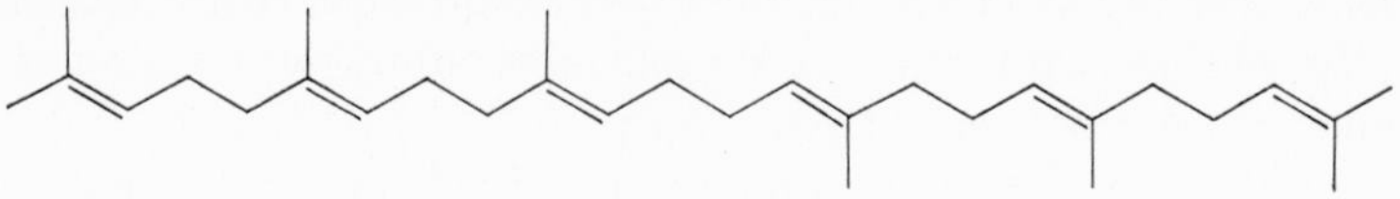

(VIII)

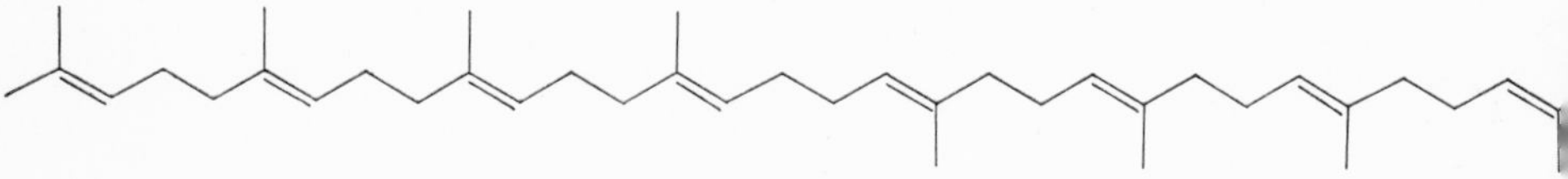

(IX)

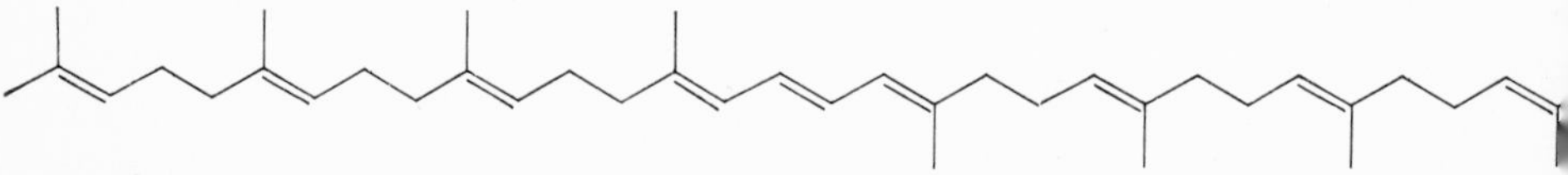

(X)

phytoene is the first 40-C unit formed and evidence for this view, in
addition to that already cited, includes (a) the direct conversion of
geranylgeranyl pyrophosphate by isolated tomato fruit plastids into
phytoene (Wells *et al.*, 1964); (b) many "carotenoid-less" mutants of
microorganisms and higher plants accumulate phytoene but not lycopersene (see Goodwin, 1964); (b) inhibition of carotenogenesis in microorganisms by diphenylamine results in the accumulation of phytoene
but not lycopersene (see Goodwin, 1963; Chichester and Nakayama,
1963); (c) under anaerobic conditions and in the absence of a suitable
electron acceptor carotenoid synthesis in *Mycobact.* spp. is inhibited and
phytoene, not lycopersene, accumulates (Rilling, 1962). Rilling points
out that a scheme, which involves the formation of lycopersene prior to
phytoene, would require an oxidizing step whereas a scheme for the
conversion of geranylgeranyl pyrophosphate into phytoene can be
written without an overall change in the oxidation state of the system.
Such a scheme is indicated in (7).

The formation of phytoene and not lycopersene as the first C-40
compound formed allows the formulation of a reason for the absence of
polycyclic tetraterpenoids, analogous to the polycyclic triterpenoids
(sterols, etc.) in Nature. The presence of the central double bond in
phytoene would prevent its folding similarly to squalene and thus
extensive cyclization initiated by OH^+ or H^+ would not be possible. It

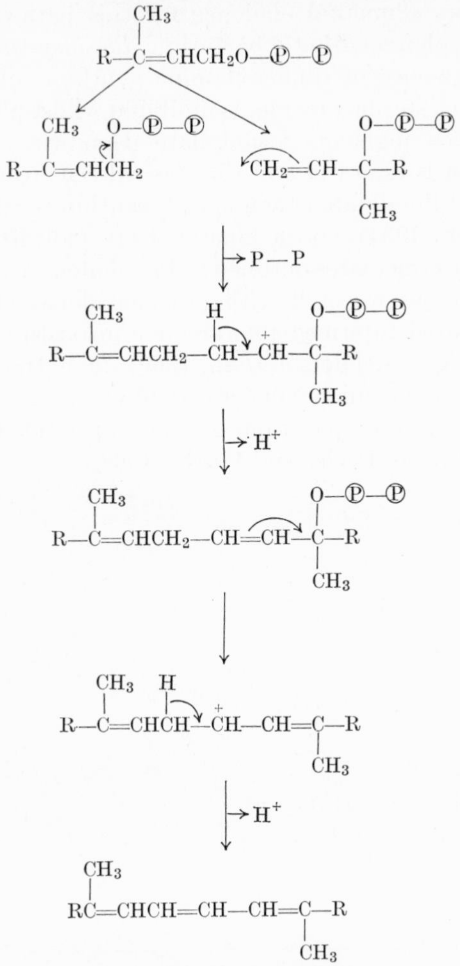

$$\text{CH}_3$$
$$|$$
$$\text{R}-\text{C}=\text{CHCH}_2\text{O}-\text{\textcircled{P}}-\text{\textcircled{P}}$$

$$\begin{array}{cc}
\text{CH}_3 & \text{O}-\text{\textcircled{P}}-\text{\textcircled{P}} \\
| & | \\
\text{R}-\text{C}=\text{CHCH}_2 & \text{CH}_2=\text{CH}-\text{C}-\text{R} \\
& | \\
& \text{CH}_3
\end{array}$$

$$\downarrow \text{P}-\text{P}$$

$$\begin{array}{ccc}
\text{CH}_3 & \text{H} & \text{O}-\text{\textcircled{P}}-\text{\textcircled{P}} \\
| & | & | \\
\text{R}-\text{C}=\text{CHCH}_2-\text{CH}-\overset{+}{\text{CH}}-\text{C}-\text{R} \\
& & | \\
& & \text{CH}_3
\end{array}$$

$$\downarrow \text{H}^+$$

(7)

$$\begin{array}{ccc}
\text{CH}_3 & & \text{O}-\text{\textcircled{P}}-\text{\textcircled{P}} \\
| & & | \\
\text{R}-\text{C}=\text{CHCH}_2-\text{CH}=\text{CH}-\text{C}-\text{R} \\
& & | \\
& & \text{CH}_3
\end{array}$$

$$\downarrow$$

$$\begin{array}{ccc}
\text{CH}_3 & \text{H} & \\
| & | & \\
\text{R}-\text{C}=\text{CHCH}-\overset{+}{\text{CH}}-\text{CH}=\text{C}-\text{R} \\
& & | \\
& & \text{CH}_3
\end{array}$$

$$\downarrow \text{H}^+$$

$$\begin{array}{ccc}
\text{CH}_3 & & \\
| & & \\
\text{RC}=\text{CHCH}=\text{CH}-\text{CH}=\text{C}-\text{R} \\
& & | \\
& & \text{CH}_3
\end{array}$$

will be seen later that the limited cyclization which occurs in carotenoids and the insertion of oxygen into the system both occur at a late stage in the biosynthetic sequence.

III. CONVERSION OF PHYTOENE INTO FULLY UNSATURATED CAROTENES

A. LYCOPENE

A scheme for the stepwise conversion of phytoene into lycopene via phytofluene, ζ-carotene and neurosporene (Fig. 5) was first proposed by Porter and Lincoln (1950) some time before the exact structures of the intermediates were elucidated. The proposals were based on the pattern of pigment distribution in various tomato mutants. Similar patterns are also observed in various mutants of *Chlorella* (Claes, 1954, 1956, 1957,

1958, 1959). Other experimental evidence for this pathway includes
(a) when cells of the photosynthetic bacterium *Rhodospirillum rubrum*
are grown in the presence of diphenylamine synthesis of the major
carotenoid component, spirilloxanthin, is inhibited whilst phytoene and
other partly saturated pigments accumulate (Goodwin and Osman,
1954); if the inhibitor is removed and the washed cells resuspended in
phosphate buffer and illuminated then spirilloxanthin is resynthesized
(Goodwin and Osman, 1954), and a kinetic study indicates that it is
synthesized via the intermediates outlined in Fig. 5 (Jensen *et al.*, 1958);
(b) in ripening tomatoes injected with [^{14}C]mevalonate the specific
activities of the isolated intermediates are not inconsistent with the
scheme outlined in Fig. 5. (Anderson *et al.*, 1960); (c) extracts of *Staph.
aureus* have been obtained which will convert phytoene into δ-carotene
(Suzue, 1960, 1961) and (d) preparations of tomato plastids will convert
phytoene into phytofluene (Beeler and Porter, 1962).

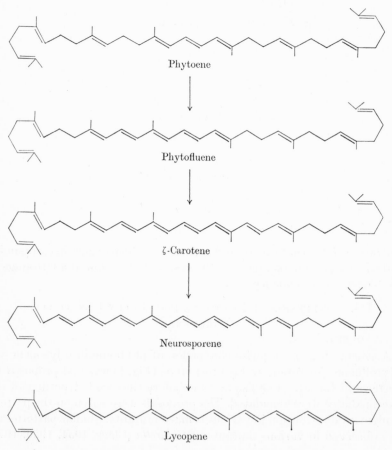

FIG. 5. The conversion of phytoene into lycopene.

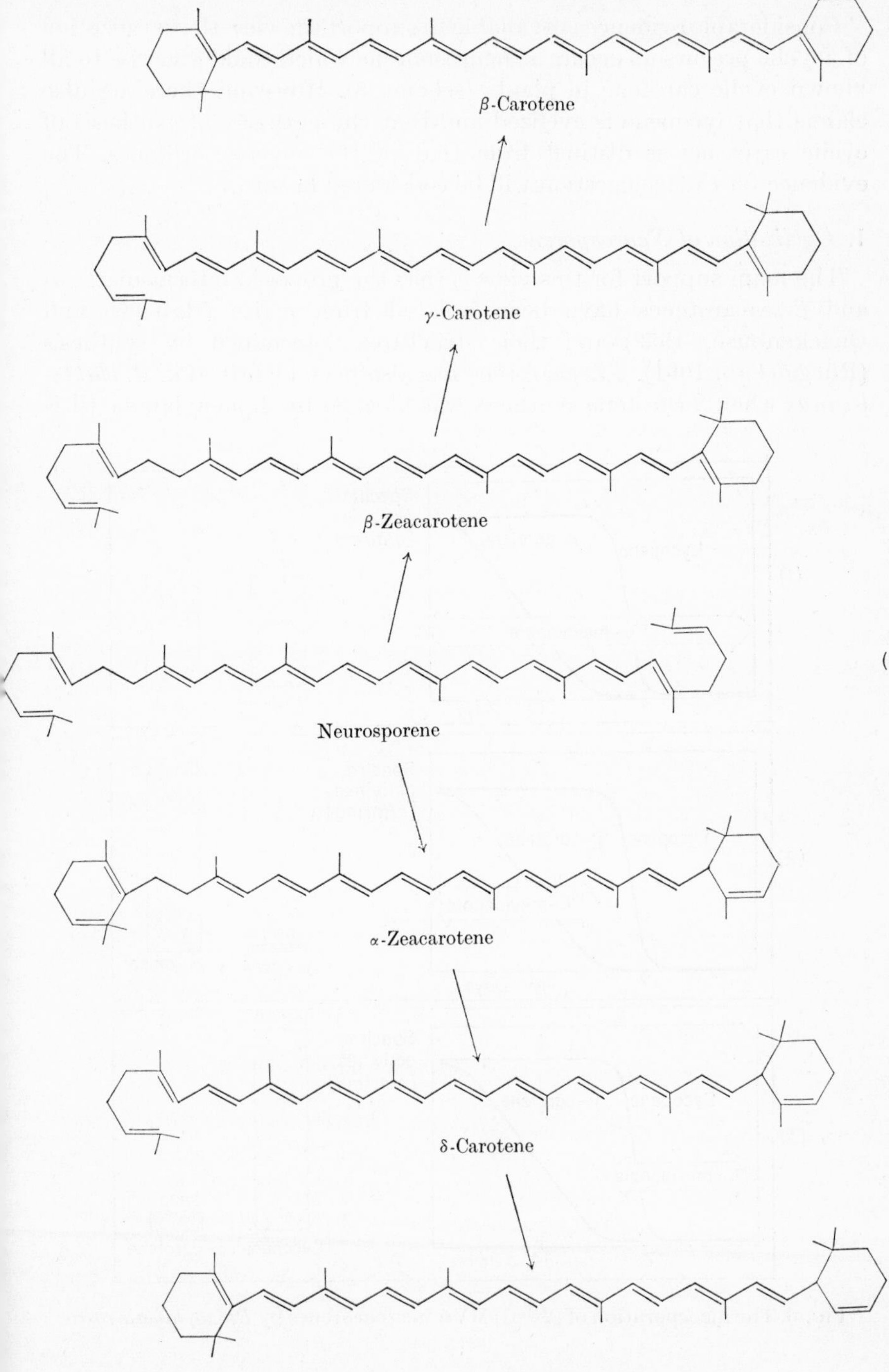

β-Carotene

γ-Carotene

β-Zeacarotene

Neurosporene

(8)

α-Zeacarotene

δ-Carotene

B. CYCLIC CAROTENES

Considerable evidence is available to support the view that cyclization of acyclic precursors occurs at neurosporene which could give rise to all known cyclic carotene in plants (scheme 8). However, there are also claims that lycopene is cyclized and that the pathway of synthesis of cyclic carotenes is distinct from that of the acyclic carotenes. The evidence for each suggestion will be considered in turn.

1. *Cyclization of Neurosporene*

The main support for this view is that the proposed intermediates α- and β-zeacarotenes have been isolated from maize (Rabourn and Quackenbush, 1959) and their structures determined by synthesis (Rüegg *et al.*, 1961). β-Zeacarotene has also been identified in *P. blakesleeanus* when β-carotene synthesis was blocked by diphenylamine [it is

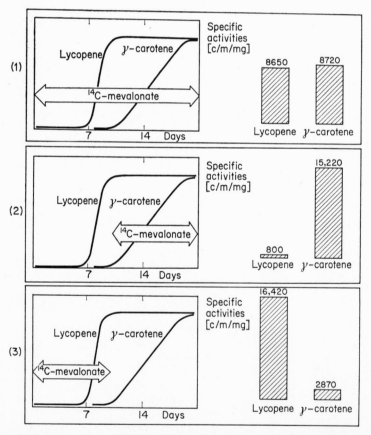

Fig. 6. The incorporation of [2-14C] MVA into carotenes by *Rhizophlyctis rosea*.

identical with pigment "X" of Goodwin and Osman, 1953]; on removal of diphenylamine β-carotene synthesis is resumed and a kinetic study of the pigment changes suggests that β-zeacarotene is an intermediate (Davies *et al.*, 1963b). β-Zeacarotene is also present in certain *Rhodotorula* spp. (Simpson, 1964). Claes (1958) found that her mutant 5/520 of *Chlorella vulgaris* when grown in the dark synthesized phytoene and other partly saturated carotenoids; on illumination β-carotene and an unidentified pigment "X" appear at the expense of phytoene etc. From the published properties of the two pigments it is likely that "X" is β-zeacarotene.

Other support for neurosporene as the branch-point is essentially negative, in the sense that evidence has been obtained that in a number of systems lycopene is not cyclized to β-carotene. For example (a) lyco-pene synthesis is inhibited in tomatoes ripened above 30° whilst β-carotene synthesis is unaffected (Goodwin and Jamikorn, 1952); the aquatic fungus *Rhizophlyctis rosea* synthesizes lycopene during the early stages of growth whilst older cultures contain both lycopene and γ-carotene; γ-carotene synthesis begins only after lycopene has reached a steady maximal level. Furthermore, if [2-^{14}C]MVA is added to a medium freshly inoculated with *R. rosea* and removed when the lycopene level has reached its maximum, then the γ-carotene eventually isolated is unlabelled although the lycopene is strongly labelled; on the other hand, if the addition of MVA is delayed until lycopene synthesis is at its maximum then the isolated γ-carotene is strongly labelled and the lycopene essentially unlabelled (Fig. 6) (B. H. Davies, quoted by Goodwin, 1963).

There is no evidence that cyclization occurs before neurosporene and B. H. Davies (unpublished experiments) has shown that cyclic ζ-carotene

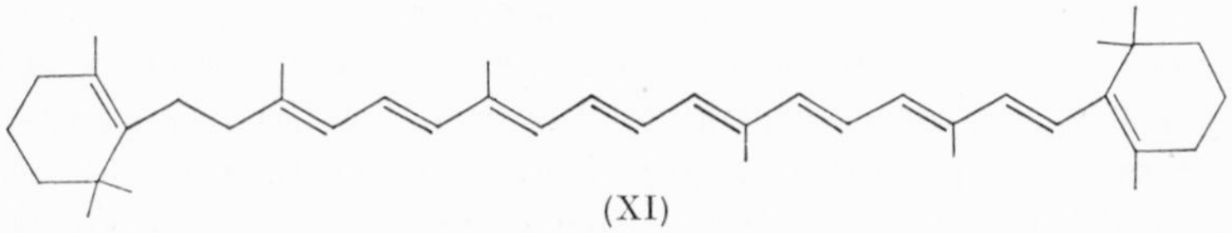

(XI)

(XI) does not occur in diphenylamine-inhibited *P. blakesleeanus*.

2. *Cyclization of Lycopene*

Evidence in favour of lycopene as the precursor of β-carotene includes the fact that in a tomato phenotype carrying the gene B obtained by back-crossing a *Lycopersicon esculentum* × *L. hirsutum* hybrid to *L. esculentum*, the usual high levels of lycopene are replaced by an equivalent amount of β-carotene (Lincoln and Porter, 1950); furthermore the fruit of the F1 generation of the high β-carotene strain contain more γ-carotene (a possible intermediate between β-carotene and lycopene) than do fruit from normal strains (Tomes *et al.*, 1954, 1956). However, the enhanced synthesis of β-carotene is, like lycopene synthesis, temperature-sensitive (Tomes, 1963); β-carotene synthesis in normal tomatoes is not temperature-sensitive (Goodwin and Jamikorn, 1952). All these observations suggest two pathways for β-carotene synthesis in the tomato, but provide no evidence for the participation of lycopene in either pathway. What appeared to be direct evidence for the participation of lycopene in β-carotene synthesis was provided by Decker and Uehleke (1961) who obtained isolated chloroplasts which converted [^{14}C]lycopene into β-carotene. Investigators in the author's laboratory have not yet confirmed these observations, but a recent short report indicates that lycopene is converted into γ-, δ- and β-carotenes by tomato fruit plastids and spinach leaf chloroplasts (Wells *et al.*, 1964).

3. *Other Pathways*

Genetic studies have been reported which indicate that the biosynthesis of cyclic and acyclic carotenoids are not directly linked. A pink mutant of *Corynebacterium michiganese* produces only acyclic carotenoids (lycopene and spirilloxanthin), and an orange mutant only cyclic carotenoids (β-carotene, cryptoxanthin and canthaxanthin). The wild strain, on the other hand, produces both types of pigment and a red back mutant only lycopene (Saperstein *et al.*, 1954); this suggests separate genetic control. Similar results have been obtained with *Rhodotorula mucilaginosa* by Villoutreix (1960). The native strain synthesizes mainly torulene and torularhodin, which are γ-carotene derivatives, whilst a mutant synthesizes β-carotene to the same extent as torularhodin is produced in the native strain. However, Simpson *et al.* (1964) have shown the same effect in *Rhodotorula gracilis* grown at different temperatures; at 5° β-carotene is the major pigment whilst at 25° β-carotene, torularhodin and torulene are present in approximately equal amounts; at both temperatures γ-carotene is at about the same level. This suggests that γ-carotene is the precursor of both β-carotene and torulin and torularhodin, and that a temperature-sensitive step subsequent to γ-carotene regulates the channelling of γ-carotene into either torulene and torularhodin or β-carotene (scheme 9).

Although the logic of the view that phytoene is the precursor of all carotenoids is compelling, and has an analogy in the triterpenoids, all of which arise from squalene, there are suggestions in the literature that other pathways exist. The incorporation of [^{14}C]-mevalonate into phytoene and β-carotene in *Neurospora crassa* does not follow a precursor/ product relationship (Krzeminsky and Quackenbush, 1960); further- more, if cells of *Rhodotorula mucilaginosa* are grown in the presence of 2-hydroxydiphenyl they are colourless and contain small amounts of all the phytoene series eccept phytofluene; if the cells are washed free from inhibitor and resuspended in phosphate buffer then β-carotene, torulene and torularhodin are synthesized but not apparently from the phytoene series (Villoutreix, 1960).

In the early work on the diphenylamine effect on *Phycomyces*, it appeared that in resuspended colourless cultures β-carotene was not being formed at the expense of the phytoene series (Goodwin, 1952); our later work indicates that such formation does occur (Davies *et al.*, 1963b) and there was never doubt that the precursor was endogenous although the presence of glucose in the resuspension medium was necessary for β-carotene synthesis; Braithwaite and Goodwin (1960) showed that if diphenylamine-inhibited cultures were grown in the presence of [^{14}C]mevalonate, then the β-carotene subsequently syn- thesized by washed suspensions was highly labelled.

IV. Formation of Xanthophylls

Almost all available evidence points to the insertion of oxygen to form xanthophylls as a late step in the biosynthetic sequence. Reports that xanthophylls are reduced to β-carotene by isolated chloroplasts (Costes, 1963) require confirmation.

Mutant 5/520 of *Chlorella vulgaris* synthesizes mainly phytoene when grown in the dark under heterotrophic conditions; on illumination in the absence of oxygen it synthesizes coloured carotenes; if the cultures are then placed in the dark in the presence of oxygen the formation of xanthophylls occurs which is parallelled by the disappearance of carotenes (Claes, 1957, 1959).

With the help of $^{18}O_2$ and $H_2^{18}O$ Yamamoto *et al.* (1962a) demons- trated that the oxygen in lutein arose in *Chlorella* from molecular oxygen and not from water; on the other hand, the oxygen in the epoxy group of violaxanthin was derived from the oxygen of water. One of the oxygen atoms in the carboxyl group of torularhodin comes from mole- cular oxygen (Simpson, 1963). This agrees with the hypothesis that the biochemical hydroxylation of a methyl group involves the direct participation of molecular oxygen and that subsequent oxidations involve the oxygen from water (Gillett, 1959) (scheme 10).

$$R.CH_3 \xrightarrow{O_2} RCH_2OH \xrightarrow{H_2O} RCOOH \qquad (10)$$

β-Carotene epoxides accumulate at the expense of β-carotene in excised tomato leaves kept in the dark in the absence of CO_2 (Glover and Redfearn, 1953). The interrelationship indicated in scheme 11 was observed in spinach leaves by Yamamoto et al. (1962b) and in *Euglena* by Krinsky (1962). No changes were observed in β-carotene, lutein or

$$\text{Violaxanthin} \underset{\text{Dark,O}_2}{\overset{\text{Light,N}_2}{\rightleftarrows}} \text{Antheraxanthin} \underset{\text{Dark,O}_2}{\overset{\text{Light,N}_2}{\rightleftarrows}} \text{Zeaxanthin} \qquad (11)$$

neoxanthin by Yamamoto et al. (1962a, b). This is in contrast with the earlier findings of Blass et al. (1959) and Sapozhnikov et al. (1959) who found a relationship between violaxanthin and lutein. Recently Bamji and Krinsky (1963) have demonstrated a conversion of antheraxanthin into zeaxanthin in lyophilized cells of *E. gracilis* to which FMN and NADPH had been added. Chloroplasts prepared by sonic oscillation of lyophilized cells require in addition to FMN and NADPH a heat-stable factor, now identified as malic acid (Bamji and Krinsky, 1964), from buffer-extracted cells for full activity. Malic acid is a source of reducing power.

Perhaps the most convincing demonstration of the late appearance of oxygen in the biosynthetic sequence leading to xanthophylls has been obtained from studies on photosynthetic bacteria.

Rhodopseudomonas spheroides when grown under anaerobic conditions produces mainly spheroidene (XII); on aeration of the cultures this pigment is almost quantitatively converted into spheroidenone (XIII) (van Niel, 1947; Goodwin et al., 1955, 1956; Davis et al., 1961; Shneour, 1962a). As mutants of *R. spheroides* have been obtained which accumulate

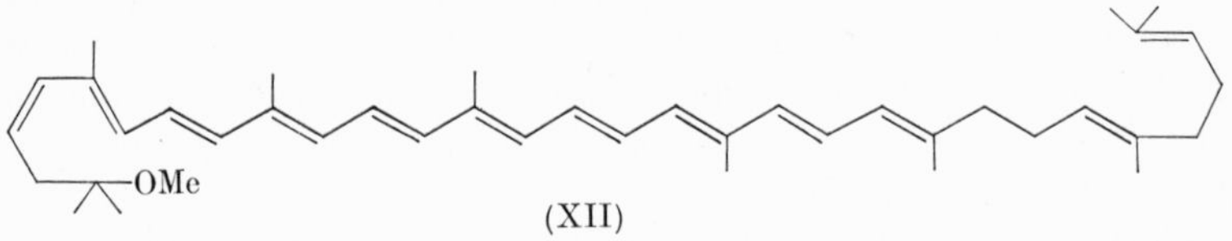

(XII)

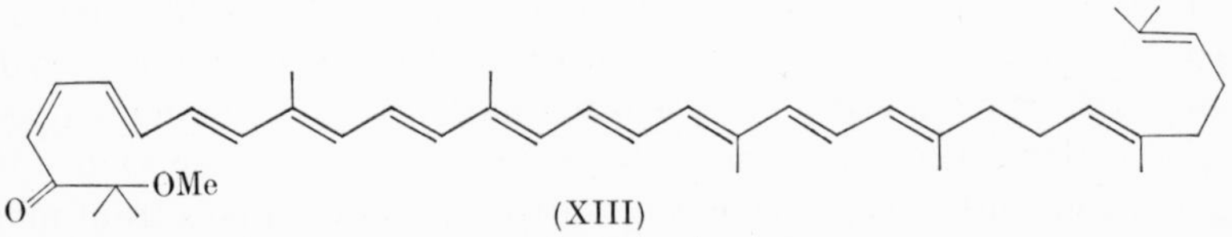

(XIII)

chloroxanthin (1-hydroxy-1,2-dihydro-neurosporene) (Nakayama, 1958; Davis et al., 1961) the main pathway (full lines) is almost certainly as indicated in scheme 12; a possible secondary pathway, where "hydroxy R" is demethylated spheroidenone, is indicated by dotted lines. With the use of $^{18}O_2$, Shneour (1962b) has demonstrated that the oxygen of spheroidenone arises from molecular oxygen, but the mechanism

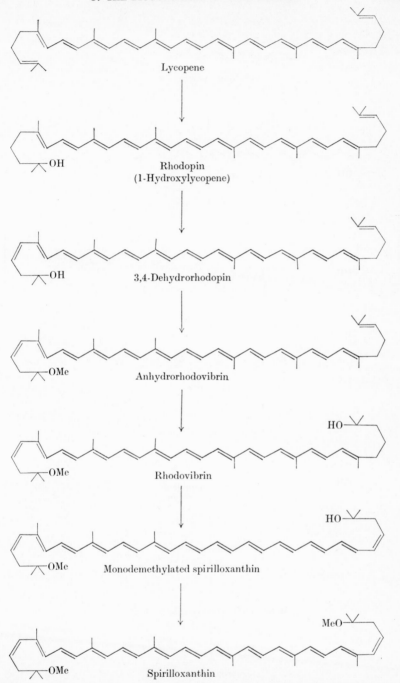

Lycopene

Rhodopin
(1-Hydroxylycopene)

3,4-Dehydrorhodopin

Anhydrorhodovibrin

Rhodovibrin

Monodemethylated spirilloxanthin

Spirilloxanthin

FIG. 7. The conversion of lycopene into spirilloxanthin in *Rhodospirillum rubrum*.

6

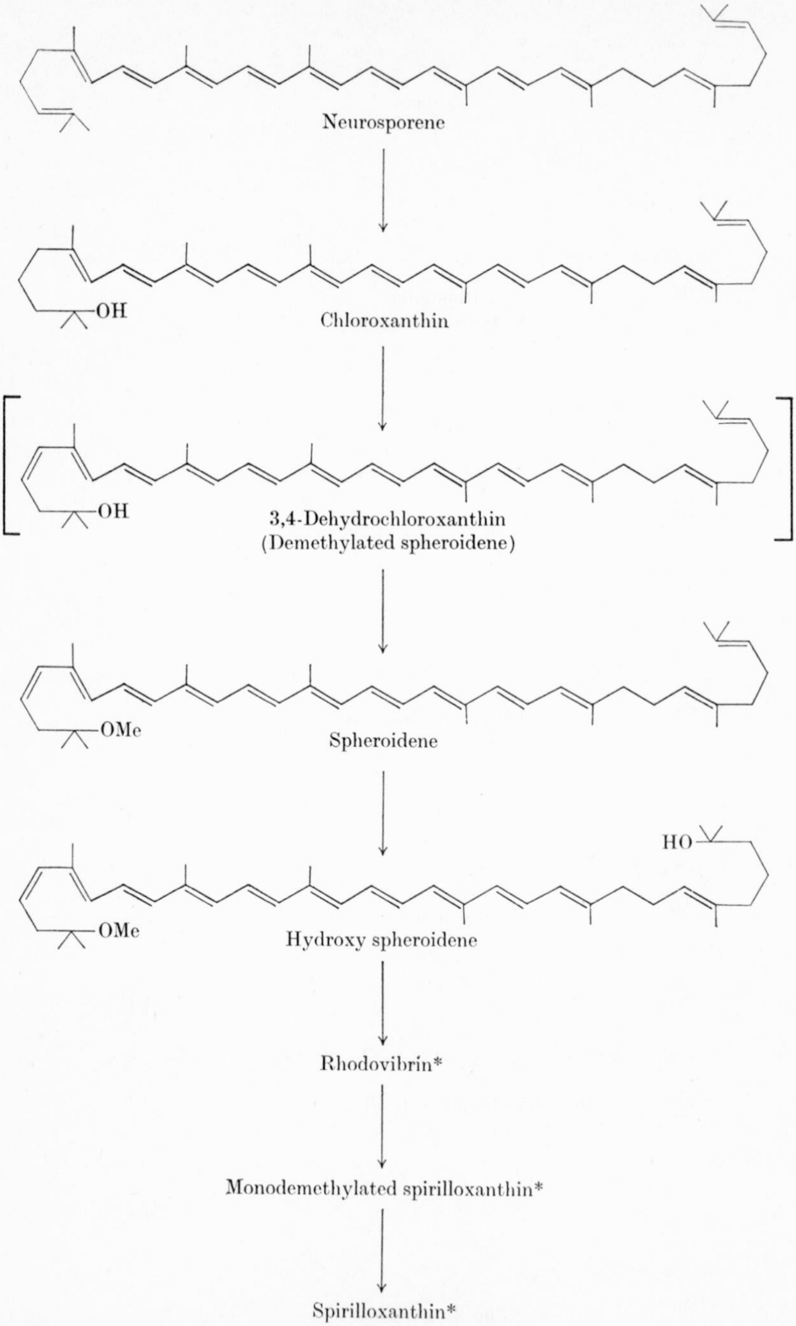

FIG. 8. The probable stepwise conversion of neurosporene into spirilloxanthin in *Rhodopseudomonas gelatinosa* (Eimhjellen and Jensen, 1964).

* For structures see Fig. 7.

eurosporene ———→ Chloroxanthin ———→ 3,4-Dehydrochloroxanthin ———→ Spheroidene

$$\begin{array}{ccc} & \downarrow ? & & \downarrow \\ \text{"Hydroxy R"} & \text{-----------→} & \text{Spheroidenone} \end{array} \quad (12)$$

involved is unknown. A very similar transformation which converts spirilloxanthin into 2-keto spirilloxanthin has been reported to occur on introducing oxygen into cultures of *Rhodopseudomonas gelatinosa* (Eimhjellen and Jensen, 1964). One of the most interesting recent developments in the studies of Jensen and her associates on the carotenoids of photosynthetic bacteria is the discovery of certain keto-derivatives in obligate anaerobes, e.g. warmingone in *Chromatium warmingii* Migula (Jensen and Schmidt, 1963) and okenone in *Chromatium okenii* Perty (Schmidt *et al.*, 1963). A possible mechanism for this reaction, a hydroxylation followed by the oxidation of the allylic hydroxyl group, [scheme 13] has been suggested by Jensen (1963b).

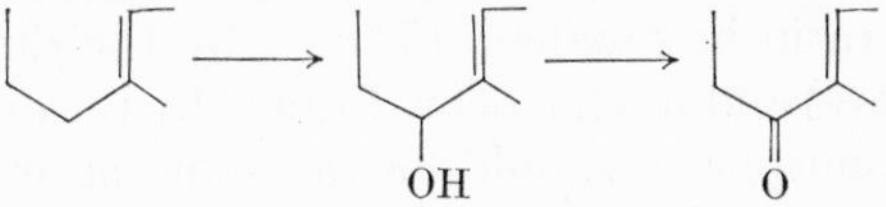

$$(13)$$

The pattern of synthesis of spirilloxanthin from lycopene in *Rhodospirillum rubrum* appears to be that indicated in Fig. 7, although none of the steps has yet been carried out enzymatically all the proposed intermediates have been detected and their structures determined (see e.g. Jensen, 1963a); kinetic studies also point in this direction (van Niel *et al.*, 1956; Jensen *et al.*, 1958). Similar observations have been observed with the purple sulphur bacterium *Chromatium* strain D (Benedict *et al.*, 1961) and *Chromatium vinosum* (Schmidt, 1963). Recently Eimhjellen and Jensen (1964) have shown that spirilloxanthin can also arise from neurosporene via chloroxanthin,3,4-dehydrochloroxanthin and spheroidene (Fig. 8).

V. STEREOSPECIFICITY OF CAROTENOID BIOSYNTHESIS

In the isomerization of isopentenyl pyrophosphate to dimethylallyl pyrophosphate a proton is lost from the carbon which originated from C-4 of mevalonic acid (scheme 5; p. 150). A similar loss of a proton occurs at each subsequent addition of isopentenyl pyrophosphate in the formation of geranyl pyrophosphate (scheme 6; p. 151), farnesyl pyrophosphate and geranylgeranyl pyrophosphate. As C-4 of mevalonic acid is a *meso* carbon atom [Caabd] the possibility existed that the enzymes concerned with the ejection of the proton from C-4 removed it stereospecifically according to the Ogston principle. This could only be tested by making C-4 asymmetric by replacing one of the hydrogens stereospecifically by tritium or deuterium. In an investigation as elegant as one could imagine Cornforth and Popják and their colleagues (Cornforth *et al.*, 1964) have synthesized two species of mevalonic acid [2-^{14}C]-4R[4-T]MVA (XIV) and [2-^{14}C]-4S[4-T]MVA (XV) in which the absolute configuration at C-4 is R* and S* respectively. If the loss of

$$
\begin{array}{cc}
\text{HOOC}\overset{*}{\underset{H_2}{C}}\!-\!\underset{T}{\overset{CH_3}{C}}\!-\!\underset{H}{\overset{OH}{C}}\!-\!CH_2OH & \text{HOOC}\overset{*}{\underset{H_2}{C}}\!-\!\underset{H}{\overset{CH_3}{C}}\!-\!\underset{T}{\overset{OH}{C}}\!-\!CH_2OH \\
(\text{XIV}) & (\text{XV})
\end{array}
$$

hydrogen at C-4 during the isomerization of isopentenyl pyrophosphate to dimethylallyl pyrophosphate and during the subsequent additions of further isopentenyl residues is stereospecific in the same sense in each case then the T/^{14}C ratio in squalene (formed by the dimerization of farnesyl pyrophosphate) and in phytoene (formed by the dimerization of geranylgeranyl pyrophosphate) should be the same as in the starting material with one species, and zero with the other. If the loss of hydrogen were not stereospecific but merely a random reaction then the ratio would be half that of the starting substrate in each case. There are other intermediate possibilities which need not be discussed. Through the generosity of Drs. Cornforth and Popják this view has been tested in the author's laboratory. With carrot root slices it has been found that the T/^{14}C ratio in phytoene synthesized in the presence of [2-^{14}C]-4R[4-T]-MVA was identical with that of the starting material; when [2-^{14}C]-4S[4-T]MVA was the substrate essentially no tritium appeared in the phytoene and the T/^{14}C ratio was zero (Goodwin and Williams, 1964); that is the 4R hydrogen is specifically retained. The same results obtained with the squalene synthesized by the carrot root preparations; this corroborated the observations of Cornforth *et al.* (1964) on squalene synthesized by rat liver preparations.

The isomerization of isopentenyl pyrophosphate to dimethylallyl pyrophosphate and its condensation with isopentenyl pyrophosphate can now be more fully described (scheme 14 and 15).

It is interesting to note that the configuration around the isolated double bonds in squalene and phytoene is *trans*. In rubber it is *cis*, and in the biosynthesis of rubber in *Hevea* sp. it is the 4S hydrogen of mevalonic acid which is retained whilst the 4R hydrogen is specifically lost (Archer *et al.*, 1964).

* The nomenclature of Cahn and Ingold.

$$
\begin{array}{c}
\text{CH}_3 \\
\diagdown \\
\text{C--C--CH}_2\text{O--}\textcircled{P}\text{--}\textcircled{P} \\
\diagup \quad | \quad | \\
\text{H}^+\ \text{CH}_2 \ \text{H} \ \text{H}
\end{array}
\longrightarrow
\begin{array}{c}
\text{CH}_3 \\
\diagdown \\
\overset{+}{\text{C}}\text{--C--CH}_2\text{O--}\textcircled{P}\text{--}\textcircled{P} \\
\diagup \quad | \quad | \\
\text{CH}_3 \ \text{H} \ \text{H}
\end{array}
\xrightarrow{\ \text{H}^+\ }
$$

$$
\begin{array}{c}
\text{CH}_3 \\
\diagdown \\
\text{C=CHCH}_2\text{O--}\textcircled{P}\text{--}\textcircled{P} \\
\diagup \\
\text{CH}_3
\end{array}
\qquad (14)
$$

$$
\begin{array}{c}
\text{CH}_3 \quad\quad \text{O--}\textcircled{P}\text{--}\textcircled{P} \quad\quad \text{CH}_3 \\
\diagdown \quad\quad\quad | \\
\text{C=CHCH}_2 \quad\quad \text{CH}_2\text{=C--C--CH}_2\text{O--}\textcircled{P}\text{--}\textcircled{P} \\
\diagup \quad\quad\quad\quad\quad\quad | \quad | \\
\text{CH}_3 \quad\quad\quad\quad\quad\quad\quad \text{H} \ \text{H}
\end{array}
\longrightarrow \quad \textcircled{P}\text{--}\textcircled{P}
$$

$$
\begin{array}{c}
\text{CH}_3 \quad\quad\quad \text{CH}_3 \\
\diagdown \quad\quad\quad\quad | \\
\text{C=CHCH}_2\text{CH}_2\overset{+}{\text{C}}\text{--C--CH}_2\text{O--}\textcircled{P}\text{--}\textcircled{P} \\
\diagup \quad\quad\quad\quad\quad | \quad | \\
\text{CH}_3 \quad\quad\quad\quad \text{H} \ \text{H}
\end{array}
\xrightarrow{\ \text{H}^+\ }
\begin{array}{c}
\text{CH}_3 \quad\quad\quad\quad \text{CH}_3 \\
\diagdown \quad\quad\quad\quad\quad | \\
\text{C=CHCH}_2\text{CH}_2\text{C=CHCH}_2\text{O--}\textcircled{P}\text{--}\textcircled{P} \\
\diagup \\
\text{CH}_3
\end{array}
\qquad (15)
$$

VI. REGULATION OF CAROTENOID BIOSYNTHESIS

A. NON-PHOTOSYNTHETIC TISSUES

A number of factors regulating carotenoid biosynthesis in non-photosynthetic tissues have been reported but most are still in the descriptive stage of investigation; very little work has yet been carried out at the biochemical level.

1. *Temperature*

The effect of temperature on lycopene and β-carotene synthesis in normal tomatoes has already been discussed in detail (p. 157). It will be remembered that above 30° lycopene but not β-carotene synthesis is inhibited; exposure to this temperature has no permanent effect on the lycopene-synthesizing system, because on returning fruit held at 30° to lower temperatures synthesis of lycopene starts up again (Went *et al.*, 1942). This explains why although usually exposed to wide temperature fluctuations, tomatoes ripen normally on the vine; the temperature at night usually drops below 30° (Sayre *et al.*, 1953).

In the mould *Phycomyces blakesleeanus* (Friend and Goodwin, 1954) and the yeasts *Rhodotorula rubra* and *R. penaus* (Nakayama *et al.*, 1954) the pigments synthesized over a wide temperature range are essentially the same, but quantitatively less at lower temperatures.

However, on one red yeast *R. gracilis* qualitative differences are observed (Skoda, 1951; Nakayama *et al.*, 1954; Simpson *et al.*, 1964). At low temperatures (8°), β and γ-carotenes predominate, whilst at higher temperature the more oxidized compounds torulene and torularhodin predominate (see also p. 158).

2. *Light*

Light increases quantitatively the level of synthesis in a number of moulds, e.g. *Phycomyces blakesleeanus* (Garton *et al.*, 1951; Chichester *et al.*, 1954), *Penicillium sclerotiorium* (Mase *et al.*, 1957). In others it triggers off carotenogenesis as in *Neurospora crassa* (Zalokar, 1955) and *Fusarium oxysporum* (Carlile, 1956). For example, if dark grown cultures of *N. crassa* are exposed to light and oxygen for a short period (1 min) and returned to darkness then, under aerobic conditions, pigment synthesis reaches a level very close to that found in continuously illuminated cultures. The effect is not temperature-dependent. In other fungi light has a qualitative effect on carotenoids; in *R. gracilis* for example, the ratio $\alpha + \beta$-carotene:torulene changes from 1·67:1 in dark grown cultures to 2·29:1 in the light (Praus, 1952).

3. *Metabolic Control*

In higher plants and moulds carotenoids are synthesized alongside sterols and related triterpenoids; the synthetic sequence for both pathways share common intermediates up to C_{15} (farnesyl pyrophosphate). An important question which can only be answered at the metabolic level is how does an organism regulate the flow of intermediates from C_{15} to sterols and to carotenoids. Only one investigation has been reported on nonphotosynthetic organisms; Yokoyama *et al.* (1962) obtained a cell-free system from *Phycomyces blakesleeanus* which would synthesize both ergosterol and β-carotene from mevalonate; NAD was required for ergosterol synthesis but not for β-carotene. The availability of NAD might therefore be a point at which metabolic control can be exerted.

B. PHOTOSYNTHETIC TISSUES

1. *Temperature*

Only one detailed investigation has been carried out on the effect of temperature on carotenoid synthesis in leaves in relation to the photoperiodicity to which plants are normally subjected. Bandurski *et al.* (1953) found that if the night temperature is maintained at 17° and the day temperature varied, then carotenoid synthesis decreases as the temperature is lowered, so that a day temperature of 4° is physiologically equivalent to darkness. At a constant day temperature (17°) variations in the night temperature has little effect on carotenogenesis, although at higher temperatures the leaves are lighter coloured because of marked changes in the anatomy of the leaf.

2. Light

In the absence of light *Chlorella vulgaris* will grow heterotrophically and produce as much carotenoid as in darkness (Goodwin, 1954). On the other hand heterotrophically grown *Euglena gracilis* v. *bacillaris* is "etiolated" and only produces small amounts of carotenoids (Goodwin and Jamikorn, 1954). The optimum light intensity for carotenogenesis on the blue-green algae *Anacystis nidulans* and *Anabaena* spp. is 400–800 ft candles (Handke, 1954).

It is well known that etiolated seedlings produce only traces of carotenoids, the majority of which are xanthophylls (Kay and Phinney, 1956; Goodwin, 1958; Goodwin and Phagpolngarm, 1960); on illumination the carotenoids are rapidly synthesized as the plants green up (Goodwin, 1958). The optimum light intensity for carotenogenesis in bean leaves is 600 ft candles (Bandurski, 1949).

If 4-day etiolated maize seedlings are exposed to red light (660 mμ) for 5 min and returned to darkness then, on examination 24 h later they contain more carotenoids than control seedlings kept continuously in the dark. This effect is nullified if the red light treatment is followed by exposure to far red light (760 mμ) for 5 min; this indicates that the response is phytochrome-mediated (Cohen and Goodwin, 1962). Similar effects are observed in peas (Henshall and Goodwin, 1964) and dwarf beans (unpublished work quoted by Mego and Jagendorf, 1961).

3. Metabolic Control

Seedlings synthesize considerable amounts of sterols during germination in the dark (Davies *et al.*, 1964) but only traces of carotenoids normally appear (see previous section). On illumination, however, as the seedlings green up and functional chloroplasts develop there is a massive synthesis not only of carotenoids but of compounds, essential to photosynthesis, which have terpenoid side chains—chlorophylls (phytol), plastoquinone (solanesol (C-45)), vitamin K_1 (phytol) and tocopherols (phytol); there is, however, no concomitant synthesis of sterol. A similar situation is observed in *Euglena gracilis* (Threlfall and Goodwin, 1964). A major problem is how light causes the terpenoid intermediates to be channelled away from sterol synthesis into synthesis of "photosynthetic terpenoids", which include the carotenoids. Recent observations in our laboratory have suggested a possible mechanism, the reality or otherwise of which is being actively investigated (Goodwin and Mercer, 1963; Goodwin, 1964b). If etiolated seedlings are excised and placed in

[2-^{14}C]mevalonate and allowed to green up then very little if any activity appears in β-carotene (Goodwin, 1958; Treharne *et al.*, 1964), in the phytol of chlorophyll (Mercer and Goodwin, 1962), and in plastoquinone (Griffiths *et al.*, 1964) (relatively rather more appears in the last compound) although they are all being rapidly synthesized; on the other hand the sterols, sterol precursors such as lanosterol and squalene, and other triterpenoids are highly labelled (Mercer and Goodwin, 1963). Conversely, if the same experiments are carried out with $^{14}CO_2$ instead of [2-^{14}C]MVA then the photosynthetic terpenoids are highly labelled and the sterols etc. only slightly labelled.

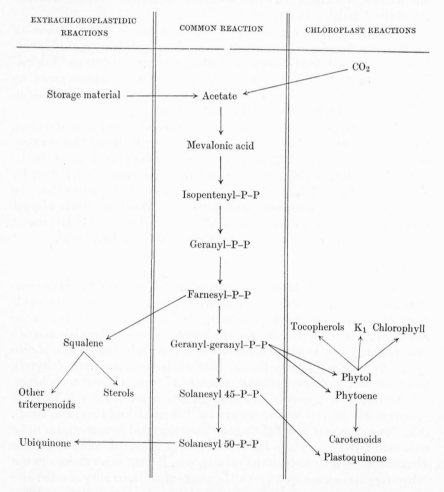

FIG. 9. Proposed compartmentalization of terpenoid biosynthesis in higher plants.

These observations have led to the view that the regulation of terpenoid synthesis in developing seedlings is achieved essentially by compartmentalization which allows two separate sites of terpenoid synthesis to exist. The sterols and pentacyclic triterpenes are synthesized extraplastidically whilst the "photosynthetic terpenoids" are synthesized in the chloroplast. Both sites of synthesis are considered to have the series of enzymes which will convert acetate (from storage material or CO_2) into the various acyclic terpenoid pyrophosphates (geranyl, farnesyl, geranylgeranyl, solanesyl, etc.). Specifically localized enzymes then form the specialized products, e.g. squalene in the cytoplasm, phytoene in the chloroplast. The overall scheme proposed is outlined in Fig. 9. Goodwin and Mercer (1963) further suggest that the chloroplast is relatively impermeable to mevalonic acid in either direction. On this view, mevalonate formed in the germinating seedling from storage material is converted into sterols which are incorporated into the membrane of the developing plastids; the failure of mevalonate to penetrate into the plastid means that it cannot be used to make photosynthetic terpenoids at a time when they are not required. Conversely, the fixation of CO_2 into mevalonate during the development of the chloroplasts from the plastids on illumination permits rapid synthesis of photosynthetic terpenoids, without any loss of essential intermediates to the cytoplasm.

REFERENCES

Agranoff, B. W., Eggerer, H., Henning, U., and Lynen, F. (1959). *J. Amer. chem. Soc.* **81**, 68.
Anderson, D. G., and Porter, J. W. (1962). *Arch. Biochem. Biophys.* **97**, 509.
Anderson, D. G., Nogard, D. W., and Porter, J. W. (1960). *Arch. Biochem. Biophys.* **88**, 68.
Archer, B. L., Barnard, D., and Cockbain, E. G. (1964). *Proc. roy. Soc.* B (in press).
Bamji, M. S., and Krinsky, N. I. (1963). *Abstr. Amer. chem. Soc.* 6-C (September).
Bamji, M. S., and Krinsky, N. I. (1964). *Fed. Proc.* **23**, 430.
Bandurski, R. S. (1949). *Bot. Gaz.* **111**, 95.
Bandurski, R. S., Scott, F. M., Pflug, M., and Went, F. W. (1953). *Amer. J. Bot.* **40**, 41.
Bataille, J., and Loomis, W. K. (1961). *Biochim. biophys. Acta* **51**, 545.
Beeler, D., and Porter, J. W. (1962). *Biochem. Biophys. Res. Comm.* **8**, 367.
Benedict, C. R., Fuller, R. C., and Bergeron, J. A. (1961). *Biochim. biophys. Acta* **54**, 525.
Blass, U., Anderson, J. M., and Calvin, M. (1959). *Plant Physiol.* **34**, 329.
Bloch, K., Chaykin, S., and Phillips, A. H. (1959). *Fed. Proc.* **18**, 193.
Braithwaite, G. D., and Goodwin, T. W. (1957). *Biochem. J.* **67**, 13P.
Braithwaite, G. D., and Goodwin, T. W. (1960). *Biochem. J.* **76**, 1, 5, 194.
Carlile, M. J. (1956). *J. gen. Microbiol.* **14**, 643.
Chichester, C. O., and Nakayama, T. O. M. (1963). *In* "Biogenesis of Natural Compounds" (P. Benfield, ed.), Pergamon Press, Oxford.

Chichester, C. O., Nakayama, T., Mackinney, G., and Goodwin, T. W. (1955). *J. biol. Chem.* **214**, 575.

Chichester, C. O., Yokoyama, H., Nakayama, T. O. M., Lukton, A., and Mackinney, G. (1959). *J. biol. Chem.* **234**, 598.

Chichester, C. O., Wong, P. S., and Mackinney, G. (1954). *Plant Physiol.* **29**, 238.

Claes, H. (1954). *Z. Naturf.* **9b**, 461.

Claes, H. (1956). *Z. Naturf.* **11b**, 260.

Claes, H. (1957). *Z. Naturf.* **12b**, 401.

Claes, H. (1958). *Z. Naturf.* **13b**, 222.

Claes, H. (1959). *Z. Naturf.* **14b**, 4.

Cohen, R. Z., and Goodwin, T. W. (1962). *Phytochemistry* **1**, 67.

Coon, M. J., Kupiecki, F. P., Dekker, E. E., Schlesinger, M. J. and del Campillo, A. (1959). *In* "Biosynthesis of Terpenes and Sterols" (G. E. W. Wolstenholme and M. O'Connor, eds.), Churchill, London.

Cornforth, J. W., Cornforth, R. H., Donninger, C., and Popják, G. J. (1964). *Proc. roy. Soc. B.* (in press).

Costes, C. (1963). *Ann. Physiol. veg.* **5**, 115.

Davies, B. H., Jones, D., and Goodwin, T. W. (1963a). *Biochem. J.* **87**, 326.

Davies, B. H., Villoutreix, J., Williams, R. J. H., and Goodwin, T. W. (1963b), *Biochem. J.* **89**, 96P.

Davies, W. E., Goodwin, T. W., and Mercer, E. I. (1964). *Analyst* (in press).

Davis, J. B., Jackman, L. M., Siddons, P. T., and Weedon, B. C. L. (1961). *Proc. chem. Soc.* p. 261.

Decker, K., and Uehleke, H. (1961). *Hoppe-Seyl. Z.* **323**, 61.

de Waard, A., Phillips, A. H., and Bloch, K. (1959). *J. Amer. chem. Soc.* **81**, 2913.

Dituri, F., Rabinowitz, J. L., Hullin, R. P., and Gurin, S. (1957). *J. biol. Chem.* **229**, 826.

Eberle, M., and Arigoni, D. (1960). *Helv. chim. acta* **43**, 1508.

Eimhjellen, K. E., and Jensen, S. L. (1964). *Biochim. biophys. Acta* **82**, 21.

Ferguson, J. J., Jr., Durr, I. F., and Rudney, H. (1959). *Proc. nat. Acad. Sci., Wash.* **45**, 499.

Folkers, K., Shunk, C. H., Linn, B. O., Robinson, F. M., Wittreich, P. E., Huff, J. W., Gilfillan, J. L., and Skeggs, H. R. (1959). *In* "Biosynthesis of Terpenes and Sterols" (G. E. W. Wolstenholme and M. O'Connor, eds.), Churchill, London.

Friend, J. S., and Goodwin, T. W. (1954). *Biochem. J.* **57**, 434.

Garton, G. A., Goodwin, T. W., and Lijinsky, W. (1951). *Biochem. J.* **48**, 154.

Gillett, J. R. (1959). *J. biol. Chem.* **234**, 1939.

Glover, J., and Redfearn, E. R. (1953). *Biochem. J.* **54**, viii.

Goodwin, T. W. (1952). *Biochem. J.* **50**, 550.

Goodwin, T. W. (1954). *Experientia* **10**, 213.

Goodwin, T. W. (1958). *Biochem. J.* **70**, 503, 612.

Goodwin, T. W. (1959a). *Advanc. Enzymol.* **21**, 295.

Goodwin, T. W. (1959b). *In* "Biosynthesis of Terpenes and Sterols" (G. E. W. Wolstenholme and M. O'Connor, eds.), Churchill, London.

Goodwin, T. W. (1964). *In* "Rodd's Chemistry of Carbon Compounds" (in press).

Goodwin, T. W., and Jamikorn, M. (1952). *Nature, Lond.* **170**, 104.

Goodwin, T. W., and Jamikorn, M. (1954). *J. Protozool.* **1**, 216.

Goodwin, T. W., and Lijinsky, W. (1952). *Biochem. J.* **50**, 268.

Goodwin, T. W., and Mercer, E. I. (1963). *In* "The Control of Lipid Metabolism" (J. K. Grant, ed.), Academic Press, London.

Goodwin, T. W., and Osman, H. G. (1954). *Biochem. J.* **56**, 222.

Goodwin, T. W., and Osman, H. G. (1953). *Arch. Biochem. Biophys.* **47**, 215.

Goodwin, T. W., and Phagpolngarm, S. (1960). *Biochem. J.* **76**, 197.

Goodwin, T. W., and Williams, R. J. H. (1964). *Proc. roy. Soc. B.* (in press).

Goodwin, T. W., Land, D. G., and Osman, H. G. (1955). *Biochem. J.* **59**, 491.

Goodwin, T. W., Land, D. G., and Sissins, M. E. (1956). *Biochem. J.* **64**, 486.

Griffiths, W. T., Threlfall, D. R., and Goodwin, T. W. (1964). *Biochem. J.* **90**, 40P.

Grob, E. C. (1959). *In* "Biosynthesis of Terpenes and Sterols" (G. E. W. Wolsten-holme and M. O'Connor, eds.), Churchill, London.

Grob, E. C., and Boschetti, A. (1962). *Chimia* **16**, 15.

Grob, E. C., and Bütler, R. (1954). *Helv. chim. acta* **37**, 1908.

Grob, E. C., and Bütler, R. (1955). *Helv. chim. acta* **38**, 1313.

Grob, E. C., and Bütler, R. (1956). *Helv. chim. acta* **39**, 1975.

Grob, E. C., Kirschner, K., and Lynen, F. (1961). *Chimia* **15**, 308.

Handke, M. H. (1954). *Wiss. nat. Z. Martin Luther Univ. Halle-Wittenberg* **4**, 89.

Hellig, H., and Popják, G. (1961). *Biochem. J.* **80**, 41P.

Henning, U., Moslein, E. M., and Lynen, F. (1959). *Arch. Biochem. Biophys.* **83**, 259.

Henshall, J. D., and Goodwin, T. W. (1964). *Photochem. Photobiol.* (in press).

Jensen, S. L. (1963a). *Acta chem. Scand.* **17**, 500.

Jensen, S. L. (1963b). *In* "Bacterial Photosynthesis" (H. Gest, A. San Pietro and L. P. Vernon, eds.), Antioch Press, Ohio.

Jensen, S. L., Cohen-Bazire, G., Nakayama, T. O. M., and Stanier, R. Y. (1958). *Biochim. Biophys. Acta* **29**, 477.

Jensen, S. L., and Schmidt, K. (1963). *Arch. Mikrobiol.* **46**, 138.

Kay, R. E., and Phinney, B. (1956). *Plant Physiol.* **31**, 226.

Krinsky, N. I. (1962). *Fed. Proc.* **21**, 92.

Krzeminski, L. F., and Quackenbush, F. W. (1960). *Arch. Biochem. Biophys.* **88**, 267.

Levy, H. R., and Popják, G. (1960). *Biochem. J.* **75**, 417.

Lincoln, R. E., and Porter, J. W. (1950). *Genetics* **35**, 206.

Lindberg, M., Yuan, C., de Waard, A., and Bloch, K. (1962). *Biochemistry* **1**, 182.

Lotspeich, F. J., Krause, R. F., Lilly, V. G., and Barnett, H. L. (1959). *J. biol. Chem.* **234** 3109.

Lotspeich, F. J., Krause, R. F., Lilly, V. G., and Barnett, H. L. (1961). *Fed. Proc.* **20**, 269.

Lynen, F., Eggerer, H., Henning, U., and Kessel, I. (1958). *Angew. Chem.* **70**, 738.

Lynen, F., Agranoff, B. W., Eggerer, H., Henning, U., and Moslein, E. M. (1959). *Angew. Chem.* **71**, 657.

Mackinney, G., Chandler, B. V., and Lukton, A. (1958). *Comm. 4th Int. Cong. Biochem.* p. 130.

Mase, Y., Rabourn, W. J., and Quackenbush, F. W. (1957). *Arch. Biochem. Biophys.* **68**, 150.

Mego, J. L., and Jagendorf, A. T. (1961). *Biochim. biophys. Acta* **53**.

Mercer, E. I., and Goodwin, T. W. (1962). *Biochem. J.* **85**, 13P.

Mercer, E. I., and Goodwin, T. W. (1963). *Biochem. J.* **88**, 46P.

Mercer, E. I., Davies, B. H., and Goodwin, T. W. (1963). *Biochem. J.* **87**, 317.

Modi, V. V., and Patwa, D. K. (1961). *Enzymologia* **23**, 27.

Nakayama, T. O. M. (1958). *Arch. Biochem. Biophys.* **75**, 352, 356.

Nakayama, T. O. M., Mackinney, G., and Phaff, H. J. (1954). *Antonie van Leeuwenhoek J. Microbiol. Serol.* **20**, 217.

van Niel, C. B. (1947). *Leeuwenhoek ned Tijdschr.* **12**, 156.

van Niel, C. B., Goodwin, T. W., and Sissins, M. E. (1956). *Biochem. J.* **63**, 408.

Pennock, J. F., Hemming, F. W., and Morton, R. A. (1962). *Biochem. J.* **82**, 11P.

Popják, G., and Cornforth, J. W. (1960). *Advanc. Enzymol.* **22**, 281.

Porter, J. W., and Lincoln, R. E. (1950). *Arch. Biochem.* **27**, 390.

Praus, R. (1952). *Chem. Listy* **51**, 1559, 1939.

Purcell, A. E., Thompson, G. A., and Bonner, J. (1959). *J. biol. Chem.* **234**, 101.

Rabourn, W. J., and Quackenbush, F. W. (1959). *Arch. Biochem. Biophys.* **44**, 159.

Rilling, H. C. (1962). *Biochim. biophys. Acta* **65**, 156.

Rüegg, R., Schwieter, U., Ryser, G., Schudel, P., and Isler, O. (1961). *Helv. chim. acta* **44**, 985, 994.

Ruzicka, L. (1959). *Proc. chem. Soc.*, p. 341.

Ruzicka, L., Eschenmoser, A., and Heusser, H. (1953). *Experientia* **9**, 357.

Saperstein, S., Starr, M. P., and Filfus, J. A. (1954). *J. gen. Microbiol.* **10**, 85.

Sapozhnikov, D. I., Maeskaya, A. N., Krasovskaya-Antropora, T. A., Prialgruskaite, L. L., and Turchino, U. S. (1959). *Biokhimiya* **24**, 34.

Sayre, C. B., Robinson, W. B., and Wishnetzky, T. (1953). *Proc. Amer. Soc. hort. Sci.* **61**, 381.

Schmidt, K. (1963). *Arch. Mikrobiol.* **46**, 127.

Schmidt, K., Jensen, S. L., and Schlegel, H. G. (1963). *Arch. Mikrobiol.* **46**, 117.

Shneour, E. A. (1962a). *Biochim. biophys. Acta* **62**, 534.

Shneour, E. A. (1962b). *Biochim. biophys. Acta* **65**, 510.

Shneour, E. A., and Zabin, I. (1958). *J. biol. Chem.* **234**, 770.

Simpson, K. L. (1963). Ph.D. thesis, University of California.

Simpson, K. L., Nakayama, T. O. M., and Chichester, C. O. (1964). *Biochem. J.* (in press).

Skoda, J. (1951). *Chem. Listy* **41**, 43.

Steele, W. J., and Gurin, S. (1960). *J. biol. Chem.* **41**, 81.

Suzue, G. (1960). *Biochim. biophys. Acta* **45**, 616; *Arch. Biochem. Biophys.* **88**, 180.

Suzue, G. (1961). *Biochim. biophys. Acta* **50**, 593.

Tavormina, P. A., Gibbs, M. H., and Huff, J. W. (1956). *J. Amer. chem. Soc.* **78**, 4498.

Tchen, T. T. (1957). *J. Amer. chem. Soc.* **79**, 6345.

Tchen, T. T. (1958). *J. biol. Chem.* **233**, 1100.

Threlfall, D. R., and Goodwin, T. W. (1964). *Biochem. J.* **90**, 40P.

Tomes, M. L. (1963). *Bot. Gaz.* **124**, 180.

Tomes, M. L., Quackenbush, F. W., and McQuistan, M. (1954). *Genetics* **39**, 810.

Tomes, M. L., Quackenbush, F. W., and Kargl, T. E. (1956). *Bot. Gaz.* **117**, 248.

Treharne, K. J., Mercer, E. I., and Goodwin, T. W. (1964). *Biochem. J.* **90**, 39P.

Varma, T. N. R., and Chichester, C. O. (1962). *Arch. Biochem. Biophys.* **96**, 265.

Varma, T. N. R., Chichester, C. O., Nakayama, T., Lukton, A., and Mackinney, G. (1959). *Nature, Lond.* **183**, 188.

Villoutreix, J. (1960). *Biochim. biophys. Acta* **40**, 434, 442.

Wells, L. W., Schelble, W. J., and Porter, J. W. (1964). *Fed. Proc.* **23**, 426.

Went, F. W., Le Rosen, A., and Zechmeister, L. (1942). *Plant Physiol.* **17**, 91.

Witting, L. A., Knaus, H. J., and Porter, J. W. (1959). *Fed. Proc.* **18**, 353.

Wuhrmann, J. J., Yokoyama, H., and Chichester, C. O. (1957). *J. Amer. chem. Soc.* **79**, 4569.

Wuhrmann, J. J., Yokoyama, H., Simpson, K., Nakayama, T. O. M., and Chichester, C. O. (1961). *Nature, Lond.* **191**, 1299.

Yamamoto, H., Chichester, C. O., and Nakayama, T. O. M. (1962a). *Arch. Biochem. Biophys.* **96**, 645.

Yamamoto, H., Nakayama, T. O. M., and Chichester, C. O. (1962b). *Arch. Biochem. Biophys.* **97**, 168.

Yokoyama, H., Chichester, C. O., Nakayama, T. O. M., Lukton, A., and Mackinney, G. (1957). *J. Amer. chem. Soc.* **79**, 2029.

Yokoyama, H., Chichester, C. O., and Mackinney, G. (1960). *Nature, Lond.* **186**, 235.

Yokoyama, H., Yamamoto, H., Nakayama, T. O. M., Simpson, K., and Chichester, C. O. (1961). *Nature, Lond.* **191**, 1299.

Yokoyama, H., Nakayama, T. O. M., and Chichester, C. O. (1962). *J. biol. Chem.* **237**, 681.

Zalokar, M. (1955). *Arch. Biochem. Biophys.* **56**, 318.

Chapter 6

PHYCOBILINS

Colm Ó hEocha

Department of Biochemistry, University College, Galway, Ireland

I. Introduction

The phycobilins are tetrapyrroles which occur as prosthetic groups of photosynthetically-active conjugated proteins (biliproteins) in some groups of algae. None of the phycobilins has been crystallized as yet and our knowledge of them is based mainly on spectral studies, both as free pigments and as constituents of their parent biliproteins. These studies indicate that at least three phycobilins occur in nature as prosthetic groups of algal biliproteins, and while a definite structure cannot yet be assigned to any of them, it is possible to make some suggestions on the basis of the known structures of animal bile pigments, or bilins.

The biliproteins which have been found in algae are either blue (phycocyanins) or red (phycoerythrins), and they fluoresce red and orange, respectively. A phycocyanin was the first algal biliprotein to be studied. In 1836 von Esenbeck of Bonn reported that a blue colouring matter, probably related to the proteins, was released on autolysis of *Oscillatoria* sp. "Das über dem grünen schlämmingen Bodensatz stehende Wasser zeigte ein sehr schönes und auffallendes Farbenspiel. Es war von oben betrachtet blutroth und gegen das licht gehalten sehr schön himmelblau." Many subsequent workers referred to the beauty of the transmitted and fluorescent colours of the algal biliproteins (see, for example, Sorby, 1877). Because of their lability they have found little practical use, although there are some reports of local usage by communities living by the sea. According to Newton (1951), the Red Alga *Ceramium rubrum*, later a classical source of phycoerythrin for experimental purposes, was once used as a source of rouge by Hebridean girls.

The shades of colour or, specifically, the visible absorption spectra of biliproteins form a basis for a broad classification. All phycoerythrins

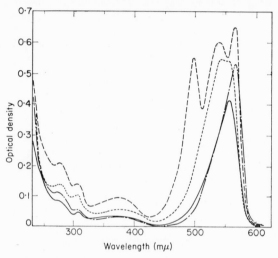

FIG. 1. Absorption spectra of aqueous solutions of phycoerythrins (pH 6–7):
— — —, R-phycoerythrin (*Ceramium rubrum*);
– – – –, B-phycoerythrin (*Porphyridium cruentum*);
–·–·–·–, C-phycoerythrin (*Phormidium persicinum*);
————, Cryptomonad phycoerythrin (*Hemiselmis rufescens*). (Ó hEocha, 1962).

have at least one absorption band between 540 and 570 mμ and all phycocyanins have an absorption band between 610 and 660 mμ. As more algae are screened for biliproteins the diversity of spectral types increases; the spectral characteristics of some of the more widely distributed biliproteins are given in Table I and Figs. 1 and 2. It should be noted that the ultra-violet spectra of phycoerythrins differ from those of phycocyanins in that they have a maximum at 305–310 mμ. References to spectra of other biliproteins, and their distribution, are given by Ó hEocha (1962). When irradiated with long wavelength ultra-violet light, aqueous solutions of biliproteins fluoresce brilliantly; the spectral maxima of the emitted radiation have been determined for many biliproteins (Table I).

TABLE I

Physical Properties of Biliproteins[a]

Biliprotein	Absorption λ_{max} (mμ) and $E^{1\%}_{1\,cm}$ where available						Fluorescence λ_{max} (mμ)	Molecular weight and pH of determination
C-phycoerythrin	275	305	~370			562 (*125*)	575	226,000 (7·2–8·3)
Cryptomonad phycoerythrin (type ii)	275	310	~370			556	580	—
B-phycoerythrin	278	307	~370		*546* (*82*)	565	578	c. 290,000 (5)
R-phycoerythrin	278	307	~370	498	540[b] (*81*)	568	578	291,000 (3–10)
C-phycocyanin	278	~350			615 (*65*)		647	138,000 (7·2–8·3)
Allophycocyanin	278	~350			(*610*)	650 (*65*)	660	134,000 (7·2–8·3)
Cryptomonad (HV-) phycocyanin	270	~350		583	(*625*) (*65*)	660		—
R-phycocyanin	278	~355		553	615 (*66*)	643	565 637	273,000 (2·5–6·0)

[a] These properties are subject to some variation depending on algal sources and methods of preparation. Sources of data: Eriksson-Quensel (1938); Airth and Blinks (1956); French et al. (1956); Hattori and Fujita (1959a); Ó hEocha and Ó Carra (1961); Ó Carra (1962a); Ó hEocha et al. (1964).

[b] Some variants of R-phycoerythrin have only a shoulder at this wavelength.

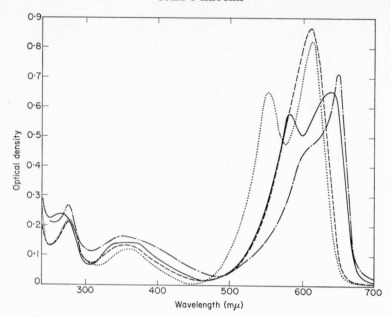

FIG. 2. Absorption spectra of aqueous solutions of phycocyanins (pH 6–7):

········, R-phycocyanin (*Porphyra laciniata*);

— — —, C-phycocyanin (*Nostoc muscorum*);

—·—·—·—, Allophycocyanin (*Nostoc muscorum*);

————, Cryptomonad (HV-) phycocyanin (*Hemiselmis virescens*, Droop).

II. OCCURRENCE

Phycobilins have been isolated only from plants of the Division Rhodophyta, Cyanophyta and Cryptophyta, i.e. Red Algae, Blue-green Algae and Cryptomonad Algae, respectively. A suggestion by Siegelman and Firer (1964) that phytochrome, a chromoprotein of higher plants, may contain a phycobilin-like prosthetic group awaits confirmation.

Phycobilin-protein complexes (biliproteins) are localized in the photosynthetic structures of algae, where they effectively extend the spectral range of chlorophyll *a*. This is of ecological importance, in coastal seawater, where daylight is attenuated rapidly and green radiation penetrates more deeply than blue or red. This is due to selective absorption and scattering of light by the water plankton and suspended matter and the absorption of blue radiation by the "yellow substance" present in these waters. Chlorophylls transmit green light but phycoerythrin, the concentration of which increases with depth of growth in Red Algae, is an effective absorber of green radiation, the energy of which it transfers to chlorophyll *a*. Biliproteins are also effective accessory pigments in the enhancement effect—the light they absorb is essential for the efficient photosynthetic utilization of the light energy absorbed by chlorophyll a itself. It has been reported that, in Red Algae, the light absorbed by phycoerythrins is much more effective in cytochrome reduction and oxygen production from water than is light absorbed by chlorophyll a, while both pigments are about equally effective in carbon dioxide reduction and cytochrome oxidation (Duysens and Amesz, 1962; Duysens and Sweers, 1963). A similar result was found in the case of the Blue-green Alga, *Anacystis nidulans*, with the difference that phycocyanin replaces phycoerythrin (Amex and Duysens, 1962). The function of the biliproteins in photosynthesis is discussed in detail in Chapter 14.

There is recent evidence (Boney and Corner, 1963) that while the role of phycoerythrin in sporelings of permanently submerged marine Red Algae is that of an accessory pigment in photosynthesis, the biliprotein functions in sporelings of intertidal Red Algae as a screen against inhibitory excess of green light from the direct rays of the sun.

The development of the cells of the Blue-green Alga *Nostoc muscorum* has been shown to be induced by light absorbed by a blue pigment, presumed to be allophycocyanin (Lazaroff and Schiff, 1962). This is a non-photosynthetic process similar to the better known growth and reproductive responses of higher plants (see Chapters 8 and 16), but it differs from these in that developmental photoinduction in the alga is reversed by green rather than far-red radiation.

The biliprotein content of attached marine Red Algae varies with season, about 2% (dry weight) being the highest reported value. Temperature and conditions of illumination during growth affect the biliprotein content of cultured algae; a high value of 24% phycocyanin (dry weight) was reported in *Anacystis nidulans* grown at 39° C and at low light intensity (Myers and Kratz, 1955). At low intensity, green was found to be more effective than blue light in stimulating the formation of phycoerythrin (Brody and Emerson, 1959), an observation of ecological interest in view of the deep penetration of green light in coastal waters. The phycobilin content of algal biliproteins is of the order 5–7%.

Algal biliproteins are soluble in dilute salt solutions and leach from disrupted algal cells. Cell breakage may be achieved by various methods including repeated freezing and thawing, grinding, blending with solid carbon dioxide, ultrasonics, and, in the case of some blue-green algae, by lysis with the enzyme lysozyme (Crespi *et al.*, 1962). Extracted biliproteins may be purified by fractional precipitation with ammonium sulphate, gel-filtration on cross-linked dextrans (Sephadex), chromatography on adsorbents such as tricalcium phosphate and zone electrophoresis (see Hjertén, 1963a, b). The importance of conducting these operations in the cold, and as expeditiously as possible, is illustrated by the fact that degradation during extraction of C-phycocyanin made it

impossible to get reproducible results in N-terminal analyses of the biliprotein when these precautions were not taken (Ó Carra, 1964). Biliproteins may be crystallized from solution in aqueous ammonium
sulphate.

Absorption spectra of purified biliproteins are presented in Figs. 1 and
2. Colourless proteins also absorb at about 278 mμ, and the value of the
ratio of the absorbancy at the principal visible maximum to that at
278 mμ may be used as a criterion for judging the purity of biliprotein
samples, highest ratios being displayed by the purest samples (see
Hattori and Fujita, 1959a). The $E_{1\,cm}^{1\%}$ values of biliproteins at the
principal maxima which are given in Table I were determined by
Ó Carra (1962a) and are, in general, in good agreement with those
reported by Hattori and Fujita (1959a) and Fujita and Hattori (1960a)
for biliproteins from different algae. It has been claimed by Hattori and
Fujita (1959b) that R-phycocyanin is an artifact, the absorption
maximum at 553 mμ (Fig. 2) being due to contamination of C-phycocyanin by phycoerythrin. These and other authors (e.g. French et al.,
1956; Haxo, 1960) have found C-phycocyanin in some species of Red
Algae, but the spectra of carefully purified preparations of R-phycocyanin from Ceramium rubrum and Porphyra laciniata are unaltered by
further extensive purification and they are crystallographically distinct
from the other biliproteins (Ó Carra, 1962a). The absorption spectrum
of R-phycocyanin (Fig. 2) lacks the peak at about 510 mμ shown by
C-phycocyanin of Porphyra tenera when contaminated by phycoerythrin
(Fig. 3, Hattori and Fujita, 1959b). R-phycocyanin must therefore be
considered a native biliprotein of some species of Red Algae.

The number of different biliproteins in algal species varies from one to
three. Red Algae usually contain phycoerythrin and one or two phycocyanins, although the blue-coloured Red Alga Porphyridium aerugineum
appears to contain only C-phycocyanin (Haxo, 1960). Blue-green algae
usually contain phycocyanin as principal biliprotein, although some
species, e.g. Phormidium ectocarpi, appear red, and contain only phycoerythrin (Haxo et al., 1955). However, it should be remembered that the
relative proportions of biliproteins in some cultured algae may be
altered by variations in the intensity and the wave-length of the illumination to which they are exposed during growth (Halldal, 1958; Ó hEocha
and Raftery, 1959; Brody and Emerson, 1959; Hattori and Fujita, 1959a)
and a discussion of distribution patterns should, ideally, be based on
analyses of algae grown under a variety of light conditions. The possible
failure to isolate biliproteins occurring in small quantities must also be
borne in mind. Extracts of some species of Phormidium, a Blue-green
Alga, contain two spectrally distinct phycoerythrins (Ó hEocha and
Haxo, 1960; Nultsch, 1962). However, the major one, C-phycoerythrin,

is converted into the second, two-peaked, phycoerythrin by various agents, including proteolytic enzymes, and this indicates that the latter is an artifact which is formed from C-phycoerythrin (Ó hEocha and Haxo,

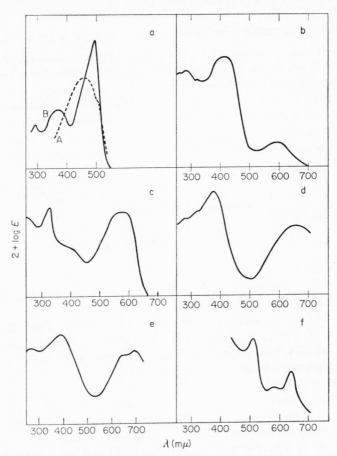

FIG. 3. Absorption spectra of bile pigments and derivatives: (a, b and c were determined in aqueous solution).

  a: Stercobilin (A), stercobilin hydrochloride (B);
  b: Mesobilirubin;
  c: Mesobiliviolin hydrochloride;
  d: Biliverdin (in methanol);
  e: Biliverdin zinc complex salt (in ethanol);
  f: Biliverdin zinc complex salt after oxidation with iodine (in ethanol). (Redrawn from Gray et al., 1961a, b, c).

1960; E. M. Ryan, D. Mitchell and C. Ó hEocha, 1963, unpublished observations). Cultured cryptomonads contain either a phycoerythrin or a phycocyanin as their major biliprotein (Ó hEocha et al., 1964).

Phycoerythrin-containing species may contain very small quantities of phycocyanin (Ó hEocha and Raftery, 1959). *Cyanidium caldarium*, an alga of uncertain classification (cf. Silva, 1962), contains two phyco-cyanins (Nichols and Bogorad, 1962).

III. Structure and Properties of the Bile Pigments

While it is conventional to represent the bile pigments as linear open-chain tetrapyrroles (as in structure I), steric considerations indicate that the molecules assume various non-linear shapes in space.

Biliverdin IXα (I) may be considered the parent substance of the naturally occurring bile pigments, as it is the first identifiable open-chain tetrapyrrole formed following oxidation of haem compounds in the presence of haem α-methenyl oxygenase, an enzyme found in liver and kidney (Nakajima *et al.*, 1963; Nakajima, 1963).

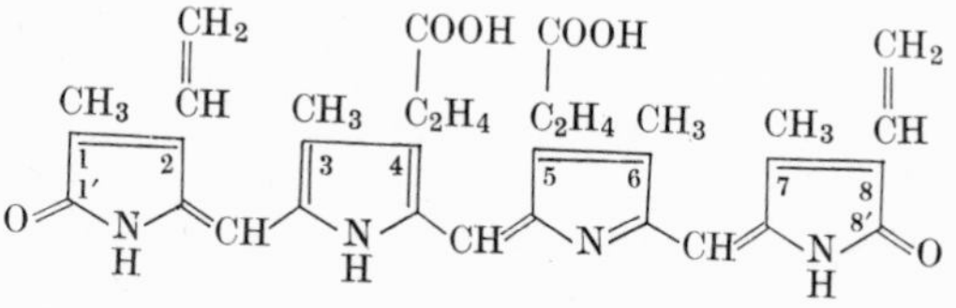

I

Biliverdin is a bilitriene which yields various other bile pigments on hydrogenation of its three bridge methine groups (—CH=). Three isomeric bilidienes (biliviolin, bilirhodin and bilirubin; Table II, structures III, IV and V, R: —CH=CH$_2$) are possible, depending on which one of the methine groups of biliverdin undergoes hydrogenation. Hydrogenation of the vinyl side-chains on positions 2 and 8 of biliverdin yields mesobiliverdin (II) which has a similar conjugated double bond system, and consequently resembles biliverdin in its optical properties (Table II). The bilidienes mesobiliviolin, mesobilirhodin and meso-bilirubin also contain ethyl side-chains. Bilenes contain only one bridge methine group (the central one of biliverdin) and may have reduced side-chains (*i*-urobilin, VI) and end-pyrrole rings (stercobilin, VII).

Properties of some bile pigments mentioned in this chapter are presented in Table II. For further information on the chemistry of the bile pigments the reader is referred to books and reviews by Lemberg and Legge (1949), Gray (1953, 1961), Siedel (1960) and Gray *et al.* (1961a, b, c.)

Until recently it was conventional to represent the bile pigments as bis-lactims (hydroxyl groups on the 1' and 8' carbons, structure I), but many of their properties are best accounted for by bis-lactam structures, as in structure I and those given in Table II. Bile pigments are ampholytes and are soluble in alkali by virtue of their carboxyl groups and in mineral acid by virtue of their nitrogen atoms. Many are also soluble in organic solvents such as chloroform, ether and ethanol and the relative solubility of bile pigments in organic and aqueous solvents is often useful in their separation. For example, i-urobilin is extracted by water from a mixture of mesobiliviolin and i-urobilin in ethereal solution.

The carboxyl groups of bile pigments may be esterified and the esters are more readily purified by adsorption chromatography than the free pigments. Most bile pigments contain the nucleophilic pyrrolenine nitrogen ($-\underset{\cdot\cdot}{N}=$), which may be protonated. The basicity of this group varies with the extent of the resonating system of the bile pigment chromophore (Gray $et\,al.$, 1961c); the longer the conjugated system the weaker the base (see below). Bile pigments are unstable in alkaline solutions and in concentrated hydrochloric acid, in which media they undergo prototropic isomerizations (Gray $et\,al.$, 1961b; Ó Carra $et\,al.$, 1964). For example, Gray $et\,al.$ (1961b) have reported that bilirubin undergoes a prototropic isomerization to dihydrobiliverdin in the presence of sodium ethoxide. Bile pigments are dehydrogenated and oxidized by concentrated nitric and perchloric acids.

Bile pigments react with divalent metal ions in non-acidic media (see Gray $et\,al.$, 1961b, c; Ó Carra, 1962b). The zinc complex salts of some bile pigments are fluorescent and, on the addition of iodine, fluorescent zinc salts of oxidized bile pigments are formed, regardless of whether the original salts are fluorescent or not (Table II).

The absorption spectra of bile pigments differ considerably from those of porphyrins, another naturally occurring series of tetrapyrrolic pigments. In neutral solvents porphyrins have four sharp, moderately intense, absorption bands in the visible spectrum and a very intense Soret band at about 400 mμ. Bile pigments lack a Soret band and their visible bands are, in general, broad (Fig. 3). Free base bile pigments have broader absorption bands than the protonated pigments (Fig. 3a); zinc salts have sharp bands, particularly after oxidation with iodine (Fig. 3e, f). The spectral changes accompanying pH changes of bile pigment solutions can be used to determine the dissociation constants of protonated bile pigments. The chromophores of verdins, violins and urobilins are basic and the basic strength increases in that order (Table II) while the extent of the resonating chromophore system decreases in the same order. Rubins are predominantly acidic in character according to Gray $et\,al.$ (1961c).

IV. The Phycobilins

Bile pigments are firmly attached to the protein moieties of algal biliproteins, in contrast to those occurring as prosthetic groups in biliproteins of other organisms. For example, the biliproteins of locusts, butterflies and the sea-hare, $Apylsia$, release their bile pigments when

Tablı

Properties of Some

Name	Class and structure no.	Structure[b]	Absorption maxime Free pigment
Biliverdin (R: —CH=CH₂)	bilitriene	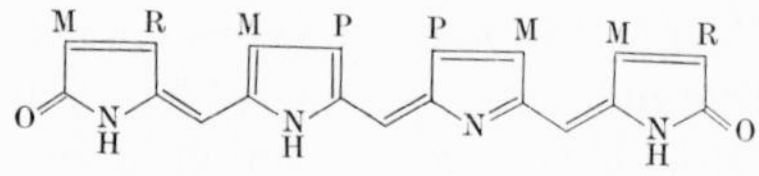 M R M P P M M R — O=⟨N-H⟩=⟨N-H⟩=⟨N⟩=⟨N-H⟩=O	377·5 640–645 (41·7) (13·4) (CHCl₃)
Mesobiliverdin (R: —CH₂—CH₃)	bilitriene II		367·5 635–640 (43·12) (13·5) (CHCl₃)
Mesobiliviolin (R: —CH₂—CH₃)	bilidiene III	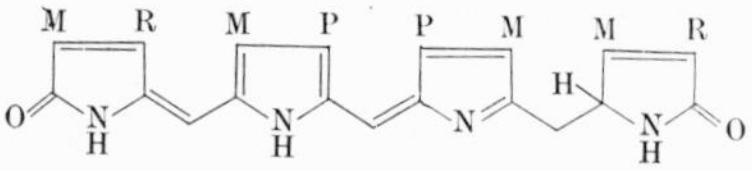 M R M P P M M R	327 565 (18·5) (12·0) (CHCl₃)
Mesobilirhodin (R: —CH₂—CH₃)	bilidiene IV	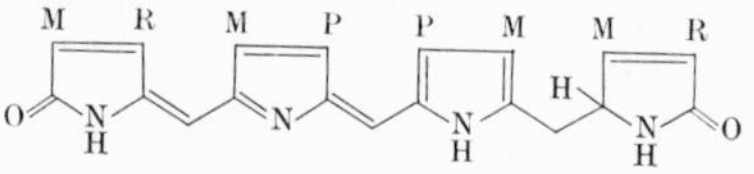 M R M P P M M R	500 (CHCl₃ + pyridine
Mesobilirubin (R: —CH₂—CH₃)	bilidiene V	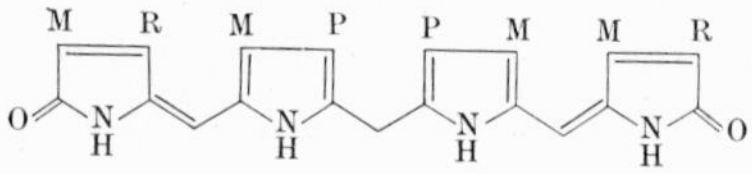 M R M P P M M R	433–434 (54·6) (CHCl₃)
i-urobilin (R: —CH₂—CH₃)	bilene VI	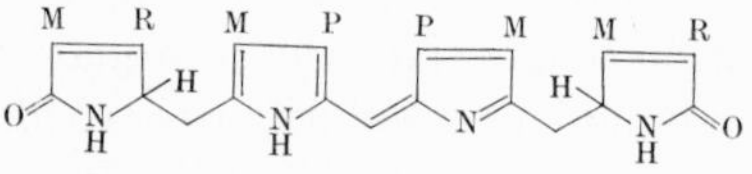 M R M P P M M R	455–460 (alkali, pH 8·6)
Stercobilin (R: —CH₂—CH₃)	bilene VII	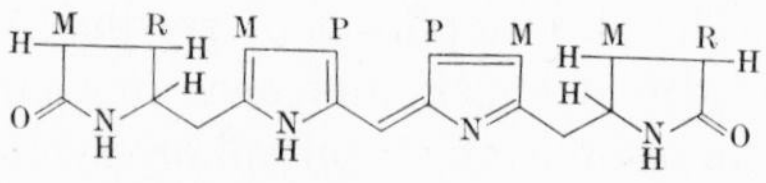 M R M P P M M R	452·5–455 (alkali, pH 8·7)

ᵃ From Gray et al. (1961a, b, c), Ó Carra (1962b) and Ó Carra et al. (1964).

they are treated with organic solvents such as methanol. Concentrated hydrochloric acid is required to release the main prosthetic groups of algal biliproteins and the low yield thus obtained has militated against structural studies of these pigments. Artifact pigments are also formed from the phycobilins under these conditions and, until recently, these e Pigments^a

) and millimolar absorbancy index where available		Colour of fluorescence of zinc complex salt	pK of conjugate acid
Protonated pigment	Zinc complex salt		
377·5 670–680 (46·35) (23·0) (5% aq. HCl)	385 695 (ethanol)	none; red after oxidation with I_2	c. 3
365 680–685 (45·8) (24·5) (5% aq. HCl)	380 695 (ethanol)	none; red after oxidation with I_2	c. 3
327·5 602·5 (22·3) (23·8) (CHCl$_3$)	340 582·5 632·5 (ethanol)	red	c. 4
312 575 (CHCl$_3$)	(540) 581 (CHCl$_3$)	orange	—
5) 420–470 (450–480) (0·1 N HCl)	451 (chloroform-methanol 1:1)	none; red after oxidation with I_2	—
499 (72·1) (CHCl$_3$)	510 (methanol)	green	7·4
499 (92·9) (CHCl$_3$)	510 (methanol)	green	7·6

M: —CH$_3$; P: —CH$_2$—CH$_2$—COOH; R: —CH$_2$—CH$_3$ or —CH=CH$_2$ (see column 1 and t).

artifacts were erroneously considered to be the prosthetic groups of algal biliproteins.

In this chapter emphasis will be placed on the three phycobilins whose spectral properties can be correlated with those of the denatured biliproteins from which they are obtained (see Section V, B).

A. PREPARATION

1. *Phycocyanobilin*

C-phycocyanin, which is the most readily available source of this pigment, is denatured with acetone and treated with 12 N HCl in the dark for 30 min at room temperature. The hydrolyzate is diluted with distilled water, centrifuged, and the supernatant extracted with chloroform with gentle shaking. The chloroform solution is shaken with dilute aqueous hydrochloric acid and the product, which remains in the chloroform layer, is a protonated phycocyanobilin (Ó hEocha, 1958). The free base is formed when the chloroform solution of phycocyanobilin hydrochloride is shaken with freshly distilled water (Ó hEocha, 1963). Because of its lability further purification of phycocyanobilin has not been found possible (Ó hEocha, 1963). The yield of phycocyanobilin from this preparation is low but owing to artifact pigment formation in acid the digestion cannot be extended. These artifacts become irreversibly attached to protein fragments and consequently extension of the acid hydrolysis results in a lower, rather than a higher, yield of pigment.

2. *Phycoerythrobilin*

The same considerations regarding time of digestion apply when phycoerythrins are treated with concentrated hydrochloric acid (Ó Carra *et al.*, 1964). The dried phycoerythrin is placed in 12 N HCl for 30 min at room temperature. The hydrolysate is diluted, neutralized with sodium acetate, the pigment extracted into ether which is then extracted with 2·8 N HCl and the phycoerythrobilin hydrochloride is finally brought into chloroform with gentle shaking. The free base phycoerythrobilin is formed after repeated shaking of the acid chloroform solution with freshly distilled water.

3. *Phycourobilin*

This pigment (Ó Carra, 1962a) is most abundant in R-phycoerythrin. It is not released when the biliprotein is treated with concentrated hydrochloric acid, but has been obtained in low yield, from chromopeptides resulting from tryptic digestion of R-phycoerythrin (C. Ó hEocha, T. B. Brennan and P. Ó Carra, 1963, unpublished observations). Dried denatured R-phycoerythrin was digested with trypsin at 30°C for 27 h at pH 7·5, using an enzyme to substrate ratio of 1:15. The digest was centrifuged and separated into red and orange-yellow zones on Sephadex G-75. After further purification on Sephadex the yellow peptide fraction was hydrolysed with silver sulphate (Paul, 1950) and the resulting urobilinoid pigment purified by chromatography on alumina.

4. *Other Phycobilins*

Lemberg and Bader (1933) were the first to show that the prosthetic groups of the phycobilins are bile pigments. Their hydrolysis was conducted with concentrated hydrochloric acid at 80° C and the resulting purified pigment from C-phycocyanin was claimed to be mesobiliviolin (see Table II). However, it is not possible to correlate the spectral properties of the pigment obtained from C-phycocyanin under these conditions with those of the parent biliprotein, and the pigment must be considered an artifact, resulting possibly from hydration of vinyl side chain(s) of phycocyanobilin under the catalytic influence of strong acid (Ó hEocha, 1963).

Another artifact pigment (phycobilin 655) was obtained, for example, when C-phycocyanin was treated by a number of procedures, including treatment with 10·9 N HCl for 20 h at room temperature (Ó hEocha, 1963). Phycobilin 655 is more stable than phycocyanobilin and has been better characterized. The relationship between these two pigments has yet to be elucidated.

Lemberg and Bader (1933) isolated a chromopeptide from R-phyco-erythrin when they digested the biliprotein with hot concentrated acid. Under these conditions, phycoerythrobilin is isomerized to a urobilin which attaches to —SH groups in proteins and the pigment examined by Lemberg is considered to be a mixture of chromopeptides of phycouro-bilin and of an artifact urobilin (Ó Carra *et al.*, 1964).

Fujita and Hattori (1962a) reported the isolation from cells of Blue-green Algae of a phycobilin which differs in properties from phyco-cyanobilin and is not obtainable from purified phycocyanin. The pigment as it occurs in the cells is water-soluble but is rendered hydrophobic by heating with 90% methanol. The authors propose that this pigment is a bilitriene (not biliverdin or mesobiliverdin, however).

Fujita and Hattori (1963b) have isolated and purified a purple phycobilin from phycoerythrin-rich cells of the Blue-green Alga *Toly-pothrix tenuis*. It differs spectrally from phycoerythrobilin and the authors consider that it may be a biosynthetic precursor of phyco-erythrin.

B. PROPERTIES

Of the phycobilins which are believed to occur in biliproteins, phyco-cyanobilin and phycoerythrobilin have been most extensively studied. Both are soluble in organic solvents such as chloroform and diethyl ether and in aqueous acids, phycoerythrobilin being the more hydrophilic of the two. Phycoerythrobilin is a somewhat stronger base than phyco-cyanobilin (Table III). Both phycobilins are unstable in alkali and in

TABLE III

Some Properties of the Phycobilins[a]

Phycobilin	Absorption maxima in chloroform (mμ)				pK of conjugate acid
	free pigment		protonated pigment		
Phycoerythrobilin	304	505	312	576	c. 6·4
Phycocyanobilin	360	612	365	630	c. 4·8

[a] Ó hEocha (1963); Ó Carra et al. (1964).

concentrated hydrochloric acid. 12 N HCl converts phycocyanobilin to a pigment having the spectral properties of mesobiliviolin while phycoerythrobilin is converted into a bilene resembling the urobilins in spectral properties. Both phycobilins may be esterified and the esters, unlike

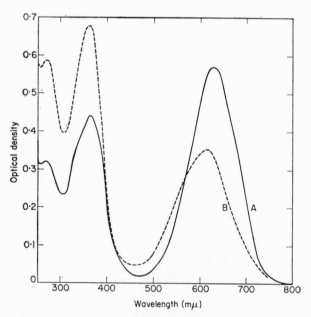

FIG. 4. Absorption spectra of equal concentrations of phycocyanobilin in chloroform. A, as hydrochloride; B, as free base. (Ó hEocha, 1963, with correction).

the free pigments are soluble in petroleum ether. The absorption spectra of the protonated and free phycobilins are given in Figs. 4 and 5 (see, also Table III).

When treated with zinc acetate, solutions of the phycobilins form zinc complex salts. These are fluorescent under ultra-violet irradiation, the emission from phycoerycyanobilin-Zn being red, phycoerythrobilin-Zn, orange, and phycourobilin-Zn green. These zinc complexes, like those of other bile pigments, are unstable under acidic conditions, when zinc ions are displaced by protons.

The position of the absorption maxima and the ratio of the absorbancies in the ultra-violet and visible are, in the case of phycocyanobilin,

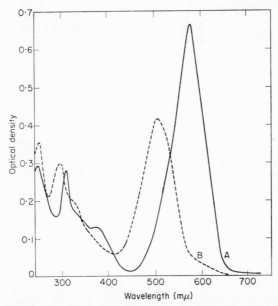

FIG. 5. Absorption spectra of equal concentrations of phycoerythrobilin in chloroform. A, as hydrochloride; B, as free base. (Ó Carra *et al.*, 1964).

intermediate between those of verdins and violins (see Tables II and III; Ó hEocha, 1963). Phycoerythrobilin, the absorption maxima of which are very close to those of a mesobilirhodin formed from *d*-urobilin (Table II, structure IV), may be dehydrogenated to a green bilitriene. It is not yet possible to assign a structure to phycocyanobilin, but structure VIII, or its side-chain isomer (IV), has been suggested for phycoerythrobilin (Ó Carra *et al.*, 1964).

$$CH_3 \quad C_2H_5 \quad CH_3 \quad \overset{\overset{\displaystyle COOH}{|}}{C_2H_4} \quad \overset{\overset{\displaystyle COOH}{|}}{C_2H_4} \quad CH_3 \quad CH_3 \quad C_2H_5$$

VIII

Phycourobilin resembles *i*-urobilin in many light absorption properties, and also in that it is oxidized by ferric chloride under conditions which leave stercobilin unaltered (Watson, 1959). The pigment obtained by silver sulphate hydrolysis (Section IV, A, 3) may be a dioxy-*i*-urobilin (Table II, structure VI; R: —CHOH—CH₃) (C. Ó hEocha, T. B. Brennan and P. Ó Carra, 1963, unpublished observations).

V. THE ALGAL BILIPROTEINS

A. PROTEIN STRUCTURE

In recent years amino acid analyses of biliproteins have been reported by Jones and Blinks (1957), Kimmel and Smith (1958) and Berns *et al.*

TABLE IV

Amino Acid Analyses of Biliproteins[a]

	Gm. of amino acid residue per 100 g of biliprotein		
Amino acid	R-phycoerythrin from Ceramium rubrum	C-phycocyanin from Nostoc muscorum	C-phycoerythrin from Phormidium persicinum
Asp	10·38	10·82	9·23
Thr	4·47[b]	5·09[b]	3·94[b]
Ser	6·75[b]	5·16[b]	3·22[b]
Glu	6·73	10·54	10·77
Pro	2·11	2·71	3·14
Gly	3·72	4·06	4·80
Ala	8·86	7·86	7·65
Val	6·31	4·23	3·95
Met	1·63	0·84	1·58
Ileu	4·44	4·44	3·96
Leu	7·39	7·69	8·02
Tyr	4·49	5·28	4·19
Phe	2·74	3·13	3·74
Lys	3·68	4·02	5·00
His	0·59	1·05	1·35
Arg	6·73	7·66	5·23
CySO₃H	3·64	0·63	0·28 (½CySS)[a]
Total	84·66	85·21	80·05

[a] Based on triplicate analyses of 20 and 70 h 6 N HCl hydrolyzates of lyophilized biliproteins (3–4 mg) on a Spinco Model 120 Analyser. R-phycoerythrin and C-phycocyanin, but not C-phycoerythrin, were oxidized with performic acid prior to hydrolysis. The figures are corrected for moisture, which was determined on a separate sample (Raftery and Ó hEocha, 1964; unpublished observations).
[b] Corrected for hydrolytic losses.

(1963). Recent analyses by M. A. Raftery and C. Ó hEocha (1964, unpublished observations) are given in Table IV. As is commonly observed, the total weight of amino acids recovered is less than the weight of biliprotein. This is accounted for, at least in part, by the weight of the phycobilins themselves and by the probable presence of carbohydrate, at least in R-phycoerythrin (Fujiwara, 1961; Raftery and Ó hEocha, 1964). Seventeen amino acids have been identified in biliproteins, all of which are characterized by a higher content of acidic (aspartic, glutamic acids) than of basic amino acids (lysine, histidine, arginine). An interesting finding is that deuteriated C-phycocyanin, obtained from the Blue-green Alga *Plectonema calothricoides* grown in D_2O, is essentially identical in amino acid composition with C-phycocyanin from the same alga grown in H_2O (Berns *et al.*, 1963). The N-terminal amino acid residue of R-, B-, and C-phycoerythrins has been identified as methionine (Ó Carra and Ó hEocha, 1962), that of C-phycocyanin as threonine, while methionine and threonine are N-terminal in R-phycocyanin (Ó Carra, 1964). Alanine and serine were identified as the C-terminal amino acids of R-phycoerythrin and C-phycocyanin respectively (Raftery and Ó hEocha, 1964).

The highest recorded values for the molecular weights of the algal biliproteins are those determined near their isoelectric points, which fall in the pH range 4.5 ± 0.25. When available, such values are given in Table I. The number of sub-units in the quaternary structures of native biliproteins is not known, but it has been suggested as a result of sedimentation and immunochemical studies that C-phycocyanin is an associating system and that the degree of association is affected by pH and biliprotein concentration (Berns *et al.*, 1963; Berns, 1963). There is evidence from column chromatography (Tiselius *et al.*, 1956), countercurrent distribution (Albertson and Nyns, 1959), zone electrophoresis and sedimentation studies (Hjerten, 1963a) that, contrary to earlier reports, R-phycoerythrin is heterogenous at pH values near neutrality. Immunochemical studies indicate that unassociated deuteriated and ordinary C-phycocyanins from *P. calothricoides* have identical primary, secondary and tertiary structures (Berns, 1963).

B. SPECTRAL PROPERTIES OF DENATURED BILIPROTEINS

The ordered three-dimensional structures of biliproteins are disrupted by various agents, including acid (Lemberg, 1930), concentrated urea solutions (Ó hEocha and Ó Carra, 1961), ethanol (Ó hEocha, 1963) and heat (Jones and Fujimori, 1961; Lavorel and Moniot, 1962; Berns *et al.*, 1963). Denaturation leads to quenching of fluorescence and to decreased absorption in the visible spectrum. It is seen from Fig. 6, which shows the spectrum of native minus denatured C-phycocyanin, that in the neutral pH range native C-phycocyanin absorbs much more in the red region of the spectrum than does the denatured biliprotein. However, the ultraviolet absorption of the biliprotein is enhanced by denaturation. Phycoerythrins are more resistant to denaturation by urea than are

phycocyanins (Ó hEocha and Ó Carra, 1961), while C-phycocyanin from
a thermophilic alga was found to denature at a higher temperature than
C-phycocyanin from an alga growing at lower temperatures (Berns,
1963). On the basis of the temperature-dependence of its fluorescence,
Moyse and Guyon (1963) concluded that C-phycocyanin is more stable
in vivo than *in vitro*.

The light absorption and fluorescence changes accompanying irreversible denaturation of biliproteins is due to disruption of non-
covalent interactions within the protein. Phycobilin residues which are
unreactive in native biliproteins owing to masking by such interactions

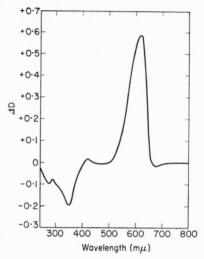

FIG. 6. The difference spectrum of native (pH 6·8) and ethanol denatured
(pH 8·0) C-phycocyanin (0·11 mg/ml). The native phycocyanin was in the sample
beam. (Ó hEocha, 1963).

do react with zinc ions, for example, after denaturation of the proteins
(Ó hEocha and Ó Carra, 1961; Lavorel and Moniot, 1962). Lavorel and
Moniot (1962) consider that the native protein configuration of C-
phycocyanin forces the phycobilin prosthetic groups to assume a rigid
co-planar structure, the disruption of which is indicated by changes in
phycobilin absorption and fluorescence.

The visible spectral properties of the protein-free phycobilins are
difficult to correlate with those of the native biliproteins. However, in the
case of denatured biliproteins the absorption maxima of the phycobilins are much closer to those of the free phycobilins, and this allows
the identification of naturally occurring phycobilins by spectrophotometry. This technique is particularly applicable when the phycobilins
are present as hydrochlorides or zinc salts, both of which have sharp

absorption peaks (cf. Section III). The similar spectral properties of denatured C-phycoerythrin and phycoerythrobilin indicates that phycoerythrobilin is the only coloured prosthetic group present in this biliprotein, while the R-phycoerythrin spectrum is reconcilable only with the presence in that chromoprotein of phycoerythrobilin and phycourobilin (Table V).

TABLE V

Absorption Maxima (mμ) of Denatured Phycoerythrins and Their Phycobilins[a]

Substance	λ_{max} in dilute aqueous acid				λ_{max} of zinc complex salt			
Phycoerythrobilin	307	(370)		556	320		(540)	583
Phycourobilin			495		c. 509			
C-phycoerythrin	307	(375)		556	320		(542)	586
R-phycoerythrin	307	(370)	498	556	320	512	(542)	586

[a] Ó Carra et al. (1964).

When more than one type of pigment is obtainable from a biliprotein under different conditions, a comparison of the spectra of the released pigments and of the denatured biliprotein may allow selection of the native phycobilin. Thus, phycocyanobilin, and not mesobiliviolin or a related bile pigment having similar spectral properties, was shown to be the native prosthetic group of C-phycocyanin (Ó hEocha, 1963). Similar reasoning indicates that phycocyanobilin is the sole prosthetic group of allophycocyanin (Ó hEocha, 1963), and that it is also present in R-phycocyanin (with phycoerythrobilin) (Ó hEocha, 1960; Ó Carra, 1962a) and in cryptomonad (HV-) phycocyanin (with an unidentified phycobilin) (Ó hEocha et al., 1964).

Ó Carra (1962a) used the spectra of denatured biliproteins to calculate the number of prosthetic groups present per molecular weight unit (as given in Table I, except in the case of C-phycocyanin where twice the value in the Table was used). He found that R- and C-phycoerythrins contain about 25 phycoerythrobilin units and that R-phycoerythrin contains, in addition, 12 phycourobilin units. R- and C-phycocyanins were reported to contain about 22 phycocyanobilin units and there are, in addition, 8 phycoerythrobilin units in R-phycocyanin. The value for C-phycocyanin agrees with that deduced from fluorescence polarization studies by Brody and Brody (1961), and it amounts to about five per cent by weight of the biliprotein.

Phycoerythrobilin is responsible for absorption at wavelengths longer than 530 mμ in phycoerythrins (Ó hEocha and Ó Carra, 1961). In

R-phycoerythrin it accounts for the two long wavelength absorption maxima of the native biliprotein, but fluorescence is seemingly emitted only by those phycoerythrobilin units which absorb at about 568 mμ. These units are involved in the non-covalent interactions of the protein, unlike the phycourobilin prosthetic groups of the same biliprotein (Ó hEocha and Ó Carra, 1961). This conclusion is based on the finding that the only visible absorption peak of R-phycoerythrin which is un-changed in position on denaturation is that due to phycourobilin (c. 498 mμ; cf. Tables I and V). Furthermore, the addition to native R-phycoery-thrin of aqueous zinc acetate to 50 mM leads to the formation of a zinc complex salt of phycourobilin, but not of phycoerythrobilin. The nature of the covalent bonds between the various phycobilins and apoproteins has not yet been established.

VI. Biosynthesis

It is only in recent years that any direct evidence has been obtained regarding the biosynthesis of biliproteins and this is based mainly on studies of action spectra of their formation. These indicate that the bio-synthetic pathways of chlorophylls and biliproteins are different. An ideal experimental organism for the study of phycocyanin biosynthesis is a heterotrophic mutant of the anomalous alga *Cyanidium caldarium* which contains C-phycocyanin and allophycocyanin but no chlorophyll (Nichols and Bogorad, 1962). The action spectrum for the formation of C-phycocyanin in young cells of this mutant has absorption maxima at 420 mμ (major peak) and 550–600 mμ. In older cells, the effectiveness of blue light (420 mμ) is decreased relative to that at longer wavelengths. The interpretation of their findings given by Nichols and Bogorad (1962) is that a haem compound serves as photoreceptor, and possibly also as precursor of C-phycocyanin, and that this compound is photochemically converted in older cells into an unidentified form more strongly activated by red light. The need for light can be dispensed with altogether in one culture medium which is presumed to contain a co-factor which replaces some reactant normally provided as a result of a photo-reaction.

The other major contribution to our knowledge of biliprotein bio-synthesis has been made by Fujita and Hattori (1960a, b, 1962b, 1963a). The organism they used was *Tolypothrix tenuis*, a Blue-green Alga which contains the biliproteins C-phycoerythrin, C-phycocyanin and allo-phycocyanin. These authors report that bile pigment precursors of C-phycoerythrin and C-phycocyanin are formed photochemically, that these precursors are photochemically interconvertible, and that, in the presence of nitrogen sources, they are converted in the dark, through intermediates, into biliproteins. This latter, dark, stage is suppressed by substances which inhibit protein biosynthesis and this is taken to indicate that the protein moieties of the biliproteins are formed *de novo*, and do not derive from proteins already existing in the cells.

Bogorad (1963) has outlined two pathways which might operate in biliprotein biosynthesis, and of these scheme B is better substantiated by the work of Fujita and Hattori. However, a final answer awaits further structural knowledge of the phycobilins and a search for enzymes in algae similar to the haem α-methenyl oxygenase of animal tissues which converts haem compounds into a bile pigment precursor (Nakajima *et al.*, 1963; Nakajima, 1963).

ACKNOWLEDGMENT

Preparation of this chapter was supported by the Air Office of Scientific Research, OAR, through the European Office of Aerospace Research, United States Air Force (Grant No. AF EOAR 63–18).

REFERENCES

Airth, R. L., and Blinks, L. R. (1956). *Biol. Bull.* **111**, 321.
Albertson, P. Å., and Nyns, E. J. (1959). *Nature, Lond.* **184**, 1465.
Amesz, J., and Duysens, L. N. M. (1962). *Biochim. Biophys. Acta* **64**, 261.
Berns, D. S. (1963). *J. Amer. chem. Soc.* **85**, 1676.
Berns, D. S., Crespi, H. L., and Katz, J. J. (1963). *J. Amer. chem. Soc.* **85**, 8.
Bogorad, L. (1963). *In* "Biogenesis of Natural Compounds" (P. Bernfeld, ed.), p. 183, Pergamon Press, Oxford.
Boney, A. D., and Corner, E. D. S. (1963). *J. Mar. biol. Ass. U.K.* **43**, 319.
Brody, S. S., and Brody, M. (1961). *Biochim. biophys. Acta* **50**, 348.
Brody, M., and Emerson, R. (1959). *Amer. J. Bot.* **46**, 433.
Crespi, H. L., Mandeville, S. E., and Katz, J. J. (1962). *Biochem. Biophys. Res. Comm.* **9**, 569.
Duysens, L. N. M., and Amesz, J. (1962). *Biochim. biophys. Acta* **64**, 243.
Duysens, L. N. M., and Sweers, H. E. (1963). *In* "Studies on Microalgae and Photosynthetic Bacteria", p. 353, Japanese Society of Plant Physiologists, Tokyo.
Eriksson-Quensel, I-B. (1938). *Biochem. J.* **32**, 585.
Esenbeck, N. v. (1836). *Liebigs Ann.* **17**, 75.
French, C. S., Smith, J. H. C., Virgin, H. I., and Airth, R. L. (1956). *Plant Physiol.* **31**, 369.
Fujita, Y., and Hattori, A. (1960a). *Plant and Cell Physiol.* **1**, 281.
Fujita, Y., and Hattori, A. (1960b). *Plant and Cell Physiol.* **1**, 293.
Fujita, Y., and Hattori (1962a). *J. Biochem., Tokyo* **51**, 89.
Fujita, Y., and Hattori, A. (1962b). *Plant and Cell Physiol.* **3**, 209.
Fujita, Y., and Hattori, A. (1963a). *In* "Studies on Microalgae and Photosynthetic Bacteria", p. 431, Japanese Society of Plant Physiologists, Tokyo.
Fujita, Y., and Hattori, A. (1963b). *J. gen. appl. Microbiol., Tokyo* **9**, 253.
Fujiwara, T. (1961). *J. Biochem., Tokyo* **49**, 361.
Gray, C. H. (1953). "The Bile Pigments," Methuen, London.
Gray, C. H. (1961). "Bile Pigments in Health and Disease," Thomas, Springfield, Ill.
Gray, C. H., Lichtarowicz-Kulczycka, A., Nicholson, D. C., and (in part) Petryka, Z. (1961a). *J. chem. Soc.* 2264.

Gray, C. H., Kulczycka, A., and Nicholson, D. C. (1961b). *J. chem. Soc.* 2268.

Gray, C. H., Kulczycka, A., and Nicholson, D. C. (1961c). *J. chem. Soc.* 2276.

Halldal, P. (1958). *Physiol. Plantarum* 11, 401.

Hattori, A., and Fujita, Y. (1959a). *J. Biochem., Tokyo* 46, 633.

Hattori, A., and Fujita, Y. (1959b). *J. Biochem., Tokyo* 46, 903.

Haxo, F. T. (1960). *In* "Comparative Biochemistry of Photoreactive Systems" (M. B. Allen, ed.), p. 339, Academic Press, New York.

Haxo, F. T., Ó hEocha, C., and Norris, P. (1955). *Arch. Biochem. Biophys.* 54, 162.

Hjertén, S. (1963a). *J. Chromatog.* 11, 66.

Hjertén, S. (1963b). *J. Chromatog.* 12, 510.

Jones, R. F., and Blinks, L. R. (1957). *Biol. Bull.* 112, 363.

Jones, R. F., and Fujimori, E. (1961). *Physiol. Plantarum* 14, 253.

Kimmel, J. R., and Smith, E. L. (1958). *Bull. Soc. chim. biol.* 40, 2049.

Lavorel, J., and Moniot, C. (1962). *J. chim. phys.* 59, 1007.

Lazaroff, N., and Schiff, J. (1962). *Science* 137, 603.

Lemberg, R. (1930). *Liebigs Ann.* 477, 195.

Lemberg, R., and Bader, G. (1933). *Liebigs Ann.* 505, 151.

Lemberg, R., and Legge, J. W. (1949). "Hematin Compounds and Bile Pigments," Interscience, New York.

Moyse, A., and Guyon, D. (1963). *In* "Studies on Microalgae and Photosynthetic Bacteria", p. 253, Japanese Society of Plant Physiologists, Tokyo.

Myers, J., and Kratz, W. A. (1955). *J. gen. Physiol.* 39, 11.

Nakajima, H. (1963). *J. biol. Chem.* 238, 3797.

Nakajima, H., Takemura, T., Nakajima, O., and Yamaoka, K. (1963). *J. biol. Chem.* 238, 3784.

Newton, L. (1951). "Seaweed Utilization," Sampson Low, London.

Nichols, K. E., and Bogorad, L. (1962). *Bot. Gaz.* 124, 85.

Nultsch, W. (1962). *Biochim. biophys. Acta* 59, 213.

Ó Carra, P. (1962a). Doctoral Thesis. The National University of Ireland.

Ó Carra, P. (1962b). *Nature, Lond.* 195, 899.

Ó Carra, P. (1964). *Biochem. J.* (in press).

Ó Carra, P., and Ó hEocha, C. (1962). *Nature, Lond.* 195, 173.

Ó Carra, P., Ó hEocha, C., and Carroll, D. (1964). *Biochem. J.* (in press).

Ó hEocha, C. (1958). *Arch. Biochem. Biophys.* 73, 207; 74, 493.

Ó hEocha, C. (1960). *In* "Comparative Biochemistry of Photoreactive Systems" (M. B. Allen, ed.), p. 181, Academic Press, New York.

Ó hEocha, C. (1962). *In* "Physiology and Biochemistry of Algae" (R. A. Lewin, ed.), p. 421, Academic Press, New York.

Ó hEocha, C. (1963). *Biochemistry* 2, 375.

Ó hEocha, C., and Haxo, F. T. (1960). *Biochim. biophys. Acta* 41, 515.

Ó hEocha, C., and Ó Carra, P. (1961). *J. Amer. chem. Soc.* 83, 1091.

Ó hEocha, C., and Raftery, M. (1959). *Nature, Lond.* 184, 1049.

Ó hEocha, C., Ó Carra, P., and Mitchell, D. (1964). *Proc. R. Irish Acad.* 63 B, 191.

Paul, K. G. (1950). *Acta chem. Scand.* 4, 239.

Raftery, M. A., and Ó hEocha, C. (1964). *Biochem. J.* (in press).

Siedel, W. (1960). *In* "Handbuch der physiologisch-und pathologisch-chemischen Analyse", Bd. IV (K. Lang and E. Lehnartz, eds.), p. 845, Springer, Berlin.

Siegelman, H. W., and Firer, E. M. (1964). *Biochemistry* 3, 418.

Silva, P. (1962). *In* "Physiology and Biochemistry of Algae" (R. A. Lewin, ed.), p. 827, Academic Press, New York.

Sorby, H. C. (1877). *J. Linn. Soc. (Bot.)* 15, 34.

Tiselius, A., Hjertén, S., and Levin, Ö. (1956). *Arch. Biochem. Biophys.* 65, 132.

Watson, C. J. (1959). *J. Lab. clin. Med.* 54, 1.

Chapter 7

PURIFICATION AND PROPERTIES OF PHYTOCHROME

W. L. BUTLER, S. B. HENDRICKS, AND H. W. SIEGELMAN

*Agricultural Marketing Service and Agricultural Research Service
U.S. Department of Agriculture, Beltsville, Maryland, U.S.A.*

I. INTRODUCTION

The essential spectral characteristics of phytochrome were ascertained from action spectra studies described in Chapter 15. The repeated reversibility of physiological responses by red and far-red light clearly indicated that the actions were mediated by a photoreceptor pigment system which existed in two interconvertible forms, one absorbing maximally near 660 mμ, P_r, and the other near 730 mμ, P_{fr}.

$$P_r \underset{730\,m\mu}{\overset{660\,m\mu}{\rightleftharpoons}} P_{fr}$$

A number of years elapsed between the description of the spectral properties of phytochrome from action spectra and the physical measurement of the pigment. The main problem in measuring phytochrome *in vivo* was the low concentration of the pigment. The molar extinction coefficients of P_r and P_{fr} were determined by detailed analyses of the degree of physiological response (internode elongation and seed germination) to known energies of light and were found to be quite high (Hendricks *et al.*, 1956). In spite of the high extinction coefficients the pigment

197

was not apparent even in albino seedlings, which showed a phytochrome-controlled response of growth (Borthwick *et al.*, 1951). Direct measurement of phytochrome ultimately required the development of spectrophotometers which could measure the absorption spectra of intact plant tissue and the finding of plant tissues which had measurable concentrations of phytochrome. The latter requirement was significant because, even with the available methods of measurement, phytochrome can still not be detected directly in many phytochrome-containing tissues. The plant response is frequently a more sensitive assay for phytochrome than current methods of physical measurement.

II. Spectrophotometric Detection

The photoreversible property of phytochrome action suggested that the pigment could be detected by measuring changes in the absorption spectra of plant tissues after irradiation with red and far-red light. The first successful physical demonstration of phytochrome was made on seedlings grown entirely in darkness to prevent the accumulation of chlorophyll (Butler *et al.*, 1959). Dark-grown seedlings were cut into small segments, pressed into a sample holder of 2-cm depth, and placed in a single-beam recording spectrophotometer in which a large area, end-window multiplier phototube was close to the sample holder. The sample was first irradiated with red light to transform P_r to P_{fr} and protochlorophyll to chlorophyll. The absorption spectrum of the sample was recorded after irradiation with red light and again after irradiation with far-red light. The difference between the spectra revealed that irradiation with far-red light increased the optical density of the sample in the red region and decreased it in the far-red region in agreement with the transformation of P_{fr} to P_r. Red light, as expected, had the opposite effect. Maximal optical density changes occurred near 660 and 730 mμ in accord with the action spectra and the changes were repeatedly reversible.

Rapid measurement of phytochrome in large numbers of samples was accomplished by use of a dual-wavelength, difference photometer devised by Birth and Norris (1963) similar in principle to the double-beam spectrophotometer developed by Chance (1951). The close juxtaposition of the multiplier phototube and the sample permitted the use of optically dense, light-scattering samples. The instrument measured the optical density difference between 660 and 730 mμ, $\Delta OD = OD_{660} - OD_{730}$. The relative amount of phytochrome in a sample was calculated from the difference between the ΔOD readings after irradiation of the sample with actinic sources of red and far-red light $\Delta(\Delta OD) = \Delta OD_{fr \text{ irrad}} - \Delta OD_{r \text{ irrad}}$. To prevent appreciable conversion of phytochrome during the measurement the intensities of the 660- and 730-mμ measuring beams were kept low.

The richest sources of phytochrome have been dark-grown seedlings. Phytochrome has been measured in dark-grown seedlings of maize, oats, barley, rice, wheat, soyabeans, peanuts, lima beans, squash, pumpkin, sunflower, red cabbage, turnip, radish, peas, kidney beans, rye grass, catalpa, morning glory, watermelon, cucumber, cotton, cowpea, and lupin. Smaller concentrations have been found in squash fruits, cauliflower heads, avocado seeds, and wheat germ. Phytochrome has not yet been measured directly in growing green plants by currently available instruments, but it has been extracted from a number of green plants and measured after concentration and partial purification (Lane et al., 1963).

III. Isolation and Purification

Purification of phytochrome has been achieved by protein separation methods combined with the spectrophotometric detection for assay. Initially, 6-day-old dark-grown maize seedlings were used as a source of the chromoprotein. However, the large amount of high molecular weight yellow contaminants not removed easily and the low yield of pigment per gram of the seedlings eliminated the use of maize. Dark-grown barley seedlings were then chosen since they contained more pigment per gram of the seedlings. The yellow contaminants were more readily removed from barley extracts, but, as will be discussed below, the ratio of the reversible absorbancy changes $\Delta A_{fr}/\Delta A_r$, for the purified solutions was generally 0·5 to 0·7, indicating that the pigment was partly denatured during the purification procedures. Up to the present time, 5-day-old dark-grown oat seedlings have provided the best yield of pigment per gram seedling with least denaturation (Siegelman and Firer, 1964).

Methods of isolating and purifying proteins from tissues of growing plants are less well established than those for seed proteins. Phytochrome can be extracted very simply from small quantities of dark-grown seedlings by grinding with alkaline buffer and sand in a mortar. Large amounts of tissue, greater than 1 kg, can be extracted with buffer in a large food chopper. Extraction with high speed homogenizers or blenders gives very poor yields of phytochrome because of probable protein denaturation caused by foaming. The main consideration in the use of an extraction buffer is to maintain the pH of the solution between 7·5 and 8·5.

Attempts to purify phytochrome by the procedures of salt fractionation, organic solvent fractionation, pH precipitation, heat, and protamine and streptomycin precipitation were generally unsatisfactory. However, recently developed column-chromatographic methods for proteins were successful. The purification scheme now used is outlined in Fig. 1, and a summary of the purification is given in Table I. The same procedure has been effective with dark-grown corn and barley seedlings. Phytochrome has been purified from dark-grown pea seedlings by Bonner

Grind 1·5 kg dark-grown oats with 1·5 litres of buffer and 75 g of cellulose; filter
↓
Centrifuge (16,000 × g, 25 min)
↓
Ultrafiltrate
↓
Centrifuge (37,000 × g, 20 min)
↓
Gel filtrate (Sephadex G-50)
↓
Calcium phosphate chromatography
↓
0·4 satd. $(NH_4)_2SO_4$ precipitation of active fractions
↓
Centrifuge (23,000 × g, 10 min)
↓
Redissolve precipitate and gel filtrate (Sephadex G-200)
↓
0·5 satd. $(NH_4)_2SO_4$ precipitation of active fractions
↓
Centrifuge (23,000 × g, 10 min)
↓
Redissolve precipitate and gel filtrate (Sephadex G-50)
↓
DEAE-cellulose chromatography
↓
0·5 satd. $(NH_4)_2SO_4$ precipitation of fractions of highest specific activity
↓
Centrifuge (23,000 × g, 10 min)
↓
Redissolve precipitate in 1 ml buffer
↓
Centrifuge (23,000 × g, 10 min)

FIG. 1. Schematic procedure for purification of phytochrome from dark-grown Clintland oats.

(1960) using ammonium sulphate precipitation, calcium phosphate adsorption, and diethylaminoethyl (DEAE)-cellulose chromatography.

Visible detection of phytochrome can be achieved in about 1 h from dark-grown oat seedlings provided all required materials are prepared in advance (Miller and Siegelman, unpublished work). An extract of

TABLE I

Summary of Purification of Phytochrome from Clintland Oats

Fraction	Volume ml	Activity (OD)/cm	Total activity (OD)/cm²	Total protein mg	Specific activity	Recovery per cent	Purification
1. Initial extract	2,500	0·0038	9·5	4,630	0·0021	100	1·0
2. Ultrafiltrate	590	0·0126	7·4	2,480	0·0030	78	1·4
3. Sephadex G-50	695	0·0108	7·5	2,010	0·0037	79	1·8
4. Calcium phosphate	166	0·0325	5·4	980	0·0055	57	2·6
5. Sephadex G-200 and ammonium sulphate precipitation	6	0·64	3·85	223	0·017	41	8·1
6. DEAE-cellulose and ammonium sulphate precipitation of highest specific activity fraction	1	0·58	0·58	4·5	0·129	6·2	61

100 g of dark-grown Norline oats is directly adsorbed on a column of di-calcium phosphate, and the phytochrome is eluted with phosphate buffer. The phytochrome can be seen on the column as a narrow, blue-green band which increases in blue colour with far-red radiation and decreases with red radiation.

Analytical electrophoretic separations of the DEAE-cellulose fraction were made by disc electrophoresis (Ornstein and Davis, 1962). A blue band, which had the photoreversible properties of phytochrome, was observed migrating down the gel column. The location of phytochrome following the electrophoretic migration was also determined directly on the gel column with the dual-wavelength difference photometer. The gel column was stained with amido black and then scanned with a densitometer. The location of phytochrome and the densitometer tracing of the stained gel column are illustrated in Fig. 2. Six protein components

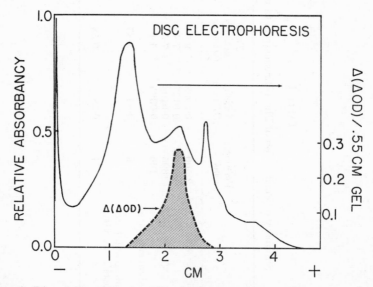

FIG. 2. Disc electrophoresis of the highest specific activity fraction of oat phytochrome after DEAE-cellulose chromatography. Densitometer tracing of amido-black-stained protein (solid line). Phytochrome absorbancy changes assayed directly on the acrylamide gel (dashed line).

are indicated by the densitometer tracing, and one of these coincides with phytochrome.

Sedimentation equilibrium centrifugation provided additional information on the heterogeneity of the DEAE-cellulose fraction. Approximately one-third of the DEAE-cellulose fraction had a molecular weight of about 90,000 and two-thirds a molecular weight of about 150,000.

Sedimentation velocity centrifugation of the DEAE-cellulose fraction did not show heterogeneity but provided a sedimentation coefficient, $s_{20,w}$, for the protein mixture of 4·5.

IV. PHOTOCHEMICAL PROPERTIES

The absorption spectra of a solution of purified phytochrome from oat seedlings (Fig. 3) show prominent bands in the red region of the spectrum and weaker absorption bands in the blue and near-ultraviolet.

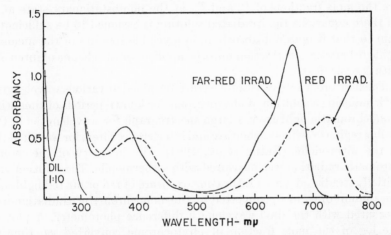

FIG. 3. Absorbance spectra of a high specific activity fraction of oat phytochrome. The spectrum at wavelengths shorter than 300 mμ was measured on a solution diluted 10-fold. After red irradiation (dotted line), and after far-red irradiation (solid line).

The photoreversible behaviour of phytochrome is independent of temperature down to $-20°$ C but is gradually lost at still lower temperatures and is not observed at $-196°$ C. Reversibility is regained on warming. Fluorescence of P_r (λ max. near 690 mμ), but not P_{fr}, has been observed *in vivo* and *in vitro* and is strongly enhanced at $-196°$ C.

The absorption band near 670 mμ in the spectrum of phytochrome after red irradiation indicated that red light did not convert all the P_r to P_{fr}; a steady-state mixture of P_r and P_{fr} was established in red light by virtue of the absorption of P_{fr} in the red region. It can be estimated from the absorption spectra (Fig. 3) that $\epsilon_{fr\,665} = 0·55\epsilon_{fr\,725}$, that $\epsilon_{r\,665} = 1·55\epsilon_{fr\,725}$, (the ϵ's are the extinction coefficients of P_r and P_{fr} at the wavelengths indicated) and that the photostationary state in red light consists of 80% P_{fr} and 20% P_r.

The photochemical transformation of phytochrome is first-order in both directions. The product of the extinction coefficient and the quantum yield can be determined from the first-order rate constant (K_λ) for the photochemical conversion of P_r or P_{fr} (Butler, 1961).

$$K_\lambda = \frac{E_\lambda \, \epsilon_{r\lambda} \, \phi_r}{P_{fr\infty\lambda}} = \frac{E_{\lambda fr\lambda} \, \phi_{fr}}{P_{r\infty\lambda}}$$

where E_λ is the intensity of monochromatic light of wavelength (Einsteins cm^{-2} sec^{-1}), $\epsilon_{r\lambda}$ and $\epsilon_{fr\lambda}$ are the extinction coefficients of P_r and P_{fr} at λ (cm^2 mole^{-1}, to base 10), ϕ_r and ϕ_{fr} are the quantum yields for the transformations of P_r and P_{fr} (mole Einstein^{-1}) and $P_{r\infty\lambda}$ and $P_{fr\infty\lambda}$ are the mole fractions of P_r and P_{fr} at the photostationary state at λ. In these equations the irradiated solution is assumed to be sufficiently thin so that it does not absorb an appreciable fraction of the incident light; otherwise, a correction must be applied for the change of intensity with sample depth.

The first-order rate constants were determined at various wavelengths by irradiating a solution of phytochrome for known periods of time with monochromatic light from a large spectrograph for wavelengths in the visible region or with a carbon arc and interference filters for wavelengths in the ultra-violet (Butler *et al.*, 1964). The intensity of the monochromatic radiation was measured with a thermopile. The solution was initially irradiated with a saturating exposure of red or far-red light and the amount of P_{fr} or P_r converted by the monochromatic irradiation was measured with the dual-wavelength difference photometer. A plot of the log of the mole fraction of phytochrome converted vs. time of

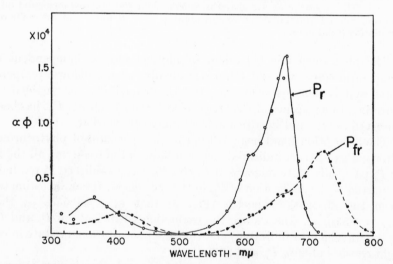

Fig. 4. The action spectra (extinction coefficient—$\alpha \times$ quantum yield—ϕ vs. wavelength) for the phototransformation of P and P_{fr} in solution.

irradiation gives a stright line whose slope is K_λ. The values of $\epsilon_{r\lambda}\phi_r$ and $\epsilon_{fr\lambda}\phi_{fr}$ can then be determined from equation 1, since E_λ, $P_{r\infty\lambda}$ and $P_{fr\infty\lambda}$ can be measured. Figure 4 is a plot of $\alpha\phi$ vs. wavelength for P_r and P_{fr} where α is the extinction coefficient expressed as litre mole^{-1} cm^{-1}, $\alpha = 0.001\epsilon$.

The action spectra for a solution of phytochrome (action is defined as the product of an extinction coefficient and quantum yield) showed that red light was more effective in converting P_r than far-red light was in converting P_{fr}: $\alpha_{r\,665}\phi_r = 16 \times 10^3$ l Einstein^{-1} cm^{-1} whereas $\alpha_{fr\,725}\phi_{fr} = 7 \times 10^3$ l Einstein^{-1} cm^{-1}. The estimate of overlap between the absorption bands of P_r and P_{fr} in the red region involved the estimate that $\alpha_{r\,665} = 1.5\alpha_{fr\,725}$. Therefore, $\phi_r = 1.5\phi_{fr}$. The action spectra also show that light absorbed by the weak absorption bands in the blue and near-ultraviolet regions is effective in converting P_r and P_{fr}.

V. *In vivo* PROPERTIES

Spectrophotometric assay has allowed studies of phytochrome properties in dark-grown seedlings. Distribution of phytochrome was examined in several dark-grown seedlings (Briggs and Siegelman, unpublished work). In monocotyledons the concentration of the pigment was highest at the tip of the coleoptile and at the junction of the mesocotyl and coleoptile. In bean and pea seedlings the highest content of phytochrome was found in the growing tip and the hypocotyl arch. The phytochrome content of the seedling generally parallels the protein content but may vary considerably.

De novo synthesis of phytochrome can be followed in dark-grown germinating seedlings. The total phytochrome content of dark-grown maize seedlings increases linearly with time for about 8 days. The phytochrome in the cotyledons of dark-grown soybeans increases rapidly during the first 5 days of imbibition and then levels off and decreases slightly over the next 5 days. However, there is no synthesis of phytochrome in the cotyledons of soybeans that fail to germinate.

Phytochrome in dark-grown seedlings was present primarily as P_r and, as such, was quite stable (Butler *et al.*, 1963). When the seedlings were briefly irradiated with red light, P_r was converted into P_{fr} and the P_{fr} formed was unstable. The total amount of photoreversible phytochrome declined over a period of several hours to about 20 to 30% of the initial amount. The phytochrome remaining was present as P_r. It was originally assumed, on the basis of difference spectra, that the red irradiation converted all the P_r to P_{fr} and that 20 to 30% of the P_{fr} formed reverted to the stable P_r form in darkness while 70 to 80% was lost. The absolute spectra showed, however, that 20% of the initial P_r was not converted by the red irradiation. Thus, most of the P_r which remained after the P_{fr} had decayed had been present throughout the dark period and was not formed by dark conversion of P_{fr} to P_r. Dark-grown seedling tissue is not suitable for measuring a dark reversion of P_{fr} to P_r because most of the P_{fr} is utilized in processes which result in the loss of photoreversible phytochrome.

VI. DENATURATION

The photoreversible absorbance of phytochrome is a property of a particular chromophoric group attached to a protein. Some reagents or conditions which affect the protein moiety alter the absorption spectra of P_r and P_{fr}. Thus, changes in the absorption spectra of the long-wavelength maxima of phytochrome can be used to study the effects of protein denaturation. In general, P_{fr} is much more susceptible to denaturation than P_r, which suggests that the protein conformation of P_r is somewhat different from that of P_{fr}.

Complete denaturation of phytochrome resulted in the loss of chromophore absorption in the region of 600 to 800 mμ (Butler et al., 1964). However, with partial denaturation, an altered phytochrome, P^*, can be obtained which is still photoreversible, $P^*_r \rightleftharpoons P^*_{fr}$. The absorption spectrum of P^*_r is similar to that of P_r except that the absorption maximum is shifted from 665 to about 660 mμ. The absorption band of P^*_{fr} is of much lower extinction than that of P_{fr} and the absorption maximum is at shorter wavelengths. The ratio of the reversible absorbancy changes in the far-red and far-red regions, $\Delta A_{fr}/\Delta A_r$, is 1·0 for native phytochrome and is in the range of 0·1 to 0·3 for the denatured P^* system (Hendricks et al., 1962).

Dark conversions between P_r and P_{fr} of native phytochrome in vitro are not appreciable. If the phytochrome is partly denatured, as indicated by a $\Delta A_{fr}/\Delta A_r$ of less than unity, however, there is an appreciable dark reversion of P^*_{fr} to P^*_r (Hendricks et al., 1962). Partial denaturation of phytochrome to the P^* system is indicated by a $\Delta A_{fr}/\Delta A_r$ ratio less than unity and dark reversion of P^*_{fr} to P^*_r. Bonner (1962) reported a dark-reversion phytochrome in vitro. The dark reversion was observed only in purified preparations.

The effect of 5 M urea on P_r is shown in Fig. 5A (Butler et al., 1964). The addition of urea caused a small hypsochromic shift of the absorption maximum, indicating denaturation of P_r to P^*_r, but no further change of the absorption spectrum occurred so long as the sample was kept in the dark. Fifteen minutes later (Fig. 5B) the absorption spectrum of P^{*r} was unchanged. On irradiation with red light P^*_r was transformed into the low-extinction P^*_{fr}. A subsequent irradiation with far red did not re-form as much P^*_r as was present initially, but the re-formed P^*_r was stable in 5 M urea. The chromophore of P^*_{fr}, however, deteriorated in urea. During 15 min as P^*_{fr} (Fig. 5c) the absorbance of P^*_{fr} decreased further, and very little P^*_r could be regained by far-red light. The rate of deterioration of P^*_{fr} in urea was more rapid in the absence of mercapto-ethanol. The effect of 5 M urea on P^*_r was reversible by dilution or

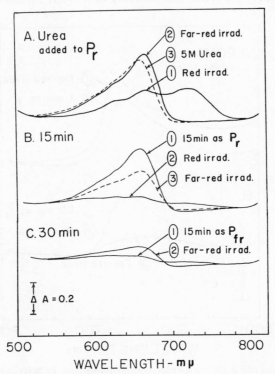

FIG. 5. Effect of 5 M urea on the absorbance spectra of phytochrome. (A) Absorbancies of phytochrome after red (1) and far-red (2) irradiation, and 1 min after adding urea to P_r (3). (B) Absorbancies of phytochrome after 15 min in darkness as P_r after addition of urea. (c) Absorbancies of phytochrome after 15 min additional in darkness as P_{fr} after addition of urea.

removal of urea by gel filtration on Sephadex G-25. Bonner (1961) found that urea caused a loss of photoreversibility and alteration in the absorbance of phytochrome.

The effects of the proteolytic enzymes, pronase and trypsin on the absorption spectra of phytochrome were similar to those of urea. Both enzymes, at a concentration of 1 mg per 1 ml, denatured P_r to P^*_r within 1 to 2 min at room temperature. The absorption spectrum of P^*_r was stable in the presence of the enzymes, but that of P^*_{fr} deteriorated. The denaturation of P to P^* probably reflects a loosening of the protein structure, which both urea and the proteolytic enzymes can effect but by different mechanisms.

Sulfhydryl reagents attacked phytochrome differentially after the phytochrome was partly denatured. N-ethyl maleimide (NEM) had little effect on either form of phytochrome. In the presence of 5 M urea, however, 5×10^{-3} M NEM immediately destroyed the absorption band

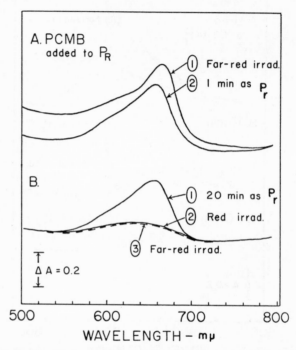

FIG. 6. Effect of 5×10^{-3} M p-chloromercuribenzoate (PCMB) on the absorbance spectra of phytochrome. (A) Absorbancies of phytochrome after far-red (1) irradiation and 1 min after adding PCMB to P_r (2). (B) Absorbancies of phytochrome after 20 min in darkness after adding PCMB to P_r, (1) and after red (2) irradiation.

of P^*_{fr} and slowly attacked the chromophore of P^*_r. Parachloromercuribenzoate (PCMB) acted similarly, but at a concentration of 5×10^{-3} M it also denatured the phytochrome without the aid of urea. The effect of 5×10^{-3} M PCMB when added to P_r is shown in Fig. 6A. The shift of the absorption maximum indicates partial denaturation to P^*_r. The 660-mμ absorption band was stable at 5×10^{-3} M PCMB, but a gradual reduction of the P^*_r absorption band was observed at 10^{-2} M. After red irradiation (Fig. 6B) the red-absorption band vanished without the concomitant formation of an absorption band in the far-red region, and irradiation with far-red light did not restore any P^*_r. Thus, an SH group, which is required for the chromophore absorption, is susceptible to attack by sulfhydryl reagents when phytochrome is present as P^*_{fr} but not when present as P^*_r, P_r, or P_{fr}.

VII. SUGGESTIONS ON CHROMOPHORE STRUCTURE

The structure of the phytochrome chromophore is still unknown. Denaturation studies clearly indicate that the photoreversible absorbance properties of the chromoprotein are dependent on a close interaction between the chromophore and the protein.

The absorption spectrum of P_r is similar to that of allophycocyanin (see Chapter 6), a biliprotein obtained from certain algae. Allophycocyanin probably has either eight or sixteen chromophores per protein molecule, while the number of chromophores per phytochrome molecule is probably one and not more than two. Thus, the ratio of the intensities of the chromophore absorption bands to that of the protein absorption band (280 mμ) is greater for allophycocyanin than for phytochrome.

The chromophores of the biliproteins were found by Lemberg to be noncyclized tetrapyroles or bile pigments (Lemberg and Legge, 1949; and Chapter 6). Ó hEocha (1963) examined the properties of the phycocyanobilin from C-phycocyanin. The general structure of bile pigments suggests several possible mechanisms for a photoreversible absorbance change. Hydrogen atoms can migrate from one portion of the molecule to another in bile pigments, and lactim-lactam tautomerism in the terminal rings of bile pigments may also function to shift absorbance (Gray, 1961). Finally, the bile pigment molecule can undergo *cis-trans* isomerization about the bridge methyne groups (—CH=). Any of these changes would be sufficient to produce the observed absorbance changes provided the system is reversible.

Other naturally occurring blue proteins are known. Blue carotenoproteins have been found in Crustacea (Wald *et al.*, 1948) but not in plants. The long-wavelength maximum of a porphyrin protein such as chlorophyll is suggestive. However, the lack of a Soret band in the absorbance spectrum of phytochrome likely precludes a cyclized tetrapyrole from being the chromophoric group. There is finally the possibility that the phytochrome chromophore may represent a new class of compounds.

VIII. RÉSUMÉ

Phytochrome has been physically measured *in vivo* and *in vitro* by spectrophotometric methods. The *in vivo* properties of phytochrome have been examined with a dual-wavelength difference photometer. The pigment has been isolated and purified by methods of protein chemistry, and photochemical and protein properties of the chromoprotein have been determined.

The spectral properties of purified phytochrome and those determined physiologically from photomorphogenic responses of higher plants (cf. Chapter 15) are identical in all important respects. The isolation and purification of phytochrome is one step toward a more complete understanding of the biochemical control of the growth and development of higher plants.

REFERENCES

Birth, G. S., and Norris, K. H. (1963). Annual Meeting of Amer. Soc. Agr. Engineers, Miami Beach, Florida, June 1963, Paper No. 63–330.

Bonner, B. A. (1960). *Plant Physiol. Suppl.* **35**, xxxii.

Bonner, B. A. (1961). *Plant Physiol. Suppl.* **36**, xlii.

Bonner, B. A. (1962). *Plant Physiol. Suppl.* **37**, xxvii.

Borthwick, H. A., Hendricks, S. B., and Parker, M. W. (1951). *Bot. Gaz.* **113**, 95.

Butler, W. L. (1961). *In* "Progress in Photobiology" (B. C. Christensen and B. Buchmann, eds.), p. 569, Elsevier, Amsterdam.

Butler, W. L., Norris, K. H., Siegelman, H. W., and Hendricks, S. B. (1959). *Proc. nat. Acad. Sci., Wash.* **45**, 1703.

Butler, W. L., Lane, H. C., and Siegelman, H. W. (1963). *Plant Physiol.* **38**, 514.

Butler, W. L., Hendricks, S. B., and Siegelman, H. W. (1964). *Photochem. Photobiol.* (in press).

Butler, W. L., Siegelman, H. W., and Miller, C. O. (1964). *Biochemistry* **3**, 851.

Chance, B. (1951). *Rev. sci. Instrum.* **22**, 634.

Gray, C. H. (1961). "Bile Pigments in Health and Disease," 101 pp., C. C. Thomas, Springfield, Illinois.

Hendricks, S. B., Borthwick, H. A., and Downs, R. J. (1956). *Proc. nat. Acad. Sci. Wash.* **42**, 19.

Hendricks, S. B., Butler, W. L., and Siegelman, H. W. (1962). *J. phys. Chem.* **66**, 2550.

Lane, H. C., Siegelman, H. W., Butler, W. L., and Firer, E. M. (1963). *Plant Physiol.* **38**, 414.

Lembert, R., and Legge, J. W. (1949). "Hematin Compounds and Bile Pigments," 749 pp., Interscience, New York.

Ó hEocha, C. (1963). *Biochemistry* **2**, 375.

Ornstein, L., and Davis, B. J. (1962). "Disc Electrophoresis," Parts I and II, 66 pp., Distillation Products Industries, New York.

Siegelman, H. W., and Firer, E. M. (1964). *Biochemistry* **3**, 418.

Wald, G., Nathanson, N., Jencks, W. P., and Tarr, E. (1948). *Biol. Bull.* **95**, 249–251.

Chapter 8

NATURE AND PROPERTIES OF FLAVONOIDS

T. Swain

*Low Temperature Research Station, Downing Street,
Cambridge, England*

I. Introduction

Nature as it surrounds us is predominantly green. It is not surprising therefore that plants, or parts of plants which are in bright contrast to this overwhelming greenness have always attracted man, and indeed other denizens of the animal kingdom. Although the various shades of yellow are pleasing to the majority of people, the most fascinating colours are those which make the deepest contrast to green, that is, various shades of red and blue. Almost all the brilliant colours of this type which are found in flowers and fruit are due to the presence of one or more of the groups of flavonoid compounds known as anthocyanins. Other classes of flavonoid compound are responsible for the yellow colour of certain flowers, although more usually this is due to the presence of carotenoid pigments. Yet other flavonoids account for the actual whiteness in most white flowers, which without them would perhaps appear almost translucent. Finally some of the brown and black pigments found in Nature are due either to the products of oxidation of flavonoid and related phenolic compounds, or to their chelates with metals.

It is the object of this Chapter to outline the structures and some of the properties of flavonoid and related compounds which are involved in pigmentation in plants. Their distribution, and contribution to flower and fruit colour, and their biosynthesis are dealt with in succeeding Chapters (9 and 10).

II. CLASSES OF FLAVONOID COMPOUNDS

The term flavonoid was first applied ten years or so ago by Geissman and Hinreiner (1952) to embrace all those compounds whose structure is based on that of flavone (2-phenylchromone, I) (L. flavus, yellow). Occasionally the term is misspelt as flavanoid, which might be a better one to use as the parent skeleton of the group is really flavan (2-phenyl-chroman) in which the heterocyclic ring is fully reduced. A number of other terms have been, and still are generically used, often in a rather loose way, to cover various groups of flavonoid compounds; for example anthoxanthin (Gr., anthos, flower; xanthos, yellow); anthochlor (Gr., chloros, pale green); chymochrome (Gr., chymos, juice; chroma, colour); and, as mentioned above, anthocyanin (Gr., kyanos, blue). This last term was the first to be introduced to describe a class of flavonoid pigments (as anthocyan) by Marquart in 1835.

It can be seen that flavone (I) consists of two benzene rings (A and B) joined together by a three carbon link which is formed into a γ-pyrone ring. The various classes of flavonoid compound differ one from another only by the state of oxidation of this 3-C link. There is a limitation to the number of structures actually found in Nature, which vary from flavan-3-ols (catechins, II) to flavonols (3-hydroxyflavones, X) (Table I). It will be noted that five classes of compounds shown in Table I, the dihydro-chalkones (3-phenylpropiophenones, III), the chalkones (phenylstyryl

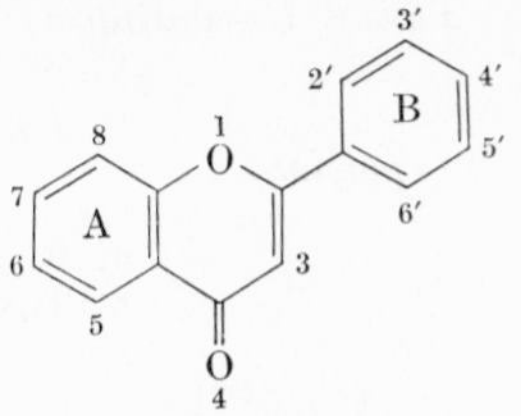

(I)

Flavone

ketones, VI; Gr. chalcos, copper), the isoflavanones (3-phenylchrom-
anones, VII), the isoflavones (3-phenylchromones, XI) and the aurones

TABLE I

The Classes of Flavonoid Compound[a]

No.	Name	Structure of 3-C portion	Typical members and position of hydroxy groups[b]
I	Flavone	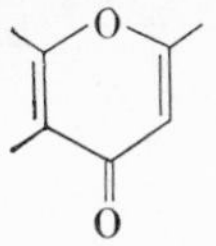	a. Apigenin; 5,7,4' b. Luteolin; 5,7,3',4'
II	Flavan-3-ol	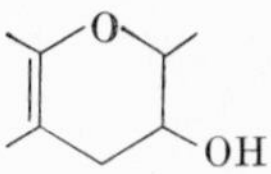	a. Catechin; 5,7,3',4' b. Gallocatechin; 5,7,3',4',5'
III	Dihydrochalkone	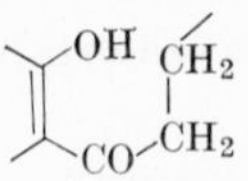	a. Phoretin; 4,2',4',6' b. Hydroxyphloretin; 3,4,2',4',6'
IV	Flavan-3,4-diols	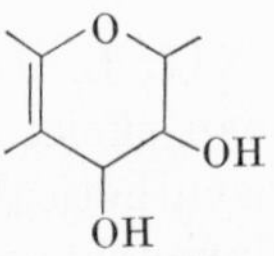	a. Leucocyanidin; 5,7,3',4' b. Leucodelphinidin; 5,7,3',4',5'
V	Flavanones	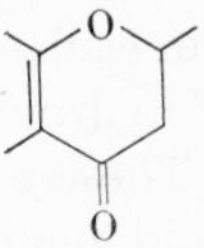	a. Naringenin; 5,7,4' b. Butin; 7,3',4' c. Eriodictoyl; 5,7,3',4'
VI	Chalkones	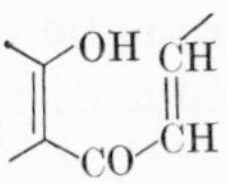	a. Butein; 3,4,2',4'
VII	Isoflavanones	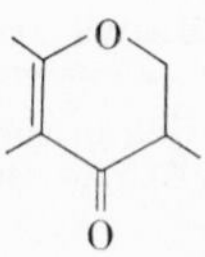	a. Padmakastein; 5,4'-dihydroxy-7-methoxy

TABLE I—continued

No.	Name	Structure of 3-C portion	Typical members and position of hydroxy groups
VIII	Dihydroxyflavonols		a. Fustin; 7,3',4' b. Taxifolin; 5,7,3',4'
IX	Anthocyanins		a. Pelargonidin; 5,7,4' b. Cyanidin; 5,7,3',4' c. Delphinidin; 5,7,3',4',5'
X	Flavonols		a. Kaempferol; 5,7,4' b. Quercetin; 5,7,3',4' c. Myricetin; 5,7,3',4',5'
XI	Isoflavones		a. Genistein; 5,7,4' b. Orobol; 5,7,3',4'
XII	Aurones		a. Sulphuretin; 6,3',4' b. Aureusidin; 4,6,3',4'

^{a} Source material: Karrer (1958), Swain and Bate-Smith (1962), Dean (1963), Seshadri (1959).

^{b} As in flavone (I), but see footnote on this page.

(2-benzylidene-3-coumaranones, XII; L. aurum, gold) do not actually possess the basic 2-phenylchroman skeleton, but they are so closely related both chemically and biosynthetically to the other types that they are always included in the flavonoid group.

The individual compounds within each class are distinguished mainly by the number and orientation of hydroxyl and methoxyl groups substituted in the two benzene rings. These groups are usually arranged in restricted patterns in the flavonoid molecule reflecting the different biosynthetic origins of the two aromatic nuclei. Thus in the A ring (I) of the majority of flavonoid compounds, hydroxyl groups are substituted at either both C_5* and C_7, or only at C_7, and generally are unmethylated. This pattern of hydroxylation follows from the acetate or malonate

* One should note the different numbering in the dihydrochalkones (III), chalkones (VI) and the aurones (XII). Here C_5 and C_7 of the flavones (I) becomes $C_{2'}$ and $C_{6'}$ (III and VI), or C_4 and C_6 (XII).

origin of this ring (see Chapter 10). The B-ring (I) of the flavonoids on the other hand is usually substituted by either one, two, or three hydroxyl or methoxyl groups. The first, which is rarely methylated, is substituted in the position para to the point of attachment of this ring to the rest of the molecule ($C_{4'}$ in I), with the second and third groups *ortho* to it at $C_{3'}$ and $C_{5'}$ these latter two groups often being methylated. The hydroxylation pattern of the B-ring thus resembles that found in the commonly occurring cinnamic acids and coumarins (e.g. XIII and XIV) and reflects their common biosynthetic origin from prephenic acid and its congeners.

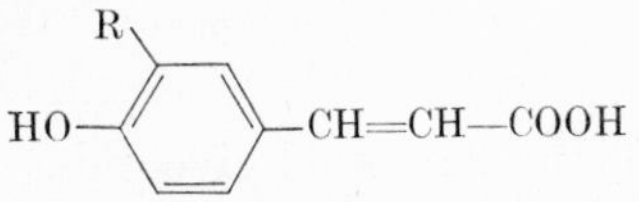

(XIII)

a. R = H; *p*-Coumaric acid
b. R = OH; Caffeic acid
c. R = OMe; Ferulic acid

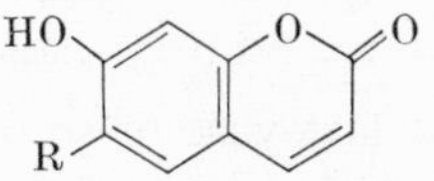

(XIV)

a. R = H; Umbelliferone
b. R = OH; Aesculetin

In most cases the flavonoid compounds exist in the plant as glycosides, that is one or more of their hydroxyl groups is joined by a semi-acetal link to a sugar. Here again, as will be discussed later, there is a restriction on the hydroxyl groups which are so affected. The sugar-free compounds are referred to as aglycones, and although their presence has often been reported in plants, it is probable that, except for non-living tissues, they are produced during the course of extraction. Most living tissues contain very active glycosidases which can work even in the presence of high concentrations of organic solvents. The presence of sugars in the molecule is undoubtedly advantageous in living tissues since it confers sap-solubility to the generally somewhat insoluble flavonoid compounds. In some cases also, notably the anthocyanins, sugars impart stability to the aglycone. Another example is that the 3-glycosides of quercetin (Xb, Table I) and myricetin (Xc) unlike the corresponding aglycones are not oxidized by phenolase, presumably because of steric reasons (Baruah and Swain, 1959; Roberts, 1960).

The sugars which have been found in flavonoid glycosides include simple hexoses and pentoses (monosides), and di- and tri-saccharides (biosides and triosides) always combined through the C_1 position usually by a β-link. In many cases, more than one phenolic hydroxyl group in the flavonoid molecule may be involved, giving rise to dimonosides and so on (e.g. cyanin, cyanidin-3,5-di-β-D-glucoside, XV). D-Glucose, occurring either alone or as part of a disaccharide, is the most common sugar in glycosides; D-galactose and L-rhamnose are less frequent, and

L-arabinose, D-glucuronic acid, and D-xylose are rather rare. Some unusual sugars have also been found; for example, apiose (XVI) in an apigenin (Ia) bioside from parsley (*Petroselinum crispum* Hoff.).

(XV)
Cyanin
(Gl = glucosyl)

(XVI)
Apiose

Until the last year or so, most of the flavonoid glycosides were each given a trivial name, often confusing and usually derived from the species or genus of plant from which they were first isolated. For example, the 3-β-L-rhamnoside of quercetin (Xb) is called quercitrin, and that from kaempferol (Xa) afzelin. This multiplicity of names makes it very difficult even for the expert to search the literature for compounds belonging to a single class, or derivatives of a single compound. In some cases different names are still being used for the same substance! A systematic rational nomenclature has been proposed for flavonoids (Freudenberg and Weinges, 1960) but until this is accepted it is to be hoped that the names of any new flavonoid glycosides which are discovered will be related to the present nomenclature of the aglycones.

As will be seen from the next chapter, flavonoid compounds are widely distributed in higher plants (Swain and Bate-Smith, 1962); glycosides of quercetin, for example, occur in 62% of the leaves of dicotyledons examined by Bate-Smith (1956). They have been isolated from all the different parts of plants, although there are usually variations in the types of compound found in the various anatomical tissues of any one plant (cf. Griffiths, 1958). In terms of plant colouring, the most striking of such plant organs are undoubtedly the flowers and fruits, but it should be remembered that flavonoids also play a part in leaf colouring especially when these are in both the young and senescent state.

In this chapter we will be dealing mainly with four classes of flavonoid glycosides which are involved directly in plant colouration. These are the anthocyanins, the flavonols, the chalkones, and the aurones. Attention will also be given to a few closely related substances such as the anhydrobases (see p. 228), and to one completely unrelated group, the betacyanins (see p. 229). Before discussing the nature and properties of these classes in detail, brief consideration must be given to the relationship between their colour and their constitution.

III. Colour and Constitution of Flavonoid Compounds

Compounds are coloured because they absorb light in the visible region of the spectrum, that is between 400 and 800 mμ. Light absorption in this region and in the ultra-violet (150 to 400 mμ) causes the excitation of electrons in the molecule, and the more firmly such electrons are bound the higher will be the energy needed, that is, the shorter will be the wavelength at which the light is adsorbed. Thus, saturated hydrocarbons shows no absorption above 160 mμ, but compounds containing double or triple bonds, or hetero atoms with non-bonded electrons show absorption at much higher wavelengths.

Graebe and Liebermann in 1868 were the first to recognize the relationship between colour and unsaturation. Some years later Witt (1888) coined the terms chromophore (Gk, phoros, bearing) for organic groups which produced colour when present in a molecule and auxochrome for other groups which deepened such colours. The relationship between unsaturation, the structure of the chromophores and colour did not become apparent, however, until the electronic theories of organic chemistry had been fully worked out.

It is now generally recognized that the presence of conjugation, chromophores and auxochromes in a molecule all act in promoting greater ease of electron transition to higher energy levels by stabilization of the resulting excited structure. In any given type of molecule the longer the conjugated chain, or the greater the number of chromophores and auxochromes, the easier are such transitions, and the longer the wavelength of absorption.

These facts are well illustrated in the flavonoid field (Table II). The

TABLE II

Spectral Characteristics of Selected Classes
of Flavonoid Compound.[c]

No.[a]	Name	Range of λ max. mμ. Band I	Band II[b]
II	Flavan-3-ols		275–280
V	Flavanones	(310–330)	275–290
I	Flavones	330–350	250–270
X	Flavonols	350–390	250–270
VI	Chalkones	360–390	(240–260)
XII	Aurones	390–430	(240–260)
IX	Anthocyanins	475–560	275–280

[a] See Table I.
[b] Values in brackets represent peaks or shoulders with absorptivities 40% or less of the main peak.
[c] Data from Jurd (1962a), and Harborne (1964a).

hydroxy-substituted flavans (catechins, IIb, and leucoanthocyanins, IVa) in which no exocyclic conjugation of the two benzene rings occurs have single banded absorption spectra like that of the simple phenols (Fig. 1). Similarly the flavanones (Va) have spectra like those of the corresponding hydroxyacetophenones, since here the hydroxy groups in the A-ring are in conjugation with the carbonyl group at C_4 (Fig. 2). However, the conjugation between the hydroxy groups of the B-ring and the carbonyl groups at C-4 becomes important in the hydroxy

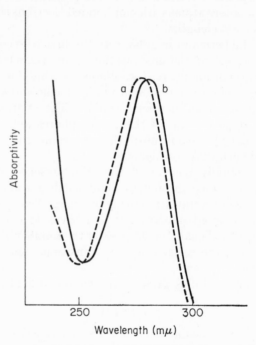

FIG. 1. The spectrum of (a) (+)-catechin (IIa) and (b) catechol (1,2-dihydroxy-benzene) in ethanol.

flavones, and the resulting spectra consist of two well separated bands of high absorptivity ($\log \epsilon > 4 \cdot 0$). The one at longer wavelength (band I) being associated with B-ring conjugation, and that at shorter wavelength (band II) with the A-ring (Fig. 3). In polyhydroxy-substituted compounds there is a great deal of overlap of individual absorption bands due to the contributions made by the various canonical forms, and many weaker bands (mainly arising from transitions of the non-bonded oxygen electrons) are masked or combined to give broad maxima. In the flavonols (X), band I moves to longer wavelengths than in the flavones owing to the contribution of the vinylic hydroxyl group at C_3 (Fig. 3). At sufficiently high concentration, solutions of flavonols absorb sufficiently in

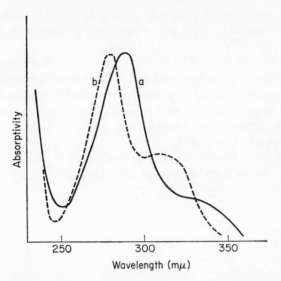

FIG. 2. The spectrum of (a) naringenin (Va) and (b) 2,4-dihydroxyacetophenone in ethanol.

the blue region of the visible spectrum to appear markedly yellow. Chalkones (VI) are also yellow and absorb in the same wavelength range as the flavonols although slightly higher, which indicates that the non-bonding electrons of the heterocyclic oxygen do not interfere greatly with conjugation in the latter substances. In aurones, band I is at an

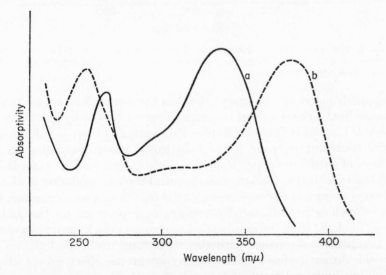

FIG. 3. The spectrum of (a) apigenin (Ia) and (b) myricetin (Xc) in ethanol.

even longer wavelength probably owing to the planarity of the 5-membered heterocyclic ring and consequent greater ease of resonance as much as any other factor (Jurd, 1962a).

The anthocyanin salts (XV) in acid solution, in which the electrons of the heterocyclic oxygen atom are involved in π bond formation, absorb at the longest wavelength of any class of flavonoid compounds (Fig. 4). It should be noted, however, that in neutral or basic solution the anthocyanins have different structures from (XV) and therefore different absorption spectra (see p. 223).

It can be seen, therefore, that as conjugation increases, flavonoid compounds absorb light at longer wavelengths. In any one class of

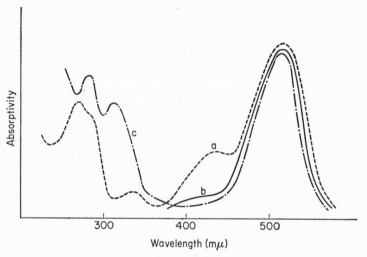

Wavelength (mμ)

FIG. 4. The spectra of (a) pelargonidin-3-glucoside (XVa), (b) pelargonidin-3,5-diglucoside, and (c) pelargonidin-3-p-coumarylglucoside-5-glucoside in 0·01% methanolic hydrochloric acid.

compounds increasing hydroxylation has the same effect, owing to the increase in the non-bonding electrons supplied by the hydroxyl group (Table III, see also Table I, Chapter 19). Naturally there is a difference in the contribution made by each hydroxyl group depending on its position of substitution (cf. Harborne, 1964a), generally in accordance with the expectation from organic chemical theory. Acylation of all the hydroxyl groups in flavonoid compounds results in a hypsochromic (to lower wavelength) shift, usually resulting in a spectrum like that of the parent nucleus. Here the non-bonded electrons of the hydroxyl-oxygens are involved in resonance with the acyl group itself. Methylation or glycoside formation has a much lesser hypsochromic effect, except where the vinylic hydroxyl group of flavonols is involved.

Finally one should remember that the spectra of all groups of flavonoid compounds are markedly altered when the phenolic hydroxyl groups are ionized (i.e. above pH 9) or involved in chelate formation with metals (Jurd, 1962a). Indeed, the formation of deeper colours when flavonoids are treated with iron alum and similar mordants, which also makes the pigments substantive, formed the basis of the old dyestuffs industry.

TABLE III

The Anthocyanidins[a]

Name and abbreviation	Substitution pattern in flavyllium salt[b]	λ max. $m\mu$[c]	Colour
Apigeninidin (Ap)	5,7,4'-Trihydroxy	476	orange yellow
Luteolinidin (Lt)	5,7,3',4'-Tetrahydroxy	493	orange
Tricetinidin (Tr)	5,7,3',4',5'-Pentahydroxy	520	—
Pelargonidin (Pg)	3,5,7,4'-Tetrahydroxy	520	scarlet red
Cyanidin (Cy)	3,5,7,3',4'-Pentahydroxy	535	bluish red
Peonidin (Pn)	Cyanidin-3'-O-methyl ether	532	bluish red
Rosinidin (Rs)	Cyanidin-7,3'-di-O-methyl ether	524	bluish red
Delphinidin (Dp)	3,5,7,3',4',5'-Hexahydroxy	546	purple blue
Petunidin (Pt)	Delphinidin-3'-O-methyl ether	546	purple blue
Malvidin (Mv)	Delphinidin-3',5'-di-O-methyl ether	542	purple
Hirsutidin (Hs)	Delphinidin-7,3',5'-tri-O-methyl ether	536	bluish red
Capseninidin (Cp)	Delphinidin-5,3',5'-tri-O-methyl ether	538	purple

[a] Data from Harborne (1962b; 1963a).   [b] Based on IX, Table I.
[c] In methanolic HCl.

For example, dyers' weld (*Reseda lutea* L.), which is the oldest known European dyestuff (Perkin and Everest, 1918), contains luteolin (Ib) which is itself hardly coloured, (λ max. 350 mμ) but which with aluminium gives an attractive yellow colour (λ max. 390 mμ).

IV. THE ANTHOCYANINS

A. INTRODUCTION

The flavonoid compounds have been the subject of investigations since the beginnings of modern organic chemistry. Compounds which could be readily isolated from plants which had been known since antiquity as a source of dyes naturally received the greatest attention. Indeed, the first flavonoid compound to be obtained in a more or less pure state was morin (XVII), which Chevreul obtained from old fustic (*Morus tinctoria* L. = *Chlorophora tinctoria* Gaudich.) in 1814 (Perkin and Everest, 1918). Most of the flavonoid compounds responsible for the tinctorial properties of natural dyestuffs had been isolated by the mid-nineteenth century, and although their structures were not determined until the researches of Perkin and Kostanecki in the 1890's, this was still twenty years before any anthocyanin had been obtained in a crystalline condition. The difficulty lay in the fact that neutral solvents were normally used for

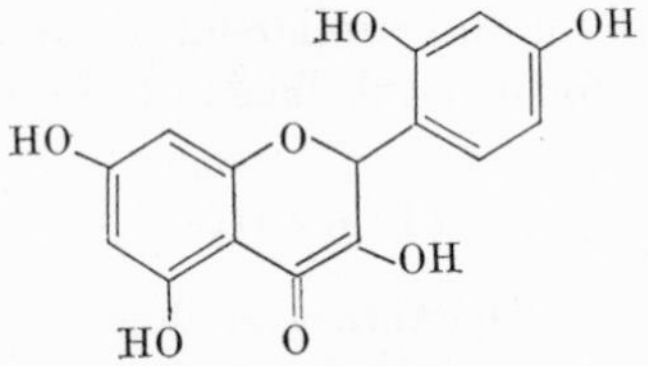

(XVII)
Morin

extraction of natural products and it was not until Willstätter and Everest (1913) recognized the oxonium nature of anthocyanins and used acids for their extraction that rapid progress could be made. These two workers isolated cyanin (XV) from cornflower and recognized that it was a diglucoside. They also proposed the terms anthocyanin and anthocyanidin for the glycosides and aglycones respectively, and introduced methods for distinguishing them based on differences in their distribution between amyl alcohol and aqueous acid. The flavyllium salt structure of the anthocyanidins (IX) was proposed by Everest (1914) one year later, and was rapidly confirmed by the brilliant synthetic work of Willstätter and his collaborators (summarized by Dean, 1963). Later Robinson and Karrer and their co-workers extended such syntheses to include all the then known common anthocyanins.

B. THE ANTHOCYANIDINS

A total of twelve anthocyanidins are known ranging from apiginidin (gesneridin) first isolated as a 5-glucoside from *Gesneria fulgens* (Robinson and Robinson, 1932) to hirsutidin, first obtained from *Primula hirsuta* (Karrer and Widmer, 1927b) (Table III). The variation in the pattern of substitution is more limited; eight of the compounds being based on two structures (Xb and c), most expected on biosynthetic grounds. The glycosides of these two anthocyanidins (cyanidin, delphinidin) together with those from pelargonidin (Xa) are the ones which most frequently occur in Nature; derivatives of the first being present in 80% of pigmented leaves, 69% of fruits and 50% of flowers. By contrast, anthocyanidins lacking a hydroxyl group at C_3 are very rare, tricetinidin, for example, having been isolated so far only from tea (*Camellia sinensis*, Roberts and Williams, 1958).

As might be expected from what was said previously, the visible colour of the anthocyanidins is dependent on the number and orientation of hydroxyl and methoxyl groups in the molecule and varies from orange yellow (apigenidin) to blue (delphinidin) (Harborne, 1958b). The colour is, however, dependent on the solvent and is bluer in alcoholic acid than in aqueous acid. Owing to the ionic character of the anthocyanidins the intensity of colour is also markedly dependent on pH, and as this is raised to near neutrality more and more of the pigment is transformed into the colourless pseudo-base form (2-hydroxy chromene) (e.g. XVIIIa → XVIIIb). According to the data of Swain and Hillis (1959)

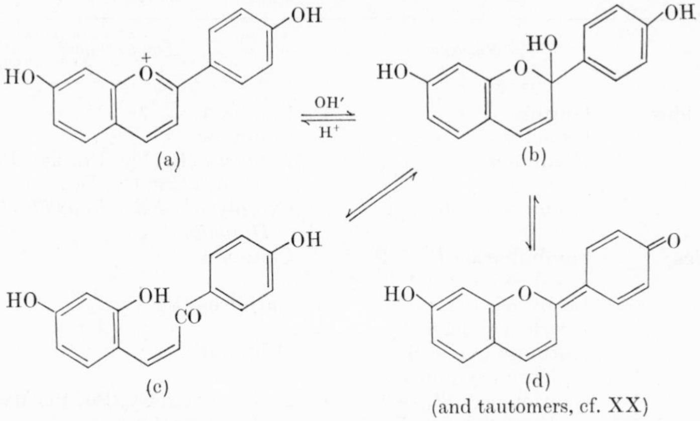

(a) (b)

(c) (d)

(and tautomers, cf. XX)

(XVIII)

Various forms of anthocyanidins

cyanin (XV) has a pK of approximately 2, but the values for other flavyllium salts may be somewhat higher (Albert, 1959). It should be noted that only band I is affected, the intensity of band II (λ max. ~ 280 mμ) hardly changing when the pH is raised from 1·0 to 6·0. The pseudo-base form can undoubtedly undergo ring opening to form the corresponding chalkone (XVIIIc), (Jurd, 1962b), and other ill-understood changes usually ensue, some of which are light-catalysed and non-reversible (Kuhn and Sperling, 1960).

At pH values above 7·0, the anthocyanidins can form anhydro bases (XVIIId) all of which have bluer shades, but which are unstable in the presence of water unless the 3-hydroxyl group is absent (XVIII, R = H). Further raising of the pH induces ionization of the phenolic hydroxyl groups, but under such basic conditions the anthocyanidins are very unstable, undergoing both cleavage and aerial oxidation, and re-acidification of such solution usually leads to poor recoveries.

C. GLYCOSIDIC FORMS

All the common anthocyanidins exist in Nature as glycosides (antho-cyanins), and often more than one derivative of a single aglycone is present in a given plant. Eighteen different types of anthocyanin glycosides are now known (Harborne, 1963a, b) and these can be divided into six classes (Table IV). The relative order of frequency of occurrence of the various monosaccharides in the anthocyanins is as stated previously (p. 215). So far L-arabinose has only been found in three plant genera,

TABLE IV

Classes of Anthocyanin Glycosides[a]

Class	Sugars	Occurrence[b]
3-Monosides	Glucose	Common
	Galactose	Common
	Rhamnose	Lathyrus (Pg, Cy, Pn, Dp, Pt)
		Plumbago (Pg, Cy, Dp, Cp)
	Arabinose (α-linked)	Cy only Rhododendron, Theobroma, Hordeum
3-Biosides	Sambubiose (β1 → 2 xylosylglucose)	Common
	Lathyrose (β1 → 2 xylosylgalactose)	Lathyrus (Pg, Cy)
	Rutinose (α1 → 6 rhamnosylglucose)	Common
	Gentiobiose (β1 → 6 glucosylglucose)	Primula (Pg, Cy, Pn, Pt, Mv) Tritonia (Pg)
	Sophorose (β1 → 2 glucosylglucose)	Common
3-Triosides	Glucosylglucosylglucose	Primula (Pg, Pn, Pt, Mv)
	2^G-xylosylrutinose	Begonia
	2^G-glucosylrutinose	Begonia and Rubus
3-Monoside-5-glucoside	Rhamnose	Lathyrus (Pg, Cy, Pn, Dp, Pt, Mv)
	Glucose	Common
3-Bioside-5-glucoside	Rutinose	Common
	Sambubiose	Matthiola (Pg, Cy) Sambucus (Cy)
	Sophorose	Rhaphanus (Pg, Cy) Brassica (Cy)
3-Bioside-7-glucoside	Sophorose	Papaver (Pg) Watsonia (Pg)

[a] From Harborne (1963a, b).
[b] Pg etc. refer to abbreviations of anthocyanins (see Table III). Only references to selected examples are given.

in each case linked to cyanidin with the unusual α-link, and xylose, only in biosides. It should also be noted that glucose is the only sugar found linked with the C_5 and C_7 hydroxyl groups. The report that *Bladhia sieboldii* contains delphinidin-7-galactoside (Yen and Huang, 1961) has been discounted by Harborne (1963b). Only a few of the wide number of possible disaccharides have been found attached to anthocyanidins. Thus only one rhamnoglucoside (rutinose, α 1 → 6), one xylosylglucoside (sambubiose, β 1 → 2) and two glucosylglucosides (sophorose, β 1 → 2; gentiobiose β 1 → 6) have been observed, the first three being relatively common. Two branched sugars have been found in *Begonia* species, both based on rutinose (2^G-glucosyl- and 2^G-xylosyl-rutinose) but along with the other trisaccharides (Table IV) are rare.

The λ max. of band I in the spectra of the glycosides of the common anthocyanins shows in all cases a hypsochromic shift from that of the aglycone. The two common classes, the 3- and 3,5-di-glycosides have similar spectral maxima, but the former all have a pronounced shoulder in the 440–460 mμ region (Fig. 4) which can be used for identification purposes (Harborne, 1958a).

Besides the glycosides proper, acylated anthocyanins have been long known but their structure has only recently been elucidated (Harborne, 1964b). In each case investigated it was shown that the sugar attached to the 3-hydroxyl group is acylated. The only acyl groups so far found in these compounds are those derived from the three common cinnamic acids, p-coumaric acid (XIIIa), caffeic acid (XIIIb) and ferulic acid (XIIIc); earlier reports on the occurrence of p-hydroxybenzoic acid (Willstätter and Mieg, 1915) and malonic acid (Karrer and Widmer, 1928) in such compounds have not been substantiated (Harborne, 1964b). The presence of the cinnamic acids can be readily demonstrated in these compounds by spectroscopic means, since the absorption spectra of the acid residues are superimposed on those of the unacylated anthocyanins (Harborne, 1958a) (see Fig. 4). The methods by which their mode of linkage was determined is described below and in Chapter 19.

D. THE CONTRIBUTIONS OF ANTHOCYANINS TO FLOWER COLOUR

As mentioned in the introduction, anthocyanins are responsible for the majority of the red and blue colours of flowers and fruits. As might be expected from a consideration of the absorption spectra (Table III) the bluer shades are usually, but not always, associated with the presence of glycosides of delphinidin and its derivatives, especially malvidin. The depth of pigmentation naturally increases with the concentration of the anthocyanin; when this is sufficiently high, as in the skins of many fruits, and especially when chlorophyll is also present, the tissue may appear almost black. The presence of small quantities of other pigments, such as carotenoids, also modifies the apparent colour of anthocyanins in flowers.

Different coloured flowers often contain the same anthocyanin (e.g. the cornflower and the rose) and it is obvious that other factors must be involved. Of these, co-pigmentation and metal chelation appear to be the most important (Harborne, 1963a). Co-pigmentation is usually associated with the presence of flavones, flavonols and flavans (condensed tannins) which change the colour to a bluer shade by modifying the actual absorption spectra of the anthocyanins themselves (see Chapter 9). The colour of anthocyanins is only markedly affected by metal chelation, especially with iron and aluminium, when the compounds possess an o-dihydroxy grouping (see Table I, Chapter 19). Several anthocyanin-metal complexes have, however, been isolated; those from cornflower (*Centaurea cyanus*) and *Lupinus polyphemus* contain, besides cyanin (XV), iron and aluminium, an unknown protein-like substance (Hayashi, 1962). Changes in the pH of the cell sap have also naturally been suggested to be responsible for variation in the colour of flowers which have the same anthocyanin. More recently this factor has been discounted because the variation in the pH of the cell sap (0·5 to 1·0 units) is suggested to be too small. It should be remembered, however, that at the normal pH of the flower (5·5), only a small part of the anthocyanin is present in the oxonium form. Small changes in the pH about this point may therefore have a much larger effect than expected on the contributions made by the forms XVIIIa–d. In any case there will be an effect of pH and of the presence of organic acids (e.g. citric acid, Hughes and Swain, 1962) on the formation of metal chelates and this aspect of pigmentation warrants further study.

Finally, the presence of colourless forms of anthocyanins have been reported in certain aquatic plants (Reznik and Neuhausel, 1959). Presumably these are present completely in the pseudo-base form, and such compounds may also easily occur in many species which have not so far been examined.

E. THE CHEMISTRY OF ANTHOCYANINS

1. *Synthesis*

The first synthesis of an anthocyanidin was carried out by Willstätter and Mallison (1914) who reduced quercetin (Xb) in poor yield to cyanidin (IXb.) In the same year Willstätter and Zechmeister (1914) carried out a total synthesis of pelargonidin (IXa) from 3,5,7-trimethoxycoumarin and p-methoxyphenyl magnesium bromide. However, the most convenient methods of synthesis of anthocyanidins, and the only ones used with success for the glycosides were devised by Robinson and his co-workers (Robinson, 1934). In these syntheses, a series of 2-O-benzoyl-(or O-tetraacetylglucosyl) -phloroglucinaldehydes were condensed with a variety of ω-hydroxy (or O-tetraacetylglucosyl)- acetophenones to produce all the common anthocyanidins and their glycosides as illustrated in the synthesis of hirsutin (XIX) (Robinson and Todd, 1932).

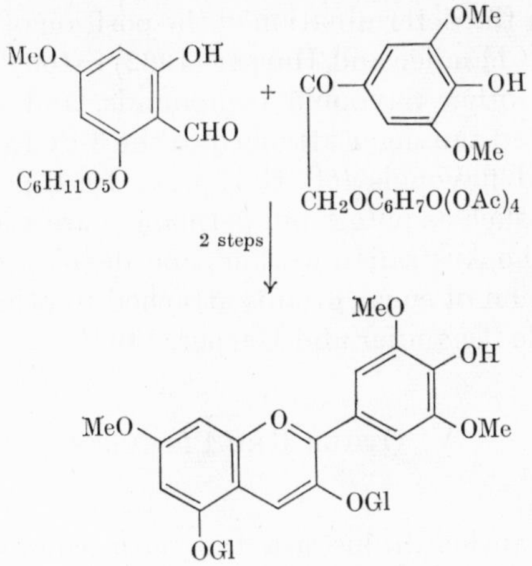

(XIX)

Hirsutin

(Gl = glucosyl)

2. Reactions

Since there are several excellent recent textbooks available (e.g. Dean, 1963; Geissman, 1962; Katritzky and Lagowski, 1960; Albert, 1959; Elderfield, 1951) the chemistry of these and other flavonoid compounds will not be dealt with in any detail. However, there are several reactions which deserve attention as they are of importance in determining the structure of anthocyanins on a microscale (see Chapter 19). Obviously the first reaction that needs to be used for this purpose is hydrolysis. Both Chandler and Harper (1961) and Harborne (1958b) have shown that when hydrolysis is carried out under mild conditions and the products examined by paper chromatography a number of structural features can be elucidated. For example, Harborne (1958b) detected seven readily separable products from the controlled hydrolysis of pelargonidin-5-glucoside-3-sophoroside; these were the known 3,5-diglucoside, the 3-sophoroside, the 3- and 5-glucosides, pelargonidin itself and the two sugars, glucose and sophorose. From these data the structure of the compound was unequivocally determined.

Mild alkali degradation under hydrogen using 10% barium hydroxide was used by Karrer to determine the structure of the anthocyanidins (Karrer and Widmer, 1927a) which under these conditions break down to give phloroglucinol (or other A-ring fragments) and the substituted benzoic acid corresponding to the B-ring. This method has not as yet been exploited on a micro-scale because the yields are so poor (about 10%, J. B. Harborne, 1964, personal communication), unlike that of mild oxidation with hydrogen peroxide developed by Karrer and de

Meuron (1932) for the determination of the position of sugar attachment in anthocyanins. Chandler and Harper (1962) extended this method on a micro scale to other flavonoid compounds, and showed that such oxidations liberated the sugar attached to the 3-hydroxyl group in both anthocyanins and flavonols (cf. Harborne, 1964b). The use of other oxidizing agents, such as potassium permanganate and ozone, were also investigated by the Australian workers and developed on a micro-scale for the investigation of sugar groups attached to other positions of the flavonoid molecule (Chandler and Harper, 1962).

V. Other Red Pigments

A. INTRODUCTION

Although the anthocyanins are the most common red colouring matters in higher plants, a number of other pigments are certainly worth a brief mention. These include, besides certain carotenoids such as lycopene (Chapter 3) and the naphthaquinones and anthraquinones (Chapter 11) the anhydrobases and the betacyanins.

B. FLAVYLLIUM ANHYDROBASES AND RELATED COMPOUNDS

As mentioned earlier all flavyllium salts yield anhydrobases (XVIIId) when treated with dilute alkali, although these are generally unstable and revert to the pseudobase form (XVIIIb) very quickly. However, two naturally occurring compounds of this class are known, carajurin (XX) from *Bignonia chica* (Chapman, *et al.*, 1927) and dracorhodin (XXI) from *Dracaena draco* L. (Robertson and Whalley, 1950). A dimer of

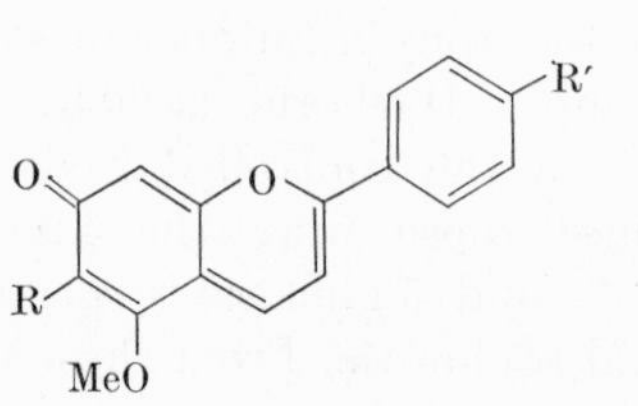

(XX) R = OH, R′ = OMe; Carajurin
(XXI) R = Me; R′ = H; Dracorhodin

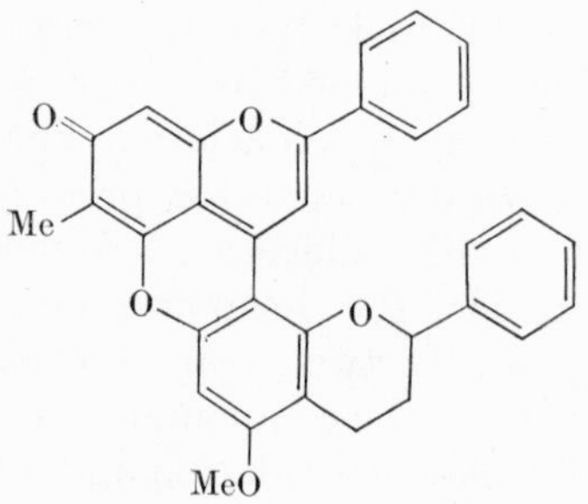

(XXII)
Dracorubin

dracorhodin, dracorubin (XXII) has also been isolated from the same tree (Robertson *et al.*, 1950). The structure of two other compounds of this type, santalin and santarubin which have been isolated from *Pterocarpus santalinus* (sandalwood) and *Baphia nitida* (camwood or barwood), has not been fully elucidated (Dean, 1963; Robertson and Whalley, 1954). The red dyestuffs obtained from the so-called soluble red woods, brazilein (XXIII) from *Caesalpinia crista* and other species, and haematin (XXIV) from *Haematoxylon campechianum* (logwood) are both produced by the aerial oxidation of two related colourless compounds, brazilin and haematoxylon which are derivatives of 4-phenyl-chroman (Robinson, 1959). Peltogynol (XXV) (from *Peltogyne porphyrocardia*) another compound closely related to the flavonoids is also

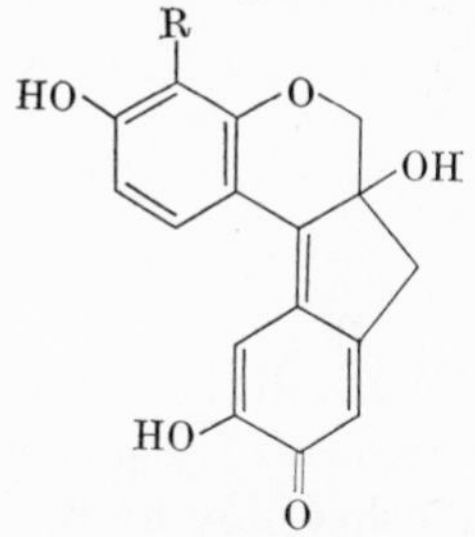

(XXIII) R = H; Brazilein
(XXIV) R = OH; Haematin

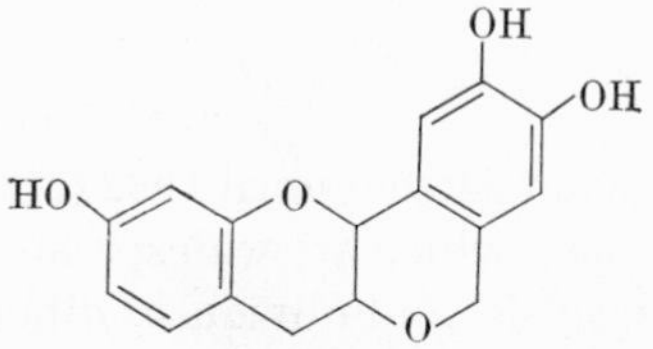

(XXV)
Peltogynol

colourless but turns red on being heated in acid solution. For some time it was regarded as a close relative of the leuco-anthocyanins (IV) until its structure was proven by Chan *et al.* (1958). It is accompanied in the wood by an epimeric form. Cyanomaclurin, is another colourless compound which in this case develops a deep blue colour on treatment with alkali. It was isolated from *Artocarpus integrefolia* by Perkin (1905), and although its structure is not completely known, Dean (1963) has suggested (XXVI) by analogy with peltogynol. Another compound of this

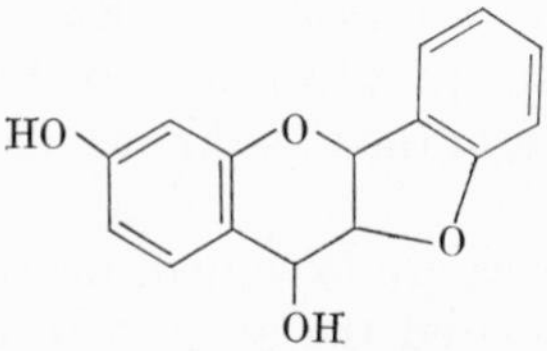

(XXVI)
Cyanomaclurin

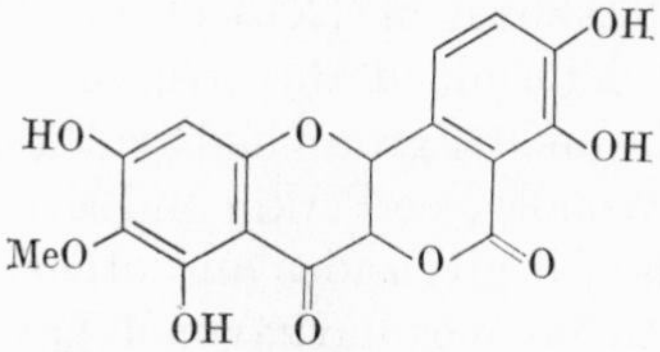

(XXVII)
Distemonanthin

group is distemonanthin (XXVII) a yellow compound isolated by King *et al.* (1954) from *Distemonanthus benthamianus*.

C. BETACYANINS AND BETAXANTHINS*

The red pigments of beetroot (*Beta vulgaris* v. *rubra*) have similar spectra to the anthocyanins (λ max. 530–545), and although they turn

*See also p. 346

yellow rather than blue, when treated with alkali, and contain nitrogen they were long assumed to have a flavonoid character (Ainley and Robinson, 1937). The structure of the aglycone betanidin (XXVIII) in

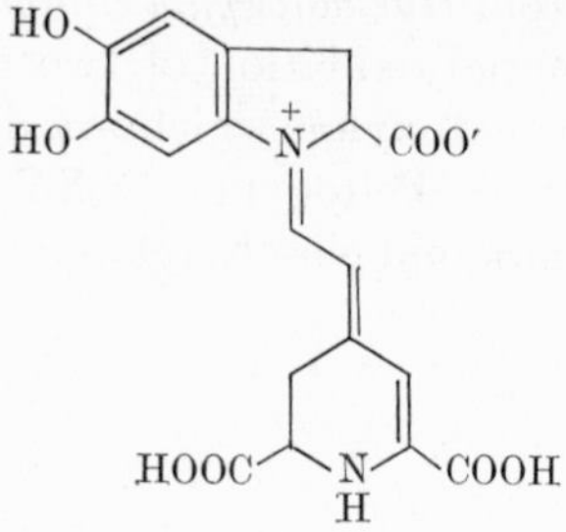

(XXVIII)
Betanidin

fact was not settled until 1962 (Mabry et al., 1962). All the red pigments of this class, which are widespread in the Centrospermae, yield betanidin on hydrolysis, and obviously differ from each other only by the nature of the sugar linked to the phenolic hydroxyl groups. The structures of the closely related yellow pigments, the betaxanthins have recently been elucidated by Piatelli et al. (1964). They have the dihydropyridine dicarboxylic acid residue of betacyanin (XXVIII) substituted with amino acid residues instead of the indole residue.

VI. The Flavones and Flavonols

A. THE AGLYCONES

Although, as mentioned above, morin (XVII) was isolated as early as 1814, the structure of these compounds was not properly elucidated until 1891 when Hertzig (1891) showed that quercetin had the molecular formula shown in (Xb) (Table I). Shortly afterwards v. Kostanecki (1893) determined the structure of chrysin (XXIX), and within ten years he and his group had synthesized most of the then known flavones and flavonols (see Perkin and Everest, 1918).

Today, if glycosides and other derivatives are excluded, nearly one hundred flavones and flavonols have been isolated, the latter class making nearly two-thirds of the total (Dean, 1963). Undoubtedly many more remain to be discovered. The compounds range in hydroxylation pattern from flavone (I) itself which occurs as a mealy deposit on the leaves of *Primula pulverulenta* (Müller, 1915) and other species, to digicitrin (XXX) from the red foxglove, *Digitalis purpurea* (Meier and Furst, 1962). Besides compounds containing a simple flavone nucleus, three C-methyl derivatives (strobochryrin, pinoquercetin and pinomyricetin) have been isolated from pine species. In each case the methyl residue is at C_6 as shown in strobochrysin (XXXI) from *Pinus strobus* (Linstedt and

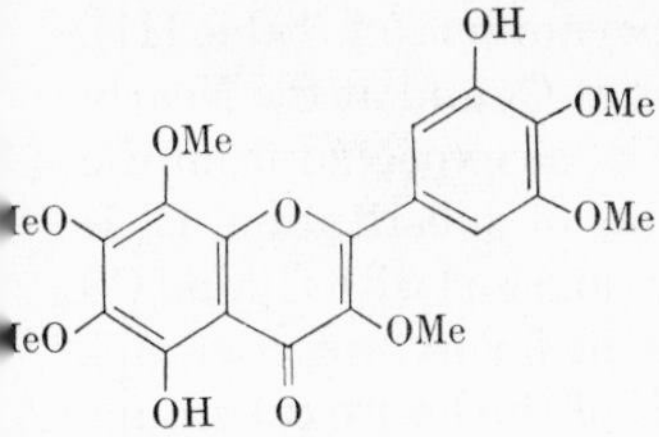

(XXX)
Digicitrin

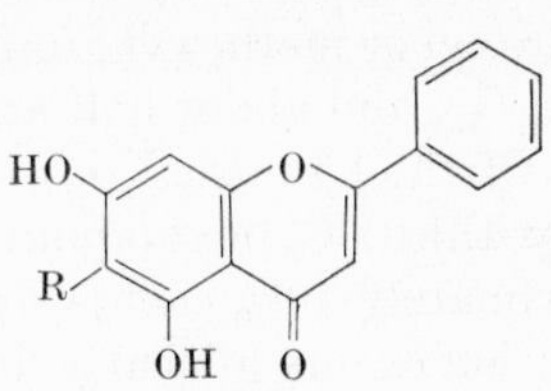

(XXIX) R = H; Chrysin
(XXXI) R = Me; Strobochrysin

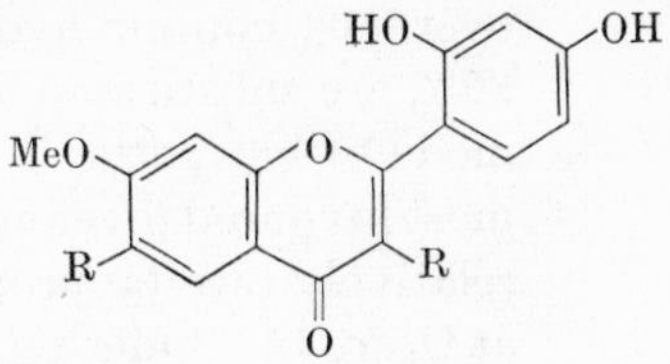

(XXXII)
R = —CH₂.CH=CMe₂
Artocarpin

Misiorny, 1951). There are four C-isopentenyl-substituted compounds, one of which, artocarpin (XXXII) from the heartwood of *Artocarpus integrefolia* (Bringi and Dave, 1956), is distinguished as being the only flavone substituted with a carbon side chain at C_3. It is accompanied in the wood by its 2'-*O*-isopentenyloxy-ether (Dave *et al.*, 1962). Six furo-

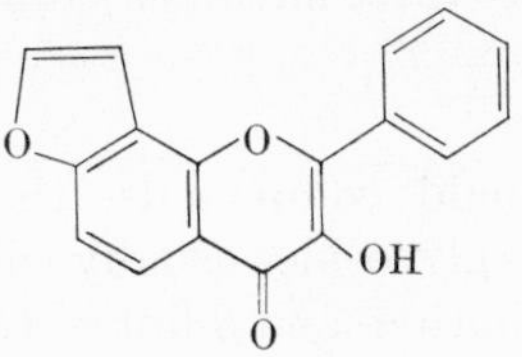

(XXXIII)
Karanjin

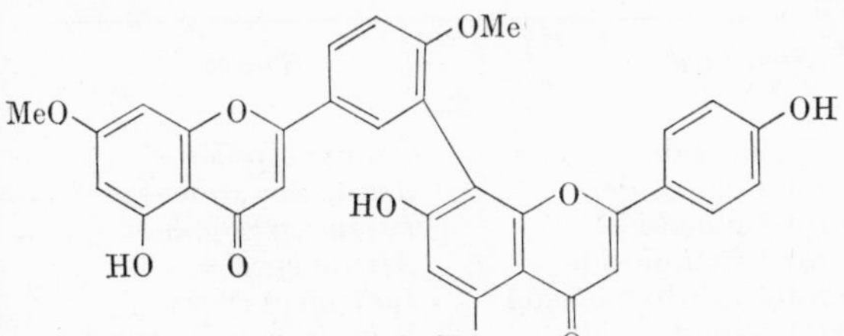

(XXXIV)
Ginkgetin

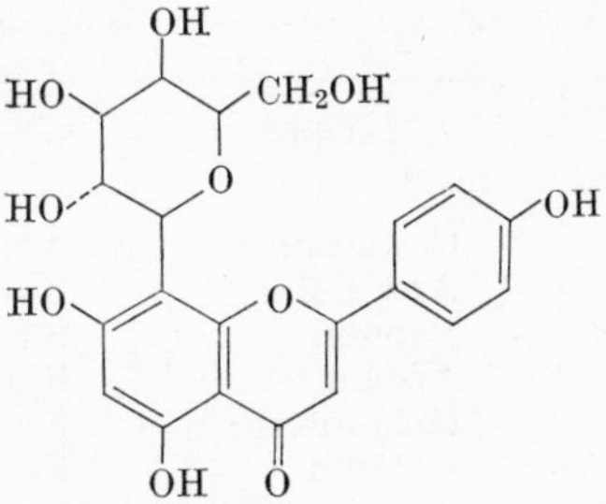

(XXXV)
Vitexin

flavones like karanjin (XXXIII) from *Pongamia glabra* (Limaye, 1936), and seven biflavonyls such as ginkgetin (XXXIV) from *Ginkgo biloba* (Baker and Ollis, 1961), are also known. Finally there is a number of glycoflavones which contain an 8-substituted C-glycosyl residue as in vitexin (XXXV) (formula from Dean, 1963) from *Vitex littoralis* (Perkin, 1898).

Although the hydroxylation patterns of the simple flavones and flavonols are more varied than those of the anthocyanidins (cf. Table III), over 90% contain hydroxyl or methoxyl groups at C_5 and at C_7. Nearly 80% are substituted at $C_{4'}$, and about half at $C_{3'}$, as expected from the mode of biosynthesis. Of the less usual positions of substitution, C_6 is most favoured (over one-third), C_8 next (about a quarter) with $C_{2'}$ and $C_{5'}$ relatively rare (approximately 10% each). Except for hydroxyl groups at C_5 (c. 15%) methylation occurs in nearly half of the hydroxyl groups at the expected positions, but is much more common (70–80%) at C_6 and C_8 (see Dean, 1963).

Many of these compounds have so far only been isolated from a single species, but the three most commonly occurring flavonols kaempferol, quercetin and myricetin (Xa, b and c, Table I) are much more widely distributed than the corresponding anthocyanidins (IXa, b and c). Indeed, in some groups of plants they can almost be regarded as common metabolites; for example, 90% of the leaves of the woody dicotyledons contain glycosides of these three flavonols (Swain and Bate-Smith, 1962).

B. THE GLYCOSIDES

As with other flavonoid compounds, the hydroxy flavones and flavonols mainly occur as glycosides usually with a β-linked sugar (Table V). L-Arabinose, occurs both α- and β-linked to the 3-hydroxyl group of quercetin, and in the first case furanoside and pyranoside forms are

TABLE V

Selected Examples of Flavonol Glycosides[a]

Name	Structure[b]	Source
Cosmosiin	Apigenin-7-glucoside	*Cosmos bipinatus*
Astragalin	Kaempferol-3-glucoside	*Astragalus sinicus*
Populin	Kaempferol-7-glucoside	*Thespesia populnea*
Afzelin	Kaempferol-3-rhamnoside	*Afzelia* species
Kaempferitrin	Kaempferol-3,7,dirhamnoside	*Indigofera errecta*
Robinin	Kaempferol-7-rhamnoside-3-galactosylrhamnoside	*Robinia pseudacacia*
Isoquercitrin	Quercetin-3-glucoside	*Gossypium herbaceum*
Quercitrin	Quercetin-3-rhamnoside	*Quercus tinctoria*
Quercimeritrin	Quercetin-7-glucoside	*Gossypium herbaceum*
Rutin	Quercetin-3-rutinoside	*Ruta graveolens*
Myricitrin	Myricetin-3-rhamnoside	*Myrica rubra*
Cannabiscitrin	Myricetin-3'-glucoside	*Cannabis indica*
Gossypitrin	Gossypetin-7-glucoside	*Gossypium* species
Gossipin	Gossypetin-8-glucoside	*Gossypium indicum*

[a] Data from Karrer (1958), Dean (1963) and Hattori (1962).
[b] Structure of aglycones, apigenin, Ia; kaempferol, Xa; quercetin, Xb; myricetin, Xc; (all in Table I) gossypetin, XXXVII.

present, giving three known isomeric compounds in all. The most common sugar is again glucose followed by galactose, rhamnose, arabinose and xylose; glucuronides are also found. There are numerous compounds containing either sugars on more than one hydroxyl group or di- and tri-saccharides. One kaempferol derivative is even reported to contain five sugar residues (Beckmann and Geiger, 1963). The structure of the complex sugars in these compounds has not been examined in many cases, probably owing to the difficulty in obtaining the higher glycosides in a pure state. In flavones the commonest position for sugar substitution is the hydroxyl group at C_7 (80%), followed by those at C_5 and $C_{4'}$. In flavonols the C_3-hydroxyl is most favoured (70%) followed by C_7 (20%), and $C_{4'}$ (5%). So far, four acylated compounds, e.g. tiliroside, the 3-p-coumarylglucoside of kaempferol (Harborne, 1964b) have been isolated, and it is to be expected that several more will be found in the future. Most plants contain more than one glycoside of any aglycone, huckleberry (*Vaccinium myrtillus*) for example having five glycosides of quercetin (Ice and Wender, 1953).

C. THE CONTRIBUTION OF FLAVONES AND FLAVONOLS TO FLOWER COLOUR

When isolated, the glycosides of flavones and flavonols vary in colour from pale cream to deep yellow depending, as stressed earlier, on the number and orientation of their hydroxyl groups (see Table I, Chapter 19). On ionization of the phenolic hydroxyl groups, the colour of solutions of all these compounds deepens, that is the λ max. undergoes a bathochromic shift, the amount being dependent on the pattern of substitution. In this case there is of course no intermediate form corresponding with the anthocyanidin pseudobases. Similar changes in colour and spectra may also be induced by protonation of the compounds in strong acids. These changes in colour with pH are fully reversible, but care must be taken with compounds, especially flavonols, which are susceptible to oxidation in basic solutions. It should also be remembered that under extreme conditions ring opening usually occurs and can lead to rearrangement or other unwanted changes. The colour and spectra of these compounds are also markedly changed by chelation with metals, and Perkin (see Perkin and Everest, 1918) made great use of the changes in colour with different metals for deducing the probable structure of several flavones. Such changes have also been used in specific colour tests for flavonols (e.g. zirconium oxychloride and citric acid, Hörhammer and Müller, 1954; see also Seikel, 1962).

Despite the yellowish colour of the three common flavonols (Xa, b and c) and their glycosides, the fact that they have been shown to be present in numerous white flowers makes it unlikely that they contribute much directly to petal colour. They may, however, be involved in the

8*

yellowish colour of some timbers. The relatively rare, more highly
substituted compounds such as quercetagetin (XXXVI) from *Tagetes
erecta* and other species (Perkin, 1902) gossypetin (XXXVII) from
Gossypium herbaceum (Perkin, 1909) and patuletin (XXXVIII) from

(XXXVI) R = OH, R' = H
    Quercetagetin

(XXXVII) R = H, R' = OH
    Gossypetin

(XXXVIII) R = OMe, R' = H
    Patuletin

Tagetes patula (Row and Seshadri, 1946), which are known to occur in
yellow flowers (see Chapter 9) are probably the most important flavone
derivatives involved in flower colour. It is, however, difficult to general-
ize, since as pointed out above, the colour of flavones and flavonols is
markedly altered both by changes in pH and more importantly by the
presence of metals. No studies of flavonol-metal complexes have been
made comparable to those made of the anthocyanins (see Hayashi, 1962;
and Chapter 9), but it is interesting that a yellow-brown complex
containing rutin (Table V) together with protein and much mineral ash
has been obtained from manufactured tobacco (Jacobsen, 1961).

Flavone and flavonol glycosides are also involved in co-pigmentation
with anthocyanins, the colour of which can be changed to bluer shades
in the presence of glycosides of the other two classes (see Chapter 9).

Most white or ivory flowers contain flavone or flavonol glycosides,
although occasionally flavonones and 3-hydroxy flavanones predominate. Albino mutants of *Antirrhinum majus* however, contain only
p-coumaric and caffeic acids (XIIIa and b) (Geissman and Harborne,
1955). Such albinos are rare, and have a quite different appearance from
the ordinary white flowers, being almost translucent. It may be concluded, therefore, that whiteness is due in part to the presence of the
flavone and flavonol glycosides, but obviously more studies are required
on this point.

D. THE CHEMISTRY OF FLAVONES AND FLAVONOLS

1. *Synthesis*

Kostanecki's early synthesis of flavones by a Claisen condensation
between suitably substituted phloracetophenones and benzoic esters
(Emilewicz *et al.*, 1899) has been superseded by the Baker-Venkataraman
(Baker, 1933) and the Allan-Robinson syntheses (Allan and Robinson,
1924). All these syntheses involve the formation and subsequent

cyclization of a suitable o-hydroxydibenzoylmethane as shown in the synthesis of quercetin (Xb), by the condensation of ω-methoxyphloracetophenone with veratric anhydride (Allan and Robinson, 1924) which goes via the intermediate (XXXIX). Flavanones and chalkones,

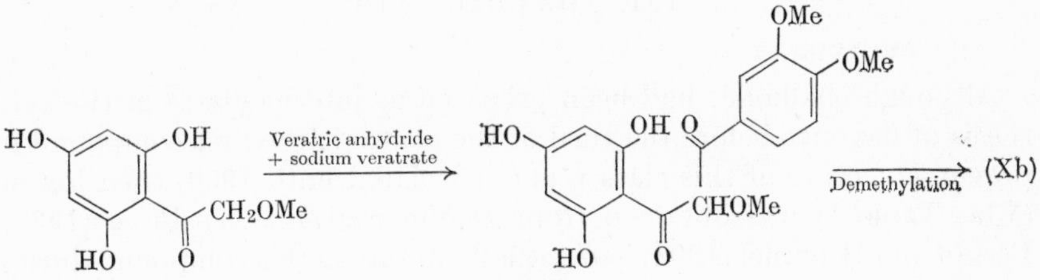

(XXXIX)

which may be readily synthesized (see p. 239), can be converted into flavones and flavonols in a variety of ways (Seshadri, 1962). For example naringenin (Va) can be converted into apigenin (Ia) by dehydrogenation of the trimethyl ether with selenium dioxide and subsequent demethylation; tetra-O-methyleriodictyol yields 5,7,3',4'-tetra-O-methylquercetin on treatment with amyl nitrite to introduce an isonitroso group at C_3 and subsequent hydrolysis with mineral acid.

2. *Reactions*

The carbonyl group in flavones and flavonols does not show the general reactions of such groups with keto reagents except Grignard reagents and 2,4-dinitrophenylhydrazine. Reduction of flavones and flavonols gives a variety of substances depending on the reagent, and often products are coloured and can be used for diagnostic purposes (Venkataraman, 1962). Magnesium or zinc with alcoholic mineral acid gives flavyllium salts; in fact cyanidin was first synthesized in this way from quercetin (Willstätter and Mallison, 1914). Catalytic reduction on the other hand gives flavan-4-ols or flavan-3,4-diols (leucoanthocyanins) (King and Clark-Lewis, 1954).

The determination of the structure of flavone and flavonol glycosides on a micro-scale makes use of similar methods to those described in connection with the anthocyanins. That is, partial hydrolysis, oxidation with hydrogen peroxide, ozone or permanganate, and alkali degradation (see p. 227), all the reactions being followed by the use of paper chromatographic and spectral methods (Harborne, 1959). As the flavones and flavonols are somewhat more stable than the anthocyanins degradation with alkali is usually carried out by fusion with solid potassium hydroxide or heating with 50% aqueous sodium hydroxide (Doporto et al., 1955). The position of sugar attachment may often be deduced by spectral means, but methylation followed by hydrolysis is also useful, a procedure difficult to apply on a micro-scale to anthocyanins (Nordström and Swain, 1953).

VII. The Chalkones*

A. THE AGLYCONES

Although chalkones had been prepared as intermediates in the synthesis of flavones before the turn of the century, the first compound of proven structure of this class was not isolated until 1939 when butein (VIa, Table I) was obtained from *Dahlia variabilis* by Price (1939). Perkin and Hummel (1904) had actually obtained this compound during the isolation of the corresponding flavanone butin (Vb) from *Butea frondosa*.

In 1921, Klein (1921) introduced the term *anthochlor* for pigments in certain yellow flowers which turned red on treatment with ammonia, and later Gertz (1938) showed that pigments of this class were especially widespread in the sub-tribe Coreopsidinae of the Compositae. Starting in 1941, Geissman and his co-workers (Geissman, 1941, see Shimokoriyama, 1962) showed that these colour changes were due to the presence of chalkones and of aurones (the first of which was isolated from *Coreopsis grandiflora* Geissman and Heaton, 1943) and their researches considerably extended the number of known chalkones and their glycosides.

At the present time, if the complex compound rottlerin (XL) from *Mallotus phillipinensis* (McGookin *et al.*, 1938), long used as a dyestuff for silk, is included, twenty naturally occurring chalkones are known (Table VI). Three of these exist in quinonoid forms such as carthamone (from safflower *Carthamus tinctoria*, Seshadri and Thakur, 1960), and may not be present in the plant as such but formed by the oxidation of the corresponding quinol (Shimokoriyama and Hattori, 1955). The variation in the substitution pattern of chalkones is limited when compared to other flavonoids since, as was pointed out by Shinoda and Sato (1928) (cf. Seshadri, 1956), chalkones having the 2',4',6'-trihydroxy substitution readily isomerize to the corresponding flavanones. Shimokoriyama (1957) has shown that several plants (e.g. *Citrus aurantium*) contain an enzyme "flavanone synthetase" which catalyses this transformation. Three chalkones listed (Table VI) as having the 2',4',6' trihydroxy grouping (e.g. carthamin) are actually present in the plant as the 2'-O-glucosides. Substitution in the B- (styryl) -ring is confined to 4-hydroxy and -methoxy, 3,4-dihydroxy and 3,4,5-trihydroxy groupings. Besides rottlerin (XL), one other complex isopentenyl compound is known, xanthohumol from *Humulus lupulus* (Hübner and

---

* American spelling, chalcone.

Riedl, 1960). α-Hydroxychalkones do not exist (cf. 3-hydroxyflavan-ones), since such compounds cyclize to 2-benzyl-2-hydroxy-3-coum-aranones, and indeed four such substances are known. These are maesopsin (XLI) (*Maesopsis eminii*, Janes *et al.*, 1961) and its 3′-hydroxy

TABLE VI

Chalkones

Name	Substitution pattern[a]	Source[b]
Isoliquiritigenin	4,2′,4′-trihydroxy	*Dahlia variabilis*
Isoliquiritigenin methyl ether	2′,4′-dihydroxy-4-methoxy	*Xanthorrhoea* resins
—[c]	2′,6′-dihydroxy-4-methoxy	*Pityrogramma chrysophylla*
Excelsin	2′-hydroxy-4′,6′-dimethoxy	*Pinus excelsa*
—[c]	2′,6′-dihydroxy-4,4′-dimethoxy	*Pityrogramma chrysophylla*
Isosalipurpurin	2′-glucosyloxy-4,4′,6′-trihydroxy	*Salix purpurea*
Neosakuranin	2′-glucosyloxy-4′,6′-dihydroxy-4-methoxy	*Prunus cerasoides*
Butein	3,4,2′,4′-tetrahydroxy	*Butea frondosa*
Robtein[d]	3,4,5,2′,4′-pentahydroxy	*Robinia pseudacacia*
Stillopsidin	3,4,2′,4′,5′-pentahydroxy	*Coreopsis stillmanii*
Okanin	3,4,2′,3′,4′-pentahydroxy	*Cylicodiscus gabunensis*
Lanceoletin	3,4,2′,4′-tetramethoxy 3′-methoxy	*Coreopsis lanceolata*
Carthamin	2′-glucosyloxy-4,3′,4′,6′-tetrahydroxy	} *Carthamus tinctoria*
Carthamone	3′,6′-quinone from carthamin	
Pedicin	2′,5′-dihydroxy-3′,4′,6′-trimethoxy	} *Didymocarpus*
Pedicellin	2′,3′,4′,5′,6′-pentamethoxy	
Pedicinin	3′,6′-dihydroxy-4′-methoxy-2′,5′-quinone	} *Pedicellata*
Methyl pedicinin	3′-*o*-methyl ether of pedicinin	
Xanthohumol[e]	4′,2′,6′-trihydroxy-4′-methoxy-5-(3,3-dimethylallyl)	*Humulus lupulus*

[a] Based on VI, Table I.
[b] Adapted from Shimokoriyama (1962), Karrer (1958) and Seshadri (1959).
[c] Nilsson (1961).
[d] Roux and Paulus (1962).
[e] Hübner and Riedl (1960).

congener alphitonin (*Alphitonia excelsa*, Birch *et al.*, 1956), and the two from *Schinopsis balansae* (King *et al.*, 1961) corresponding in hydroxylation pattern to butein and its 4-*O*-methyl ether. The compound pon-gamol (XLII) (*Pongamia glabra*, Narayanaswamy *et al.*, 1954) is interesting, however, since it is a β-hydroxy chalkone in which ring closure to the corresponding flavone is blocked by the methylation of the *O*-hydroxy group.

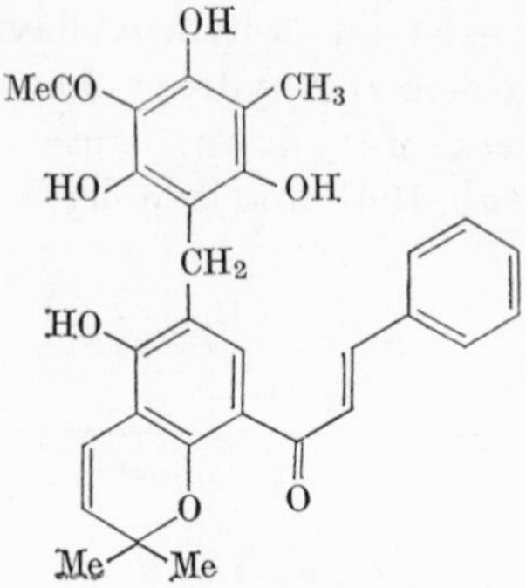

(XL)
Rottlerin

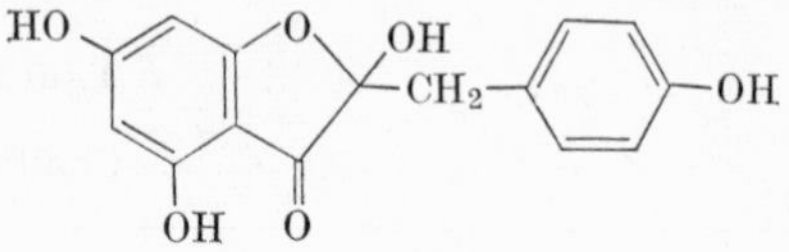

(XLI)
Maesopsin

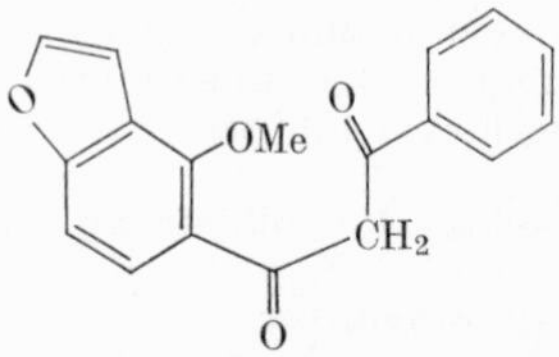

(XLII)
Pongamol

B. THE GLYCOSIDES

Like other flavonoids most of the simple chalkones exist in the plant as glycosides, but in this case glucose is the only sugar, either alone or in biosides, which has been found so far. For example, Harborne (1963b) isolated four glycosides of 4,2′,4′-trihydroxychalkone from *Ulex europaeus* (see Chapter 19). Usually the compounds co-occur with the glucosides of the corresponding flavanone and aurone, e.g. in *Dahlia variabilis* (Nordström and Swain, 1956). This is not surprising in view of the relative ease of interconversion of chalkones and flavanones, and the reported presence of an enzyme which catalyses this step (see above) and also another catalysing the oxidation of chalkones to aurones in *Cosmos sulphureus* and *Coreopsis lanceolata* (Shimokoriyama and Hattori, 1953).

C. THE CONTRIBUTION OF CHALKONES TO FLOWER COLOUR

All the chalkones so far isolated are yellow to orange in colour, the position of λ max. increasing with increasing number of hydroxyl groups, and, of course, being markedly affected by changes in pH and the presence of metals. Because of their deep colour they are undoubtedly responsible for the colour of the flowers and woods in which they occur. The two chalkones isolated from the underside of the leaves of the fern

Pityrogramma Chrysophylla var. *heyderi* (Table IV) are responsible for the orange colour of the sori (Nilsson, 1961); it is interesting that the white coloured variant (var. *marginata*) has the corresponding dihydro-chalkones (cf. III, Table I), and a nearly related species with yellow sori (*P. triangularis*) has the closely related compound ceroptene (XLIII)

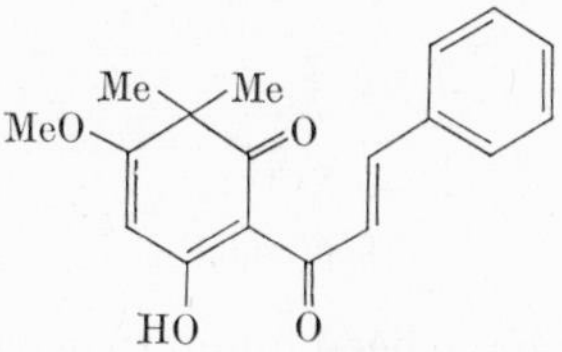

(XLIII)

Ceroptene

(Nilsson, 1959). The chalkones are, however, probably very limited in their distribution and may therefore be comparatively unimportant as colouring matters with regard to Nature as a whole (see also Chapter 9).

D. THE CHEMISTRY OF CHALKONES

The synthesis of chalkones is relatively easy, as they are obtained by the condensation of suitable hydroxyacetophenones with benzaldehydes in the presence of base. The yields however are often rather poor. They are readily cleaved by strong alkali and on treatment with dilute alkali or acid (usually the latter) undergo partial or complete ring closure to the corresponding flavanones. The spectral changes which accompany this isomerization (cf. Table II) are a good indication of the presence of chalkones. This conversion does, however, make the identification of chalkone glycosides somewhat difficult, and cleavage is best carried out enzymatically (Harborne, 1963b). Methylation, other than with diazomethane and demethylation, often gives poor yields of product, since the vinyl ketone structure leads to ready polymerization. The position of sugar attachment is therefore probably best determined by spectroscopic means (Harborne, 1963b).

VIII. THE AURONES

A. THE STRUCTURES OF AURONES AND THEIR CONTRIBUTION TO FLOWER COLOUR

As described above Geissman and Heaton (1943) isolated the first aurone (the name suggested by Bate-Smith and Geissman, 1954, for the class hitherto known as benzylidene-3-coumaranones) from *Coreopsis grandiflora* and called it leptosidin (XLIV). Since that time only five other aurones have been found, their substitution pattern being similar to the other flavonoids all containing a hydroxyl group at C_6 (Table VII).

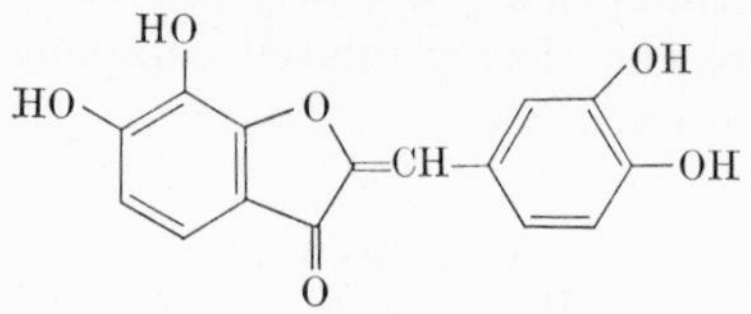

(XLIV)

Leptosidin

Like chalkones, they have been found to occur only as glucosides, and it has been remarked that those which occur in Compositae are never derived from phloroglucinol (Shimokoriyama and Geissman, 1960), but this is not so as demonstrated by the presence of bracteatin in *Helenium*

TABLE VII

Aurones

Name	Structure[a]	Source[b]
Sulphuretin	6,3′,4′-trihydroxy	*Cosmos sulphureus*
Aureusidin	4,6,3′,4′-tetrahydroxy	*Antirrhinum majus*
Rangusin[c]	Aureusidin 6-O-methyl ether	*Melanorrhea* sp.
Maritimetin	6,7,3′,4′-tetrahydroxy	*Coreopsis maritima*
Leptosidin	7-O-methyl ether of maritimetin	*Coreopsis grandiflora*
Bracteatin[d]	4,6,3′,4′,5′-pentahydroxy	*Helichrysum bracteatum*

[a] Based on XII, Table I.
[b] Adapted from Shimokoriyama (1962).
[c] King *et al.* (1962).
[d] Hänsel *et al.* (1962).

bracteatum (Hansel *et al.*, 1962) (see Table VII). Their spectral characteristics and hence their colour are similar to chalkones, except they usually have somewhat higher λ max. and thus they are responsible for the deeper colour of the flowers in which they occur. However, again like chalkones, their distribution is very limited.

B. THE CHEMISTRY OF AURONES

The aurones are readily synthesized by condensing suitable aldehydes with β-coumarones, themselves made by cyclization of ω-chloro-2-hydroxyacetophenones. The ease of condensation enables glucosides to be synthesized without difficulty (Farkas and Pallos, 1960).

Like the other flavonoids discussed previously the aurones are degraded by alkali to yield A and B ring fragments. They also react with cyanides to give the isomeric flavones and may be oxidized by alkaline hydrogen peroxide under suitable conditions to give flavonols.

Determination of the structure of aurones on a micro-scale follows the conventional patterns described earlier (Harborne, 1962a) and as they are more stable than chalkones, methylation and other manipulations present little difficulty (Nordström and Swain, 1956).

IX. OTHER FLAVONOID COMPOUNDS

In general the flavanones (V) and their 3-hydroxy- derivatives (VIII), isoflavones (XI) and the rare isoflavanones (VII), are probably not involved directly in plant colouration except as mentioned earlier in white flowers. Flavanones and 3-hydroxyflavanones, especially those having vicinal hydroxy groups (e.g. VIIIb) are, however, susceptible to oxidation and yield brown pigments which in some cases are probably responsible for the browning of flowers as they wither. Nevertheless most of the brown pigments produced from flavonoids appear to be formed by the oxidation of catechins (flavan-3-ols, II) and leuco-anthocyanins (flavan-3,4-diols, III) and their oligomers and polymers (flavolans). Indeed these polymeric forms, which are in fact condensed tannins, are themselves coloured. The actual structure of such compounds is not known, except that they are formed by polymerization of flavans, and that this can happen in several different ways (see Goldstein and Swain, 1963). It appears likely that some oxidative coupling occurs (Hathway and Seakins, 1957; Hathway, 1959) and leads to the formation of polyquinones. Such quinones are brown in colour and are relatively stable since they are not reduced by either ascorbic acid or potassium ferrocyanide but only by borohydride (Swain, 1963).

The leuco-anthocyanins are extremely widespread in plants (Bate-Smith, 1956, 1962), especially the woody dicotyledons, 60% of which have these compounds in their leaves. They occur predominantly in the polymeric form (flavolans, Swain, 1962), and are present in specially high concentration in heartwoods (Roux, 1962). In fact the distinctive dark colour by which most heartwoods are recognized, is almost always due to the presence of flavolans; species which do not contain these compounds (e.g. the box, *Buxus sempiverens*) have no distinctive heartwood (Dr. E. C. Bate-Smith, personal communication). Flavolans and their oxidation products are also responsible for the brown colour of autumn leaves. Senescent green leaves, when freed from chlorophyll by extraction with organic solvents, show the presence of large amounts of insoluble brown pigment, which is of a leuco-anthocyanin nature (cf. Hillis and Swain, 1959). This apparently is the partial cause of the dull olive colour of these mature leaves. When such leaves are dried slowly, the chlorophyll disappears, and the flavolans are further oxidized to give the deep brown appearance characteristic of many autumn leaves.

The leuco-anthocyanins, besides giving rise to brown pigments, occasionally may impart pink colours to wood owing to their partial conversion into anthocyanidins.

The browning described above may or may not be due to enzyme-catalysed oxidations, but the discolouration which ensues when fresh parts of plants are cut certainly is. This is generally most noticeable in the case of fruits, such as the apple, or other fleshy organs like the potato tuber, but it does occur in all plant tissues having the requisite enzyme system and a suitable substrate. In the majority of cases browning is due to the oxidation of hydroxy flavans (Siegelman, 1955); indeed in tea and chocolate, the desirable colour of the beverage is due to the products of this reaction (see Swain, 1962). However, other non-flavonoid phenolic compounds such as tyrosine and arbutin (Hattori and Sato, 1963) may be involved as well as the naphthoquinones and related compounds described in Chapters 11 and 12.

In some cases darkening may also be caused by the formation of metal chelates (cf. Hughes and Swain, 1962) but no well-authenticated cases appear to have been reported other than in foods (see Swain, 1962).

In conclusion many other phenolic compounds are undoubtedly involved in plant pigmentation, as may be seen from Chapters 11 and 12, but it may safely be stated that the flavonoids offer the greatest variation in colour, which is remarkable when one considers the rather narrow range of structural types that they represent.

ACKNOWLEDGMENT

I should like to acknowledge the help given by Dr. J. B. Harborne in the preparation of this chapter.

REFERENCES

Ainley, A. D., and Robinson, R. (1937). J. chem. Soc. 449.
Albert, A. (1959). "Heterocyclic Chemistry," Athlone Press, London.
Allan, J., and Robinson, R. (1924). J. chem. Soc. 125, 2192.
Baker, W. (1933). J. chem. Soc. 1381.
Baker, W., and Ollis, W. D. (1961). In "Recent Developments in the Chemistry of Natural Phenolic Compounds" (W. D. Ollis, ed.), Pergamon, Oxford.
Baruah, P. B., and Swain, T. (1959). J. Sci. Food Agric. 10, 125.
Bate-Smith, E. C. (1956). Sci. Proc. Roy. Dublin Soc. 27, 165.
Bate-Smith, E. C. (1962). J. Linn. Soc. (Bot.) 58, 95.
Bate-Smith, E. C., and Geissman, T. A. (1954). Nature, Lond. 167, 688.
Beckmann, S., and Geiger, H. (1963). Phytochemistry 2, 281.

Birch, A. J., Ritchie, E., and Speake, R. N. (1960). *J. chem. Soc.* p. 3593.

Bringi, N. V., and Dave, K. G. (1956). *Sci. Proc. Roy. Dublin Soc.* **27**, 93.

Chan, W. R., Forsyth, W. G. C., and Hassall, C. H. (1958). *J. chem. Soc.* p. 3174.

Chandler, B. V., and Harper, K. A. (1961). *Austral. J. Chem.* **14**, 586.

Chandler, B. V., and Harper, K. A. (1962). *Austral. J. Chem.* **15**, 114.

Chapman, E., Perkin, A. G., and Robinson, R. (1927). *J. chem. Soc.* p. 3015.

Dave, K. G., Telang, S. A., and Venkataraman, K. (1962). *Tetrahedron Letters* **1**, 9.

Dean, F. M. (1963). "The Naturally Occurring Oxygen Ring Compounds," Butterworths, London.

Doporto, M. L., Gallagher, K. M., Gowan, J. E., Hughes, A. C., Philbin, E. M., Swain, T., and Wheeler, T. S. (1955). *J. chem. Soc.* p. 4249.

Elderfield, R. C. (Ed.) (1951). "Heterocyclic Compounds," vol. II, J. Wiley, New York.

Emiliwicz, T., Kostanecki, St. v., and Tambor, J. (1899). *Ber. dtsch. chem. Ges.* **32**, 2448.

Everest, A. E. (1914). *Proc. roy. Soc.* **87** B, 449.

Farkas, L., and Pallos, L. (1960). *Chem. Ber.* **93**, 1272.

Freudenberg, K., and Weinges, K. (1960). *Tetrahedron* **8**, 336.

Geissman, T. A. (1941). *J. Amer. chem. Soc.* **63**, 656.

Geissman, T. A. (Ed.) (1962). "The Chemistry of Flavonoid Compounds," Pergamon, New York.

Geissman, T. A., and Harborne, J. B. (1955). *Arch. Biochem. Biophys.* **55**, 447.

Geissman, T. A., and Heaton, C. D. (1943). *J. Amer. chem. Soc.* **65**, 677.

Geissman, T. A., and Hinreiner, E. (1952). *Bot. Rev.* **18**, 77.

Gertz, O. (1938). *Kgl. physiograf. Sällskop Lund Förh* **8**, 62.

Goldstein, J. L., and Swain, T. (1963). *Phytochemistry* **2**, 371.

Graebe, J., and Liebermann, F. (1868). *Ber. dtsch. chem. Ges.* **1**, 106.

Griffiths, L. A. (1958). *Biochem. J.* **70**, 120.

Hänsel, R., Langhammer, L., and Albrecht, A. G. (1962). *Tetrahedron Letters*, 599.

Harborne, J. B. (1958a). *Biochem. J.* **70**, 22.

Harborne, J. B. (1958b). *J. Chromatography* **1**, 473.

Harborne, J. B. (1959). *J. Chromatography* **2**, 581.

Harborne, J. B. (1962a). *Phytochemistry* **1**, 203.

Harborne, J. B. (1962b). *Fortschr. Chem. org. Nat.* **20**, 165.

Harborne, J. B. (1963a). In "Chemical Plant Taxonomy" (T. Swain, ed.), pp. 359–388, Academic Press, London.

Harborne, J. B. (1963b). *Phytochemistry* **2**, 85.

Harborne, J. B. (1964a). In "Methods in Phenolic Chemistry" (J. B. Pridham, ed.), (in press) Pergamon, Oxford.

Harborne, J. B. (1964b). *Phytochemistry* **3**, 151.

Hathway, D. E. (1959). *Biochem. J.* **70**, 34.

Hathway, D. E., and Seakins, J. W. T. (1957). *Biochem. J.* **67**, 239.

Hattori, S. (1962). In "The Chemistry of Flavonoid Compounds" (T. A. Geissman, ed.), Pergamon, New York.

Hattori, S., and Sato, M. (1963). *Phytochemistry* **2**, 385.

Hayashi, K. (1962). In "The Chemistry of Flavonoid Compounds" (T. A. Geissman, ed.), pp. 248–287, Pergamon, New York.

Hertzig, J. (1891). *Monatsh.* **12**, 172.

Hillis, W. E., and Swain, T. (1959). *J. Sci. Food Agric.* **10**, 135.

Hörhammer, L., and Müller, K. H. (1954). *Arch. Pharm.* **287**, 310.

Hübner, H., and Riedl, W. (1960). *Chem. Ber.* **93**, 312.

Hughes, J. C., and Swain, T. (1962). *J. Sci. Food Agric.* **13**, 229.

Ice, C. H., and Wender, S. H. (1953). *J. Amer. chem. Soc.* **75**, 50.

Jacobsen, J. S. (1961). *Arch. Biochem. Biophys.* **93**, 580.

Janes, N. F., King, F. E., and Morgan, J. W. W. (1961). *Chem. and Ind. Rev.* p. 346.

Jurd, L. (1962a). *In* "The Chemistry of Flavonoid Compounds" (T. A. Geissman, ed.), pp. 107–155, Pergamon, New York.

Jurd, L. (1962b). *Chem. & Ind. Rev.* p. 1197.

Karrer, P., and de Meuron, G. (1932). *Helv. chim. acta* **15**, 507.

Karrer, P., and Widmer, R. (1927a). *Helv. chim. acta* **10**, 5.

Karrer, P., and Widmer, R. (1927b). *Helv. chim. acta* **10**, 758.

Karrer, P., and Widmer, R. (1928). *Helv. chim. acta* **11**, 837.

Karrer, W. (1958). "Konstitution und Verkommen der Organischen Pflanzenstoffe," Birkhäuser, Basel.

Katritzky, A. R., and Lagowski, J. M. (1960). "Heterocyclic Chemistry," Methuen, London.

King, F. E., and Clark-Lewis, J. W. (1954). *J. chem. Soc.* 1399.

King, F. E., King, T. J., and Stokes, P. J. (1954). *J. chem. Soc.* 1954, 4594.

King, F. E., King, T. J., and Rustidge, D. W. (1962). *J. chem. Soc.* p. 1192.

King, H. G. C., White, T., and Hughes, R. B. (1961). *J. chem. Soc.* p. 3234.

Klein, G. (1921). *Sitzber. Akad. Wiss. Wien* **130**, 247.

Kostanecki, St. v. (1893). *Ber. dtsch. chem. Ges.* **26**, 2901.

Kuhn, H., and Sperling, W. (1960). *Experientia* **16**, 237.

Limaye, D. B. (1936). *Rassayanam* **1**, 1.

Linstedt, G., and Misiorny, A. (1951). *Acta chem. scand.* **5**, 1.

Mabry, T. J., Wyler, H., Sassu, G., Mercier, M., Paritch, J., and Dreiding, A. S. (1962). *Helv. chim. acta* **45**, 640.

Marquart, L. C. (1835). "Eine chemisch-physiol. Abhandlung," Bonn.

McGookin, A., Percival, A. B., and Robertson, A. (1938). *J. chem. Soc.* p. 309.

Meier, W., and Furst, A. (1962). *Helv. chim. acta* **45**, 232.

Müller, H. (1915). *J. chem. Soc.* **107**, 78S.

Narayanaswamy, S., Ragaswami, S., and Seshadri, T. R. (1954). *J. chem. Soc.* p. 1871.

Nilsson, M. (1959). *Acta chem. scand.* **13**, 750.

Nilsson, M. (1961). *Acta chem. scand.* **15**, 211.

Nordström, C. G., and Swain, T. (1953). *J. chem. Soc.* 2764.

Nordström, C. G., and Swain, T. (1956). *Arch. Biochem. Biophys.* **60**, 329.

Perkin, A. G. (1898). *J. chem. Soc.* **73**, 1019.

Perkin, A. G. (1902). *Proc. chem. Soc.* **18**, 75.

Perkin, A. G. (1905). *J. chem. Soc.* **87**, 715.

Perkin, A. G. (1909). *J. chem. Soc.* **95**, 1855.

Perkin, A. G., and Everest, A. E. (1918). "The Natural Organic Colouring Matters," Longmans, Green, London.

Perkin, A. G., and Hummel, I. J. (1904). *J. chem. Soc.* **85**, 459.

Piatelli, M., Minale, L., and Prota, G. (1964). *Phytochemistry* **3** (in press).

Price, J. R. (1939). *J. chem. Soc.* p. 1017.

Reznik, H., and Neuhausel, R. (1959). *Z. Bot.* **47**, 471.

Roberts, E. A. H., and Williams, D. M. (1958). *J. Sci. Food Agric.* **10**, 217.

Roberts, E. A. H. (1960). *Nature, Lond.* **185**, 536.

Robertson, A., and Whalley, W. B. (1950). *J. chem. Soc.* p. 1882.

Robertson, A., and Whalley, W. B. (1954). *J. chem. Soc.* p. 2794.

Robertson, A., Whalley, W. B., and Yates, J. (1950). *J. chem. Soc.* p. 3117.

Robinson, G. M., and Robinson, R. (1932). *Biochem. J.* **26**, 1647.

Robinson, R. (1934). *Ber. dtsch. chem. Ges.* **67** *A*, 85, 98.

Robinson, R. (1959). *In* "The Chemistry of the Carbon Compounds" (F. H. Rodd, ed.), vol. IX B, Elsevier, Amsterdam.

Robinson, R., and Todd, A. E. (1932). *J. chem. Soc.* p. 2299.

Roux, D. G. (1962). *Chem. & Ind. Rev.* p. 278.

Roux, D. G., and Paulus, E. (1962). *Biochem. J.* **82**, 324.

Row, L. R., and Seshadri, T. R. (1946). *Proc. Ind. Acad. Sci.* **23** *A*, 140.

Seikel, M. K. (1962). *In* "The Chemistry of Flavonoid Compounds" (T. A. Geissman, ed.), pp. 34–69, Pergamon, New York.

Seshadri, T. R. (1956). *Sci. Proc. Roy. Dublin Soc.* **27**, 177.

Seshadri, T. R. (1959). *Tetrahedron* **6**, 169.

Seshadri, T. R. (1962). *In* "The Chemistry of Flavonoid Compounds" (T. A. Geissman, ed.), pp. 156–196, Pergamon, New York.

Seshadri, T. R., and Thakur, R. S. (1960). *Curr. Sci. India* **29**, 57.

Shimokoriyama, M. (1957). *J. Amer. chem. Soc.* **79**, 4199.

Shimokoriyama, M. (1962). *In* "The Chemistry of Flavonoid Compounds" (T. A. Geissman, ed.), pp. 286–316, Pergamon, New York.

Shimokoriyama, M., and Geissman, T. A. (1960). *J. org. Chem.* **25**, 1956.

Shimokoriyama, M., and Hattori, S. (1953). *J. Amer. chem. Soc.* **75**, 2277.

Shimokoriyama, M., and Hattori, S. (1955). *Arch. Biochem. Biophys.* **54**, 93.

Shinoda, J., and Sato, S. (1928). *J. pharm. Soc.* (*Japan*) **48**, 791.

Siegelman, H. W. (1955). *Arch. Biochem. Biophys.* **56**, 97.

Swain, T. (1962). *In* "The Chemistry of Flavonoid Compounds" (T. A. Geissman, ed.), Pergamon, New York.

Swain, T. (1963). *Proc. Int. Congr. Pur. Appl. Chem.*, London.

Swain, T., and Bate-Smith, E. C. (1962). *In* "Comparative Biochemistry" (M. Florkin and H. S. Mason, eds.), vol. IIIa, pp. 755–810, Academic Press, New York.

Swain, T., and Hillis, W. E. (1959). *J. Sci. Food Agric.* **10**, 63.

Venkataraman, K. (1962). *In* "The Chemistry of Flavonoid Compounds" (T. A. Geissman, ed.), pp. 70–106, Pergamon, New York.

Willstätter, R., and Everest, A. E. (1913). *Liebigs Ann.* **401**, 189.

Willstätter, R., and Mallinson, G. (1914). *Sitz. Kgl. Preuss. Akad. Wiss.* **1914**, 769.

Willstätter, R., and Mieg, W. (1915). *Liebigs Ann.* **408**, 61.

Willstätter, R., and Zechmeister, L. (1914). *Sitz. Kgl. Preuss. Akad. Wiss.* **1914**, 886.

Witt, E. (1888). *Ber. dtsch. chem. Ges.* **21**, 325.

Yen, P., and Huang, P. (1961). *Tetrahedron* **12**, 181.

Chapter 9

FLAVONOIDS: DISTRIBUTION AND CONTRIBUTION TO PLANT COLOUR

J. B. HARBORNE

John Innes Institute, Hertford, England

I. INTRODUCTION

Water-soluble pigments of the flavonoid group (i.e. anthocyanins, flavonols and flavones) are very widely distributed in nature. The intensely coloured anthocyanins are most abundantly present in petals and fruits, but also occur in leaves, roots and tubers. In leaves of many plants, their presence is presumably masked by the ubiquitous chlorophyll, but purple-red anthocyanin colour sometimes appears either in young or in dying leaves. Flavonols and flavones are also very common leaf constituents, but their pale yellow or cream colours are again masked by chlorophyll. In contrast to chlorophylls, carotenoids and quinones, flavonoid pigments are characteristic only of higher plants, being virtually absent from lower phyla.

The most significant function of the sap-soluble flavonoids is their ability to impart colour to the plants in which they occur. They are responsible for most orange, scarlet, crimson, mauve, violet and blue colours, as well as contributing much to yellow, ivory and cream flowers.

247

The only other considerable groups of colouring matters in higher plants are the lipid-soluble chlorophylls and carotenoids. Chlorophylls a and b provide the prevailing green of plant leaves and the carotenoids are the most important sources of yellow colours in flowers and fruits. These lipid pigments are considered in other chapters in this volume, but the relative contributions of carotenoids and flavonoids to yellow colour will be considered in a later section in this chapter.

It is difficult to evaluate the precise importance of flavonoid colours in nature. They occur in all parts of the plant and pigmentation must, in some cases, be fortuitous and without obvious function. Flower colour, however, is important for attracting bees, butterflies and other animals to ensure fertilization. Indeed, the association between bee activity and flower colour has long been studied (Sprengel, 1793; Darwin, 1876; see also Manning, 1956a). Bees can discriminate four basic colours and natural evolution of plants towards producing blue flowers must be associated with the bees' preference for this colour (von Frisch, 1950). The fact that many inbreeding plants, such as the sweet pea, have brilliant anthocyanin colours in their petals does not contradict this, since, as Stebbins (1959) has pointed out, self-pollinating plants are almost certainly derived from cross-pollinating ancestors. In contrast to bees, birds are sensitive to red colours and certain species are important pollinators of tropical flowers.

The importance of anthocyanin colour in fruits such as the strawberry, cherry, blackcurrant and so on as an aid to seed dispersal by animals is self-evident. Both fruit and flower colour give immense aesthetic pleasure to man and conscious selection for colour varieties among garden plants and horticultural crops has been practised for a very long time. For example, it is possible that colour varieties of the potato tuber were prized by the Peruvian peasants even in pre-Inca times (Salaman, 1949); and colour "breaks" in the tulip were known and preserved in European gardens as far back as the sixteenth century (McKay and Warner, 1933).

Serious study of the water-soluble plant pigments may be dated from the time of Robert Boyle, who showed in 1664 that the purple pigment of *Viola tricolor* was a natural indicator, becoming green in alkaline and red in acid solution. The term "anthocyanin" was coined by Marquart in 1835 and the basic chemistry of flavones and anthocyanins was worked out at the turn of the nineteenth century by von Kostanecki and Willstätter in Germany and Perkin in this country. The isolation and determination of structure of cyanin, the principal anthocyanin of the cornflower, by Willstätter and Mallison in 1915 remain a landmark in the study of flavonoid pigments. During the period 1930 to 1940, the chemistry of flower colour variation was intensively studied by geneticists and biochemists at the John Innes Institute. In active collaboration with the Robinsons and their school at Oxford, who were the first to synthesize the natural anthocyanins, these workers laid the foundation for our present knowledge of the subject. The valuable contributions of Karrer and his co-workers in Zurich and of Hayashi in Japan must also be mentioned.

In recent years with the development of more accurate and refined analytical techniques, determinations of the structures of all the more important water-soluble pigments have been completed (Geissman, 1962; Harborne, 1962a; Dean, 1963). Even the structure of the elusive and labile beetroot pigment, betanin, the "nitrogenous anthocyanin" of Ainley and Robinson (1937), has been solved with the aid of nuclear magnetic resonance spectroscopy (Mabry et al., 1962). Work has also gone forward on the contributions of co-pigmentation, metal-complexing and pH to the blueing of flower colours, but many of the factors responsible for subtle differences in shade and tone in flowers are still undetermined.

In this chapter, our present knowledge of the chemical factors controlling plant colour will be reviewed and some of the gaps remaining in our understanding of the subject will be mentioned. Earlier reviews dealing inter alia with flavonoids and flower colour are those of Blank (1947, 1958), Paech (1954), Reznik (1956), Scott-Moncrieff (1936), Lawrence (1950) and Beale (1941).

II. NATURAL DISTRIBUTION

The main facts about the natural distribution of the flavonoid pigments are well known and have been discussed recently by Swain and Bate-Smith (1962), Harborne (1963a) and Harborne and Simmonds (1964), so that only the main outlines need be given here. It is convenient to consider the anthocyanins first and then deal with the flavonols and related substances.

Many surveys of the naturally occurring anthocyanins have been carried out, not only among temperate (Lawrence et al., 1939; Beale et al., 1941) but also among tropical plants (Forsyth and Simmonds, 1954). The floras of Australia (Gascoigne et al., 1948), the Galapagos Islands (Taylor, 1940), Japan (Hayashi and Abe, 1955) and the Himalayas (Acheson, 1956) have received special attention. It is clear that anthocyanins are characteristic of higher plants, being of particularly frequent occurrence in the angiosperms (both mono- and dicotyledons). There are only a few records of their occurrence in gymnosperms; e.g., cyanidin 3-monoside is reported in cones of Picea obovata (Beale et al., 1941). They have been found in one moss genus, Bryum (Bendz et al.,

1962) and are probably present in ferns, though evidence for their presence in the latter group is based only on the results of surveys (Price *et al.*, 1938; Hayashi and Abe, 1953) and needs confirmation. Anthocyanins certainly appear to be absent from lower plants such as the algae, fungi and bacteria (see, e.g. Robinson and Robinson, 1934; Alston, 1958).

Although anthocyanins occur in most higher plant orders, they are completely replaced by the nitrogenous betacyanins in nine of the ten families comprising the order Centrospermae. The taxonomic implications of the presence of normal anthocyanins in the tenth family, the Caryophyllaceae, have been reviewed elsewhere (Harborne and Simmonds, 1964; Swain, 1963).

While anthocyanins based on pelargonidin, cyanidin and delphinidin and their methyl ethers are by far the most common, a few pigments that lack the usual 3-hydroxyl group are known. These are rare in nature, being recorded only in the four dicotyledonous families, Bignoniaceae, Gesneriaceae, Sterculiaceae and Theaceae in the Gramineae and in the moss, *Bryum*.

The distribution of flavonols and flavones closely follows that of the anthocyanins. A leaf survey of 1,000 angiosperms has shown that the frequency of occurrence of the three common flavonols, quercetin, kaempferol and myricetin are 56, 48 and 10% respectively (Swain and Bate-Smith, 1962). A careful search would probably reveal that every higher plant contained a flavone or flavonol in one part or another. Flavonoids which contribute to yellow colour are of more restricted occurrence than the common flavonols. The anthochlor pigments—chalkones and aurones—occur abundantly only in the Compositae, but have been noted in the Gesneriaceae, Leguminosae, Scrophulariaceae, Oxalidaceae, Ranunculaceae and Solanaceae. Yellow flavonols, such as quercetagetin, gossypetin and hibiscetin, have also only been found so far in a few plants, notably those belonging to the Primulaceae, Ericaceae, Malvaceae and Compositae.

III. CONTRIBUTION TO FLOWER COLOUR

The contribution of flavonoids to flower colour and their importance in relation to other pigments are summarized in Table I. The descriptions of colour here are rather broad; for more precise notes on the colours of individual flowers, Colour Charts, such as those of Wilson (1938) and Wanscher (1953), should be consulted. The colours in Table I refer to that of the corolla or petal; it should, perhaps, be pointed out that flavonoids also contribute to pigmentation in other parts of the flower, be it sepal, bract, stamen, style or pollen. Anthocyanins have, for example, been isolated from style and stamen of *Anemone*, from sepals

TABLE I

Contribution of Flavonoids to Flower Colour

Colour[a]	Pigments[b]	Examples
ivory and cream	flavones (e.g. apigenin) and/or flavonols (e.g. quercetin)	ivory *Antirrhinum majus* or *Dahlia variabilis*
yellow	(a) carotenoid alone	yellow *Rosa*
	(b) flavonol alone (i.e. quercetagetin)	*Primula vulgaris*
	(c) aurone alone	yellow *Antirrhinum majus*
	(d) carotenoid and flavonol or chalkone	*Lotus corniculatus, Ulex europeaus*
orange	(a) carotenoid alone	*Lilium regale*
	(b) pelargonidin and aurone	*Antirrhinum majus*
scarlet	(a) pure pelargonidin	*Pelargonium, Salvia splendens*
	(b) cyanidin and carotenoid	*Tulipa* cultivar
	(c) cyanidin and flavonoid	*Chasmanthe* and *Lapeyrousa*
brown	cyanidin on carotenoid background	*Cheiranthus cheiri, Rosa* cv. "Cafe", *Primula polyanthus*
magenta or crimson	pure cyanidin	red *Camellia hortense*, red *Begonia* cultivars
pink	pure peonidin	*Paeonia, Rosa rugosa*
mauve or violet	pure delphinidin	*Verbena, Brunfelsia calycina*
blue	(a) cyanidin and co-pigment	*Meconopsis betonicifoail*
	(b) cyanidin as metal complex	*Centaurea cyanus*
	(c) delphinidin[c] and co-pigment	*Plumbago capensis*
	(d) delphinidin as metal complex	*Delphinium*, blue *Lupinus*
	(e) delphinidin[c] at "alkaline" pH	*Primula sinensis*
black (purple black)	delphinidin (at high concentration)	*Tulipa* cv. "Queen of the Night", *Viola × wittrockiana* (pansy)

[a] Green flowers (e.g. of *Helleborus foetidus*) are presumably pigmented by chlorophyll. Chlorophyll appears in some plants (*Tulipa*) in immature petals, only to disappear as the flower matures.

[b] For brevity, the pigment aglycones only are given, but it should be remembered that flavonoids practically always occur in flowers in glycosidic form.

[c] Present here in a partly methylated form.

of many tuber-bearing *Solanum* and from bracts (floral leaves) of *Poinsettia* and *Musa*.

The various points about flower colour shown in Table I will be amplified in the following sections.

A. THE ANTHOCYANINS

1. *Hydroxylation and Colour*

The most important flower pigments are undoubtedly the anthocyanins. For example, of 832 dicotyledonous species in the British flora

TABLE II

Colour of the Three Major Anthocyanidins

Structure:	pelargonidin	cyanidin	delphinidin
Name: (abbreviation)	(Pg)	(Cy)	(Dp)
$\lambda_{max}^{MeOH-HCl}$ (mμ):	520	535	545
$\lambda_{max}^{aqu. HCl}$ of the 3-glycoside (mμ):	492	507	516
Colour:	orange-red	magenta	mauve

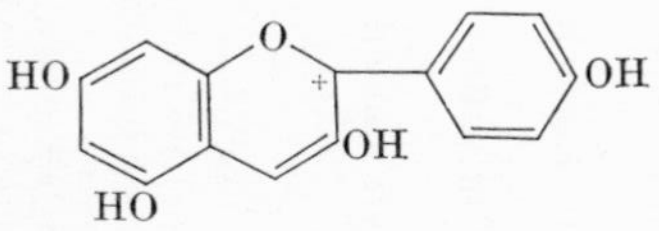

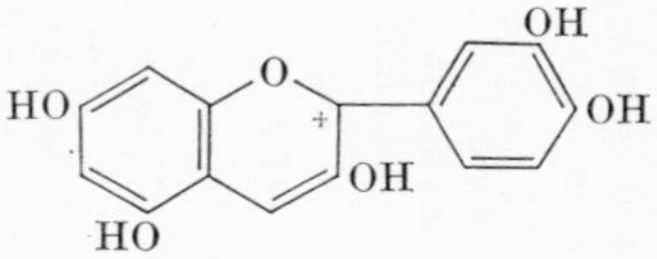

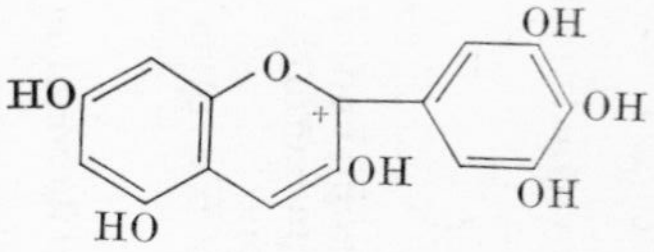

surveyed (cf. Beale *et al.*, 1941), no less than 49% have anthocyanins in the wild type or in a naturally occurring variety. The contribution of anthocyanins to flower colour is basically simple. There are three main pigments: pelargonidin (Pg), cyanidin (Cy) and delphinidin (Dp), which differ in structure only by the number of their hydroxyl groups (Table II). Neglecting the present complications of glycosylation, methylation and co-pigmentation, these three pigments, either singly or as mixtures, provide the whole range of flower colour from pink, orange and scarlet to mauve, violet and blue. Broadly speaking, all pink, scarlet and orange-red flowers have pelargonidin, first isolated from the garden *Pelargonium*, all crimson and magenta flowers have cyanidin, which occurs typically in the crimson rose, and mauve and blue flowers have

TABLE III

Relation between Colour and Anthocyanidin Type in Trinidad Plants

| Flower colour | No. of species containing | | | | | Totals |
	Dp	Dp+Cy	Cy	Cy+Pg	Pg	
yellow-red	0	0	6	3	6	15
red	7	6	57	14	8	92
bluish-red	21	8	19	1	0	49
reddish-blue	19	5	4	0	0	28
blue	11	1	2	0	0	14

delphinidin, a pigment named after *Delphinium*. In considering the relative contributions in more detail of pelargonidin, cyanidin and delphinidin, their general occurrence in nature will be discussed first, before their occurrence in colour varieties of garden plants are considered. The two aspects are inter-related, since both depend on the fact that selection for blue colour has occurred during the evolution of higher plants.

The many surveys of anthocyanins that have been carried out show that the distribution of Pg, Cy and Dp types is strongly correlated with flower colour. Some typical results, obtained by Forsyth and Simmonds (1954) in a study of 247 Trinidad plants, are shown in Table III. In a survey of Australian flora, Gascoigne *et al.* (1948) obtained similar results, observing, for example, that Dp was present in 90% of the blue-flowered species. In the remaining 10%, blueing is presumably produced by strong co-pigmentation of cyanidin (see later).

While there is clearly a relationship between flower colour and geographical distribution, earlier suggestions by Beale *et al.* (1941) that anthocyanidin type is simply related to climate now seem to be unsatis-

TABLE IV

Occurrence of Anthocyanidin Types in Flower Colour Mutants of Garden Plants[a]

Plant	Colour forms	No. of varieties examined	Percentage occurrence of			Accompanying flavonols[c]
			Pg	Cy	Dp[b]	
Lathyrus odoratus (sweet pea)	cerise, pink[d] and salmon	7	100	0	0	Km
	crimson and carmine	5	0	100	0	Km, Qu
	mauve and blue	9	0	0	100	Km, Qu, My
Verbena hybrida (verbena)	pale pink	2	100	0	0	
	scarlet-magenta	1	95	5	0	
	pink	1	80	20	0	Km, Qu, Ap
	scarlet	2	85	10	5	
	maroon	1	40	30	30	
	purple-blue	2	0	15	85	My, Qu, Km, Lu, Ap
	purple	2	0	10	90	Lu, Ap
	white	1	0	0	0	
Hyacinthus orientalis (hyacinth)	deep red "Scarlet O'Hara"	—	90	10	0	
	pink "Pink Perfection"	—	60	40	0	
	mauve "Lord Balfour"	—	20	80	0	Ap, Km
	mauve "Mauve Queen"	—	0	100	0	
	blue "Delft Blue"	—	0	10	90	
	pale blue "Springtime"	—	0	0	100	

Streptocarpus hybridae[e] (cape primrose)	pink	—	100	0	0	Ap, Km
	salmon	—	80	20	0	Ap
	rose and magenta	—	0	100	0	Ap, Lu
	mauve and blue	—	0	0	100	Ap, Lu
Primula sinensis[e] (Chinese primrose)	orange and coral	—	90	10	0	Km
	maroon, mauve and blue	—	0	0	100	Km, Qu, My
Lupinus polyphyllus (lupin)	pink and red	3	40	60	0	Qu, Km, Lu, Ap
	purple, mauve and blue	3	0	20	80	Lu, Ap
Tulipa (tulip)	red and orange	48	46	48	6	Km, Qu
	pink, crimson and deep red	38	36	56	7	}
	black, purple and violet	21	6	32	61	Km, Qu, My

[a] Except in the case of *Tulipa* (Shibata and Ishikura, 1960), data are from Harborne (1962a, 1963a and unpublished results).
[b] Dp = delphinidin; Cy = cyanidin; Pg = pelargonidin. Pigments present in *Lathyrus*, *Primula* and *Streptocarpus* are mainly methylated (i.e. peonidin, petunidin and malvidin are present).
[c] Km = kaempferol; Qu = quercetin; My = myricetin; Lu = luteolin; Ap = apigenin.
[d] Two pink shades also contain traces of cyanidin.
[e] Forms of known genotype were examined in these cases.

factory. Thus, the view that high pelargonidin and low delphinidin frequencies are characteristic of tropical floras appears to be incorrect: Forsyth and Simmonds (1954) found that the Trinidad plants contained fewer Pg and Dp types (17% and 41%) and more Cy types (67%) than temperate plants. Delphinidin predominates in alpine floras because blue-flowered plants are so common here; thus Acheson (1956), in a survey of Himalayan plants, found 28 Dp-, 17 Cy- and 1 Pg-containing species.

When wild plants are brought into cultivation, mutations occur in the direction: Dp → Cy → Pg (Beale, 1941). Mutant forms have been preserved in many garden plants and among these flowers there is again excellent correlation between colour and anthocyanidin type (Table IV). In a few plants (e.g. *Lathyrus odoratus*) genetic factors controlling hydroxylation are involved in epistasy and so are absolute in their action: pure Dp, Cy and Pg types predominate. In others (e.g. *Primula sinensis*), intermediate cyanidin types are absent and the main mutation affecting hydroxylation, K → k, is from Dp to Pg; only traces of Cy are present in the kk mutant.

In most garden plants, varieties containing mixtures of anthocyanidin types are quite as common as those having single pigments. Flowers with mixtures are of the expected intermediate colour shades. Good examples here are *Verbena* and the garden hyacinth (Table IV). At the other extreme, there are plants (e.g. *Tulipa*) in which forms having single anthocyanidins in their petals are rare and the colour range is due to the presence of varying proportions of the three main types. Shibata and Ishikura (1960), who analysed 107 tulip varieties, found that the majority had mixtures of all three pigments; nevertheless, there is still a good correlation between the predominating type and colour (Table IV).

In some garden plants, pelargonidin forms have not yet been isolated. This is true, for example, of the cultivated *Cyclamen*, in which Dp and Cy types only are known and the colour range extends from deep purple to purplish-red (van Bragt, 1962). In *Delphinium*, orange and red forms have recently been produced by skilful hybridization (Legro, 1963), but their pigments have not yet been submitted to chemical analysis. Pelargonidin is not found among the flower colour forms of the tuber-bearing *Solanum* for a different reason, i.e. because selection for colour has taken place, unusually, in the tuber and not in the flower (Dodds and Long, 1955).

By contrast with the plants mentioned above and in Table IV, there are plants which are not able to synthesize delphinidin and in which colour variation is more restricted. One example is the garden rose, most varieties of which contain cyanidin and in which mutations to pelargonidin are of rather rare occurrence. The orange-red varieties available today are derived from the dwarf polyantha "Paul Crampel", which was introduced about 1930. This orange-flowered variety is unusual in that it back mutates somatically to produce crimson-flowered offshoots, which are pigmented by cyanidin. A second example is *Dahlia variabilis*, a plant in which cyanic colour is due to cyanidin or pelargonidin or their mixture. A third example is *Antirrhinum majus*, magenta forms of which have cyanidin and pink forms pelargonidin. Two wild *Antirrhinum* species (*A. cornutum* and *A. nuttallianum*) have blue delphinidin-containing flowers (Harborne, 1963b), so that there is a reasonable chance that a blue snapdragon will be produced one day.

A rare change that affects the hydroxylation pattern of anthocyanidins, and hence colour, is the loss of the 3-hydroxyl group. Pigments lacking this 3-hydroxyl, analogous otherwise to delphinidin, cyanidin and pelargonidin, are much nearer the yellow end of the colour spectrum; thus tricetinidin has $\lambda_{max}^{MeOH-HCl}$ 520, luteolinidin $\lambda_{max}^{MeOH-HCl}$ 493 and apigeninidin $\lambda_{max}^{MeOH-HCl}$ 476 mμ. Plants containing these pigments have orange-red (*Gesneria cuneifolia*, *Rechsteineria cardinalis*) or orange-yellow flowers (*Kohleria eriantha*). The striking russet-orange flowers of *Columnea* × *banksii* and *C. stavengeri* contain a pigment of a similar nature.

Substitution of a hydroxyl group in the 6-position also has a hypsochromic effect on colour and the 6-hydroxy derivatives of pelargonidin, cyanidin and delphinidin have been synthesized (Charlesworth and Robinson, 1934). A novel pigment having the spectral properties of 6-hydroxypelargonidin ($\lambda_{max}^{MeOH-HCl}$ 497 mμ) occurs in the tangerine-coloured flowers of *Impatiens aurantiaca* (Clevenger, 1964). This substance, aurantinidin, however, differs chromatographically from the synthetic pigment (J. B. Harborne, unpublished data) so that its structure is still in doubt.

2. *Methylation of Anthocyanins*

Methylation of some of the hydroxyl groups of the anthocyanidin molecule has a small reddening effect on colour. This is apparent from a consideration of the absorption spectra of the known methylated pigments (Table V).

Few examples of this reddening of flower colour can be quoted, because the effect of methylation is frequently obscured by other factors, particularly by co-pigmentation. However, the relative amounts of the various methylated pigments have been measured in several mutants of *Primula sinensis*, all of which are recessive for the co-pigment gene B. The results (Table VI) support the thesis that methylation has a reddening effect (Harborne and Sherratt, 1961). Another example is *Rosa*, in

9

which cyanidin-peonidin mixtures are found almost exclusively in pinker varieties (*Rosa rugosa* and derived hybrids) whereas crimson and deeper red varieties have only cyanidin (Harborne, 1961).

While pigments based on malvidin, peonidin and petunidin are quite

TABLE V

Long Wave Absorption Maxima of Methylated Anthocyanidins

	$\lambda_{\text{max. (m}\mu)}^{\text{MeOH-HCl}}$	$\Delta\lambda$
Delphinidin derivatives:		
parent compound (Dp)	546	—
3′-O-methyl ether (petunidin) (Pt)	546	0
3′,5′-di-O-methyl ether (malvidin) (Mv)	542	4
7,3′,5′-tri-O-methyl ether (hirsutidin) (Hs)	536	10
5,3′,5′-tri-O-methyl ether (?) (capensinidin) (Cp)	538	8
Cyanidin derivatives:		
parent compound (Cy)	535	0
3′-O-methyl ether (peonidin) (Pn)	532	3
7,3′-di-O-methyl ether (rosinidin) (Rs)	524	11

common, 5- or 7-O-methylated anthocyanins are very rare; in this case, the hypsochromic effect of methylation is more pronounced (8 to 11 mμ). Unfortunately, this is not reflected to any extent in flower colour, because of other modifying factors. Thus the flower colour of the

TABLE VI

Methylated Pigments in *Primula sinensis*

Variety	Flower colour	Percentage composition		
		Dp	Pt	Mv
"Duchess Fern Leaf"	blue	100	0	0
"Reading Pink"	pink	37	51	13
"Oak Tongue"	maroon	5	29	65

capensinidin-containing *Plumbago capensis* is sky-blue, the result of strong co-pigmentation of the anthocyanin by the flavonol, azalein (5-O-methyquercetin 3-rhamnoside) (Harborne, 1962b). Again, although *Primula rosea* (containing rosinidin) has distinctive rose-pink petals, *Primula* species having hirsutidin (e.g. *Primula cashmiriana*, *P. hirsuta*) cannot be distinguished by their flower colour from those having mal-vidin (e.g. *P. obconica, P. lichiangensis*).

3. Glycosylation of Anthocyanidins

Although glycosylation of the 3-hydroxyl group of anthocyanidins has a relatively large hypsochromic effect (-15 mμ) in the visible region of the spectrum, glycosylation is not an important factor in flower colour, because anthocyanidins always occur in flowers with at least one sugar attached to the 3-hydroxyl group. It is true that there have been reports from time to time of anthocyanidins being isolated in the free state from flowers; e.g. from *Begonia* spp. (Bopp, 1957), *Camellia japonica* (Hayashi and Abe, 1953) and *Lathyrus hirsutus* (Pecket, 1960). The isolation of free anthocyanidins from these flowers does not neces-sarily mean that they occur as such *in vivo*, since some 3-glycosides, and notably 3-pentosides, are labile and invariably undergo partial hydrolysis during extraction and isolation with acid-containing sol-vents. Thus, re-examination in this laboratory of flower pigments of the plants mentioned above failed to disclose the presence of any free aglycones; significantly, however, a cyanidin 3-pentoside was detected in one *Begonia* species and a malvidin 3-rhamnoside in *Lathyrus hirsutus*.

From the point of view of flower colour, the nature of the 3-substituted sugar is immaterial; all 3-glycosides of a particular anthocyanidin have the same visible spectra. Although 3-glycosides and 3,5-diglycosides (the two major classes of anthocyanins) have almost identical visible maxima, the substitution of a sugar in the 5-position does have a small effect on colour. Thus, the 3,5-diglucosides of pelargonidin, peonidin and malvidin differ from the corresponding 3-glycosides by being fluorescent in solution. This is probably related to the intensity of colouration in the flowers in which they occur; petals of *Pelargonium* and *Punica granatum*, containing pelargonidin 3,5-diglucoside, do have an intensely orange appearance. Acylation of the sugar residues of such glycosides with *p*-coumaric or caffeic acid partly quenches this fluorescence; thus acylated pelargonidin 3,5-diglucosides occur in the duller scarlet blooms of *Salvia splendens* and *Monarda didyma*.

Anthocyanins with sugars attached to the 3- and 7-positions, instead of the more usual 3- and 5-positions, are very rare in nature. Only one such pigment, pelargonidin 3-sophoroside-7-glucoside, is known (Har-borne, 1962a) and this has a visible maximum ($\lambda_{max}^{MeOH-HCl}$ 498 mμ) different from pelargonidin 3-glucoside ($\lambda_{max}^{MeOH-HCl}$ 507 mμ) and the 3,5-diglucoside ($\lambda_{max}^{MeOH-HCl}$ 504 mμ). The flowers which contain it, *Papaver orientalis* and some forms of *P. nudicaule*, are distinctly more orange-yellow in colour than the scarlet *Papaver rhoeas*, which contains pelargonidin and cyanidin 3-sophoroside.

4. Quantitative Effects

Variations in the amounts of anthocyanin in the petal have profound effects on colour and large discontinuous differences in anthocyanin content have been noted in the flowers of some plant varieties. At one end of the scale, low pigment concentrations give flowers with a faint pinkish blush (e.g. the rose "Madame Butterfly") and at the other, concentrations are found in the deep purple-black petals of the tulip "Queen of the Night" or of the pansy "Jet Black".

Rather few quantitative measurements have been made, mainly because reliable extinction values for most anthocyanins have only been readily available in recent years. In making such measurements, allowance must be made for variations due to the environment, age of the petal and so on. Values obtained by the early workers (quoted by Blank (1958)) are, for cyanin in cornflower, 0·05 to 0·7% of the dry weight in normal varieties and 13 to 14% in some dark-purple forms. Similarly, flowers of *Pelargonium peltatum* were found to have 1% and *P. zonale* 6 to 14% of the dry weight as pigment.

More recently, Harborne and Sherratt (1961) have found that the orange "Dazzler" mutant of *Primula sinensis* has three times as much pelargonidin glucoside as the coral form. This difference in anthocyanin concentration (3·2 as compared with 1·1% dry weight) is under monogenic control. A single gene also appears to separate deep and pale mauve colour forms of *Solanum iopetalum*, which differ in anthocyanin concentration by a factor of four (J. B. Harborne, unpublished data). Deep purple forms of *Torenia fournieri* have as much as nine to ten times as much pigment as pale forms. Anthocyanin concentration is here controlled by two complementary genes and hybrids between the two forms have intermediate quantities and colours (Endo, 1962). A gene controlling anthocyanin concentration in *Pisum* increases pigment in the petal wing more than in the petal standard; pigment ratios in intense and pale phenotypes are 1:5·5 for the wings and 1:2·5 in the standard (Harborne, 1964).

Pigment concentrations in petals of *Dianthus caryophyllus* and *Antirrhinum majus* have been measured by Geissman and his co-workers in connection with genetical studies. In red carnations, Geissman and Mehlquist (1947) found pelargonidin 3-glucoside to occur in the ratios of 4:2:1 in petals of different intensity; magenta forms contained 2·4% of their dry weight as cyanidin 3-glucoside. In *Antirrhinum*, Jorgensen and Geissman (1955) found that the concentration of cyanidin

3-rutinoside in magenta forms varied (0·3 to 1·4% dry weight) inversely with the aurone concentration (see also below, p. 265).

To summarize, it is clear that anthocyanin concentration in the flower varies within the range from 0·01 to 15% dry weight and is controlled in a very precise manner by genetic factors in certain plants.

5. *Co-pigmentation*

The phenomenon of co-pigmentation, the blueing of anthocyanin colour *in vivo* by flavones and related substances was discovered independently by Robinson and Robinson (1931) and by Lawrence (1932). It is easily demonstrated *in vitro*. At room temperature aqueous acid extracts of co-pigmented flowers are bluer in tone than those of unco-pigmented petals. On heating, the loose co-pigment-pigment complex is dissociated and there is a reddening in colour; on cooling, the colour reverts to the original blue shade. While the co-pigment in most flowers which show this phenomenon is probably a flavone glycoside or a hydrolyzable tannin and can be removed by ethyl acetate extraction, some unrelated substances will co-pigment with anthocyanins in the test tube; examples are 2-hydroxyxanthone, narcotine and papaverine.

Recently, co-pigmentation has been studied in more detail in a few selected plants. In *Primula sinensis*, in which plant it is under simple genetic control (Scott-Moncrieff, 1936), the spectral shift shown by the malvidin 3-glucoside of maroon flowers (**bb** types) when co-pigmented with flavone to give mauve flowers (**BB** types) is 5 mμ (the λ max. in aqueous acid changes from 516 to 521 mμ). The two flavonols responsible, i.e. kaempferol 3-gentiobioside and 3-gentiotrioside, occur in both genotypes though in amounts varying with the genotype. Measurements in two different families showed that co-pigmented forms had three and five times more flavonol than the unco-pigmented varieties (Harborne and Sherratt, 1961).

A blue rose has long been searched for; the rather unsatisfactory mauve and purple varieties (e.g. "Reine de Violette") so far available contain the cyanidin 3,5-diglucoside of crimson roses co-pigmented with large amounts of gallotannin. The spectral shift in rose is from 507 to 512 mμ (Harborne, 1961). A rather unusual co-pigment, the C-glucosidic xanthone mangiferin (Bate-Smith and Harborne, 1963) is present in *Iris* cultivars and produces, by interaction with delphinidin 3-(*p*-coumaroylrutinoside)-5-glucoside, a range of colours through red and mauve to blue.

Blueness in flowers of *Lathyrus* is due to co-pigmentation of delphinidin, petunidin and malvidin 3-rhamnoside-5-glucosides (Harborne, 1963c) with kaempferol and quercetin glycosides. Pecket and Selim (1962) have demonstrated this by hybridizing a species with red flowers, which lack flavonols, with one having cream flowers, containing flavonols. The resulting hybrid *L. clymenum* × *ochrus*, had the expected mauve coloured flowers. In addition, colour differences between wing and standard in cyanic flowers of *Lathyrus*, *Pisum* and *Vicia* are probably a result of variations in amount of these co-pigments.

While the above co-pigment-pigment complexes are stable in aqueous acid, they are dissociated by heating or by the addition of alcohol. Stronger anthocyanin-flavone complexes, which are stable to alcohol, have been isolated from time to time from plants, notably from *Spirodela oligorrhiza*, *Delphinium consolida* and *Columnea* × *banksii*.

Hayashi (1962), in reviewing the factors controlling blueness in flowers, tends to dismiss co-pigmentation as being a rather minor factor. However, it is certainly a widespread phenomenon and, furthermore, it is patent that in the very many flowers which contain pigments which are methylated in the B ring and which thus cannot complex with metal (e.g. malvidin and peonidin—see below, Section 6), some other factor besides metal chelation must be responsible for blueing; in such cases, co-pigmentation is the only known available mechanism.

6. *Metal Complexing*

Chelation of anthocyanins with metal ions is, besides co-pigmentation, the other major factor responsible for blueing the flower pigments of higher plants. Although we know little about the chemistry of co-pigmentation, our knowledge of the metal complexes is more complete. Recently, chelated anthocyanins have been isolated from five plant species by expressing the plant sap followed by precipitation with alcohol or ether. While these complexes are unstable *in vitro* and are dissociated by acid or on ion-exchange columns, they are undoubtedly more stable *in vivo* than pigments which are not similarly protected.

The pure blue pigment "protocyanin" from the cornflower, *Centaurea cyanus*, has been the most studied. Bayer (1958) and Bayer *et al.* (1960) showed that it contained cyanidin 3,5-diglucoside complexed with ferric iron and aluminium and also that it had spectral properties very similar to those of synthetic anthocyanin metal complexes. In a parallel study, Hayashi *et al.* (1961) collected flowers from 7,200 plants to obtain 600 mg of purified protocyanin (yield 0·03%). Their material contained magnesium (rather than aluminium) as the second metal accompanying iron in the complex. Potassium was also present, but this was removable by dialysis. In a later paper, these workers (Saito *et al.*, 1961) reported that protocyanin had a molecular weight of 20,000, was composed of cyanin, magnesium, iron and potassium in the ratio 8:2:1:24, and contained peptide, polysaccharide and flavone-like material as an integral part of its structure. Cornflower blue does therefore seem to require both metal chelation and the presence of a suitable polysaccharide. The idea that the absorption of anthocyanin onto polysaccharide is involved in flower colour variation is by no means a new one and was introduced by Robinson and Robinson (1939) to explain blueing in *Centaurea* and other plants. Bopp (1958) has more recently invoked the idea of colloidal state to explain the colour change from blue to red which occurs in certain *Streptocarpus* hybrids as the flowers develop.

The metal complexes of several other plants have been studied in less detail (Table VII). Blue forms of *Lupinus* contain a delphinidin-aluminium-iron complex but the pelargonidin in red lupins is not complexed (Bayer, 1959). Thus an essential factor for formation of stable metal complexes is the presence in the anthocyanin of a free *o*-dihydroxy grouping. Spectral studies of the effect of aluminium chloride on anthocyanins in solution have also shown this (Geissman, *et al.*, 1954). The blue pigment of *Commelina* has a chelating metal in its structure (Mitsui *et al.*, 1959) whereas, curiously, a violet pigment in *Viola* has potassium as its only metal (Hayashi and Takeda, 1962). Colour changes in the sepal of *Hydrangea macrophylla* have long been studied (cf. Chenery, 1948), but only recently has it been shown that blue forms definitely contain a metal complex. The anthocyanin in both red and blue forms is delphinidin 3-glucoside (Robinson, 1939). The colour change from red to blue is controlled by the availabilities of nitrogen, phosphorus and potassium salts to the plant, which have a large effect on the accumulation of the chelating metals, aluminium and molybdenum (Asen *et al.*, 1959).

Thus, the requirements for blueing by metal chelation are: (a) an anthocyanin which contains a catechol nucleus (i.e. a delphinidin, petunidin or cyanidin glycoside); (b) a chelating metal (Al, Mg or Mo); and (c) an internal mineral balance which promotes availability of the chelating metal(s).

7. *Effect of pH*

Solutions of anthocyanins are red in acid, blue in alkali and the pH of the cell sap was once considered to be an important factor in flower colour. However, a survey by Shibata *et al.* (1949) of the cell sap of 200 plants showed that flowers were all acidic (pH about 5·5), irrespective of colour. Nevertheless, small changes of pH within the acid range appear to have some effect on flower colour. Thus Scott-Moncrieff (1936) noted differences of 0·5 and 1 pH units between red and mauve colour forms of *Primula sinensis*, *P. acaule* and *Papaver rhoeas*. In *P. sinensis*, the change of pH from 5·4 to 6·2 has a blueing effect and is controlled by the gene **R**, which is independent of factors controlling co-pigmentation and methylation. Changes in colour from red to mauve and purple,

TABLE VII

Composition of Blue or Violet Pigments which Contain Metals

Plant species	Colour	Anthocyanin	Metals present	Other constituents
Centaurea cyanus	blue	Cy 3,5-diglucoside	Fe^{3+}, Mg^{2+} and K^+	peptide, flavone and polysaccharide
Commelina communis	blue	Dp 3-(p-coumaroyl-rutinoside)-5-glucoside	Mg^{2+} and K^+	polysaccharide
Hydrangea macrophylla	blue	Dp 3-glucoside	Mo^{3+} and Al^{3+}	—
Viola × wittrockiana	violet	Dp 3-(p-coumaroyl-rutinoside)-5-glucoside	K^+	—
Lupinus polyphemus	blue	Dp 3,5-diglucoside	Al^{3+} and Fe^{3+}	polysaccharide

which occur during flower development, have also been ascribed to pH effects (Robinson, 1939).

8. *Anthocyanins on a Yellow Background*

Many colour effects are produced by interaction of anthocyanins with other pigments. The co-pigment effects of the cream flavones have already been discussed, but the effects of co-occurrence with yellow pigments have not yet been mentioned. A good example here is the garden snapdragon, which contains yellow aurone pigments but no carotenoids. Mixtures of cyanidin with these aurones give orange-red colours, while mixtures of pelargonidin and aurone give orange-yellow shades. High anthocyanin concentration is here related to low aurone concentration and vice versa; the interaction of factors controlling pigment synthesis has a considerable effect on flower colour (Jorgensen and Geissman, 1955). The general effect of anthocyanins occurring with water-soluble yellow pigments is such that cyanidin-containing flowers appear as if they have pelargonidin. Examples of flowers having cyanidin and water soluble, but unidentified, yellow pigments are the yellow-red petals of *Lapeyrousia cruenta*, *Chasmanthe* and *Crocosma masonorum* (Harborne, 1963a) and those of *Tecomaria capensis* and *Holmskioldia sanguinea* (Forsyth and Simmonds, 1954).

When anthocyanins and lipid-soluble yellow pigments co-occur, the resulting flower colour is more often brown than orange. This may be because, whereas water-soluble yellow pigments are in the cell vacuole with the anthocyanins, carotenoids are located in the plastids. Brown colours formed by magenta cyanidin on a yellow carotenoid background can be seen in the wallflower *Cheiranthus cheiri*, in *Primula polyanthus* and in rose varieties, e.g. the coffee coloured "Café". Brown colours are not confined to the flower; brown anthers of the flowers of some *Solanum* plants are coloured by the petunidin glycoside, petanin, on a carotenoid background.

9. *Flower Colour Changes*

Besides colour variation between mutants of garden plants which has formed the basis of the discussion up to this point, there are also the alterations in colour undergone by individual flowers as they develop, mature, fade and die. These changes are very pronounced in a few plants (e.g. from yellow to red in *Cheiranthus mutabilis*) and have therefore attracted the attention of pigment chemists. The assumption that such changes are due to the interconversion of one kind of pigment into another is most unlikely, however attractive the hypothesis that a colour change from yellow to red is due to the *in vivo* reduction of flavonol to anthocyanidin. Thus, tracer and enzymatic studies show

9*

that flavonoid and carotenoid pigments, although often described as "end products" of metabolism, are regularly "turned over" in the plant. Furthermore, both Reznik (1961) and Hess (1963) have shown that the initiation and rate of flavonol synthesis in petals of *Primula obconica* and *Petunia* are quite independent of those of anthocyanin synthesis.

More probably, explanations for colour changes during the life of a flower lie in differential rates of pigment synthesis, and in alterations of pH and of availability of metal ions. These factors operating singly or together will inevitably produce effects on flower colour.

Two examples may be mentioned. First, the popular rose "Masquerade" is yellow in bud, orange-yellow when freshly open and deep red before fading. It is clear that yellow carotenoid is produced at an early stage of development, whereas the synthesis of the anthocyanin, cyanin, is delayed until maturity. Significantly, the undersides of red petals have yellow patches, indicating that anthocyanin synthesis in this variety is particularly light-dependent. Second, the flower of *Hibiscus mutabilis* changes during the course of one day from yellow in the morning to pink in the evening. If the pigment of the yellow flower (quercetin 7-glucoside) were the precursor of the cyanidin 3,5-diglucoside in the pink flower (Subramanian and Swamy, 1964), this would involve not only a reduction but also a complex re-arrangement of the glycosidic pattern. It is much more likely that anthocyanin synthesis is delayed, but the product ultimately masks the pale yellow colour of the quercetin glycoside.

10. *Flower Patterns and Virus Breaks*

It is not possible to discuss the chemistry of flower colour without a brief mention of flower patterns. These are quite elaborate in such plants as the foxglove, violet, orchid, iris and primrose. Patterns are usually due to local increase in pigment production in some areas of the petal (e.g. the foxglove). Alternatively, a second pigment is locally superimposed on the main colouring matter (e.g. the dark purple spot in some poppy flowers is due to cyanidin on a pelargonidin background). Patterning is under complex genetic control and occasionally genes controlling patterns are mutable and their effects vary with the environment. Some patterns are related to the needs of insect vectors; the "honey lines" of *Streptocarpus* and many other flowers direct the bees towards the nectar (Manning, 1956b).

Some colour patterns have quite a different cause: that is, virus infection. Virus breaks in tulips were first reported in the literature in 1568. The effect of virus is to inhibit anthocyanin in some areas of the petals; the variegated forms, once so popular, are now rapidly being replaced by healthy self-coloured varieties. Virus infection has a mottling effect on flower colour in the garden stock, *Matthiola incana*, and may either increase anthocyanin colour or inhibit it (Feenstra *et al.*, 1963). The concentration of flavonol in virus-infected "white" flowers is higher than that in healthy white flowers, but there is no simple relationship between inhibition of anthocyanin and increase in flavonol. Precisely how the virus inhibits or stimulates pigment synthesis in these flowers is still obscure.

B. CHALKONES, AURONES AND FLAVONES

1. *Yellow Flower Colour*

In considering the contribution of flavonoids to yellow flower colour, it is necessary to point out at the outset that the commonly occurring flavonols and flavones, which are often incorrectly stated to be yellow pigments, do not contribute significantly to yellow flower colour. It is true that the common flavonols, myricetin, quercetin and kaempferol, are pale yellow in the solid state. Nevertheless, their 3-glycosides (and they always occur in petals in glycosidic form) are either colourless or pale buff in colour. Furthermore, the spectral maxima of the majority of flavonol glycosides lie at about 340–360 mμ and there is very little absorption above 380 mμ.

Flavonoids which do contribute to yellow colour can be considered under the following four headings.

(1) The *anthochlor pigments* (chalkones and aurones) are deep yellow in colour and characteristically change to red when the petal is treated with ammonia vapour (Gertz, 1938). Chalkones have absorption maxima at 370 to 390 mμ, aurones at 390 to 420 mμ. They are the principal yellow colouring matters in *Dahlia* and *Antirrhinum* but, more frequently, co-occur with carotenoids (e.g. in *Coreopsis, Oxalis, Ulex*). They seem to be of rather restricted distribution (see p. 250), but they may be more common than is now thought.

(2) *Quercetagetin* and related compounds. Quercetagetin (6-hydroxy-quercetin) has long been known (Latour and Magnier de la Source, 1877) to occur in the African marigold, *Tagetes erecta*, but its contribution here to flower colour is masked by the predominance of carotenoids (Rao and Seshadri, 1941). Recent work in this laboratory has shown that quercetagetin and related compounds are important yellow flower pigments in their own right. Quercetagetin is the principal pigment, together with 6-hydroxykaempferol, in the primrose, *Primula vulgaris*, and occurs, with carotenoid, in most other yellow *Primula* species (e.g. the cowslip, *P. veris*). It is also a major pigment in *Rhododendron*; a survey showed it to be present in six out of nine yellow-flowered species but absent from all of eight white-flowered species, in which plants it was replaced by

quercetin. Quercetagetin has also been found in yellow flowers of *Dianthus knappii*, *Coronilla glauca*, *Papaver nudicaule* and *Lotus corniculatus*. The isomeric 8-hydroxyquercetin (gossypetin) is also an important pigment in yellow cotton flowers, *Gossypium*.

The common flavonols probably contribute to yellow flower colour when (a) they are methylated or (b) they are present in certain unusual glycosidic forms. Thus, a myricetin methyl ether (probably syringetin) contributes to yellow colour in the meadow pea, *Lathyrus pratensis*, and isorhamnetin (quercetin 3′-methyl ether) may do the same in the common marigold, *Calendula officinalis*. Quercetin 7- and 4′-glucosides have absorption spectra similar to quercetin itself and may therefore provide some yellow in gorse, *Ulex europaeus*, in *Rosa foetida* and in other petals in which they occur. A third possibility—that flavonols contribute to yellow flower colour when complexed with metals such as aluminium (compare the anthocyanin-metal complexes, p. 262)—has yet to be demonstrated *in vivo*.

(3) *Anthocyanins with unusual hydroxylation patterns* (e.g. apigeninidin, λ max. 476 mμ) and their presence in orange-yellow flowers have already been discussed in a previous section (p. 257).

(4) *Nitrogenous yellow pigments* are mentioned here because several unidentified pigments of this type have been considered to be nitrogenous flavones, by analogy with the "nitrogenous anthocyanins" which are now known to have alkaloid-like structures (the betacyanins). In this category are nudicaulin, the pigment of the Iceland poppy and of *Meconopsis cambrica*, and the various water-soluble yellow pigments of the Centrospermae (e.g. *Celosia cristata*). Since their structures are not known, they will not be further considered here.

Chemical studies of yellow-petalled plants have rarely included a consideration of both flavonoids and carotenoids so that it is difficult to estimate the relative contributions of the two types of pigment to yellow colour. No detailed surveys have been carried out and broad surveys, based on the relative solubilities of crude petal extracts in ether and in water, could be very misleading since water-soluble carotenoid-like pigments are known. Crocetin, the pigment of *Crocus sativus*, was isolated in 1818 by Aschoff (cf. Karrer, 1958); a similar pigment has recently been noted in *Nemesia strumosa* and no doubt others exist in nature. Because of these difficulties, the data collected together in Table VII must be considered to present only an incomplete, and probably biased, assessment of the relative importance of flavonoids and carotenoids. The following points may be noted:

(1) The most surprising fact that emerges is that there is a relatively large number of plants which are coloured yellow by both flavonoid and carotenoid (classes I and II in Table VIII). This is rather surprising,

TABLE VIII

Distribution of Flavonoids and Carotenoids in Yellow-flowered Plants

Plant	Flavonoids[a]	Carotenoids[b]
I. *Plants having flavonoids and known carotenoids*		
Ulex europaeus (gorse)	2′,4′,4-trihydroxychalcone, 3,7,4′-trihydroxyflavone, quercetin 7- and 4′-glucoside	α- and β-carotene, violaxanthin, taraxanthin
Lotus corniculatus (birdsfoot trefoil)	quercetagetin methyl ether	α- and β-carotene
Tagetes erecta	quercetagetin	lutein
Calendula officinalis	isorhamnetin	β- and γ-carotene, lycopene
II. *Plants having flavonoids and unidentified carotenoids*		
Coreopsis spp.	butein, sulphuretin, maritimetin, leptosidin	not known
Oxalis cernua	aureusidin	not known
Helichrysum bracteatum	bracteatin	not known
Rosa foetida	quercetin 4′-glucoside	not known
Gossypium spp.	gossypetin	not known
Lathyrus pratensis	syringetin (?)	not known
Coronilla glauca	quercetagetin	not known
III. *Plants having only flavonoids*		
Rhododendron spp.	quercetagetin	absent
Antirrhinum majus yellow forms	aureusidin, bracteatin	absent
Primula vulgaris (primrose)	quercetagetin, 6-hydroxykaempferol	traces of carotenoid present around "eye"
Dianthus knappii	quercetagetin	absent
Dahlia variabilis	2′,4′,4-trihydroxychalcone, butein, sulphuretin	absent
Cosmos sulfureus	butein and sulphuretin	unidentified red pigment (non-carotenoid) also present
IV. *Plants having colourless flavonoids and coloured carotenoids*		
yellow *Tulipa*	kaempferol and quercetin	violaxanthin
yellow *Lilium*	kaempferol and quercetin	violaxanthin
yellow *Crocus*	kaempferol	α-, β- and γ-carotene, lycopene

[a] All pigments occur in glycosidic form; normally not mentioned here unless it is significant to colour.
[b] Data from Goodwin (1952).

because, in producing other flower colours, nature tends to be economical in the pigments used.

(2) The available data suggest that most plants fall into class IV:

i.e. they have colourless flavonoids and yellow or orange carotenoids (see also Seybold, 1954). By contrast, plants having only flavonoids (class III) are relatively few in number.

(3) A fifth class—plants with carotenoids and lacking flavonoids—no doubt exists but the author was unable to find a suitable example because of the meagre information available on this subject.

(4) Both kinds of yellow pigment may contribute to flower colour in different species of the same genus. For example, of two yellow-petalled *Paeonia* species examined recently, one (*P. lutea*) had a carotenoid and the other (*P. trollioides*) a chalkone. Similarly, in *Rhododendron* six species had quercetagetin and three (presumably) carotenoid.

To summarize, while present available studies show that carotenoids contribute more to yellow colour in higher plants than do flavonoids, future studies may well bring flavonoids into equal prominence with them.

2. Cream, Ivory and White Flower Colour

A large proportion of higher plants have white, ivory or cream flowers; in addition, cyanic-flowered plants in cultivation not infrequently produce acyanic (white) mutants. The vast majority of such flowers have "colourless" flavones or flavonols. Surveys of white-flowered wild plant species by Roller (1956) and Reznik (1956) showed that 86% of the sample contained kaempferol and 17% quercetin; luteolin and apigenin also commonly occur. Dihydroflavonols, leucoanthocyanidins and flavanones are of less frequent occurrence in such flowers.

Although not visible to the human eye, these pigments absorb strongly in the ultraviolet and can be "seen" by bees and, presumably, other insects; thus, they may serve some purpose in the plant. The presence of these flavonoids also adds "body" to the flower petal to give a cream or ivory appearance. Thus, the albino mutant in *Antirrhinum majus* (a rare form which lacks flavones altogether) is readily distinguished in its appearance from ivory flavone-containing flowers of the same plant. There are also several different white forms of *Dahlia variabilis*: some have the flavones (luteolin, apigenin) present in cyanic forms, others have the flavonols, kaempferol and quercetin, and yet others (e.g. "Clare White") have flavanones (Nordström and Swain, 1958), but no true albino is known. In fact, white petals which completely lack flavonoids of any kind are very rare. Besides the albino snapdragon, the only other examples known to the author are certain strains of *Petunia* and *Pisum*. Such plants are of great interest from the point of view of flavonoid biogenesis (cf. Geissman and Harborne, 1955).

The biogenetic relationship of the ivory flavones to the anthocyanins is now well established (see e.g. Harborne, 1962c) and some examples of the co-occurrence of structurally-related anthocyanins and flavones are given in Table IV. For a complete discussion of flavonoid biosynthesis, the reader is referred to Chapter 10.

IV. CONTRIBUTION TO LEAF COLOUR

Anthocyanins are the only flavonoids which are visible in leaves and their contribution may be considered under three headings: (1) red pigment formed transiently in young leaves but disappearing as the leaves mature; (2) permanent leaf pigmentation; and (3) autumnal colouring. One general point about leaf anthocyanins is that they are simpler in structure than those of flowers. Indeed, cyanidin (as the 3-glucoside) is the characteristic pigment in the leaf in all stages of its growth and other anthocyanidins are much less frequent (Lawrence *et al.*, 1939).

A. TRANSIENT LEAF COLOURS

Young leaves of many higher plants, at an early stage in development, produce a flush of anthocyanin which disappears rapidly as the leaves mature. Price and Sturgess (1938) surveyed 200 species from 110 genera and identified the anthocyanin in 93% of this sample as a cyanidin 3-glycoside. In a narrower survey, Reznik (1956) found cyanidin in nine species, delphinidin in four and peonidin in three.

The cause of anthocyanin formation at this stage in leaf development is probably that sugar accumulates in the tissues in amounts in excess of the immediate requirements for growth. Indeed, anthocyanin synthesis in leaves seems to be rather closely related to carbohydrate metabolism. Experiments with tomato seedlings show that under any environmental or cultural stress (i.e. high light intensity, nitrogen starvation, feeding of sucrose, removal of "carbohydrate sinks" or low temperatures), quantities of petunidin glycoside accumulate (Hussey, 1963). If subjected to both a high light intensity and conditions which stop growth, the tomato plant becomes deep purple and the chlorophyll green is completely masked.

Other conditions leading to anthocyanin accumulation in leaves include viral or fungal infection, treatment with growth regulators or wounding. For example, purple tinges appear on leaves of leaf roll-infected potatoes as a consequence of the disturbed translocation caused by this virus. With regard to wounded tissue, Bopp (1959) surveyed 191 species and found anthocyanin accumulation around the wound in 20% of this sample.

The transient anthocyanin soon disappears as the plant grows away, but it is not known whether the pigment produced in the juvenile stage is destroyed by enzyme [i.e. by anthocyanase (Huang, 1955) or by an oxidase (Bopp, 1957)] or is "diluted out" as the cells divide and multiply.

B. PERMANENT LEAF COLOUR

While anthocyanin colour is rather widespread in young and autumnal leaves, it is rather uncommon as a permanent leaf feature. While cyanidin is again the most usual pigment (present in twenty-eight out of thirty-six types surveyed by Reznik (1956)), delphinidin types are known and pelargonidin also occurs.

Many of the plants that show leaf colouration are of considerable ornamental value. The copper beech, a "sport" from the normal green *Fagus sylvatica*, is pigmented with the 3-galactosides of cyanidin and pelargonidin. Cyanidin glycosides also provide permanent colours in *Begonia* (*B. rex* has a deep purple-red leaf), in *Coleus* (notable for the striking anthocyanin patterning), in *Rosa*, in *Acer* and in *Rubus*. Intense leaf anthocyanin colour is sometimes correlated with deep colours in the flowers; the dark magenta form of *Antirrhinum* is one example. One of the most intensely pigmented of all plants is the red cabbage, *Brassica oleracea*.

Primula and *Solanum* plants are unusual in having delphinidin derivatives in their leaves. In *Primula sinensis*, leaf pigmentation is correlated with that of the flower; thus, **K** types have delphinidin in both plant parts, whereas **kk** types have mainly pelargonidin in the flower and mainly cyanidin and peonidin in leaves. Leaf pigments are commonly less methylated than those of the flower (Harborne and Sherratt, 1961). In *Solanum* plants and in the tomato, the prevailing leaf pigment is petunidin (Harborne, 1960) and one wild potato species, *S. microdontum*, has a remarkably intensely pigmented purple-black stem, together with normal green leaves.

Anthocyanins differing from the usual type occur in the leaves of members of the Gesneriaceae. This is not surprising since apigeninidin and luteolinidin have been detected in flowers of plants of this family. Unusual "pigments" are present in leaves of aquatic plants, which, according to Reznik and Neuhäusel (1959), have anthocyanins present in a colourless leucobase form. Treatment of the leaves with cold acid liberates anthocyanin, so these compounds are not leucoanthocyanidins. In passing, it may be mentioned that colourless leucobase forms of anthocyanin have also been found in flowers, e.g. in white blooms of *Lespedeza hortensis* (Hayashi and Abe, 1953) and in some, but not all, white *Iris* varieties (Werckmeister, 1955; Harborne, unpublished data).

Anthocyanin colour in leaves is often localized in its distribution. It sometimes occurs only on the undersurface (e.g. *Hoffmannia ghies-*

breghtii), or in the leaf hairs (e.g. *Gynura aurantiaca*). Permanent anthocyanin in leaf appears to lack function; many plants with red leaves are variants of a more normal green form. However, the presence of anthocyanin does not appear to be a handicap; the plants are able to photosynthesize normally.

C. AUTUMNAL COLOURING

Autumnal colouring is well known to be provided by both anthocyanins and carotenoids. Anthocyanin colouration is particularly striking in certain genera (*Acer* and *Pyrus*, for example) and is dependent on climatic factors for its full development. The pigment of autumnal leaves is almost always the simplest anthocyanin, cyanidin 3-glucoside. Hayashi and Abe (1953) analysed seventy-four plants from twenty-five families and found a cyanidin 3-glucoside in all of them. Again, Reznik (1956) found cyanidin in forty-seven out of forty-nine plants; autumnal leaves of forty-five species had a quercetin glycoside as well. While it is assumed that anthocyanin formation in autumn is connected with the liberation of sugar (from starch degradation) in dying leaves, no quantitative measurements correlating these two factors have yet been made.

V. CONTRIBUTION TO FRUIT COLOUR

As in the leaves and flowers, anthocyanin is a major contributor to colour in the fruits of higher plants. Not unnaturally, most attention has been given to the pigments of edible fruits. One or other of the six common anthocyanidins provide colour here (Table IX); the glycosidic

TABLE IX

Anthocyanidins of Edible Fruit

Anthocyanidin	*Fruit*
pelargonidin	passion fruit, strawberry[a]
cyanidin	apple (skin), pear (flesh), mulberry, blackberry, raspberry, cherry, plum, peach, sloe, red currant, elderberry and cranberry[b]
cyanidin and delphinidin	blackcurrant, "blood" orange (juice), "red" banana (skin)[c]
delphinidin	pomegranate (juice), aubergine (skin), whortleberry and grape[d]

[a] Wild strawberry has a 1:1 mixture of Pg and Cy, whereas cultivated strawberry has Pg, with only traces of Cy (Sondheimer and Karash, 1956).
[b] Also contains peonidin.
[c] Pigments are methylated (peonidin and malvidin); the pigment of the more common yellow-skinned cultivars is carotenoid.
[d] Also contains petunidin and malvidin.

patterns of the pigments of most of these fruits are known (see Harborne, 1964) but are not given since glycosylation is not immediately relevant to colour production. Ornamental fruits have also been studied; for example, cyanidin and peonidin 3-galactosides are known to pigment the red berries of *Ardisia crispa* and a petunidin glycoside is present in the purple-black berries of the deadly nightshade, *Atropa belladonna* (Harborne, 1963b).

As indicated in Table IX, anthocyanin colour is sometimes present throughout the fruit (e.g. raspberry), but, in other cases, is confined to the juice (e.g. blood orange) or the skin (e.g. apple). Among the legumes, anthocyanin may colour the pod of some species (e.g. strains of *Pisum sativum*) or the seed coat of others (e.g. *Pisum nepalensis*, *Phaseolus vulgaris*, *Phaseolus multiflorus*). The seed coat pigments of the various colour forms of the broad bean have been studied in great detail by Feenstra (1960), who has isolated from them all six common anthocyanidins, as well as several flavonol glycosides and some leucoanthocyanidins.

Many of the factors modifying anthocyanin colour in flowers presumably also operate in the fruit, but little work has been done on this aspect of fruit colour. Differences in pigment concentration are mainly responsible for the distinctive appearance of the two main groups of cherry varieties, the "black" (actually purple) and the "white" (actually pale red) cherry. The colours in the skin and flesh of the cherry are controlled by different genes, and yellow cherry cultivars, e.g. "Stark's Gold", lack anthocyanin in the flesh but have a yellow carotenoid in the skin. Metal complexing rather than co-pigmentation is presumably responsible for most of the blue colours in plant berries; thus Chenery (1948) found that 87% of 154 blue fruited species were strong aluminium accumulators.

VI. Conclusion

In summarizing the contribution of flavonoids to flower colour, one has the striking paradox that, although the chemical basis of colour is relatively simple (e.g. all anthocyanins are derived from one structure, cyanidin), there exists in nature an infinite number of different flower colours. Thus, it is rare to find two plant species, even in the same genus, with exactly the same flower tone. Again, many cultivated plants exhibit a remarkable amount of colour variation; over 1,000 rose varieties are listed and the majority differ in some degree in respect of their colour properties.

One explanation for this paradox is that, while the chemical basis is simple, there are many modifying factors, several of which might operate at the same time in the same species. Some of these modifying factors (e.g. metal complexing) have received attention and their effects on flower colour have been recorded. However, even in the case of the blueing effect of metals on anthocyanin colour, it is not clear how closely the pigment complexes, isolated by the mildest of extraction methods, are related to the *in vivo* situation; more work is clearly needed to answer this point. Also, there must be some additional factors modifying flower colour which have not yet been studied at all. For example, the actual physical structure of the petal surface must play a role in determining the colour of many flowers, but this has yet to be demonstrated.

Recent surveys have shown that the flavones and anthocyanins are, together, probably as widespread among higher plants as the carotenoids. The ability to synthesize flavonoids is clearly universal to the angiosperms. One striking illustration of this point is provided by the weedy composite, *Happlopappus gracilis*; although the mature plant has green leaves, yellow flowers and shows no trace of anthocyanin, large amounts of two cyanidin glycosides are produced by the plant when its cells are grown in tissue culture in the presence of light (Harborne, 1964a). There is little doubt that anthocyanin synthesis can be initiated in all plant cells, if the right environment is provided and genetic factors inhibiting synthesis are absent.

Since little work has been done on the basic structures of flavonoid pigments since the nineteen-thirties, it is, sometimes, assumed that there are no new flavonoids in nature remaining to be studied. This is by no means so; for example, the structures of several novel anthocyanidins present in orange-flowered plants are being investigated in this laboratory at the present time. With regard to the yellow water-soluble pigments, there are still large gaps in our knowledge. Thus, although the yellow pigment, nudicaulin, was isolated from *Papaver nudicaule* by Price *et al.* as long ago as 1939, it is not yet known if this substance is a flavonoid or not. Likewise, the yellow colouring matters of the Centrospermae, substances of considerable taxonomic interest, still remain to be identified.*

Little is known about the function of flavonoids in plants, apart from their role as pigments. The transient synthesis of anthocyanin in young or dying leaves seems to be related to carbohydrate metabolism but this idea certainly needs further experimental confirmation. By contrast, anthocyanin production in permanently coloured leaves, e.g. of *Coleus*, is quite unrelated to the environment or starch synthesis. The reason why pigment is present in one *Coleus* leaf cell but absent from the adjacent one is by no means clear (Commoner and Zucker, 1953) and the problem will not be answered until more is known about the biochemical basis of cellular differentiation.

* The structures of three betaxanthins have recently been elucidated by Piatelli *et al.* (1964). They are similar in structure to the betacyanins and are not related to the flavones, as was once thought.

REFERENCES

Acheson, R. M. (1956). *Proc. roy. Soc. B* **145**, 549.

Ainley, A. D., and Robinson, R. (1937). *J. chem. Soc.* 446.

Alston, R. E. (1958). *Amer. J. Bot.* **45**, 689.

Asen, S., Stuart, N. W., and Siegelman, H. W. (1959). *Proc. Amer. Soc. hort. Sci.* **73**, 495.

Bate-Smith, E. C., and Harborne, J. B. (1963). *Nature, Lond.* **198**, 1307.

Bayer, E. (1958). *Chem. Ber.* **91**, 1115.

Bayer, E. (1959). *Chem. Ber.* **92**, 1062.

Bayer, E., Nether, K., and Egeter, H. (1960). *Chem. Ber.* **93**, 2871.

Beale, G. H. (1941). *J. Genet.* **42**, 197.

Beale, G. H., Price, J. R., and Sturgess, V. C. (1941). *Proc. roy. Soc. B* **130**, 113.

Bendz, G., Martensson, O., and Terenius, L. (1962). *Acta chem. scand.* **16**, 1183.

Blank, F. (1947). *Botan. Rev.* **13**, 241.

Blank, F. (1958). In "Encyclopedia of Plant Physiology" (K. Paech and M. V. Tracey, eds.), vol. 10, p. 300, Springer Verlag, Berlin.

Bopp, M. (1957). *Planta* **48**, 631.

Bopp, M. (1958). *Z. Naturf.* **13b**, 669.

Bopp, M. (1959). *Z. Bot.* **47**, 197.

Boyle, R. (1664). "Experiments and Considerations Touching Colours," London.

Bragt, J. van (1962). *Meded. LandbHoogesch., Wageningen* **62**, 1.

Charlesworth, E. H., and Robinson, R. (1934). *J. chem. Soc.* 1619.

Chenery, E. M. (1948). *Ann. Bot. N.S.* **12**, 121.

Clevenger, S. (1964). *Canad. J. Biochem.* **42**, 154.

Commoner, B., and Zucker, M. L. (1953). In "Growth and Differentiation in Plants" (W. E. Loomis, ed.), pp. 339–392, Iowa State College Press, Ames.

Darwin, C. (1876). "The Effects of Cross and Self Fertilisation in the Vegetable Kingdom," Murray, London.

Dean, F. M. (1963). "Naturally Occurring Oxygen Ring Compounds," Butterworth, London.

Dodds, K. S., and Long, D. H. (1955). *J. Genet.* **53**, 136.

Endo, T. (1962). *Jap. J. Genet.* **37**, 284.

Feenstra, W. J. (1960). *Meded. LandbHoogesch., Wageningen* **60**, 1.

Feenstra, W. J., Johnson, B. L., Ribereau-Gayon, P., and Geissman, T. A. (1963). *Phytochemistry* **2**, 273.

Forsyth, W. G. C. and Simmonds, N. W. (1954). *Proc. roy. Soc. B* **142**, 549.

Frisch, K. von (1950). "Bees, their Vision, Chemical Senses and Language," Cornell, Ithaca, New York.

Gascoigne, R. M., Ritchie, E., and White, D. R. (1948). *J. roy. Soc. N.S.W.* **82**, 44.

Geissman, T. A. (ed.) (1962). "Chemistry of the Flavonoid Compounds," Pergamon Press, Oxford.

Geissman, T. A., and Harborne, J. B. (1955). *Arch. Biochem. Biophys.* **55**, 447.

Geissman, T. A., and Mehlquist, G. A. L. (1947). *Genetics* **32**, 410.

Geissman, T. A., Jorgensen, E. C., and Harborne, J. B. (1953). *Chem. Ind.* 1389.

Gertz, O. (1938). *Kgl. Physiograf. Sällskap. Lund*, Förh. **8**, 62.

Goodwin, T. W. (1952). "Comparative Biochemistry of the Carotenoids," Chapman and Hall, London.

Harborne, J. B. (1960). *Biochem. J.* **74**, 262.

Harborne, J. B. (1961). *Experientia* **17**, 72.

Harborne, J. B. (1962a). *Fortschr. Organ. Naturst.* **20**, 165.

Harborne, J. B. (1962b). *Arch. Biochem. Biophys.* **96**, 171.

Harborne, J. B. (1962c). *In* "Chemistry of the Flavonoid Compounds" (T. A. Geissman, ed.), pp. 598–617, Pergamon Press, Oxford.

Harborne, J. B. (1963a). *In* "Chemical Plant Taxonomy" (T. Swain, ed.), pp. 359–388, Academic Press, London.

Harborne, J. B. (1963b). *Phytochemistry* 2, 85.

Harborne, J. B. (1963c). *Phytochemistry* 2, 327.

Harborne, J. B. (1964a). *Rep. Innes hort. Instn.* 45.

Harborne, J. B. (1964b). *In* "Biochemistry of Phenolic Compounds" (J. B. Harborne, ed.), pp. 129–169, Academic Press, London.

Harborne, J. B., and Sherratt, H. S. A. (1961). *Biochem. J.* 78, 298.

Harborne, J. B., and Simmonds, N. W. (1964). *In* "Biochemistry of Phenolic Compounds" (J. B. Harborne, ed.), pp. 77–124, Academic Press, London.

Hayashi, K. (1962). *In* "Chemistry of Flavonoid Compounds" (T. A. Geissman, ed.), pp. 248–285, Pergamon Press, Oxford.

Hayashi, K., and Abe, Y. (1953). *Misc. Rep. Res. Inst. nat. Resour., Tokyo* 29, 1.

Hayashi, K., and Abe, Y. (1955). *Bot. Mag., Tokyo* 68, 299.

Hayashi, K., and Takeda, K. (1962). *Proc. imp. Acad. Japan* 38, 161.

Hayashi, K., Saito, N., and Mitsui, S. (1961). *Proc. imp. Acad. Japan* 37, 393.

Hess, D. (1963). *Planta* 59, 567.

Huang, H. T. (1955). *J. Agric. Food Chem.* 3, 141.

Hussey, G. C. (1963). *J. exp. Bot.* 14, 326.

Jorgensen, E. C., and Geissman, T. A. (1955). *Arch. Biochem. Biophys.* 55, 389.

Karrer, W. (1958). "Konstitution und Vorkommen der organischen Pflanzenstoffe," p. 744, Birkhaüser-Verlag, Basel.

Latour and Magnier de la Source (1877). *Bull. soc. chim. Paris* 228, 337.

Lawrence, W. J. C. (1932). *Nature, Lond.* 129, 834.

Lawrence, W. J. C. (1950). *Symp. Biochem. Soc.* 4, 3.

Lawrence, W. J. C., Price, J. R., Robinson, R., and Robinson, G. M. (1939). *Phil. Trans.* 230 *B*, 149.

Legro, R. A. H. (1963). *J. R. hort. Soc.* 88, 13.

Mabry, T. J., Wyler, H., Sassu, G., Mercier, M., Parikh, J., and Dreiding, A. S. (1962). *Helv. chim. acta* 45, 640.

Manning, A. (1956a). *New Biology* 21, 59.

Manning, A. (1956b). *Behaviour* 9, 114.

Marquart, L. Cl. (1835). "Die Farben der Blüthen, Eine chemischphysiologische Abhandlung," Bonn.

McKay, M. B., and Warner, M. F. (1933). *Nat. Hort. Mag.* 178.

Mitsui, S., Hayashi, K., and Hattori, S. (1959). *Proc. imp. Acad. Japan* 35, 169.

Nordström, C. G., and Swain, T. (1958). *Arch. Biochem. Biophys.* 73, 220.

Paech, K. (1954). *Ann. Rev. Plant Physiol.* 6, 273.

Pecket, R. C. (1960). *New Phytol.* 59, 138.

Pecket, R. C., and Selim, A. R. A. A. (1962). *Nature, Lond.* 195, 620.

Piattelli, M., Minale, L., and Prota, G. (1964). *Phytochemistry* (in press).

Price, J. R., and Sturgess, V. C. (1938). *Biochem. J.* 32, 1658.

Price, J. R., Sturgess, V. C., Robinson, R., and Robinson, G. M. (1938). *Nature, Lond.* 142, 356.

Price, J. R., Robinson, R., and Scott-Moncrieff, R. (1939). *J. chem. Soc.* 1465.

Rao, P. S., and Seshadri, T. R. (1941). *Proc. Indian Acad. Sci.* 14A, 289.

Reznik, H. (1956). *S.B. heidelberg. Akad. Wiss. Math.-naturwiss. Kl., Abhandl.* 125.

Reznik, H. (1961). *Flora* 150, 454.

Reznik, H., and Neuhäusel, R. (1959). *Z. Bot.* 47, 471.

Robinson, G. M. (1939). *J. Amer. chem. Soc.* 61, 1606.

Robinson, G. M., and Robinson, R. (1931). *Biochem. J.* **25**, 1687.

Robinson, G. M., and Robinson, R. (1934). *Biochem. J.* **28**, 1712.

Robinson, G. M., and Robinson, R. (1939). *J. Amer. chem. Soc.* **61**, 1605.

Roller, K. (1956). *Z. Bot.* **44**, 477.

Saito, N., Mitsui, S., and Hayashi, K. (1961). *Proc. imp. Acad. Japan* **37**, 484.

Salaman, R. N. (1949). "The History and Social Influence of the Potato," Cambridge University Press.

Scott-Moncrieff, R. (1936). *J. Genet.* **32**, 117.

Seybold, A. (1953–4). *S.B. heidelberg Akad. Wiss. Math.-naturwiss. Kl.* **2** *Abh.* 31.

Shibata, M., and Ishikura, N. (1960). *Jap. J. Bot.* **17**, 230.

Shibata, K., Hayashi, K., and Isaka, T. (1949). *Acta phytochim., Tokyo* **15**, 17.

Sondheimer, E., and Karash, C. B. (1956). *Nature, Lond.* **178**, 648.

Sprengel, C. K. (1793). "Das entdeckte Geheimnis der Natur im Bau und in der Befruchtung der Blumen."

Stebbins, G. L. (1959). *In* "Vistas in Botany" (W. B. Turrill, ed.), pp. 258–290, Pergamon Press, London.

Subramanian, S. S., and Swamy, M. N. (1964). *Curr. Sci. (India)* **33**, 112.

Swain, T. (ed.) (1963). "Chemical Plant Taxonomy," Academic Press, London.

Swain, T., and Bate-Smith, E. C. (1962). *In* "Comparative Biochemistry" (M. Florkin and H. S. Mason, eds.), vol. III, pp. 755–809, Academic Press, New York.

Taylor, T. W. J. (1940). *Proc. roy. Soc. B* **129**, 230.

Wanscher, J. H. (1953). *K. Vet Højsk Aarsskr.* 91.

Werckmeister, P. (1955). *Der Züchter* **25**, 315.

Werckmeister, P. (1960). *Bull. Amer. Iris Soc.* 25.

Willstätter, R., and Mallison, H. (1915). *Liebigs Ann.* **408**, 147.

Wilson, R. F. (1938). "Horticultural Colour Chart."

Chapter 10

BIOSYNTHESIS OF FLAVONOIDS *

H. Grisebach

*Chemisches Laboratorium der Universität Freiburg i.Br.,
Freiburg i.Br., Germany*

I. Introduction

Early in the structural work on flavonoids it was noted that there were certain regularities in the pattern of hydroxyl or methoxyl group substitution. With few exceptions the oxygen-containing substituents in ring A are in the *meta* position, as in phloroglucinol or resorcinol, whereas in ring B they are in the *ortho* position to each other (3', 4' and 5'). Since the substitution pattern in ring B corresponds in many cases to that in *p*-coumaric acid, caffeic acid and other phenylpropane derivatives in plants, Sir Robert Robinson postulated as early as 1921 that flavonoids are biogenetically derived from a C_6–C_3 and a C_6 unit (ring A). Early support for this hypothesis came from the study of the genetics of

---

* I wish to thank my wife for the translation of the manuscript.

flower colour (Lawrence and Scott-Moncrieff, 1935; Scott-Moncrieff, 1936). In albino mutants of the snapdragon (*Antirrhinum majus*), for instance, glucose esters of *p*-coumaric and caffeic acids were present which have the same substitution pattern as that present in ring B of the flavonoids occurring in the coloured genotypes (Geissman and Harborne, 1955; Harborne and Corner, 1961).

Although the general hypothesis of Robinson seemed to be correct, reviews on the subject of flavonoid biosynthesis as late as 1952 (e.g. Geissman and Hinreiner, 1952) presented a confusing picture of ideas on

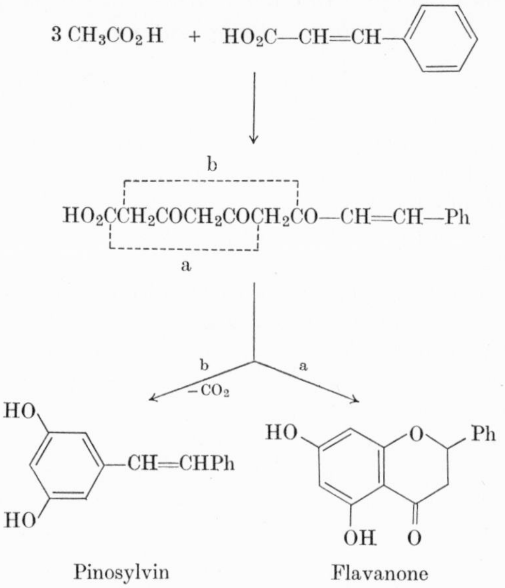

FIG. 1. Hypothesis for the formation of flavonoids and stilbenes (Birch and Donovan, 1953).

specific precursors and on the mechanism of biosynthesis. In 1953 an important theoretical contribution to the subject was made by Birch and Donovan, who put forward the hypothesis that flavonoids arise from the addition of three acetate units to cinnamic acid or a related compound. They also postulated that the stilbenes, e.g. pinosylvin, could be derived from the same precursor by a different type of cyclization (Fig. 1). Birch's hypothesis, which in the meantime has been shown to be fully correct, stimulated further work with radioactive precursors which has contributed much to our knowledge of flavonoid biosynthesis. A number of reviews of this work have appeared (Bogorad, 1958; Grisebach, 1962a, b; Neish, 1960; Grisebach and Ollis, 1961; Birch, 1962). In this chapter an attempt will be made to present a comprehensive picture of our present-day knowledge in this field.

II. Precursors of Flavonoids

It is now certain that ring A of the flavonoids is formed by a head-to-tail condensation of three acetyl (malonyl) units, while ring B and carbon atoms 2, 3 and 4 originate from an intact phenylpropane unit (Fig. 2). This biosynthetic pattern was found in the formation of cyanidin (Grisebach, 1957, 1958), quercetin (Underhill *et al.*, 1957; Watkin *et al.*, 1957; Geissman and Swain, 1957; Shibata and Yamazaki, 1958), catechin (Comte *et al.*, 1960; Zaprometov, 1962) and phloretin (Hutchinson *et al.*, 1959).

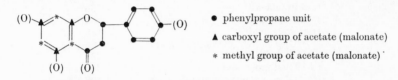

● phenylpropane unit

▲ carboxyl group of acetate (malonate)

* methyl group of acetate (malonate)

FIG. 2. Origin of the carbon atoms in the flavane skeleton.

A. THE PHENYLPROPANE PRECURSOR

A number of phenylpropane compounds can serve as precursors for ring B and C-atoms 2, 3 and 4. The most effective precursors are L-phenylalanine, cinnamic acid and *p*-hydroxycinnamic acid. The phenylpropane compounds themselves are formed in higher plants as in bacteria by the well-known pathway via shikimic and prephenic acids (Neish, 1960). In order to compare the efficiencies of several precursors the dilution of the specific radioactivity of the compound administered or the percentage of administered ^{14}C converted into quercetin was determined (Underhill *et al.*, 1957; Watkin and Neish, 1960). Table I shows the dilution values obtained with a number of precursors for quercetin in buckwheat (*Fagopyrum tataricum*).

While this method makes it possible to determine approximately the relative efficiency with which various compounds can serve as precursors, the question remains as to the nature of the actual biological phenylpropane intermediate which condenses with acetate or malonate (see following section) to form the $C_6-C_3-C_6$ intermediate. Most likely this intermediate is cinnamic acid and/or *p*-coumaric acid (Reznik, 1960). *Trans*-cinnamic acid can be formed in the plant by the direct elimination of ammonia from L-phenylalanine which is catalysed by the enzyme phenylalanase. In the same way *trans-p*-coumaric acid can arise from tyrosine by the action of the enzyme tyrase (Fig. 3) (Neish, 1961; Koukol and Conn, 1961). Tyrase has so far been found only in grasses (Gramineae). Similarly *trans*-caffeic acid can be formed in various plants by the deamination of β-(3,4-dihydroxyphenyl)-L-alanine (DOPA) (Macleod and Pridham, 1963). However, caffeic acid is a much poorer precursor of quercetin than is cinnamic or p-coumaric acid (Table I). Formation of cinnamic acid by the postulated pathway (Underhill *et al.*,

TABLE I

Comparison of [^{14}C]-Compounds as Precursors of Quercetin in Buckwheat (Underhill *et al.*, 1957)

Compound administered	Dilution[a]
Shikimic acid[b]	36
L-Phenylalanine[b]	66
Cinnamic acid[c]	148
[β-^{14}C]-p-hydroxycinnamic acid	185
[β-^{14}C]-caffeic acid	1,268
[β-^{14}C]-sinapic acid	4,240
[β-^{14}C]-m-methoxycinnamic acid	4,502
Phenylacetic acid[c]	7,260
Protocatechuic acid	11,840
p-Hydroxybenzoic acid	14,350
[β-^{14}C]-ferulic acid	578,000

[a] Specific activity of compound administered divided by specific activity of quercetin.
[b] Randomly labelled.
[c] Carboxyl labelled.

1957) phenylpyruvic acid → phenyllactic acid → cinnamic acid does not seem to take place (Gamborg, 1962). The incorporation of phenyllactic acid into quercetin (Table I) seems to occur indirectly via phenylpyruvic acid → phenylalanine → cinnamic acid (Gamborg *et al.*, 1962).

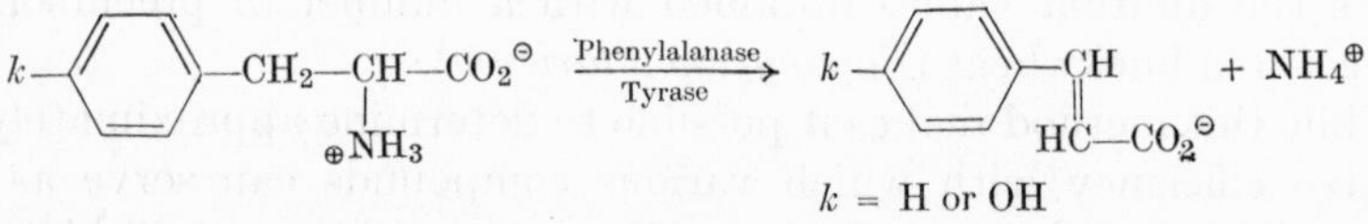

$$k\text{—}\langle\text{—}\rangle\text{—}CH_2\text{—}CH\text{—}CO_2^{\ominus} \quad \xrightarrow[\text{Tyrase}]{\text{Phenylalanase}} \quad k\text{—}\langle\text{—}\rangle\text{—}\underset{HC\text{—}CO_2^{\ominus}}{\overset{CH}{\|}} \quad + \quad NH_4^{\oplus}$$

$$\underset{\oplus NH_3}{}$$

k = H or OH

FIG. 3. Enzymatic formation of cinnamic and p-coumaric acid.

Since the deamination reaction is irreversible, the intact incorporation of cinnamic acid into the flavonoids proves that the amino acids themselves do not take part in the condensation to the C_6–C_3–C_6 compound.

B. FORMATION OF RING A

It was believed earlier that the flavane skeleton could arise by condensation of a cinnamic acid with phloroglucinol itself (e.g. Pachéco,

1956). That phloroglucinol cannot be a precursor was shown in a competition experiment by Watkin *et al.* (1957): When buckwheat cuttings were given $^{14}CO_2$ as the only source of radioactive carbon, the quercetin formed was equally labelled in rings A and B. When unlabelled phenylalanine was given at the same time as $^{14}CO_2$ the activity of ring B was only one-tenth that of ring A. In contrast, simultaneous administration of phloroglucinol with $^{14}CO_2$ resulted in a uniformly labelled quercetin. In the same kind of experiment myo-inositol could be excluded as a precursor of ring A of quercetin.

On the basis of numerous experiments Kursanov (1954) suggested that the catechin tannins are formed to a large extent by the pathway D-glucose → myo-inositol. However, [^{14}C]-myo-inositol is not incorporated into catechin in tea leaves; neither is myo-inositol a precursor of cyanidin in red cabbage (Weygand *et al.*, 1957).

The specific incorporation of acetate into ring A of cyanidin in a head-to-tail fashion as predicted by Birch's hypothesis was proved by a

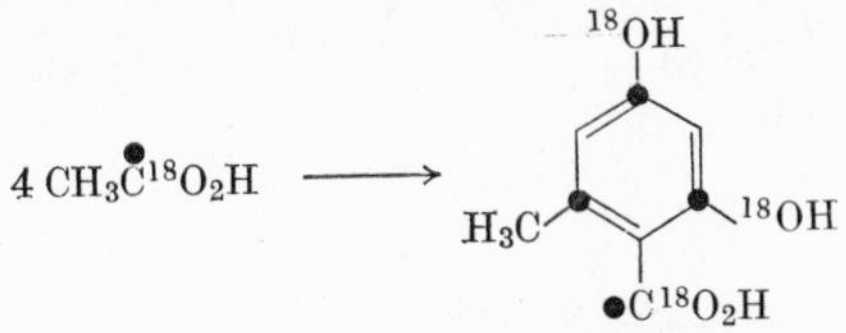

$$4 \ CH_3\overset{\bullet}{C}^{18}O_2H \longrightarrow$$

FIG. 4. Origin of the oxygen atoms in orsellinic acid ($\bullet = {}^{14}C$).

complete degradation of ring A of cyanidin (Grisebach, 1957). By analogy with fatty acid biosynthesis and the results which have been obtained in the study of the biosynthesis of other acetate-derived natural products (Lynen and Tada, 1961) one must assume that malonyl-CoA and not acetyl-CoA is the biological intermediate in the formation of ring A of the flavonoids. Although there is as yet no experimental proof for the participation of malonate in the case of flavonoid biosynthesis, there cannot be much doubt that acetate is incorporated via malonyl-CoA, because for energetic reasons the polyketoacid chain can be formed only by malonyl-CoA (Lynen and Tada, 1961).

Experiments with [1-^{14}C-^{18}O]-acetate (Gatenbeck and Mosbach, 1959) have proved that the oxygen in the phenolic hydroxyl groups of orsellinic acid (Fig. 4) comes from the carboxyl group of acetate (malonate). By analogy with this and similar experiments with other phenolic substances (Gatenbeck, 1960) it can be assumed that the oxygen of the hydroxyl groups in positions 5 and 7 of the flavonoids as well as the oxygen atom of the heterocyclic ring also originate from the carboxyl group of malonate.

III. INTERMEDIATES AND ENDPRODUCTS OF BIOSYNTHESIS

A. CHALKONES

Condensation of an activated cinnamic acid (probably the CoA-ester) with three molecules of malonyl-CoA would lead to the formation of a β-polyketoacid which would then—probably owing to the surface structure of the enzyme—undergo intramolecular ring closure, whereby the first stable intermediate formed should be a chalkone (Fig. 5).

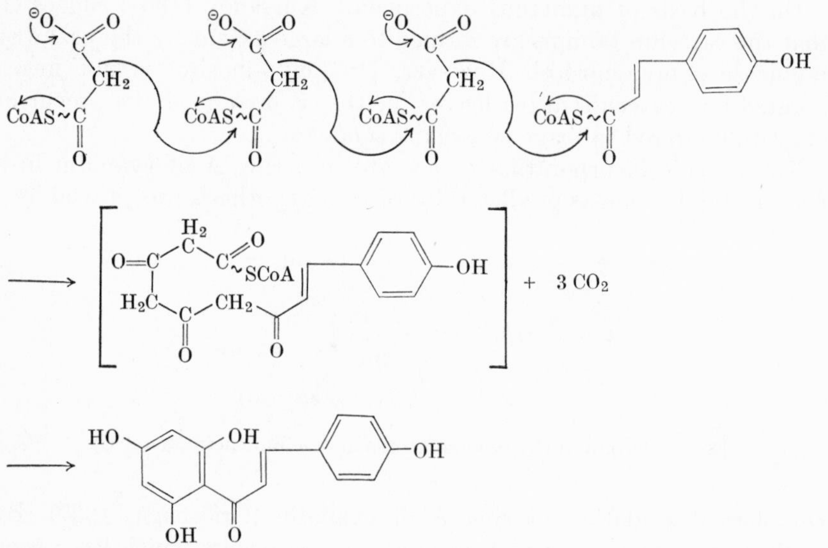

FIG. 5. Hypothetical formation of a chalkone from p-coumaryl-CoA and malonyl-CoA.

If this assumption is true, then chalkones would be the first C_6–C_3–C_6 intermediates in flavonoid biosynthesis which can be isolated. In the last years a series of experiments with [^{14}C]-chalkones have been carried out which indicate that these compounds do occupy a central position in flavonoid metabolism. First of all, the participation of 2',4,4',6'-tetrahydroxychalkone or its 2'-glucoside in the biosynthetic pathway could be demonstrated by a competition experiment between [3-^{14}C]-cinnamic acid and the unlabelled chalkone. When red cabbage seedlings were fed only [3-^{14}C]-cinnamic acid on the one hand and [3-^{14}C]-cinnamic acid plus unlabelled chalkone on the other hand, the specific activity of the cyanidin isolated was very much smaller in the second case (Table II) (H. Grisebach and L. Patschke, 1963, unpublished observations).

Direct proof for the participation of the [^{14}C]-chalkone glucoside was its incorporation into cyanidin in red cabbage and into cyanidin and

TABLE II

Competition Experiment with 2′,4,4′,6′-Tetra-
hydroxychalkone-2′-glucoside in Red Cabbage
Seedlings

Compound administered	Spec. activity of cyanidin (cpm/mmole)
[3-^{14}C]-Cinnamic acid (7·5 μmole)	487,200
[3-^{14}C]-Cinnamic acid (7·5 μmole) + chalkone (15 μmole)	225,300

quercetin in buckwheat (*Fagopyrum esculentum*). The radioactivity in the products was localized in the expected positions, as was demons-trated by degradation (Fig. 6) (Grisebach and Patschke, 1961).

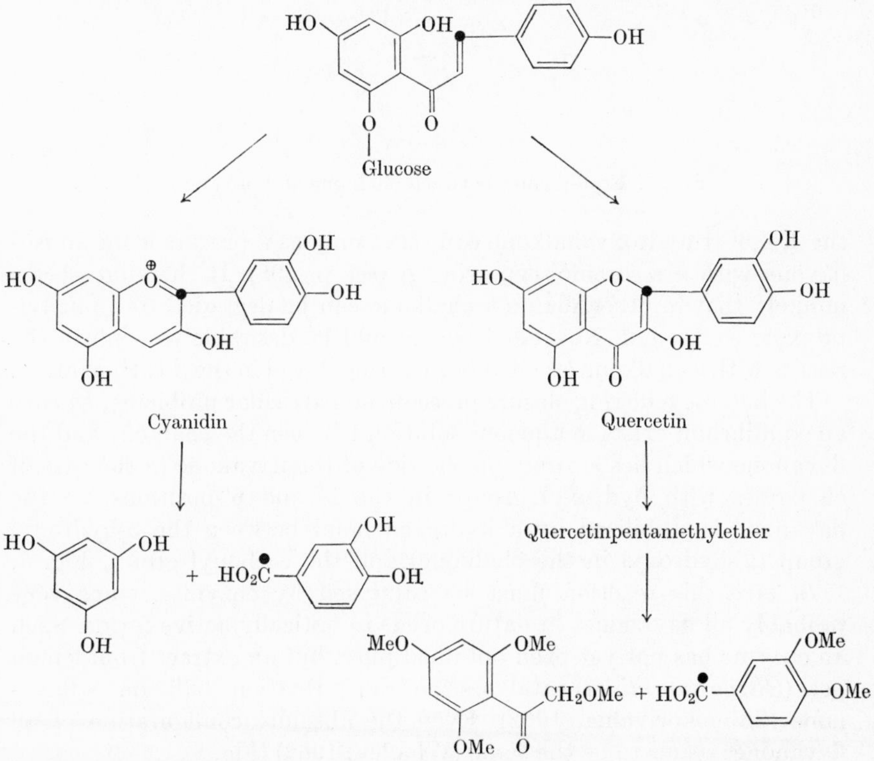

FIG. 6. Incorporation of 2′,4,4′,6′-tetrahydroxy-[β-^{14}C]-chalkone-2′-glucoside into cyanidin and quercetin and degradation of the latter compounds (● = ^{14}C).

The question can now be raised whether in the biosynthesis of various flavonoids chalkones with different patterns of oxidation in rings A and B occur as intermediates, or whether all the compounds can be derived from a single chalkone with the sites of nuclear oxidation shown in Fig. 6. The fact that this chalkone is incorporated into both cyanidin and quercetin indicates that a change in the oxidation stage of the C_3-chain as well as the introduction of an additional hydroxyl group *ortho* to the one already present in ring B can take place at the level of a C_6–C_3–C_6 intermediate.

However, some uncertainty remains as to the validity of this conclusion, because the results discussed above would also have been obtained if the chalkone had been degraded to a phenylpropane compound prior to incorporation into the flavonoids. Such a degradation could be excluded in experiments with chana germ (*Cicer arietinum L.*). In this plant the 2',4,4',6'-tetrahydroxychalkone is incorporated only into an isoflavone with phloroglucinol-type substitution in ring A and

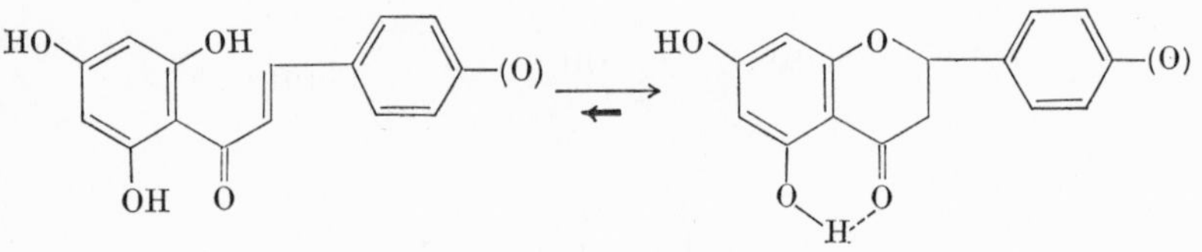

FIG. 7. Equilibrium between chalkone and flavanone.

the 4,4',6'-trihydroxychalkone can serve only as a precursor for an isoflavone with a resorcinol-type ring A (see p. 296). It therefore seems unlikely that in other plants a chalkone can be degraded to a phenylpropane compound. Nevertheless it would be desirable to confirm the results with a chalkone labelled both in ring A and in the β-carbon atom.

The heterocyclic ring closure presents no particular problems. *In vitro* an equilibrium exists in aqueous solution between the chalkone and the flavanone which lies entirely on the side of the flavanone in the case of chalkones with hydroxyl groups in the 2' and 6'-positions, as the flavanone is stabilized by a hydrogen bond between the 5-hydroxyl group (2'-hydroxyl in the chalkone) and the carbonyl group, Fig. 7.

In vivo this reaction must be catalysed by enzymes, since very probably all flavanones in nature occur in optically active forms. Such an enzyme has not yet been obtained pure, but an extract from lemon peel (*Citrus aurantium*) catalyses the transformation chalkone → flavanone (Shimokoriyama, 1962). Even the absolute configuration of all flavanones seems to be the same (Whalley, 1962) (Fig. 8).

Stabilization of the chalkones can also occur through hydrogenation of the double bond to form dihydrochalkones. The dihydrochalkone phlorizin from *Malus* species is easily formed in the plant from the corresponding chalkone, as has been demonstrated by experiments in which the [^{14}C]chalkone was administered to apple tree leaves (Fig. 9) (Grisebach and Patschke, 1962).

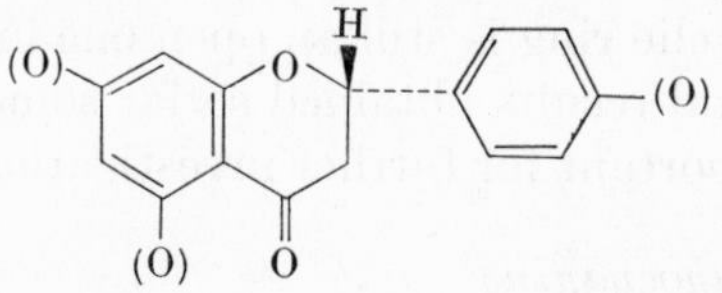

FIG. 8. Absolute configuration of flavanones.

It has already been mentioned that according to Birch's hypothesis a different cyclization of the poly-β-keto precursor could lead to the formation of a stilbene. This prediction has been verified experimentally

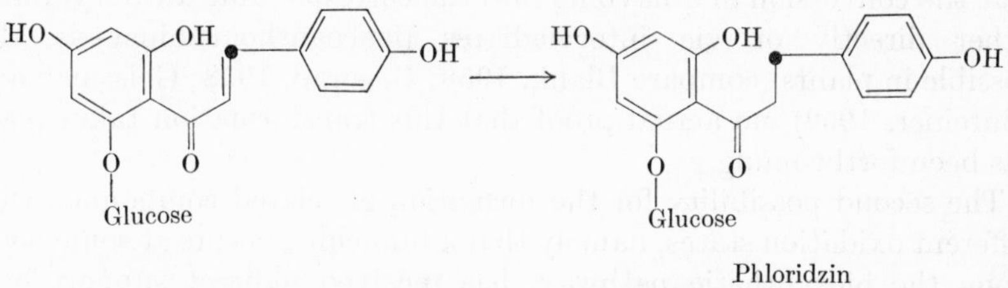

FIG. 9. Formation of phloridzin ($\bullet = {}^{14}$C).

by several workers (Billek and Kindl, 1962; Hillis and Hasegawa, 1962; Ibrahim and Towers, 1962; von Rudloff and Jorgensen, 1963). Thus, for example, the distribution of activity in pinosylvin monomethyl ether

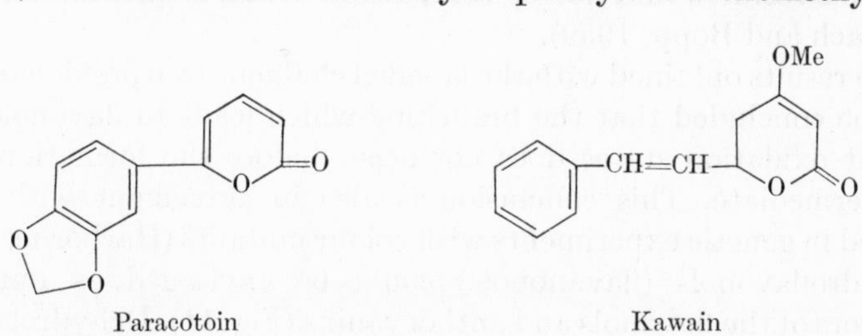

FIG. 10. Compounds which could arise by condensation of cinnamic acid with one or two acetate units.

after administration of [1-^{14}C]-acetate and [U-^{14}C]-phenylalanine to pine twigs is consistent with the Birch scheme (Fig. 1).

The naturally occurring aromatic derivatives of monocyclic α-pyrones, such as paracotoin and kavain (Fig. 10), can be envisaged as condensation products of cinnamic acids with only one or two acetate units (Mors *et al.*, 1962).

B. VARIATIONS IN THE OXIDATION STATE OF THE HETEROCYCLIC RING

The question of the formation of flavonoids differing in the oxidation state of the heterocyclic ring is still an open one in many respects, but from the experimental results obtained so far some conclusions can be drawn which are important for further investigations.

1. *Flavonols and Anthocyanins*

The much discussed suggestion that the flavonols might be precursors of the anthocyanins probably goes back to the observation made by Willstätter and Mallison (1914), who succeeded in reducing quercetin to cyanidin *in vitro* with magnesium in aqueous methanolic hydrochloric acid. While some experimental observations give support to the idea that the conversion of a flavonol into the corresponding anthocyanin—either directly or via intermediates (leucoanthocyanins)—is also possible in plants (compare Blank, 1958; Bogorad, 1958; Geissman and Hinreiner, 1952), no actual proof that this transformation takes place has been forthcoming.

The second possibility for the formation of related compounds with different oxidation states, namely that a branching occurs at some point along the biosynthetic pathway, has received indirect support in a number of investigations (see earlier reviews).

When buckwheat seedlings are fed with [^{14}C]phenylalanine and the specific activity of the products is plotted against time, the curves of cyanidin and quercetin run parallel and reach a maximum at the same time. This result would not be compatible with a sequential formation (Grisebach and Bopp, 1959).

From results obtained with the labelled chalkone (see previous section) it can be concluded that the branching which leads to flavonoids with different oxidation states does not occur before the formation of the C_{15} intermediate. This conclusion is also in agreement with results obtained in genetic experiments with colour mutants (Harborne, 1962a).

Dihydroflavonols (flavanonols) could be envisaged as immediate precursors of the flavonols and anthocyanins (Fig. 11). Dehydrogenation of the naturally occurring dihydroflavonols to flavonols is easily achieved *in vitro* since the H-atoms at C-2 and C-3 in these compounds are in *trans* position. Conversion of dihydroflavonols into anthocyanins, which have the same oxidation state, might take place by the mechanism indicated in Fig. 11. This scheme does not, however, satisfactorily explain the results obtained in studies of the light-dependent formation of flavonols and anthocyanins (see Section V). These results indicate that anthocyanin

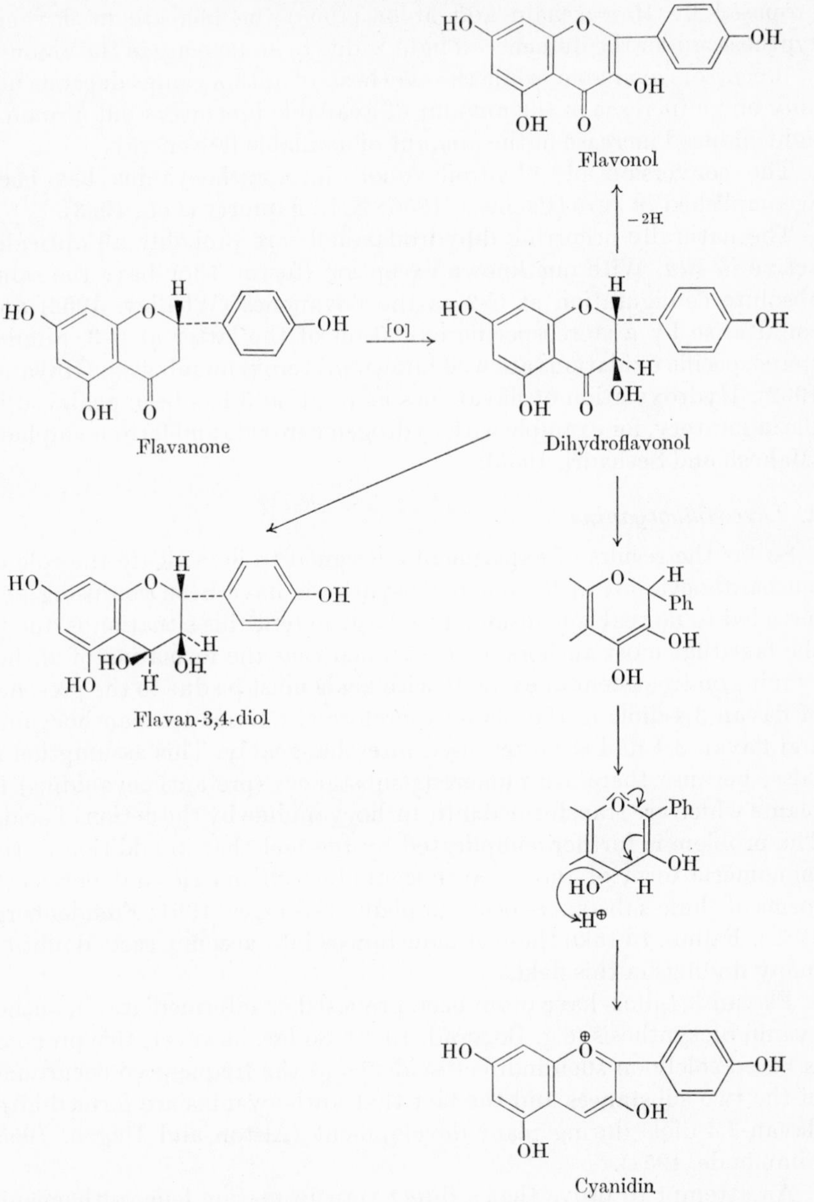

FIG. 11. Possible conversion of dihydroflavonols into flavanols, anthocyanins and flavan-3,4-diols.

synthesis is physiologically more complex than flavonol synthesis: flavonols can be synthesized in the dark, but anthocyanins are formed in many plants only in the presence of light. According to a hypothesis

10

proposed by Harraschain and Mohr (1963) the increase in flavonol synthesis under the influence of light is due to an increase in the amount of precursors available, while the synthesis of anthocyanins depends not only on an increase in the amount of available precursors but also on a light-induced increase in the amount of available free energy.

The conversion of dihydroflavonols into anthocyanins has been accomplished *in vitro* (Pachéco, 1956; Krishnamurty *et al.*, 1963).

The naturally occurring dihydroflavonols are probably all optically active *in situ*. With one known exception (fustin) they have the same absolute configuration at C-2 as the flavanones (Whalley, 1962) and could arise by a stereospecific oxidation of the latter at C-3. Similar stereospecific oxidations are well known in steroid metabolism (Hayano, 1962). Hydroxylation of flavanones at position 3 has been achieved in the laboratory, for example with hydrogen peroxide and ferrous sulphate (Mahesh and Seshadri, 1955).

2. *Leucoanthocyanins*

So far the results of experiments designed to investigate the role of leucoanthocyanins in flavonoid biosynthesis have been confusing and have led to no real conclusion. To a large extent this situation is due to the fact that most authors have assumed that the formation of antho-cyanins on treatment of extracts with acids must be due to the presence of flavan-3,4-diols in the plant; therefore the terms leucoanthocyanin and flavan-3,4-diol are often used interchangeably. This assumption is false, because there are numerous substances (pro-anthocyanidins) in plants which are transformed into anthocyanidine by the action of acids. The problem is further complicated by the fact that in addition to the monomeric form of the proanthocyanidins oligomeric and polymeric forms of these substances occur in plants (Weinges, 1961; Freudenberg, 1962). Failure to take these circumstances into account casts doubt on many findings in this field.

Flavan-3,4-diols have often been proposed as intermediates in antho-cyanin biosynthesis (e.g. Bogorad, 1958). So far, however, this proposal is based solely on such indirect evidence as the frequent co-occurrence of the two substances and the fact that anthocyanins are formed after flavan-3,4-diols during plant development (Alston and Hagen, 1955; Simmonds, 1954).

An attempt to prove that a direct transformation leucoanthocyanin → anthocyanin can take place has been made with *Impatiens balsamia* (Bopp and Matthiss, 1962). After a single feeding of [carboxyl-^{14}C]-phenylalanine the specific activity of leucoanthocyanin at first increases and then decreases after the appearance of anthocyanin. When the specific activities of the two compounds are plotted against time, the decreasing portion of the leucoanthocyanin curve intersects the anthocyanin curve approximately at its maximum. From these results it was concluded that in the hypocotyls of *Impatiens* leucoanthocyanin is a direct precursor of anthocyanin. However, since at least a part of the proanthocyanins are very probably present in oligomeric or polymeric form (see above), the application of the criteria set up by Zilversmit *et al.* (1943) for the relationship between the activity/time curves of precursor and product seems questionable in this case.

Moreover, the work of these authors offers no proof that the leucoanthocyanins in *Impatiens* are identical with flavan-3,4-diols and consequently presents no evidence that the latter are precursors of anthocyanins. It is more probably that the flavan-3,4-diols are biosynthetic end-products (which can lead to polymeric forms). Here again the branching from the main pathway could take place at the level of the dihydroflavonols (Fig. 11).

3. Catechins

Preliminary experiments with tea leaves (*Thea sinensis*) have shown that 2′,4,4′,6′-tetrahydroxychalkone is incorporated into catechin and epicatechin (H. Grisebach and L. Patschke, 1963, unpublished observations).

Catechin itself seems to be a metabolic end product, since radioactive d-catechin which was taken up by *Chamaecyparis pisifera* cuttings was not transformed into other flavonoids, for example quercetin or taxifolin (Hasegawa and Yasue, 1962).

4. Aurones

Aurones with a resorcinol-type ring A such as sulfuretin (Fig. 12) are invariably found to occur together with the corresponding chalkones (e.g. sulfuretin with butein, etc.), and in view of the ready conversion of

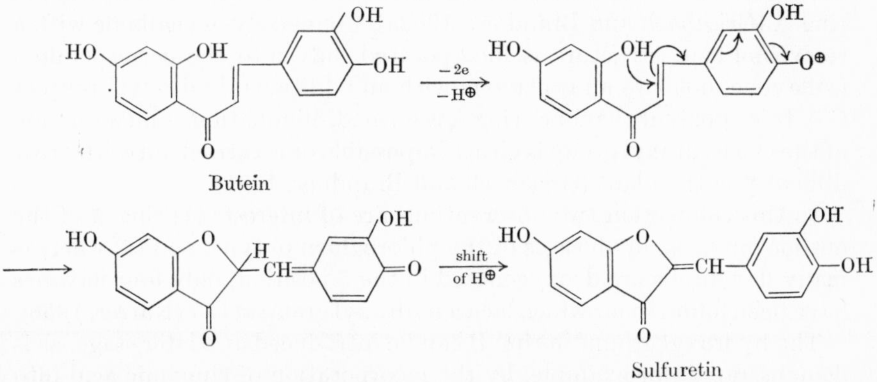

FIG. 12. Hypothesis for the formation of aurones (Geissman, 1963).

chalkones into aurones by oxidation under physiological conditions it is quite likely that aurones are formed by direct oxidation of chalkones in the plant (Geissman and Fukushima, 1948; Geissman et al., 1956; Shimokoriyama and Geissman, 1960) (Fig. 12). Extracts from *Cosmos sulphureus* and *Coreopsis lanceolata* can convert hydroxychalkone glycosides into aurones (Shimokoriyama and Hattori, 1953). Since, however, such a conversion also takes place very readily *in vitro* it is difficult to establish the enzymatic nature of this reaction. This difficulty would also be encountered in experiments with labelled chalkones.

C. OXYGEN SUBSTITUENTS IN RINGS A AND B

In considering the question of the biogenetic origin of the oxygen functions in ring A, a distinction must be made between the hydroxyl groups in positions 5 and 7 and the heterocyclic oxygen atom on the one hand and the rarely occurring oxygen substituents in positions 6 and 8 on the other hand. It has already been pointed out earlier (p. 283) that the former oxygen functions almost certainly originate from the carboxyl group of malonate, whereas the latter must be introduced later.

In the case of flavonoids with a resorcinol-type structure in ring A the hydroxyl group at C-5 must be eliminated at an as yet unknown stage of the biosynthesis. Birch (1957) assumes that this elimination takes place via the reduction of a carbonyl group in the hypothetical poly-β-ketoacid (Fig. 1). On the other hand, enzymes have been found in animal organisms which can eliminate a phenolic hydroxyl group, probably via the dihydro compound (Daly and Witkop, 1963).

The investigation of the incorporation of chalkones with different substitution patterns into isoflavones (p. 296) support the Birch hypothesis, since a chalkone with a phloroglucinol-type structure can function as a precursor only for an isoflavone with the same pattern of oxidation in ring A, not for an isoflavone having a resorcinol-type substitution in ring A (Grisebach and Brandner, 1962a). Conversely, a chalkone with a resorcinol-type structure is incorporated only into the corresponding isoflavone, not into an isoflavone with an additional hydroxyl group at C-5. It is apparent that once ring A is formed, elimination or introduction of the C-5 hydroxyl group is either impossible or is carried out with great difficulty in the plant (Grisebach and Brandner, 1961).

In this connection two observations are of interest: (1) ring A of the anthocyanins is, in all cases of the phloroglucinol type, and (2) whereas many flavon(ol)s are deoxygenated in the 5 position, only four flavones have been found so far which lack a hydroxyl group at C-7 (Karrer, 1958).

The hydroxyl groups in ring B can be introduced at a later stage, as is demonstrated, for example, by the incorporation of cinnamic acid into quercetin. Since p-hydroxycinnamic acid is a much better precursor for quercetin than 3,4-dihydroxycinnamic acid (caffeic acid) (Table I, p. 282) the introduction of the 3' or 5' hydroxyl group most probably takes place not at the cinnamic acid stage but at the level of the C_{15} intermediate (chalkone).

Experiments with colour mutants (Harborne, 1962a) indicate that the enzymes involved in hydroxylation are very specific, in contrast to the phenolase complex. Mason (1955) considers it probable that phenolases catalyse the hydroxylation of flavonoids, but the extreme specificity points to enzymes of the phenylalanine hydroxylase type (Kaufman, 1962).

Anthocyanins with few substituents are formed earlier in blossom development than are the more highly substituted anthocyanins. In three pure lines of *Petunia hybrida* the order of appearance was cyanidin, delphinidin, päonidin, petunidin, and malvidin. It has been assumed that the reason for this order of appearance lies in the sequential activity of the substitution-determining genes (Hess, 1963a). In the course of these experiments it was also proved that all the enzymes necessary for anthocyanin synthesis are present in flower buds (Hess, 1963b).

In this connection it should be mentioned that flavonoids are synthesized only in certain cells or tissues. In seedlings of *Sinapis alba* L. for example the anthocyanins in the cotyledons are located only in the epidermis, whereas in the hypocotyl they occur exclusively in the subepidermal layer (H. Kleiber and H. Mohr, 1963, personal communication).

D. FORMATION OF GLYCOSIDES

It is probable that glycosylation occurs late in the biosynthetic sequence; possibly it is the last step. Experimental support for this assumption has been gained from the study of the genetic control of glycosylation (Harborne, 1962b) and more directly from the isolation of enzymes which catalyse the glycosylation of flavonols. A cell-free extract from mung beans (*Phaseolus vulgaris*) catalyses the formation of quercetin-β-D-glucuronide from uridine diphosphate-glucuronic acid and quercetin (Marsh, 1960). From the same plant Barber (1962) isolated an enzyme which catalyses the formation of rutin from UDP-L-rhamnose and quercetin-3-β-glucoside. UDP-L-rhamnose is formed in bean leaves from UDP-D-glucose. The results of the latter experiment are also in agreement with the conclusions drawn from other studies that synthesis of mono-, di-, and triglycosides is a step-by-step process involving separate additions of monosaccharides to flavonoids (Harborne, 1963).

The sugar residue in the C-glycosides (e.g. vitexin) is attached to a highly anionoid centre in the aglycone. These could also be formed from the aglycone and an activated sugar like UDPG.

E. BIFLAVONYLS

The structures of the biflavonyls (Fig. 13) strongly support the suggestion that their biosynthesis involves oxidative coupling of free radicals derived either from apigenin or a closely related compound, in association with O-methylation (Baker *et al.*, 1963). Enzymes which can

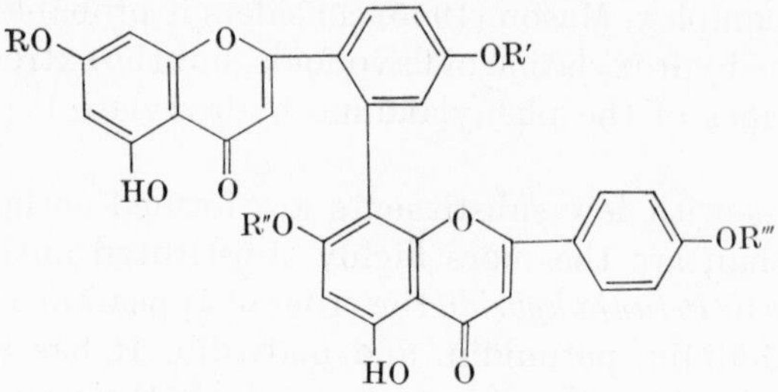

FIG. 13. Structure of biflavonyls.

catalyse such a coupling reaction have not yet been isolated from plants which contain biflavonyls, but an enzyme extract from leaves of *Crypto-meria japonica* causes a similar coupling of totarol to form podotarin (Bocks and Cambie, 1963) (Fig. 14).

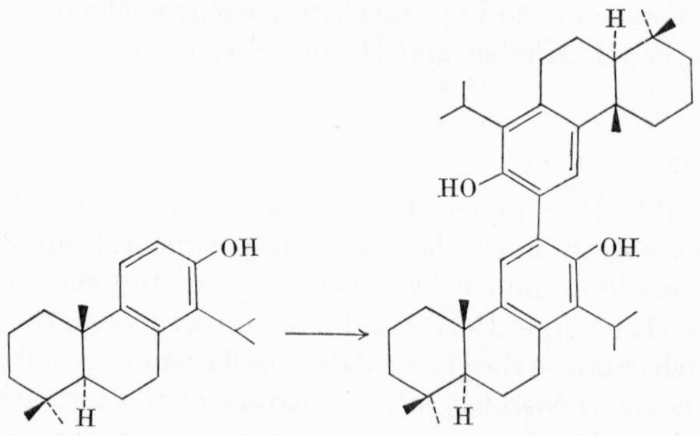

Totarol   Podotarin

FIG. 14. Enzymatic coupling of totarol.

VI. ISOFLAVONOIDS

A. ISOFLAVONES

While the biosynthesis of all flavan derivatives almost certainly proceeds along the same basic course, a special biosynthetic position must be assigned to the isoflavones which are derivatives of 3-phenyl-benzo-γ-pyrone (Fig. 15). Since branching occurs at C-3, ring B and carbon atoms 2, 3 and 4 of the isoflavones cannot originate from an intact phenylpropane precursor.

Theories for the formation of the isoflavone carbon skeleton were developed by a number of authors. Geissman and Hinreiner (1952), Robinson (1955) and Whalley (1956) suggested that a phenyl migration

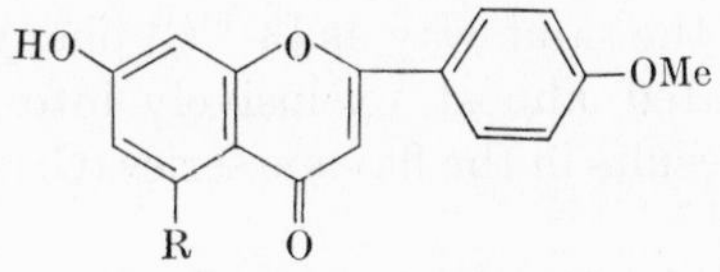

FIG. 15. Formononetin, R = H; Biochanin-A, R = OH.

might take place in the course of the biosynthesis, whereas others considered such a rearrangement to be unlikely (Warburton, 1954). Another possibility proposed for the formation of isoflavones was the condensation of a phenylacetic acid unit with phloroglucinol, followed by ring-closure with formic acid or its biological equivalent (Geissman and Hinreiner, 1952; Robinson, 1955).

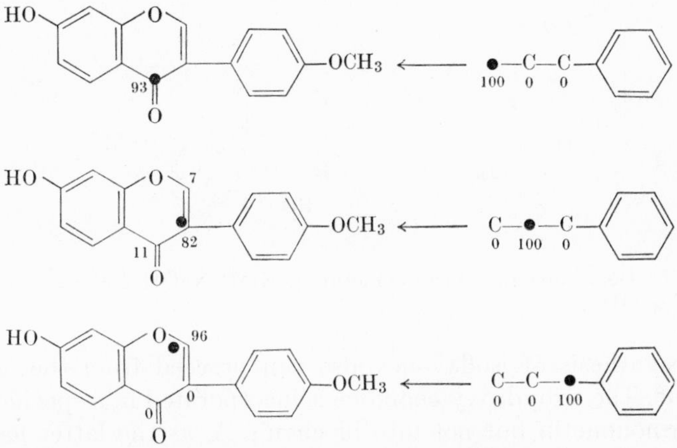

FIG. 16. Distribution of radioactivity in formononetin with [1-^{14}C]-, [2-^{14}C]- and [3-^{14}C]-phenylalanine as precursor. The numbers represent percentage activity.

Investigations of isoflavone biosynthesis were carried out with red clover (*Trifolium pratense*) and chana germ (*Cicer arietinum*). The former contains formononetin (7-hydroxy-4'-methoxy isoflavone), the latter, formononetin and biochanin A (5,7-dihydroxy-4'-methoxyiso-flavone) (Fig. 15). The incorporation of [carboxyl-^{14}C], [2-^{14}C] and [3-^{14}C]-phenylalanine into formononetin results in the distribution of radioactivity shown in Fig. 16, as could be demonstrated by degradation of the isoflavone (Fig. 17) (Grisebach, 1959; Grisebach and Doerr, 1959). These results prove unequivocally (1) that the carboxyl group of phenyl-alanine is not lost and consequently the biosynthesis cannot involve a C_6–C_2 precursor, and (2) that a phenyl migration takes place in the course of the biosynthesis.

In chana germ [3-^{14}C]-cinnamic acid is incorporated into formononetin and biochanin A in the same way as [3-^{14}C]-phenylalanine and [1-^{14}C]-acetate is incorporated almost exclusively into ring A, as would be expected from the results in the flavone series (Grisebach and Brandner, 1961).

Experiments in which [β-^{14}C]-4,4′,6′-trihydroxychalkone-4′-glucoside was administered to red clover and chana germ led to the conclusion that

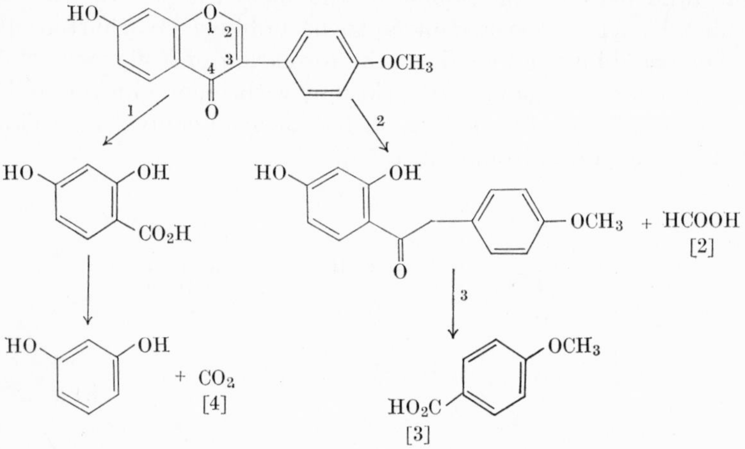

FIG. 17. Degradation of formononetin. 1. KOH/NaOH 250°; 2. 0·4 N NaOH; 3. KMnO$_4$, OH$^-$.

the biosynthesis of isoflavones also can proceed from the level of a chalkone. The trihydroxy-chalkone is incorporated in a specific manner into formononetin but not into biochanin A, as the latter has an additional hydroxyl group in ring A. In contrast, 2′,4,4′,6′-tetrahydroxy-chalkone-4′-glucoside-[β-^{14}C] is a good precursor for biochanin A whereas it is incorporated only to a very small extent or not at all into formononetin (Fig. 18) (Grisebach and Patschke, 1960; Grisebach and Brandner, 1961; Grisebach and Brandner, 1962a). Because of the very small amount of activity found in formononetin in this experiment it seems doubtful that a reductive elimination of the hydroxyl group from the phloro-glucinol ring is possible (see Section III, C). These experiments also provide proof for the intact incorporation of a C_6–C_3–C_6 compound into formononetin and biochanin A, since a degradation to a C_6–C_3 compound

prior to incorporation would result in radioactive labelling in both isoflavones, as was shown in the experiments with cinnamic acid or phenylalanine.

After feeding [3-^{14}C]-cinnamic acid to chana germ it is possible to
isolate radioactive 4,4',6'-trihydroxychalkone by dilution analysis.
Furthermore, the transformation of the chalkone into formononetin is
brought about to a small extent by cell-free extracts of chana germ
(Grisebach and Brandner, 1962b). Therefore the chalkone must either

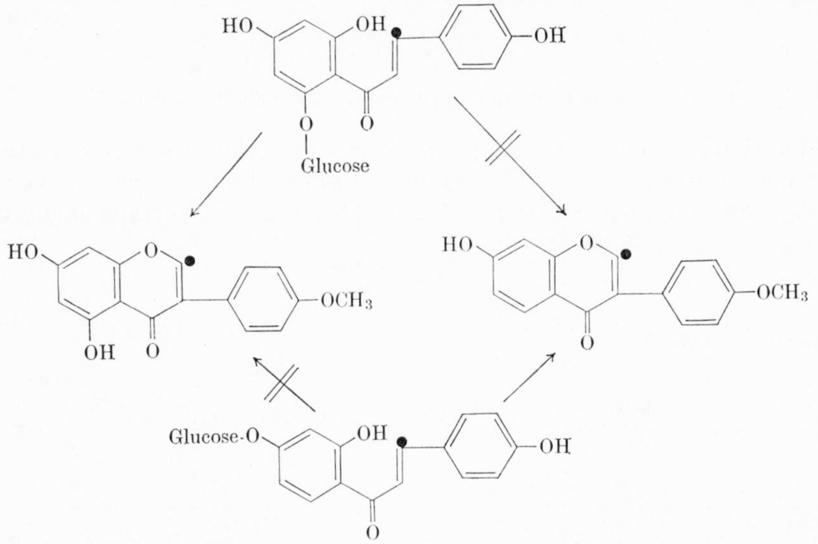

FIG. 18. Incorporation of tri- and tetrahydroxychalkone into formononetin and
biochanin-A. ● labelled atom.

be a direct intermediate in the biosynthesis or in rapid equilibrium with
such an intermediate.

The results discussed above prove that the phenyl migration takes
place at the stage of a C_6–C_3–C_6 precursor. The nature of this precursor
is not yet known.

In vitro the rearrangement of suitable substituted chalkone epoxides
leads to isoflavones (Algar and McKenna, 1944; Grisebach, 1961).
However, this rearrangement involves not a phenyl but a benzoyl group
migration (Fig. 19) (House *et al.*, 1957; Barz, 1962). It is therefore
probable that the phenyl migration during the biosynthesis of isoflavones does not occur until after closure of the heterocyclic ring, the
stereochemical conditions for such a rearrangement being favourable.

In the case of flavanols, *in vitro* rearrangements involving an aryl
10*

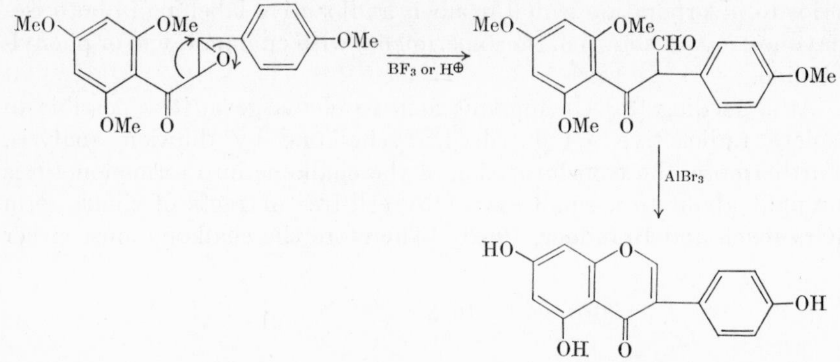

FIG. 19. *In vitro* formation of isoflavones from chalkone epoxides.

migration have been known for a long time. Thus the treatment of tetra-*O*-methylcatechins with PCl₃ results in the formation of some isoflavene (Fig. 20) (Freudenberg *et al.*, 1926). This type of rearrangement is

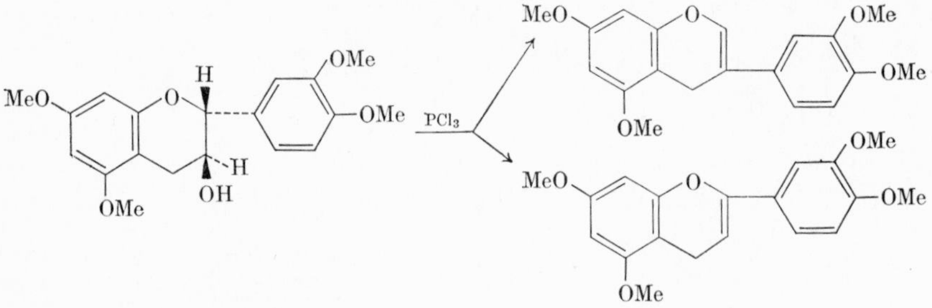

FIG. 20. Rearrangement of tetra-*O*-methylcatechin.

favoured by the neighbouring group effect and can take place with retention of optical activity (e.g. Clark-Lewis and Korytnyk, 1958).

In the case of flavanones a rearrangement to an isoflavone under the

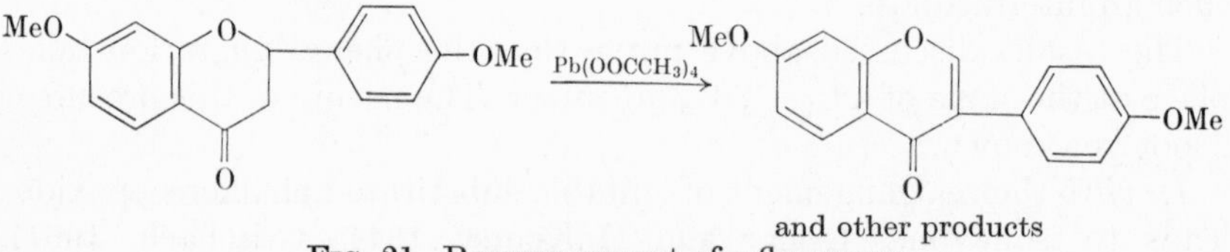

and other products

FIG. 21. Rearrangement of a flavanone.

influence of lead tetra-acetate has been discovered, which is considered to be a radical reaction (Fig. 21) (Cavill *et al.*, 1954).

A rearrangement of a dihydroflavonol (flavanonol) involving the migration of the aryl group on the heterocyclic ring has not yet been described in the literature. The 2(ax)H:3(ax)H *trans* structure of the naturally occurring dihydroflavonols would make the 1,2-aryl shift via a phenonium cation intermediate possible (Fig. 22). *In vivo* such a rearrangement might be initiated by the elimination of a pyrophosphate

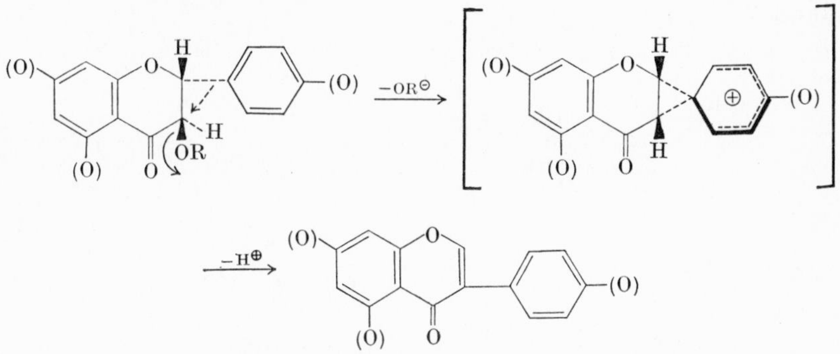

FIG. 22. Hypothetical rearrangement of a dihydroflavonol.

group as an anion, but efforts to detect phosphate esters of flavonols in plants have so far been unsuccessful (Brandner, 1962).

Another interesting and so far unsolved question, is whether the isoflavanones are intermediates in the formation of isoflavones or whether they are formed by hydrogenation of the latter.

B. 3-ARYLCOUMARINS

The 3-arylcoumarin pacchyrrhizin and a number of coumaranocoumarins, for example coumestrol, occur in *Leguminosae*. On biochemical and taxonomic grounds it was postulated that the biosynthesis of these compounds is related to that of the isoflavones rather than to that of the coumarins (Grisebach, 1959; Bate-Smith, 1959a).

Experiments on the biosynthesis of coumestrol in lucerne (*Medicago sativa*) have proved this hypothesis to be correct. With [3-^{14}C]-cinnamic acid as the precursor the total radioactivity was located in the carbonyl group of the lactone ring (C-2) of coumestrol, as was shown by degradation to 2-(2,4-dimethoxyphenyl)-6-methoxy-benzofuran-3-carboxylic acid and decarboxylation of the latter (Fig. 23). [1-^{14}C]-Acetic acid was almost exclusively incorporated into ring A of coumestrol (Grisebach and Barz, 1963).

Furthermore, [β-^{14}C]-4,4′,6′-trihydroxychalcone-4′-glucoside is incorporated into coumestrol in the same manner as it is into isoflavones (Fig. 23). The dilution of the specific activity of the chalcone upon incorporation into coumestrol is somewhat greater than upon incorporation into the isoflavones formononetin and daidzein, which also occur in lucerne (Grisebach and Barz, 1964).

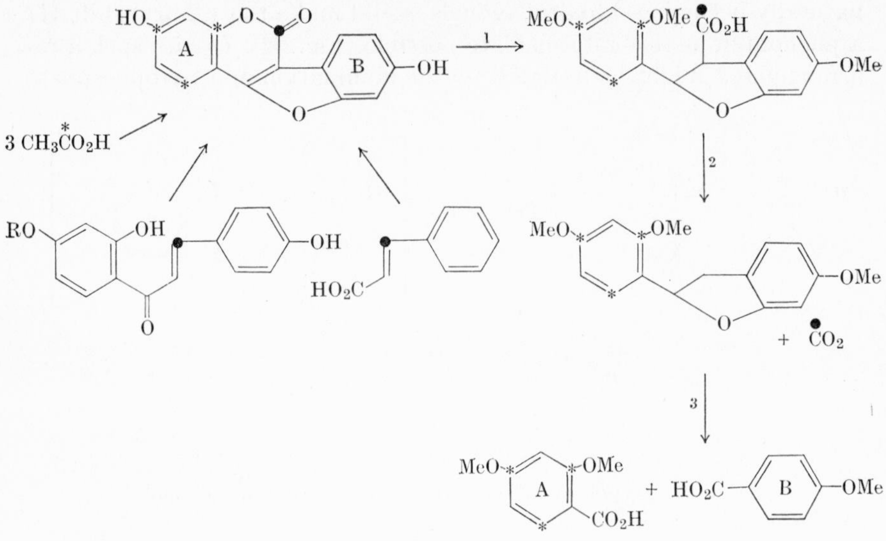

FIG. 23. Incorporation of various precursors into coumestrol. 1. $(CH_3)_2SO_4$, OH^-; 2. Δ 290°; 3. $KMnO_4$.

These results lead to the conclusion that the chalkone is a common intermediate in the biosynthesis of both coumestrol and the isoflavones, but the question is still open whether coumestrol is formed from an iso-

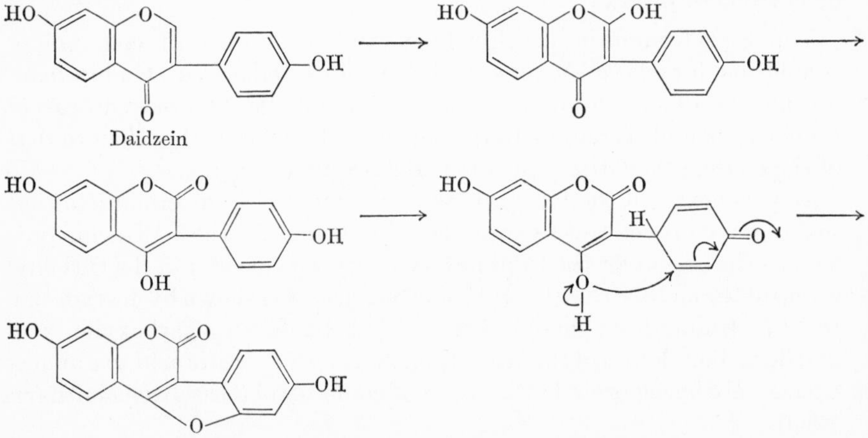

FIG. 24. Hypothetical formation of coumestrol from daidzein.

flavone, for example by oxidation at C-2, as is assumed by Bate-Smith (1959b) (Fig. 24), or whether coumestrol and the isoflavones are formed independently from a common precursor.

Also unanswered is the question of the origin of the 2′-hydroxyl group occurring frequently in the isoflavonoids or the origin of the oxygen in the 2'-ether linkage characteristic of homopterocarpin, pterocarpin, coumestrol and wedelolactone. This 2'-oxygen may originate from o-hydroxycinnamic acid. Alternatively, the 2'-ether linkage could be formed by addition of oxygen at C-4 to a quinonoid form of ring B (Fig. 24) (Whalley, 1961).

C. ROTENOIDS

The rotenoids (e.g. rotenone, Fig. 25) bear an obvious structural relationship to the isoflavones. Theoretical biosynthetic relationships

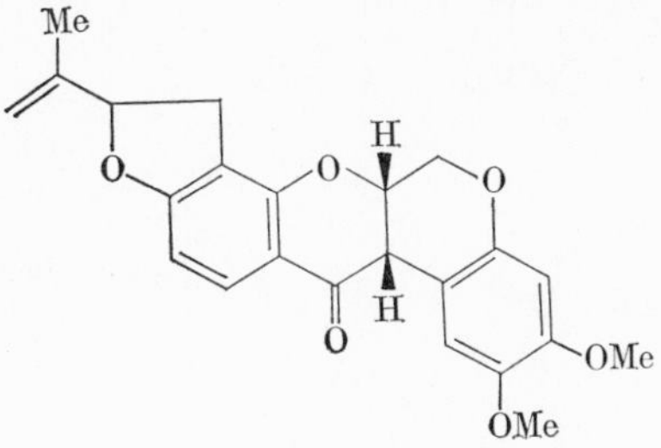

FIG. 25. Rotenone.

between rotenoids and isoflavones have been discussed in detail by Grisebach and Ollis (1961). It can be assumed that the methylene bridge in the rotenoids is derived from a C_1-precursor. Several plausible schemes for the formation of rotenoids can be visualized. On the basis of recent results in the alkaloid field it is tempting to assume that the biosynthesis

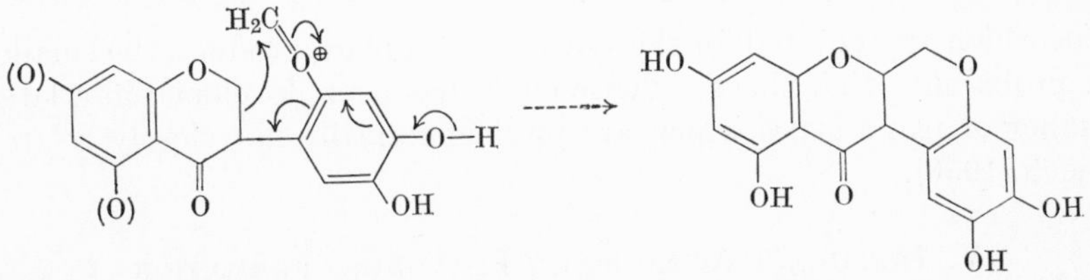

FIG. 26. Hypothetical formation of a rotenoid from a 2'-methoxyisoflavone.

of rotenoids proceeds by oxidation of 2'-methoxy-isoflavones or related products (Fig. 26). Such a pathway would have some resemblance to the formation of the "berberine bridge" from an N-methyl group (Barton et al., 1963; Battersby et al., 1963) and to the formation of the methylene-dioxy group from a methoxyl and a hydroxyl group (Fig. 27) (Barton et al., 1962). So far, however, no experimental evidence is available in this field.

Although the isoflavones fit into the biosynthetic pathway leading to the flavonoids, they have a special position owing to the fact that their biogenesis involves the unusual rearrangement with aryl migration. This special position can also be recognized phytogenetically in that isoflavones and compounds related biogenetically to them have so far been found almost exclusively in the Leguminosae, whereas flavonoids occur in all flowering plants. This may be an expression of Paech's "Häufigkeitsregel" in which he pointed out that the more numerous the

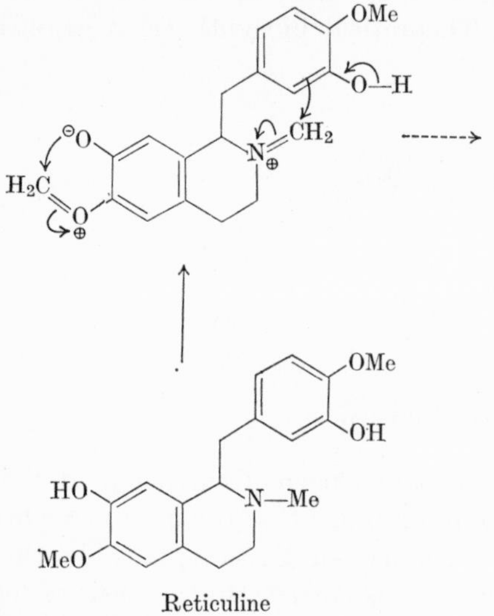

FIG. 27. Origin of the "berberine carbon" and the methylene-dioxy group from an N-methyl and O-methyl group respectively.

steps which are required for the synthesis of a plant product, the smaller the probability that this synthetic chain has been developed in a large number of plant types which are phylogenetically not closely related (Paech, 1950).

V. INFLUENCE OF LIGHT ON FLAVONOID FORMATION

In many cases light is necessary for the initial formation of anthocyanins in the plant cell and in all cases investigated it promotes anthocyanin production. The formation of flavones is also strongly stimulated by the action of light. This effect of light is apparently independent of photosynthesis.

The influence of light of various wavelengths on anthocyanin formation has been investigated by Siegelman and Hendricks (1957), Mohr (1957) and Kandeler (1958). In mustard seedlings, for instance, anthocyanin formation is controlled by two photoreactions. One of these reactions is governed by the well-known red, far-red pigment system (phytochrome), that is, optimal anthocyanin formation can be induced with light of 660 mμ. This induction can be reversed by subsequent irradiation with light of 730 mμ. The phytochrome system is practically saturated after a very short time of irradiation (low energy reaction). The other photoreaction is a high-energy reaction the action spectrum of which shows peaks in the blue and the far-red range of the visible spectrum (Mohr, 1957). Whereas Siegelman and Hendricks assume that the high energy reaction is directly involved in the biosynthetic pathway of anthocyanin formation, Mohr considers it very probable that the influence of light is always indirect and that the biosynthetic pathway itself does not include a photochemical reaction. The latter conclusion is based on results of experiments with mustard and buckwheat seedlings which have shown that anthocyanin synthesis and synthesis of flavones is controlled by light in precisely the same way as are the other photoresponses more closely related to growth processes, such as inhibition of hypocotyl lengthening, opening of the plumular hook etc. (Mohr, 1962; Mohr and van Nes, 1963; Harraschain and Mohr, 1963).

VI. INHIBITORS

In their investigation of anthocyanin biosynthesis in *Spirodela oligorrhiza* Thimann and his colleagues found a number of compounds which inhibit anthocyanin formation. These inhibitors can be divided into three groups: (1) Cu-binding substances, for example phenylthiocarbamide (Edmondson and Thimann, 1950); (2) compounds which influence pyrimidine and purine metabolism, among which azaguanine had the strongest inhibitory effect (Thimann and Radner, 1955a); and (3) sulphur-containing compounds including ethionine and methionine, of which the nature of the inhibitory effect is as yet not clear (Thimann and Radner, 1955b).

In later work it was found that ribonuclease inhibits anthocyanin formation in *Spirodela* and in corn-leaf discs. Inhibition in *Spirodela* occurred over a concentration range from 0·10 mg/ml to 1·0 mg/ml, and the 50% inhibition point was at about 0·33 mg/ml (2×10^{-5} M). In contrast, deoxyribonuclease causes no inhibition of anthocyanin formation (Radner and Thimann, 1963). From these results and from the previous experiments with the anti-metabolites of the RNA bases the authors conclude that "anthocyanin formation is controlled by an unstable nucleic acid analogous to the messenger RNA of bacteria".

However, it is unlikely that ribonuclease degrades only an RNA which is specifically responsible for anthocyanin synthesis, and consequently the existence of such an RNA is not proved by these experiments.

Another type of inhibitor was found in p-fluorocinnamic acid and the other p-halo-cinnamic acids which cause an inhibition of anthocyanin synthesis in red cabbage seedlings. At a concentration of 300 μg p-fluorocinnamic acid per 25 seedlings the anthocyanin content is approximately equal to that of the dark controls. p-Fluorocinnamic acid also inhibits flavonol synthesis in buckwheat seedlings (Grisebach and Kellner, 1964), but in flowers of *Petunia hybrida* no inhibition of anthocyanin synthesis was observed (D. Hess, 1963, personal communication). Since cinnamic acid is an immediate precursor for flavonoid formation, the inhibition with the p-halocinnamic acids is probably more specific than the inhibition with the above mentioned compounds.

Several herbicides, such as 2,2-dichloropropionic acid, inhibit anthocyanin synthesis in flowers of *Salvia splendens* (Asen *et al.*, 1963).

VII. CONCLUSIONS

The use of [^{14}C]-precursors has led to the confirmation of the hypothesis for the biosynthesis of flavonoids proposed by Birch and beyond this to the accumulation of much new information. From the experimental material presented it can be concluded with near certainty that the chalkones, or compounds bearing a very close structural relationship to them, serve as central intermediates in flavonoid metabolism from which anthocyanins, flavonols, aurones, catechins, isoflavones and 3-aryl-coumarins can be formed.

The many successful results obtained in this field in the last few years must not, however, obscure the fact that as yet no conclusive proof has been presented for the existence of relationships such as those proposed in Fig. 11 (p. 289) for example. The use of isotopically-labelled compounds will undoubtedly continue to be of importance in the elucidation of the as yet unsolved problems in flavonoid biosynthesis, but it will also be necessary to carry out investigations with the enzymes of flavonoid metabolism.

Only with the aid of at least partly purified enzyme preparations will a study of individual reaction steps and their mechanisms be possible.

From experimental results to date it has become more and more evident that the cinnamic acids occupy a central position in plant metabolism. Their condensation with malonate leads to flavonoids, stilbenes, and other compounds. They are reduced to coniferyl and sinapyl alcohols, the precursors of lignin. Cyclization of o-hydroxy-cinnamic acids results in the formation of coumarins, and degradation of cinnamic acids leads to benzoic acids (e.g. Grisebach and Vollmer, 1963). Furthermore, recent investigations indicate that cinnamic acids can in some cases also serve as precursors in alkaloid biosynthesis (e.g. Suhadolnik and Zulalian, 1963). These relationships are illustrated in Fig. 28. So far the only proven mode of formation of the cinnamic acids in

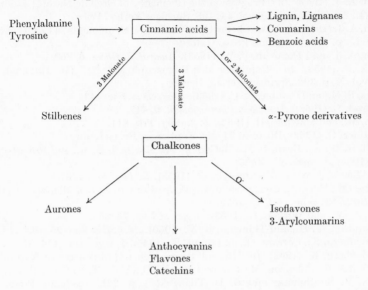

_O_→ means that an 1,2-aryl shift is involved

FIG. 28. Biogenetic relationships between cinnamic acids and natural phenolic compounds.

plants is that from phenylalanine and tyrosine. Consequently the availability of these amino acids together with the formation of malonate are the prerequisites for the biosynthesis of flavonoids.

REFERENCES

Algar, J., and McKenna (1944). *Proc. R. Irish Acad.* **49**, 225.
Alston, R. E., and Hagen, C. W. (1955). *Nature, Lond.* **175**, 990.
Asen, S., Jansen, L. L., and Hilton, J. L. (1963). *Nature, Lond.* **185**.
Baker, W., Finch, A. C. M., Ollis, W. D., and Robinson, K. W. (1963). *J. chem. Soc.* 1477.
Barber, G. A. (1962). *Biochem. Biophys. Res. Comm.* **8**, 204.
Barton, D. H. R., Kirby, G. W., and Taylor, J. B. (1962). *Proc. chem. Soc.* 340.
Barton, D. H. R., Hesse, R. H., and Kirby, G. W. (1963). *Proc. chem. Soc.* 267.
Barz, W. (1962). Diplomarbeit Universität Freiburg/Br., Germany.
Bate-Smith, E. C. (1959a). *In* "Vistas in Botany" (W. B. Turrill, ed.), p. 120, Pergamon Press, London.
Bate-Smith, E. C. (1959b). *In* "The Pharmacology of Plant Phenolics" (J. W. Fairbairn, ed.), p. 69, Academic Press, London.
Battersby, A. R., Francis, R. J., Hirst, M., and Staunton, J. (1963). *Proc. chem. Soc.* 268.

Billek, G., and Kindl, H. (1962). Öst. Chem. Ztg. 63, 273.

Birch, A. J., and Donovan, F. W. (1953). Austral. J. Chem. 6, 360.

Birch, A. J. (1957). In "Progress in the Chemistry of Organic Natural Products" (L. Zechmeister, ed.), vol. 14, 198, Springer Verlag, Wien.

Birch, A. J. (1962). In "The Chemistry of Flavonoid Compounds" (T. A. Geissman, ed.), p. 618, Pergamon Press, Oxford.

Birch, A. J., and Donovan, F. W. (1953). Austral. J. Chem. 6, 360.

Blank, F. (1958). In "Handbuch der Pflanzenphysiologie" (W. Ruhland, ed.), vol. X, p. 300, Springer-Verlag, Berlin.

Bocks, S. M., and Cambie, R. C. (1963). Proc. chem. Soc. 143.

Bogorad, L. (1958). Ann. Rev. Plant Physiol. 9, 417.

Bopp, M., and Matthiss, B. (1962). Z. Naturf. 17b, 811.

Brandner, G. (1962). Doctoral Thesis, Freiburg i. Br. Germany.

Cavill, G. W. K., Dean, F. M., McGookin, A., Marshall, B. M., and Robertson, A. (1954). J. chem. Soc. 4573.

Clark-Lewis, J. W., and Korytnyk, W. (1958). J. chem. Soc. 2367.

Comte, Ph., Ville, A., Zwingelstein, G., Favre-Bonvin, J., and Mentzer, C. (1960). Bull. Soc. chim. biol. 42, 1079.

Daly, J. W., and Witkop, B. (1963). Angew. Chem. 75, 555.

Edmondson, Y. H., and Thimann, K. V. (1950). Arch. Biochem. 25, 79.

Freudenberg, K., Carrara, G., and Cohn, E. (1926). Liebigs Ann. 446, 87.

Freudenberg, K. (1962). In "Recent Progress in the Chemistry of Natural and Synthetic Colouring Matters and Related Fields" (T. S. Gore, B. S. Joshi, S. V. Sunthankar and B. D. Tilak, eds.), p. 221, Academic Press, New York.

Gamborg, O. L. (1962). Lecture at the International Symposium on the Chemistry of Natural Products, Brussels.

Gamborg, O. L., Wetter, L. R., and Neish, A. C. (1962). Phytochemistry 1, 159.

Gatenbeck, S. (1960). Svensk. kem. Tidskr. 72, 188 (and references cited therein).

Gatenbeck, S., and Mosbach, K. (1959). Acta chem. scand. 13, 1561.

Geissman, T. A. (1963). In "Comprehensive Biochemistry" (M. Florkin and E. H. Stotz, eds.), p. 235, Elsevier, Amsterdam.

Geissman, T. A., and Fukushima, D. K. (1948). J. Amer. chem. Soc. 70, 1686.

Geissman, T. A., and Harborne, J. B. (1955). Arch. Biochem. Biophys. 55, 447.

Geissman, T. A., and Hinreiner, E. (1952). Bot. Rev. 18, 77.

Geissman, T. A., and Swain, T. (1957). Chem. & Ind. 984.

Geissman, T. A., Harborne, J. B., and Seikel, M. K. (1956). J. Amer. chem. Soc. 78, 825.

Grisebach, H. (1957). Z. Naturf. 12b, 227.

Grisebach, H. (1958). Z. Naturf. 13b, 335.

Grisebach, H. (1959). Z. Naturf. 14b, 802.

Grisebach, H. (1961). In "Recent Developments in the Chemistry of Natural Phenolic Compounds" (W. D. Ollis, ed.), p. 69, Pergamon Press, Oxford.

Grisebach, H. (1962a). Planta Medica 10, 385.

Grisebach, H. (1962b). In "Recent Progress in the Chemistry of Natural and Synthetic Colouring Matters and Related Fields" (T. S. Gore, B. S. Joshi, S. V. Sunthankar and B. D. Tilak, eds.), p. 301, Academic Press, New York.

Grisebach, H., and Barz, W. (1963). Z. Naturf. 18b, 466.

Grisebach, H., and Barz, W. (1964). Z. Naturf. (in press).

Grisebach, H., and Bopp, M. (1959). Z. Naturf. 14b, 485.

Grisebach, H., and Brandner, G. (1961). Z. Naturf. 16b, 2.

Grisebach, H., and Brandner, G. (1962a). *Experientia* [Basel] **18**, 400.
Grisebach, H., and Brandner, G. (1962b). *Biochim. biophys. Acta* **60**, 51.
Grisebach, H., and Doerr, N. (1959). *Z. Naturf.* **15b**, 284.
Grisebach, H., and Kellner, S. (1964). *Z. Naturf.* (in press).
Grisebach, H., and Ollis, W. D. (1961). *Experientia* [Basel] **11**, 1.
Grisebach, H., and Patschke, L. (1960). *Chem. Ber.* **93**, 2326.
Grisebach, H., and Patschke, L. (1961). *Z. Naturf.* **16b**, 645.
Grisebach, H., and Patschke, L. (1962). *Z. Naturf.* **17b**, 857.
Grisebach, H., and Vollmer, K. O. (1963). *Z. Naturf.* **18b**, 753.
Harborne, J. B. (1962a). *In* "The Chemistry of Flavonoid Compounds" (T. A. Geissman, ed.), p. 593, Pergamon Press, Oxford.
Harborne, J. B. (1962b). *In* "The Chemistry of Flavonoid Compounds" (T. A. Geissman, ed.), p. 610, Pergamon Press, Oxford.
Harborne, J. B. (1963). *Phytochem.* **2**, 85.
Harborne, J. B., and Corner, J. (1961). *Arch. Biochem. Biophys.* **92**, 192.
Harraschain, H., and Mohr, H. (1963). *Z. Bot.* **51**, 277.
Hasegawa, M., and Yasue, M. (1962). *Nippon Ringaku Kaishi* **44**, No. 9, 244. [C.A. **58**, 1727c (1963)].
Hayano, M. (1962). *In* "Oxygenases" (O. Hayaishi, ed.), p. 181, Academic Press, New York.
Hess, D. (1963a). *Planta* **59**, 567.
Hess, D. (1963b). *Z. Bot.* **51**, 142.
Hillis, W. E., and Hasegawa, M. (1962). *Chem. & Ind.* 1330.
House, H. O., Reif, D. J., and Wasson, R. L. (1957). *J. Amer. chem. Soc.* **79**, 2490 (and earlier publications).
Hutchinson, A., Taper, C. D., and Towers, G. H. N. (1959). *Canad. J. Biochem. Physiol.* **37**, 901.
Ibrahim, R. K., and Towers, G. H. N. (1962). *Canad. J. Biochem. Physiol.* **40**, 449.
Kandeler, R. (1958). *Ber. dtsch. bot. Ges.* **71**, 34.
Karrer, W. (1958). "Konstitution und Vorkommen der organischen Pflanzenstoffe," p. 579 and 673, Birkhäuser Verlag, Basel.
Kaufmann, S. (1962). *In* "Oxygenases" (O. Hayaishi, ed.), pp. 129–179, Academic Press, New York.
Koukol, J., and Conn, E. E. (1961). *J. biol. Chem.* **236**, 2692.
Krishnamurty, H. G., Krishnamoorthy, V., and Seshadri, T. R. (1963). *Phytochem.* **2**, 49.
Kursanov, A. L. (1954). "Synthese und Umwandlung der Gerbstoffe in der Teepflanze," VEB Verlag Volk und Gesundheit, Berlin.
Lawrence, W. J. C., and Scott-Moncrieff, R. (1935). *J. Genet.* **30**, 155.
Lynen, F., and Tada, M. (1961). *Angew. Chem.* **63**, 519.
Macleod, N. J., and Pridham, J. B. (1963). *Biochem. J.* **88**, 45P.
Mahesh, V. B., and Seshadri, T. R. (1955). *J. chem. Soc.* 2533.
Marsh, C. A. (1960). *Biochim. biophys. Acta* **44**, 359.
Mason, H. S. (1955). *In* "Advances in Enzymology" (F. F. Nord, ed.), vol. 16, 145, Interscience, New York.
Mohr, H. (1957). *Planta* **49**, 389.
Mohr, H. (1962). *Annu. Rev. Plant Physiol.* **13**, 465.
Mohr, H., and van Nes, E. (1963). *Z. Bot.* **51**, 1.
Mors, W. B., Magalhães, M. T., and Gottlieb, O. R. (1962). *In* "Progress in the Chemistry of Organic Natural Products" (L. Zechmeister, ed.), vol. 20, p. 158, Springer Verlag, Wien.
Neish, A. C. (1960). *Ann. Rev. Plant Physiol.* **11**, 55.

Neish, A. C. (1961). *Phytochem.* **1**, 1.

Pachéco, H. (1956). *Bull. Soc. chim. Fr.* 1600.

Paech, K. (1950). "Biochemie und Physiologie der sekundären Pflanzenstoffe," p. 29, Springer-Verlag, Berlin.

Radner, B. S., and Thimann, K. V. (1963). *Arch. Biochem. Biophys.* **102**, 92.

Reznik, H. (1960). *In* "Ergebnisse der Biologie," p. 14, Springer-Verlag, Berlin.

Robinson, R. (1955). "The Structural Relations of Natural Products," p. 41, Clarendon Press, Oxford.

von Rudloff, E., and Jorgensen, E. (1963). *Phytochem.* **2**, 297.

Scott-Moncrieff, R. (1936). *J. Genet.* **32**, 117.

Shibata, S., and Yamazaki, M. (1958). *Pharm. Bull., Tokyo* **6**, 42.

Shimokoriyama, M. (1962). *In* "The Chemistry of Flavonoid Compounds" (T. A. Geissman, ed.), p. 289, Pergamon Press, Oxford.

Shimokoriyama, M., and Geissman, T. A. (1960). *J. org. Chem.* **25**, 1956.

Shimokoriyama, M., and Hattori, S. (1953). *J. Amer. chem. Soc.* **75**, 2277.

Siegelman, H. W., and Hendricks, S. B. (1957). *Plant Physiol.* **32**, 393.

Simmonds, N. W. (1954). *Nature, Lond.* **173**, 402.

Suhadolnik, R. J., and Zulalian, J. (1963). *Proc. chem. Soc.* 216.

Thimann, K. V., and Radner, B. S. (1955a). *Arch. Biochem. Biophys.* **58**, 484.

Thimann, K. V., and Radner, B. S. (1955b). *Arch. Biochem. Biophys.* **59**, 511.

Underhill, E. W., Watkin, J. E., and Neish, A. C. (1957). *Canad. J. Biochem. Physiol.* **35**, 219, 229.

Warburton, W. K. (1954). *Quart Revs.* **8**, 68.

Watkin, J. E., and Neish, A. C. (1960). *Canad. J. Biochem. Physiol.* **38**, 559.

Watkin, J. E., Underhill, E. W., and Neish, A. C. (1957). *Canad. J. Biochem. Physiol.* **35**, 230.

Weinges, K. (1961). *Chem. Ber.* **94**, 3032.

Weygand, F., Brucker, W., Grisebach, H., and Schulze, E. (1957). *Z. Naturf.* **12b**, 222.

Whalley, W. B. (1956). *Chem. & Ind.* 1049.

Whalley, W. B. (1961). *In* "Recent Developments in the Chemistry of Natural Phenolic Compounds" (W. D. Ollis, ed.), Pergamon Press, Oxford.

Whalley, W. B. (1962). *In* "The Chemistry of Flavonoid Compounds" (T. A. Geissman, ed.), p. 450, Pergamon Press, Oxford.

Willstätter, R., and Mallison, H. (1914). *S.-B. preuß. Akad. Wiss., physik.-math. Kl.* 769.

Zaprometov, M. N. (1962). *Biokhimiya* **27**, 366.

Zilversmit, D. B., Entenmann, C., and Fishler, M. C. (1943). *J. gen. Physiol.* **26**, 325.

Chapter II

QUINONES: NATURE, DISTRIBUTION AND BIOSYNTHESIS

R. H. THOMSON

Department of Chemistry, University of Aberdeen, Scotland

I. INTRODUCTION

At the present time approximately two hundred quinones have been isolated from vegetable sources, the great majority occurring in flowering plants and fungi, including lichens. Representatives have also been found in the bacteria and algae but not, as yet, in the mosses or ferns. They provide a range of colour from pale yellow (e.g. tectoquinone) to almost black (e.g. thelephoric acid), and a diversity of structure extending from simple benzoquinones to polycyclic compounds containing eight rings. *o*-Quinones are uncommon. The lipid-soluble ubiquinones and vitamins K, of particular biochemical interest, are relatively simple quinones bearing long alkenyl side chains which belong to the growing group of isoprenoid quinones, but as they are not pigments they are not considered here. Some of the isoprenoid quinones are simply terpenes in a relatively high state of oxidation but the majority are of mixed biogenetic origin with an isoprenoid group attached to an aromatic system. Most of these colouring matters arise by the acetate-malonate pathway, and the shikimic acid route to aromatic compounds is seldom utilized

309

for quinone biosynthesis. However, there are still many quinones of uncertain origin and the recently discovered mitomycins, which are N-heterocyclic compounds, raise new problems.

II. Anthraquinones

It is convenient to begin with the anthraquinones as they form the largest and most compact group showing very little variation in skeletal structure, and many of them have an oxygenation pattern characteristic of acetate-derived aromatic compounds. They occur* frequently as glycosides and as mixtures of closely related pigments, about half of them in the bark, wood and roots of flowering plants, especially Rubiaceae, some of which were used for centuries as natural dyestuffs. A smaller group is found in the Rhamnaceae, Polygonaceae and Leguminosae, and extracts of these plants are still used as purgatives. The remainder are chiefly mould metabolites occurring especially in *Penicillium* and *Aspergillus* spp.; a few have been encountered in lichens but anthraquinones are rare in the higher fungi. It has been shown that the fungal components of lichens (e.g. *Cladonia cristatella, Xanthoria parietina*) can elaborate anthraquinones in pure culture (Castle and Kubsch, 1949; Tomaselli, 1963).

Emodin (II) is a typical anthraquinone and the most widely distributed, being found in higher and lower fungi, in lichens (as a methyl ether), and in higher plants including monocotyledons (*Iridaceae*, (Henriquez Ulloa, 1960), *Liliaceae*†, (Penas Goas, 1950)). In an early paper on the acetate hypothesis (Birch and Donovan, 1955) emodin was regarded as the "theoretical" structure to be expected from head-to-tail condensation of seven acetate units (I), followed by cyclization, oxidation and decarboxylation, the other fungal anthraquinones being derived by introduction and/or removal of oxygen (e.g. IV), oxidation of the side chain (e.g. III), O-methylation, etc. at appropriate stages. This has been amply confirmed by subsequent experimental work with [^{14}C]-acetate on the biosynthesis of helminthosporin (Birch *et al.*, 1958a and b), cynodontin (Birch *et al.*, 1961), islandicin (IV) (Gatenbeck, 1960a) and emodin (II) (Gatenbeck, 1958). In addition to establishing the origin of the carbon skeleton Gatenbeck (1960a) also showed, by feeding *Penicillium islandicum* with [^{14}C-^{18}O]-acetate, that three oxygen functions in islandicin, and four in emodin, were labelled with ^{18}O and hence were derived from the carbonyl group of acetic acid as required by theory, although the exact position of the labelled oxygen was not determined.

---

* For detailed references to botanical sources see Thomson (1957, 1962).
† Rhein (III) (*Kniphofia* spp.) (Boross, 1963) and related pigments also occur in *Liliaceae* (van Oudtshoorn, 1964).

It is now known that the actual chain building unit in fatty acid bio-synthesis is malonyl coenzyme-A (formed by reversible carboxylation of acetyl coenzyme-A), and recent work with micro-organisms has established that $[2\text{-}^{14}C]$-malonate is incorporated into several "acetate-derived" phenolic compounds. This biosynthetic modification requires that the first unit in a β-polyketide chain is supplied by acetic acid (or some other monobasic acid); for example, orsellinic acid (Bentley and Keil, 1961) and 6-methylsalicylic acid (Bu'Lock and Smalley, 1961) are formed by condensation of one acetate and three malonate units, with

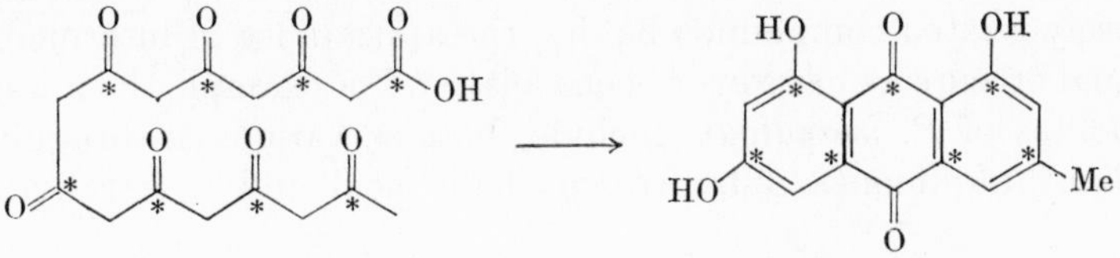

(I)

(II) Emodin

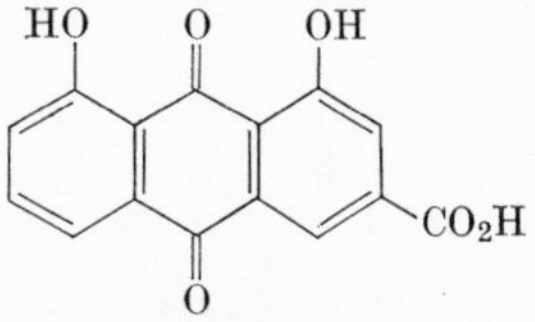

(III) Rhein

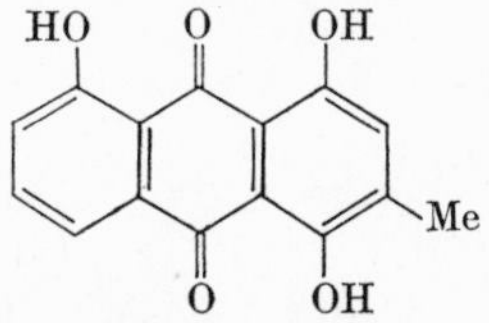

(IV) Islandicin

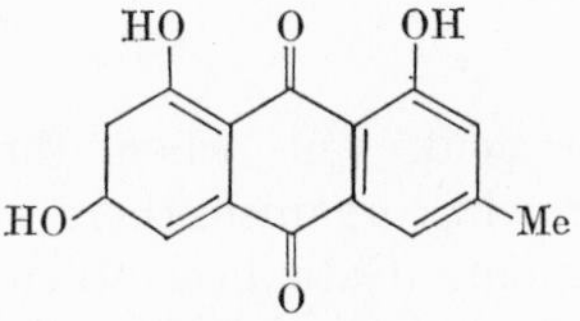

(V) Flavoskyrin

loss of carbon dioxide. A further consequence is that in labelling experiments using acetate, higher incorporation of ^{14}C is to be expected at the first unit (in anthraquinones the β-methyl group and the neighbouring carbon atom), which is in agreement with experimental observations (Birch, 1962). Shibata and Ikekawa (1963) have shown that rugulosin (VI) is biosynthesized by this route.

Rugulosin and flavoskyrin (V), both *Penicillium* metabolites, represent intermediate stages in the biosynthesis of dianthraquinones and anthraquinones, respectively. Flavoskyrin can be easily dehydrated (aromatized) *in vitro* to chrysophanol (III; Me in place of CO_2H), one of the commonest natural quinones. When *P. brunneum* was fed with $[2\text{-}^{14}C]$-malonate radioactive carbon was incorporated into rugulosin but isotopic analysis showed that the labelling was insignificant in the β-methyl groups and the adjacent C-3 and C-3′ carbon atoms; on the other hand when [1-^{14}C]-acetate was used as the precursor, with or without added [^{12}C]-malonate, incorporation of ^{14}C was higher at C-3 and C-3′ than in the other radioactive carbon atoms. These results show that the anthracene nuclei in rugulosin are biosynthesized from one acetate and seven malonate units. Gatenbeck (1962) has reached a similar conclusion with respect to the origin of islandicin, and by implication all the fungal anthraquinones arise in this way.

Although the anthraquinones are sometimes accompanied in Nature by closely related compounds having the appearance of intermediates, no actual precursors have ever been isolated. For example the numerous metabolites of *P. islandicum* include, besides various anthraquinones and dianthraquinones, 3-hydroxyphthalic acid and a tetrahydroxy-

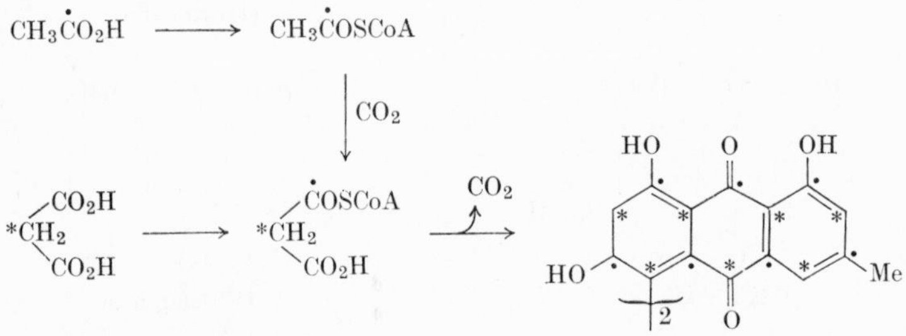

(VI) Rugulosin

benzophenone-carboxylic acid, but when these compounds were labelled and fed to the growing organism there was no incorporation of radiocarbon into the pigments (Gatenbeck, 1960b). Moreover, the rate studies of Gatenbeck (1960c) show that islandicin (IV), its 5,5′-dimer iridoskyrin, and rugulosin (VI), the "apparent precursor" of the latter, are biosynthesized independently, and Kikuchi and Nakahara (1961) and Kikuchi (1962) deduce from their work on pigment formation in various strains of *P. islandicum* that each compound in the monomer-dimer pairs, islandicin-iridoskyrin and catenarin-dicatenarin, is derived competitively from a common precursor at enzyme level (see also Shibata, 1962).

It appears that an assembly of acetate and malonate units undergoes a sequence of reactions on an enzyme surface, but only after an irreversible step (possibly cyclization or aromatization) has been completed are molecules released into the surrounding medium (Ehrensvärd and Gatenbeck, 1961). Birch (1962) has suggested that malonyl coenzyme-A might be held on active centres by salt formation or in other ways;

release of carbon dioxide during chain formation would simultaneously detach the molecule from the enzyme surface. Thereafter no further reaction takes place affecting the main carbon skeleton although minor changes such as chlorination or side chain oxidation are possible, e.g. the formation of skyrin (5,5'-di-emodin) precedes that of oxyskyrin which in turn appears before skyrinol in cultures of *P. islandicum* (both these latter compounds are formed by side chain oxidation, β-Me $\rightarrow$ β-CH$_2$OH) (Kikuchi and Nakahara, 1961).

Structural variation in the emodin group lies chiefly in the number and position of the phenolic groups, ranging from one in (VII) (*Pachybasium*

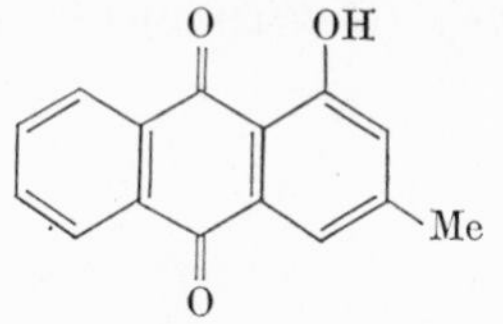

(VII)

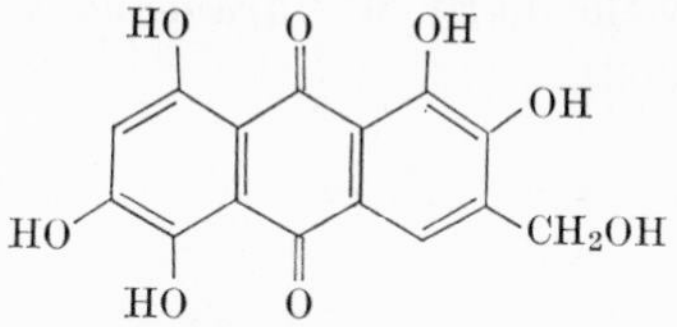

(VIII) Asperthecin

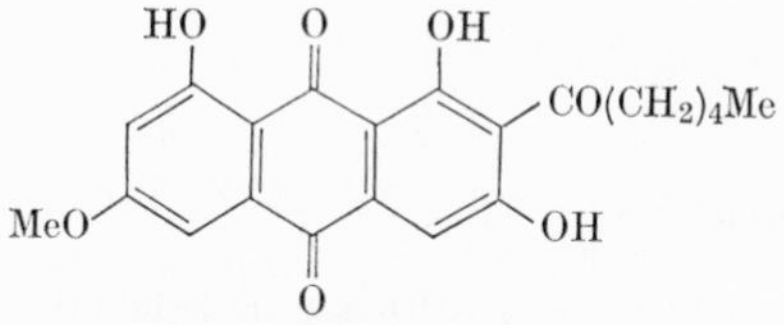

(IX) Solorinic acid

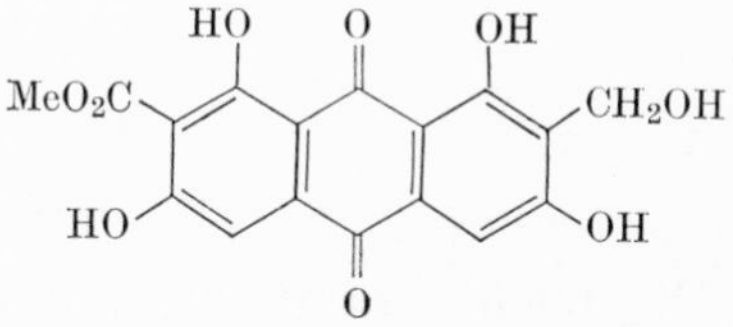

(X) Rhodocladonic acid

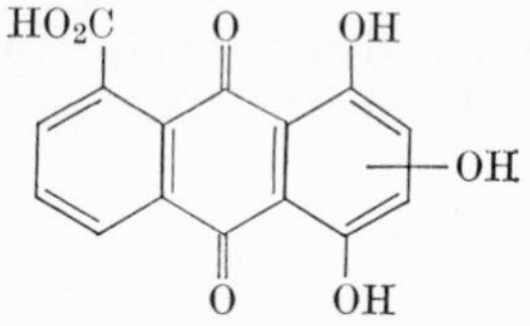

(XI) Boletol

candidum) to five in (VIII) (*Aspergillus nidulans*). In nagliovensin the β-side chain has three carbon atoms and in the lichen pigment solorinic acid (IX), which is a β-substituted 1,3,6,8-tetrahydroxyanthraquinone, there is a six-carbon side chain. These features are unexceptional but the α-side chain in boletol (XI), which occurs in *Boletus* spp. (higher fungi), is unusual, and the origin of the second side chain in rhodocladonic acid (X) (*Cladonia* spp.) and the quinone (XII) (*Curvularia lunata*) (Bohlmann *et al.*, 1961) is not clear. Normal acetate-malonate biogenesis, plus the introduction of an "extra" carbon atom from the C$_1$ pool, could obviously account for the formation of (X) and (XII); alternatively (XII) could arise by condensation of two linear β-polyketide chains as

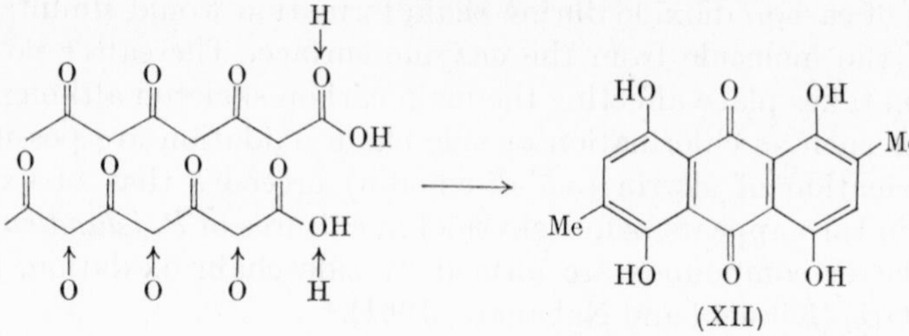

(XII)

indicated above. As prenylation has not been observed in the anthra-quinone series, it is interesting to note the existence of harunganin (XIII) in the bark of *Harungana madagascariensis* (*Guttiferae*) (Stout *et al.*, 1962).

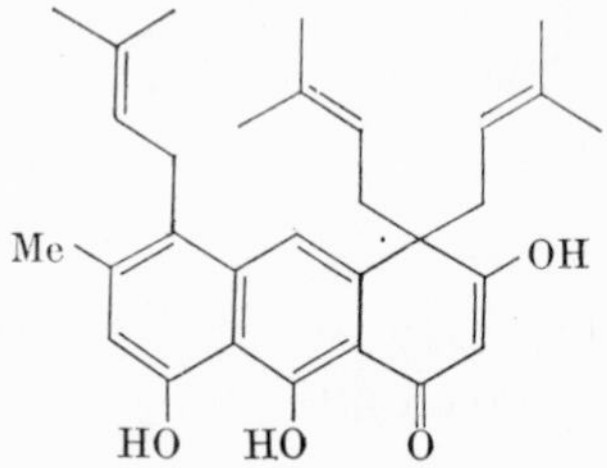

(XIII) Harunganin

The mould *Aspergillus versicolor* produces a number of related xan-thone and anthraquinone pigments with rather unusual oxygen ring systems fused to the main carbon skeleton. One of these is averufin (XIV) which may be regarded as a 2-substituted 1,3,6,8-tetrahydroxy-anthraquinone. Pusey and Roberts (1963) suggest that it arises by aldol

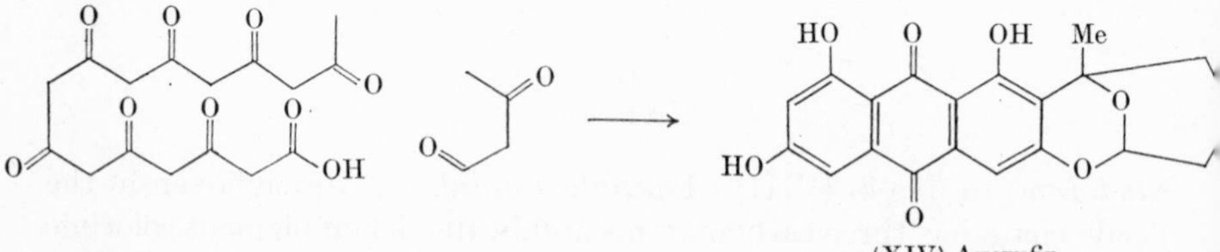

(XIV) Averufin

reaction of a C_{16} β-polyketide with a C_4 (acetoacetaldehyde) chain, followed by the usual condensations and cyclic acetal formation. A unique structural variation is seen in the aza-anthraquinone phom-azarin (XV), an orange pigment elaborated by the fungus *Phoma terrestris* which also produces cynodontin, a normal anthraquinone. Labelling studies have shown that at least eight acetic acid residues are incorporated during biosynthesis, together with a nitrogenous com-ponent (Birch *et al.*, 1961, 1964).

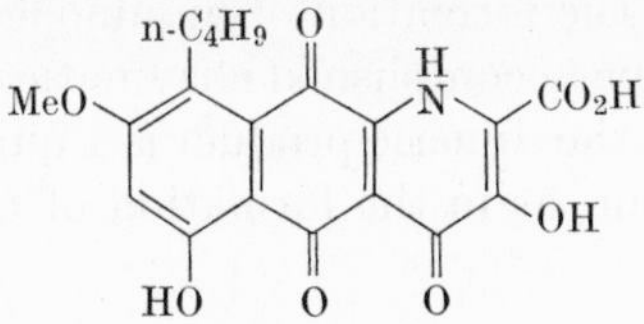

(XV) Phomazarin

Most of the anthraquinones found in higher plants fall into two groups. Those found in the *Rhamnaceae, Polygonaceae* and *Leguminosae* resemble the fungal quinones and some (emodin, chrysophanol, islandicin) occur in both Divisions. It is therefore reasonable to assume that the emodin-type quinones found in flowering plants originate from acetate, and the occasional occurrence of the corresponding anthrones supports this view. However, the origin of the numerous anthraquinones elaborated by *Rubiaceae* is less clear. More than a dozen are substituted only in one ring, half of them containing one, two or three hydroxyl groups but no carbon side chain. This is not an obviously "acetate-derived" substitution pattern nor is that of rubiadin (XVI), which appears frequently.

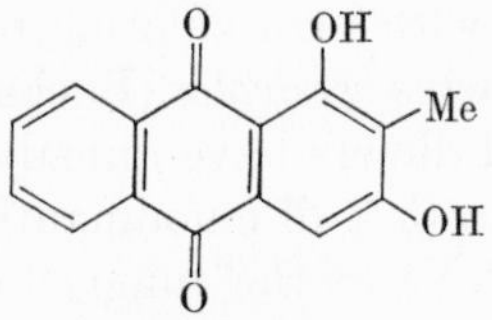

(XVI) Rubiadin

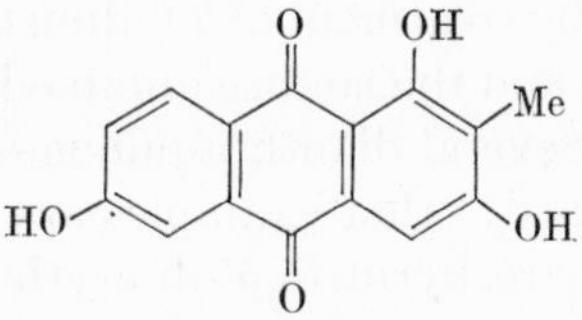

(XVII) Colucidin

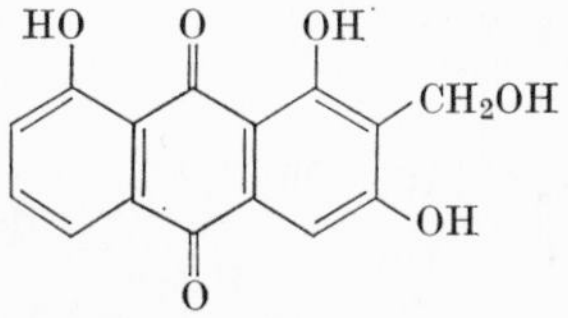

(XVIII) Coelulatin

On the other hand both colucidin (XVII) (Briggs, 1962), which occurs with rubiadin and anthragallol in *Coprosma lucida*, and coelulatin (XVIII) (Bowie *et al.*, 1962), also found with rubiadin in *Coelospermum* spp., do resemble the fungal pigments. Unfortunately, no experimental work has been recorded on the biosynthesis of these quinones. 2-Methylanthraquinone (tectoquinone) which occurs in teak, may have a mixed biogenetic origin and is discussed later (p. 329).

It has become clear in recent years that the oxidative coupling of plant phenols to form dimers and polymers is a common phenomenon, and leads *inter alia* to the formation of diquinones and extended quinones. The process can be accomplished enzymatically or by a variety of inorganic oxidants. If the dimeric product is a quinol further oxidation to a quinone may ensue, as in the formation of the extended quinone

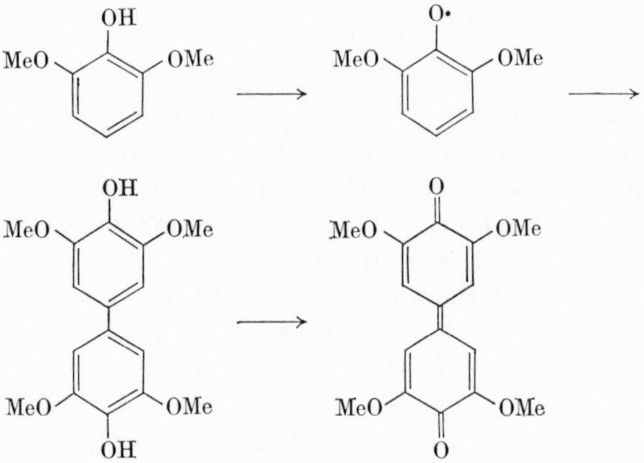

(XIX)

(XIX) by treatment of 2,6-dimethoxyphenol with ferric chloride, or with oxygen and the laccase obtained from *Polystictus versicolor* (Bocks *et al.*, 1962). Several dianthraquinones and related dimers have already been mentioned; other examples are penicilliopsin (5,5'-di-emodinanthrone) and fusaroskyrin (5,5'-di-erythroglaucin) (XX) in the fungi, and the

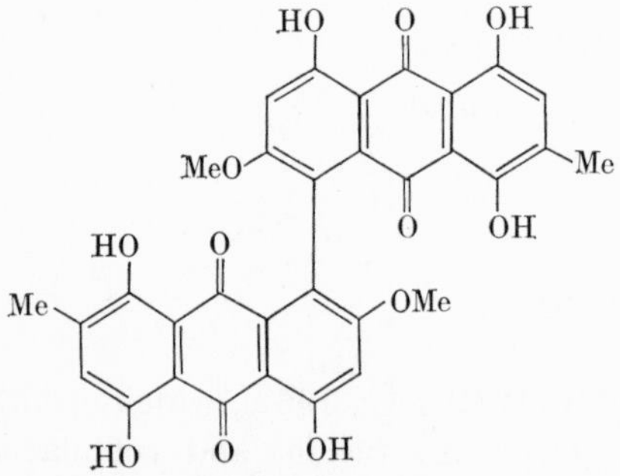

(XX) Fusaroskyrin

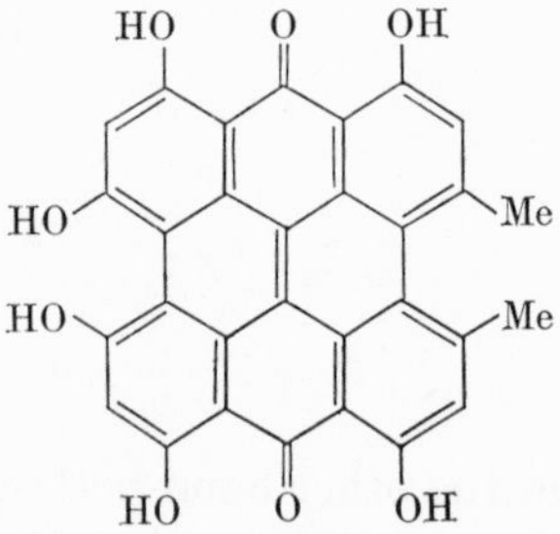

(XXI) Hypericin

sennosides (glucosides of 10,10'-dirheinanthrone) and hypericin (XXI) in flowering plants. The latter, which is formed by stepwise intramolecular coupling, is a common pigment in *Hypericaceae*, and in *H. hirsutum* it occurs together with emodinanthrone, and the intermediate dehydrodianthrone and helianthrone (Brockmann, 1957).

III. NAPHTHAQUINONES

About twenty naphthaquinones have been found in flowering plants, scattered through almost as many families, and a few occur in micro-organisms. They may be present in roots, wood, bark, leaves or fruit, but the presence of lawsone (2-hydroxy-1,4-naphthaquinone) and its methyl ether in the flowers of *Impatiens* spp. (*Balsaminaceae*) is unusual. Lawsone is also the colouring principle of henna, an ancient dye obtained by crushing the leaves of *Lawsonia alba* (*Lythraceae*), still used in Eastern countries as a cosmetic. The root of Dyer's Bugloss (*Alkanna tinctoria*), which contains alkannin (LXXXI), was formerly an important natural dyestuff, and its optical isomer shikonin (*Lithospermum ery-throrhizon*) was used at one time to dye Tokyo Violet. One or other of these pigments, derived from a related plant *Arnebia hispidissima*, is still used in India for colouring food (Jain and Mathur, 1964).

The biosynthesis of naphthaquinones has not been investigated but inspection of formulae suggests that most of them are of acetate-malonate origin; several possess additional terpenoid side chains and are con-sidered separately (see p. 328). The structure of flaviolin (XXII) (*Asper-gillus* spp.) was correctly predicted on the basis of the acetate theory

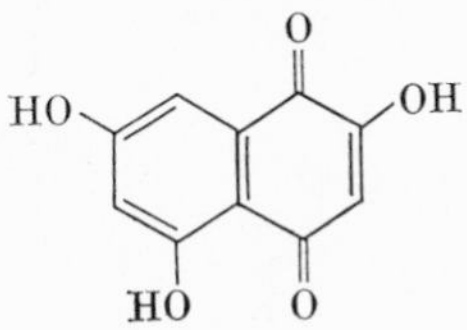

(XXII) Flaviolin

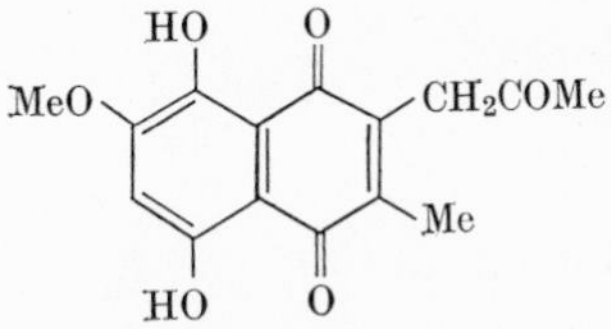

(XXIII) Javanicin

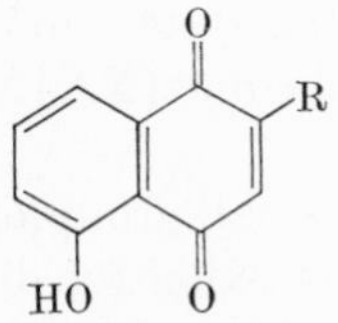

(XXIV) Juglone (R = H)
Plumbagin (R = Me)

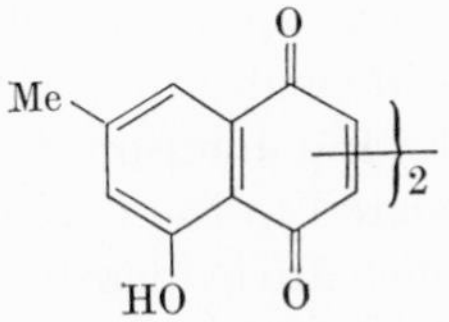

(XXV) Diospyrin

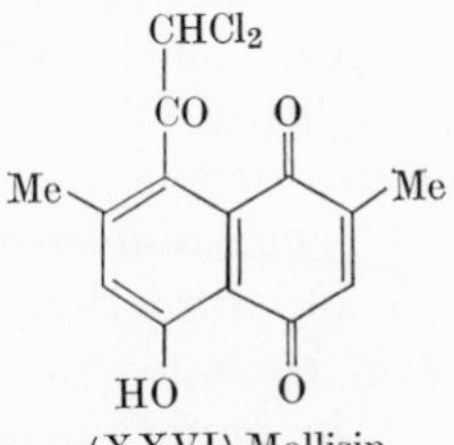

(XXVI) Mollisin

(Birch and Donovan, 1954), and structure (XXIII) is preferred for javanicin (*Fusarium* spp.) on the same grounds. Plumbagin (XXIV; R = Me) occurs in at least three families of higher plants, including *Ebenaceae*, which also provides an *o*-quinone and a dimer (XXV) (Kapil and Dhar, 1961). Juglone (XXIV; R = H) is found only in the *Juglandaceae* where it occurs in a reduced form as a glucoside. In contrast to the anthraquinones, the naphthaquinones do not exist as glycosides. The fungal quinone mollisin (XXVI) (*Mollisia* spp.) (Overeem, 1962) is noteworthy for its rare dichloroacetyl group, and xanthomegnin (XXVII) (*Trichophyton megnini*) (Just *et al.*, 1963) has a lactone structure unusual amongst naphthaquinones. Actinorhodin (XXVIII), another dimer, (*Streptomyces coelicolor*) is the sole naphthaquinone representative in

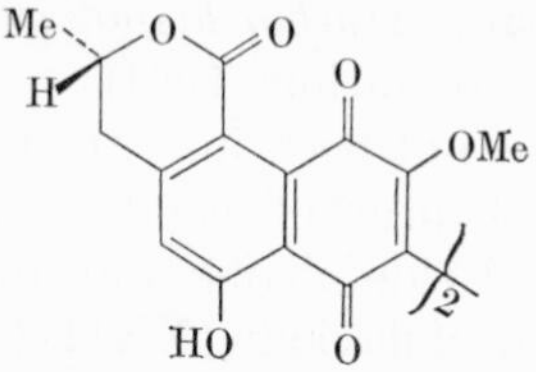

(XXVII) Xanthomegnin

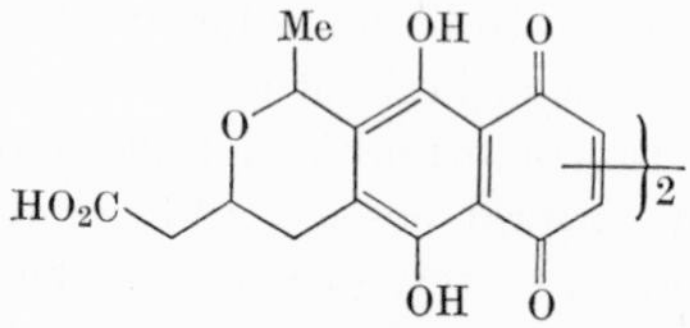

(XXVIII) Actinorhodin

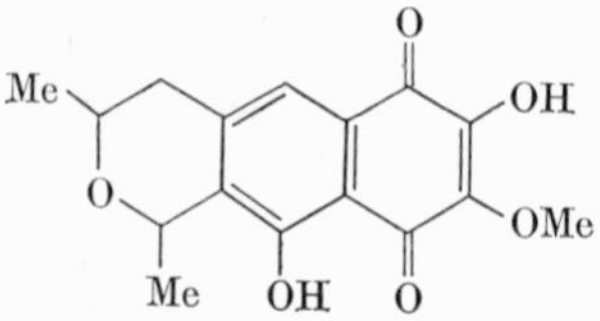

(XXIX) Ventilagone

bacteria (Brockmann *et al.*, 1962). The pyran ring system in the latter is also present in eleutherin (*Iridaceae*) and ventilagone (XXIX) (*Rhamnaceae*) (Cooke and Johnson, 1964).

Closely related to the naphthaquinones is a small group of perylenequinones which are evidently biosynthesized via oxidative dimerization of naphthalene precursors. The studies of Allport and Bu'Lock (1958, 1960) have revealed an interesting sequence of events in the metabolism of the large Ascomycete *Daldinia concentrica*. From the wild fungus it is possible to extract the almost black 4,9-dihydroxyperylene-3,10-quinone (XXX) and the dinaphthyl (XXXI). Laboratory cultures of unpigmented strains, which are deficient in oxidase, do not produce dimers but rather a series of "acetate-derived" C_8 and C_{10} benzenoid compounds, and the mono- and dimethyl ethers of 1,8-dihydroxynaphthalene which are almost certainly of similar origin. The diol is evidently the precursor of all the naphthalene metabolites; in the wild state, it is oxidized to the dimer (XXXI) which then undergoes either further intramolecular coupling leading to the perylenequinone (XXX) or intermolecular oxidation to form the black polymer (XXXII). A

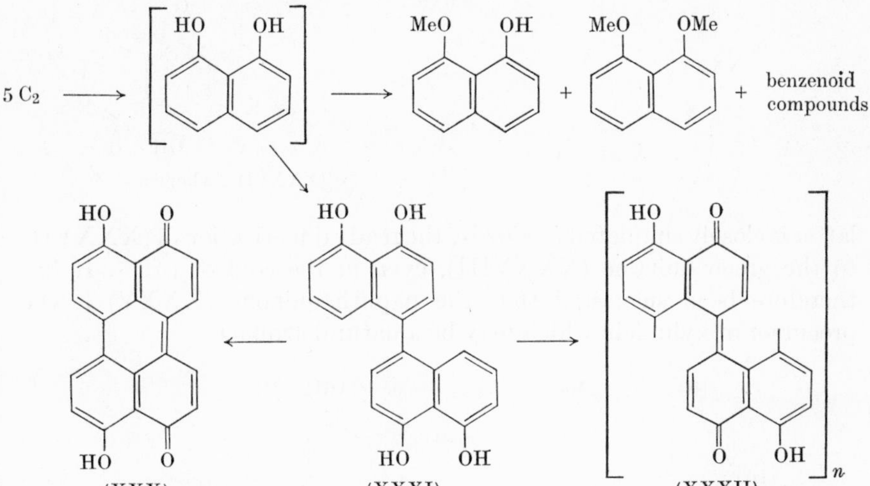

similar course of events seems likely in the biosynthesis of the other perylenequinones elaborated by Elsinöe spp. (e.g. XXXIII) (Batterham and Weiss, 1963), *Phyllosticta caryae* (phycarones) (Hackeng *et al.*, 1963), and *Cercosporina Kikuchii* (cercosporin) (Kuyama, 1962), which appear

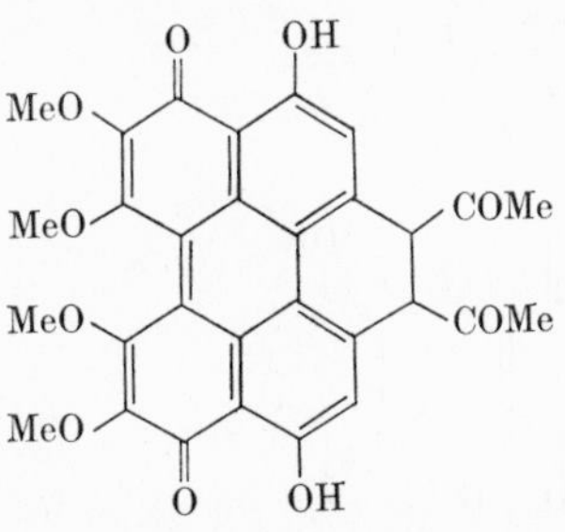

(XXXIII) Elsinochrome A

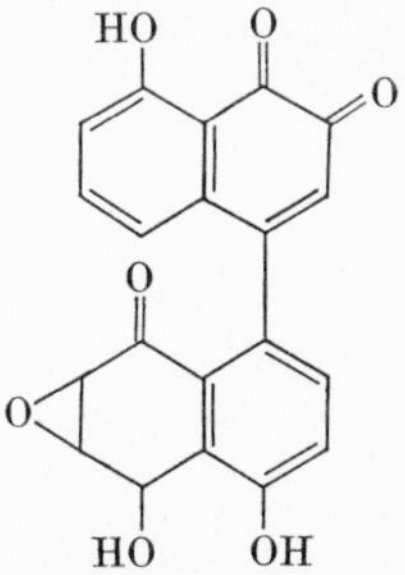

(XXXIV) Mycochrysone

to be very similar, if not identical in structure. Two other interesting pigments, which belong to this group biogenetically, are the orange-red mycochrysone (XXXIV), a metabolite of an unnamed Discomycete (Read and Vining, 1963), and xylindein (XXXVI) (Blackburn *et al.*, 1962), a green pigment produced by the Ascomycete *Chlorociboria aeruginosa* which has been used for staining wood. The formation of the

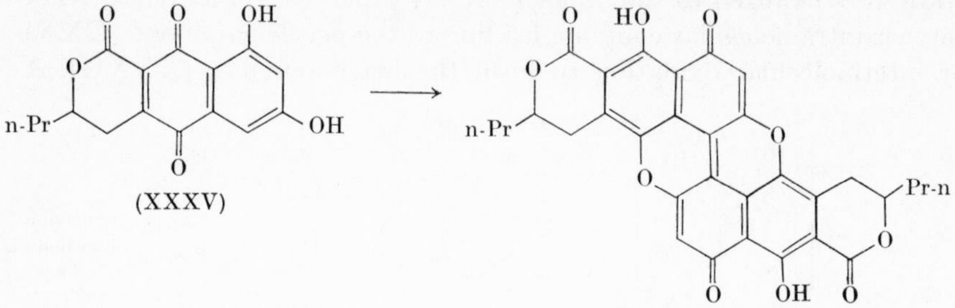

(XXXV)

(XXXVI) Xylindein

latter is closely simulated *in vitro* by the ready dimerization of (**XXXVII**) to the green quinone (**XXXVIII**), even in the cold at pH 7. It has therefore been suggested that the naphthaquinone (**XXXV**) is the precursor of xylindein which may be a natural artefact.

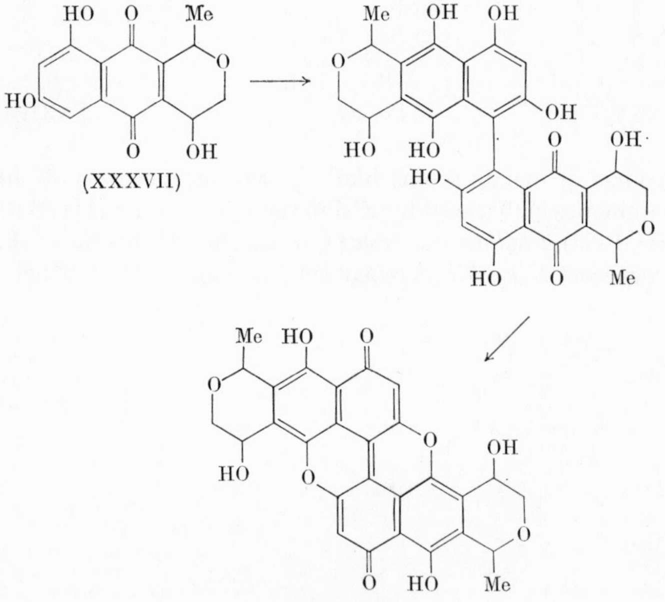

(XXXVII)

(XXXVIII)

IV. BENZOQUINONES

These pigments can be divided into several small groups, each with common structural features and usually limited distribution. The majority are fungal metabolites. The lower fungi (chiefly *Penicillium* and *Aspergillus* spp.) produce simple derivatives of benzoquinone and toluquinone such as (**XXXIX**) (yellow) and (**XL**) (violet-black), or analogous diquinones like oosporein (XLI) (red) which is fairly widely distributed. The characteristic benzoquinones of the higher fungi, principally Agaricaceae and Polyporaceae, are brown terphenyl deriva-

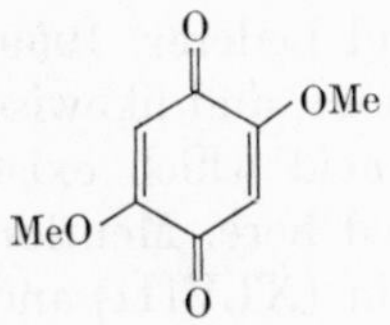

(XXXIX) 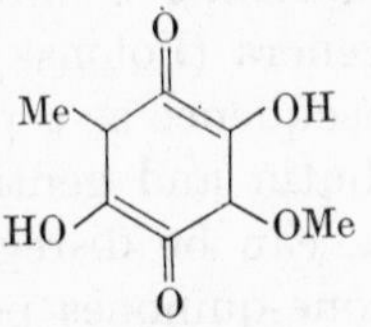   (XL) Spinulosin 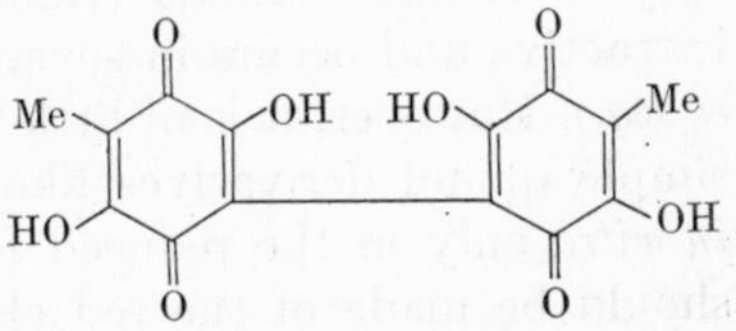   (XLI) Oosporein

tives of which polyporic acid (XLII) is typical. Polyporic acid and the almost black thelephoric acid (XLIII) are also found in lichens. Phlebiarubrone (XLIV), an *o*-quinone of the same series (the only

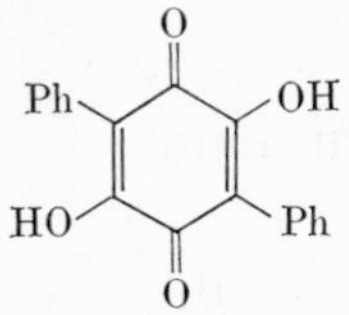

(XLII) Polyporic acid 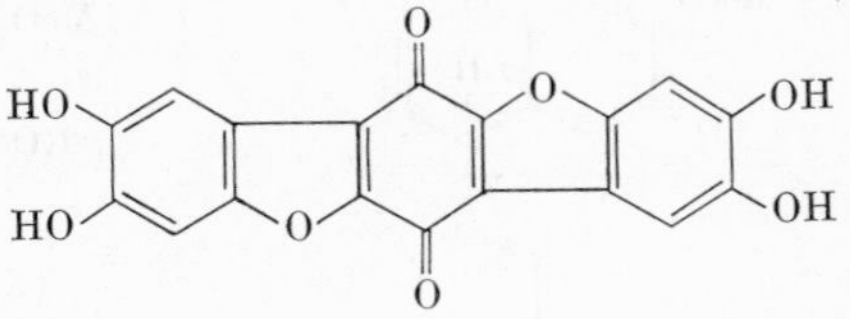   (XLIII) Thelephoric acid

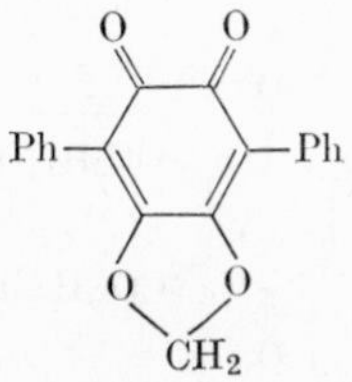

(XLIV) Phlebiarubrone

natural *o*-benzoquinone) was recently isolated from laboratory cultures of the Basidiomycete *Phlebia strigosozonata* (McMorris and Anchel, 1963). Among flowering plants, the Myrsinaceae elaborate a small group of

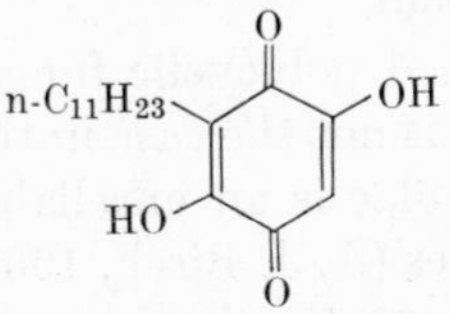

(XLV) Embelin 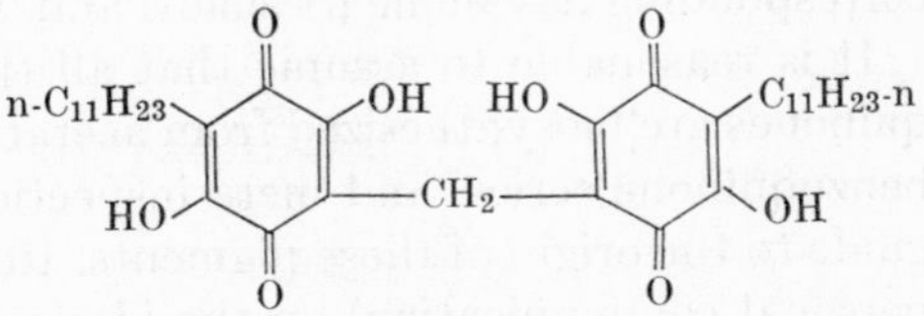   (XLVI) Vilangin

orange benzoquinones having long alkyl side chains. The best known example is embelin (XLV), present in the ripe berries of *Embelia ribes* together with the diquinone vilangin (XLVI) (Rao and Venkateswarlu, 1961). Vilangin can easily be obtained from embelin by treatment with

11

formaldehyde. The recently discovered dalbergiones (dalbergenones) (XLVII) are confined so far to *Dalbergia* and *Machaerium* (Leguminosae) heartwoods whereas 2,6-dimethoxybenzoquinone, formerly reported only in *Adonis vernalis* (Ranunculaceae), is now known as a wood extractive and occurs in several genera (Polonsky and Lederer, 1959, *et seq.*). However, it is of little consequence as a pigment, and likewise simple quinol derivatives like arbutin and gentisic acid which exist *in vitro* only in the reduced form, can be disregarded here. Mention should be made of the red chalkone-quinones pedicin (XLVIII) and carthamone (XLIX), although biogenetically they are flavonoids. The pedicins (XLVIII) occur with related flavonoids on the leaves of *Didymocarpus pedicellata* (Gesneraceae), whereas carthamone and its

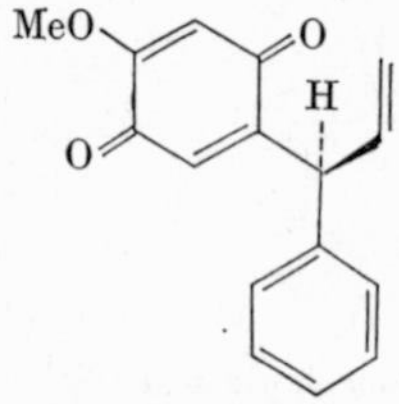

(XLVII) Dalbergione

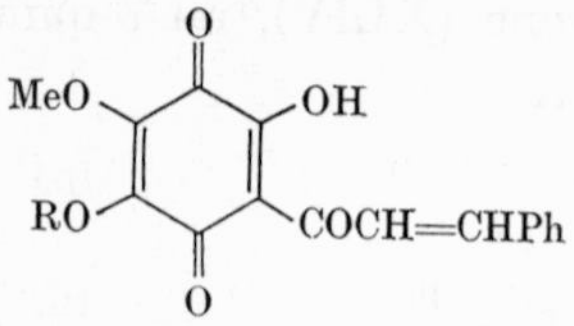

(XLVIII) Pedicin (R = H)
Methylpedicine (R = Me)

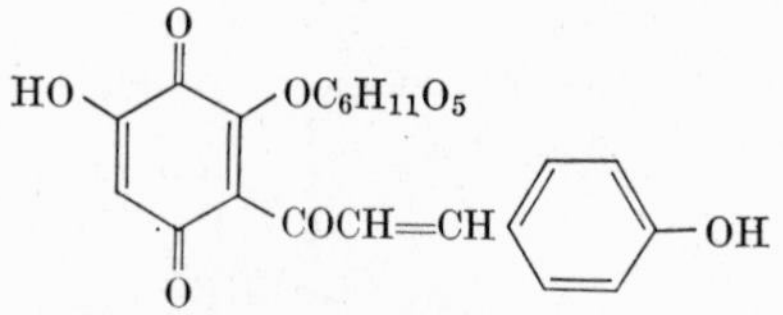

(XLIX) Carthamone

congeners are found in the orange-red flowers of *Carthamus tinctorius* (Compositae) which were formerly used for dyeing purposes. In the white and ivory flowers, carthamone is replaced by its quinol and the corresponding flavanone (Seshadri and Thakur, 1960).

It is reasonable to assume that all the condensed polycyclic fungal quinones are biosynthesized from acetate, but this is not the case in the benzoquinone series, and mere inspection of formulae is an unreliable guide to the origin of these pigments. Recent studies (A. J. Birch, 1963, personal communication) on the biosynthesis of aurantiogliocladin (L) show that the acetate origin originally suggested (Birch *et al.*, 1958a) is wrong, and it may be derived from phenylalanine despite the fact that 6-methylsalicylic acid is incorporated as a unit in cultures of *Gliocladium roseum*.

On the other hand recent work on the formation of fumigatin (LI) in cultures of *Aspergillus fumigatus* supports the view that this quinone is "acetate-derived". [1-^{14}C]-Acetate, [2-^{14}C]-acetate and [^{14}C]-L-

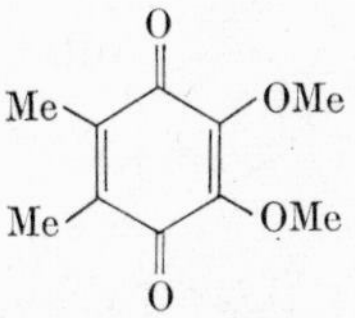

(L) Aurantiogliocladin 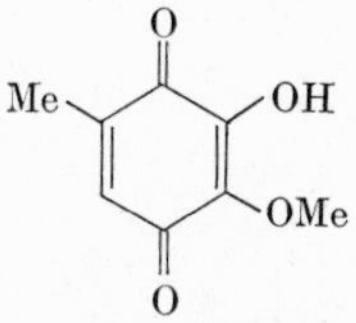   (LI) Fumigatin

methionine were incorporated as expected (Pettersson, 1963). It was also shown that added orsellinic acid could be directly transformed into fumigatin, by hydroxylation at position 5 and further oxidation, although this does not establish that orsellinic acid is a natural precursor.

In the terphenyl group of quinones the hydroxylation pattern in the benzenoid rings (4'- or 3',4'-) is reminiscent of the B ring in flavonoids. This suggests an origin from shikimic acid but no convenient means of testing this idea was available until the discovery of volucrisporin (LV) in cultures of the hyphomycete *Volucrispora aurantiaca*. The origin of this red terphenylquinone is unusual, and so is its *m*-hydroxylated structure and the absence of oxygen functions on the quinone nucleus (cf. XLII). Feeding experiments with labelled precursors showed that shikimic acid, phenylalanine, phenyllactic acid, and *m*-tyrosine were readily incorporated but acetate and cinnamate were not. Read *et al.* (1962) therefore suggest that volucrisporin arises by condensation of two C_6–C_3 units, most likely phenylpyruvic acid, which is *m*-hydroxylated before condensation (LII). Since neither tyrosine nor 3,4-dihydroxyphenylalanine was incorporated into the pigment, a hydroxylation-dehydroxylation process is apparently not involved and the method by which *m*-hydroxyl groups are introduced is not known. The sequence (LII) → (LV) leads to volucrisporin, the central ring in (LIII) being at the oxidation level found in the other terphenylquinones. The other members of the group could therefore arise similarly from the appropriate C_6–C_3 precursors. The possibility of rearrangement to a branched C_6–C_3 intermediate prior to condensation cannot be entirely excluded although labelling experiments showed that 1,2-migration of the aryl group does not take place.

The dalbergiones (XLVII), which are evidently C_6–C_3–C_6 compounds, are closely related to the 4-phenylcoumarins found in *Dalbergia sissoo*. It has been suggested (Grisebach, 1961) that these compounds may be formed via two successive 1,2-aryl migrations (cf. isoflavone biosynthesis). Seshadri (1957) envisaged the condensation of a phenol with a C_9 unit, possibly in the form of a β-keto-acid, but a more attractive

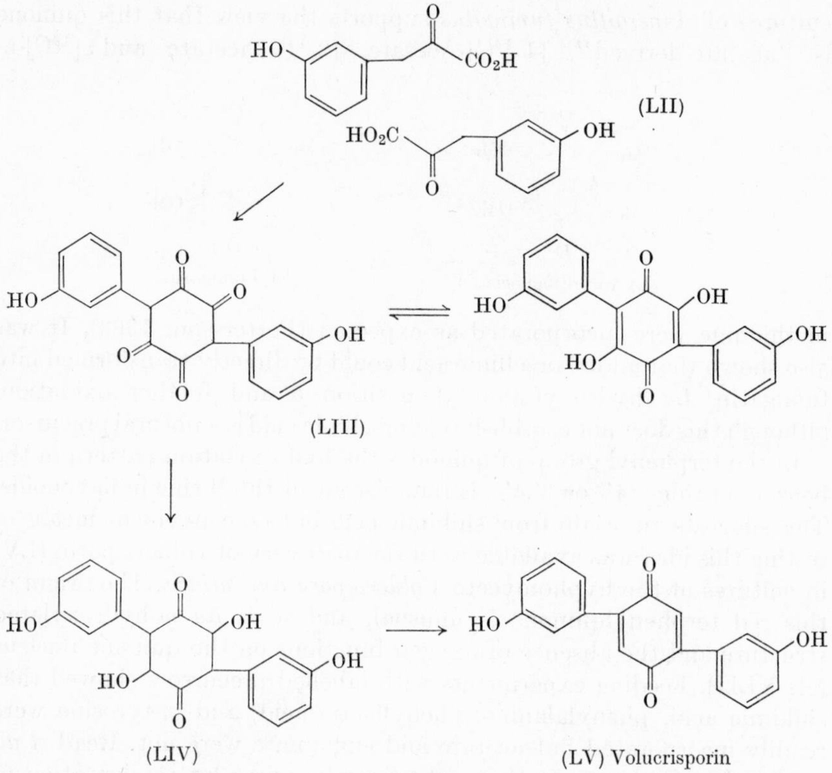

(LII)

(LIII)

(LIV)

(LV) Volucrisporin

hypothesis, proposed by W. D. Ollis (1963, personal communication), is that a phenol condenses with a cinnamyl pyrophosphate (LVI), a process analogous to prenylation with $\gamma\gamma$-dimethylallyl pyrophosphate. On this

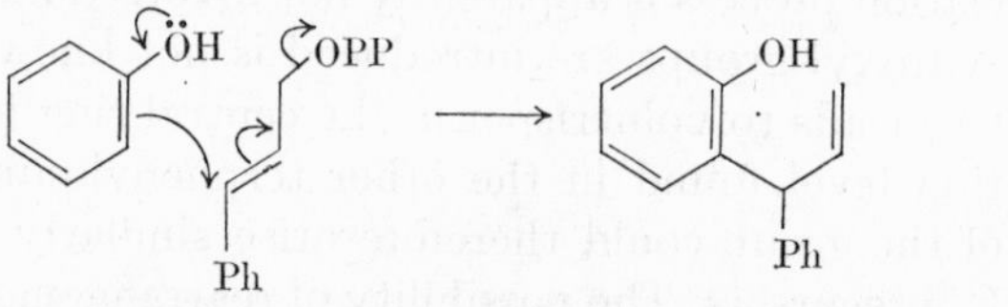

(LVI)

view the quinone ring in the dalbergiones originates from acetate-malonate and the C_9 unit from shikimic acid.

V. NAPHTHACENEQUINONES

This unique group of red, antibiotic, pigments is confined to the Actinomycetales, especially Streptomycetes; the only other natural products having this tetracyclic carbon skeleton are the tetracyclines and probably the quinocycline pigments (Cosulich *et al.*, 1963), which are also Streptomycete metabolites, and perhaps heliomycin (*Actinomyces flavochromogenes* (var. *heliomycin*) (Grinev *et al.*, 1963).* (For a recent review see Brockmann, 1963.)

They occur either as glycosides (cinerubins, rhodomycins, rutilantins—collectively, anthracyclines) in combination with unusual amino-sugars, or as free aglycones (pyrromycinones, rhodomycinones—collectively, anthracyclinones) which are denoted by Greek letters. ϵ-Pyrromycinone (rutilantinone) is the aglycone common to pyrromycin (LVII), the cinerubins and the rutilantins (Brockmann *et al.*, 1960), and there appears to be considerable variation in the carbohydrate moieties. All the aglycones possess the same carbon skeleton (apart from occasional loss of an ester group, e.g. LIX) and have the same absolute configuration at their asymmetric centres (except η-pyrromycinone (LVIII) which is

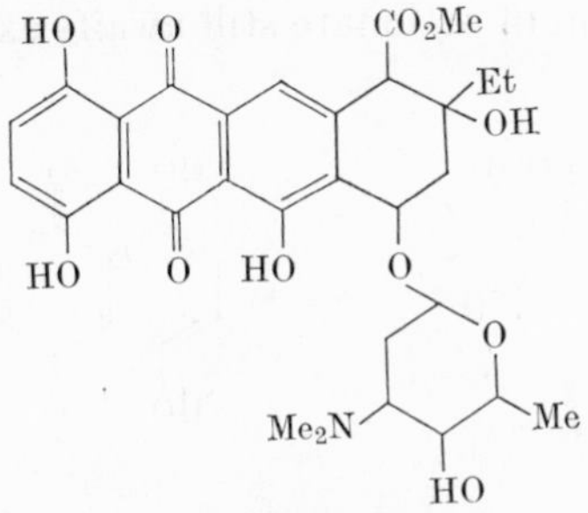

(LVII) Pyrromycin

fully aromatic) (Brockmann Jr., and Legrand, 1963), but they differ in the number and arrangement of the hydroxyl groups as may be seen in structures (LVIII) to (LXI). In contrast to the anthraquinones only α-hydroxyl groups are present.

The appearance of oxygen functions on alternate carbon atoms in these molecules is a clear indication of their acetate derivation and when [1-^{14}C]-acetate was fed to a rutilantin culture it was incorporated into the aglycone (ϵ-pyrromycinone) as expected. Isotopic analysis showed that only *nine* acetate units were incorporated and the activity of the ethyl groups and of carbon-9 was much less than that of the other labelled carbon atoms, and their labelling moreover was random. Evidently the ethyl group is not formed by C-methylation of a β-polyketide chain derived solely from acetate and must have a different biosynthetic origin. The nature of this was established by feeding [1-^{14}C]-propionate to the same organism which then produced ϵ-pyrromycinone labelled selectively at C-9 (LXIII) (Ollis *et al.*, 1960)

* Little information is available.

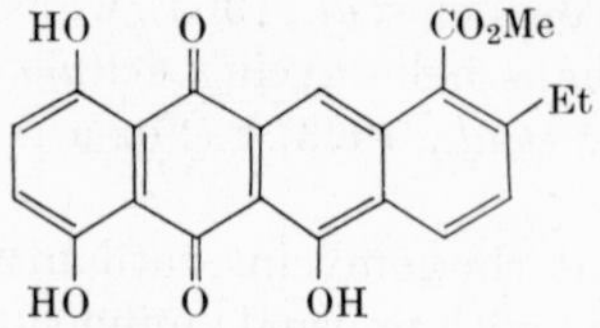

HO O CO₂Me / Et ... (LVIII) η-Pyrromycinone

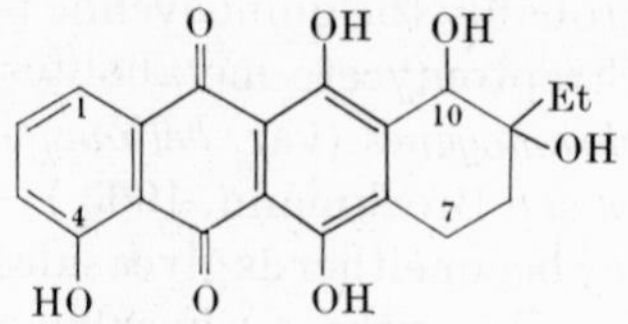

(LIX) γ-Rhodomycinone*

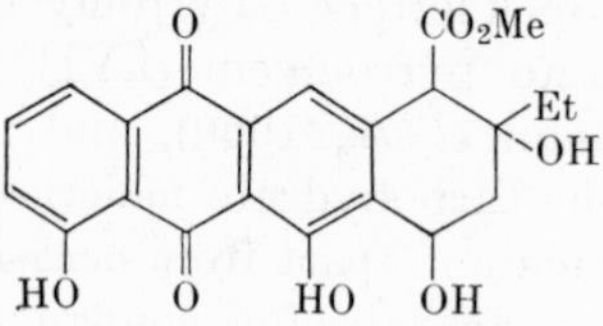

(LX) Aklavinone

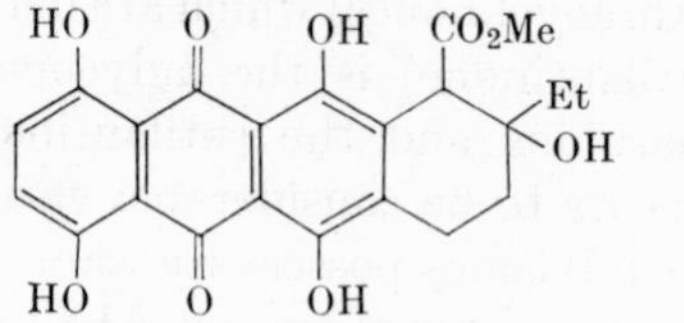

(LXI) ε-Isorhodomycinone

showing that the starter acid in the naphthacene biosynthesis is propionic acid. The participation of malonate still awaits experimental confirmation.

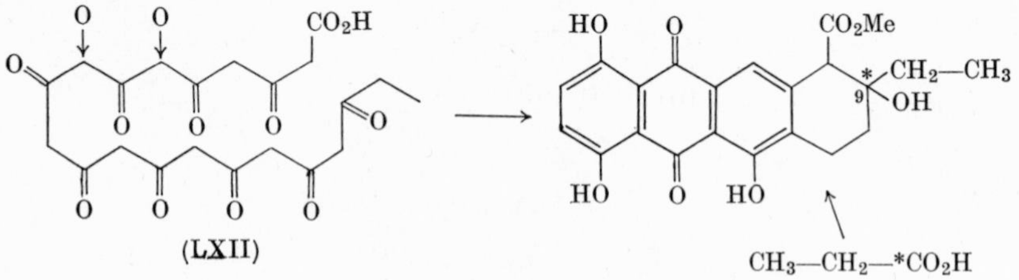

(LXII)

$CH_3—CH_2—*CO_2H$

(LXIII)

VI. PHENANTHRAQUINONES

As phenanthraquinones, analogous to the fungal anthraquinones, can be built up (on paper) by suitable coiling and condensation of a β-polyketide chain, it is surprising that until recently the only natural phenanthraquinones were of terpenoid origin (see p. 327) apart from a compound, denticulatol, isolated from a Chinese species of *Rumex* (Chi *et al.*, 1947), which appears to be a dihydroxy-methyl-9,10-phenanthraquinone of uncertain structure. This gap is now filled by the discovery of piloquinone (LXV), the principal red pigment elaborated by *Streptomyces pilosus* (Polonsky *et al.*, 1963). A biogenetic scheme in which isocaproic acid is the starter unit of a β-polyketide chain can be envisaged but the French workers point out that piloquinone, like the naphthacenequinone pigments, is also a C_{21} Streptomycete metabolite and could arise from the *same* propionate-acetate (malonate) precursor (LXII) = (LXIV).

* Or isomer with OH at C-1 instead of C-4.

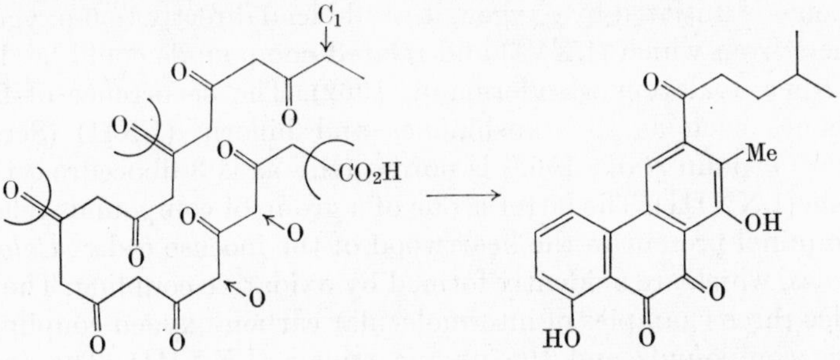

(LXIV)   (LXV) Piloquinone

VII. ISOPRENOID QUINONES

In a large number of natural products an isoprenoid unit is attached to an aromatic system. About half the quinones in this category are of mixed biogenetic origin and the rest are completely isoprenoid, i.e. "terpene quinones", and therefore call for illustration rather than

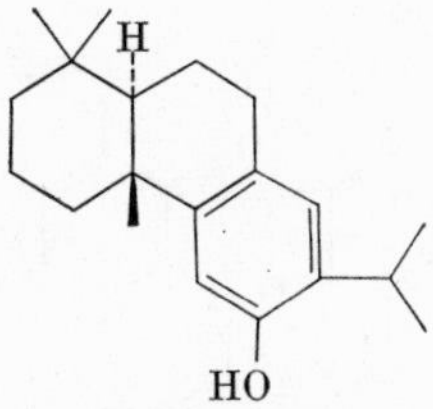

(LXVI) Ferruginol 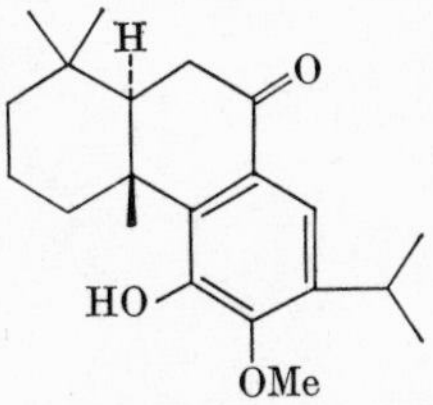   (LXVII) Cryptojanonol

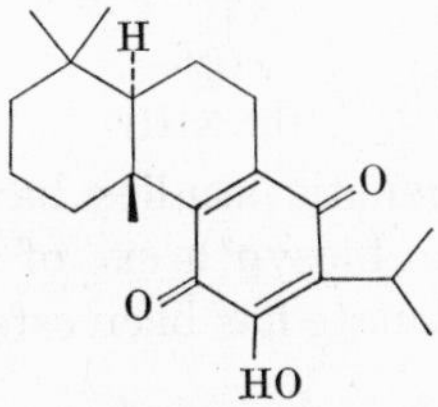

(LXVIII) Royleanone 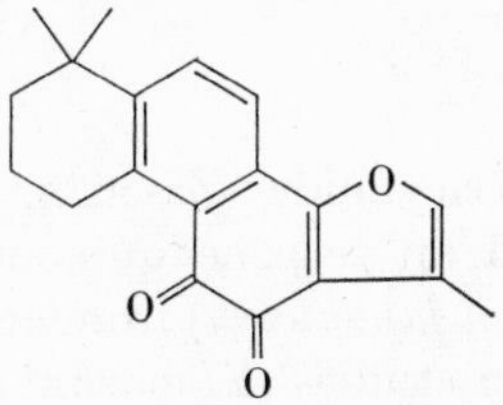   (LXIX) Tanshinone II

discussion in this chapter. They have a limited distribution in flowering plants and in the Gymnospermae. As can be seen by comparison of compounds (LXVI) to (LXIX) the royleanones (Compositae) (Edwards *et al.*, 1962) and tanshinones (Labiatae) are diterpenes in a high state of oxidation, but are otherwise unexceptional. Thymoquinone (LXX) (Coniferae) and perezone (LXXI) (Compositae) are similarly related to mono- and sesquiterpenes, respectively. ApSimon and Edwards (1961) point out that if the final cyclization to form ring C in the biogenesis of diterpenes is initiated by oxygen, it would lead directly to 6-oxygenated products from which (LXVI) and related compounds could be derived by further oxidation (Sandermann, 1962). The occurrence of further o-quinones such as the tanshinones and biflorin (LXII) (Scrophulariaceae) (Comin et al., 1962) is noteworthy as is 3-libocedroxythymoquinone (LXXIII). The latter is one of a group of compounds related to thymoquinol present in the heartwood of the incense cedar, Calocedrus decurrens, which are evidently formed by oxidative coupling. The group includes three examples of intermolecular carbon-oxygen coupling, two dimeric compounds and the unique trimer (LXXIII). The coupling products can be formed in vitro from p-methoxythymol by oxidation

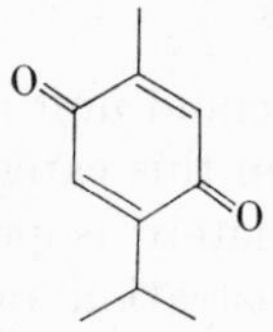

(LXX) Thymoquinone 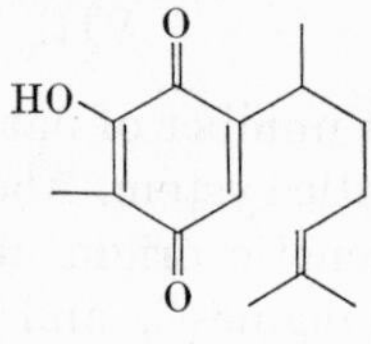   (LXXI) Perezone

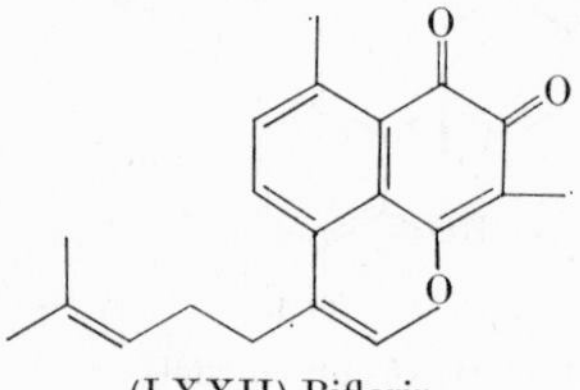

(LXXII) Biflorin

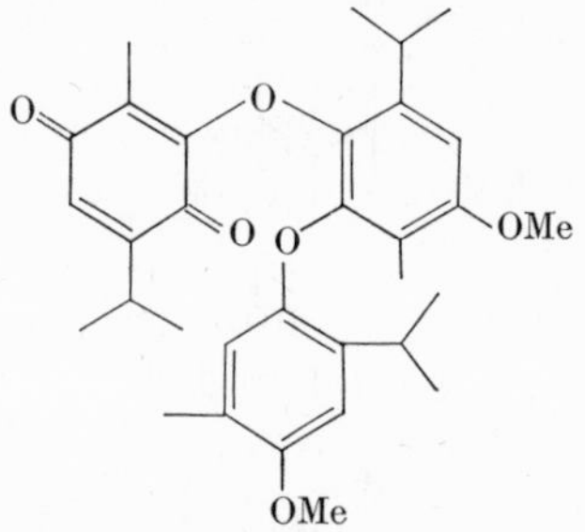

(LXXIII)

with ferricyanide (Zavarin, 1958). No biogenetic studies have been reported on terpene quinones although the biosynthesis of thymol (Orthodon japonicum) from acetate via mevalonate has been established by tracer studies (Yamazaki et al., 1963).

The terpenoid quinones of mixed biogenetic origin include the widely occurring ubiquinones, plastoquinones and vitamins K which are discussed separately in Chapter 13. The others are chiefly C_{15} compounds (LXXIV to LXXVI) occurring in tropical heartwoods (Bignoniaceae and Verbenaceae) although there are isolated examples in Proteaceae and Gesneraceae (LXXIV). Here again no experimental work on the biogenesis of these quinones is on record but there can be little doubt that the C_5 unit is derived from mevalonate and is presumably introduced by alkylation of a naphthol with γγ-dimethylallyl pyrophosphate, for which parallels exist (Ollis and Sutherland, 1961). Nothing is known of the origin of the aromatic part of these pigments which, like the vitamins K, have no substituents in the benzenoid ring. In this connection it has been pointed out (Sandermann and Dietrichs, 1957) that lapachol (LXXVI)

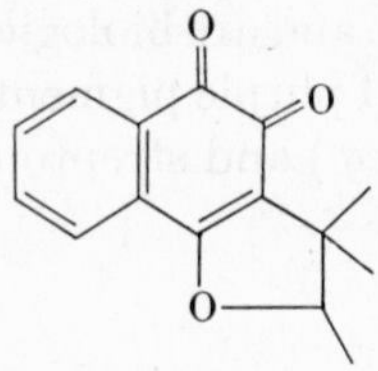

(LXXIV) Dunnione

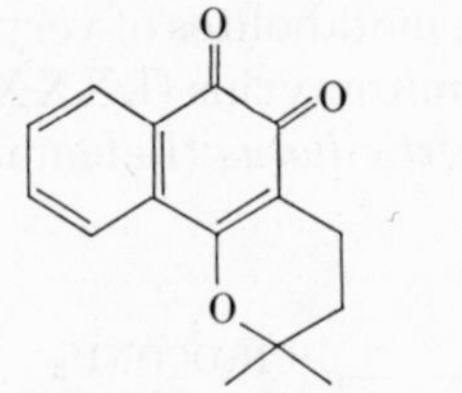

(LXXV) β-Lapachone

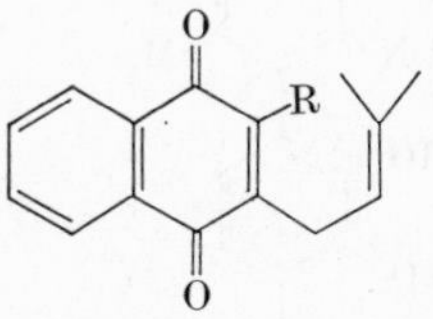

(LXXVI) Lapachol (R = OH)
Desoxylapachol (R = H)

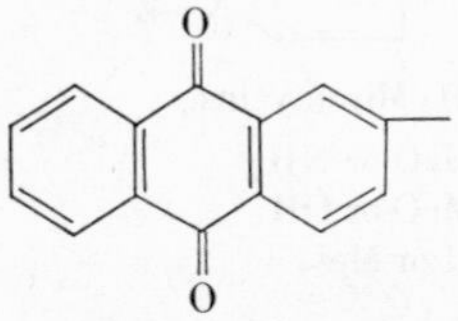

(LXXVII) Tectoquinone

and desoxylapachol (LXXVI) (Sandermann and Simatupang, 1963) may be biogenetically related to tectoquinone (LXXVII) and related anthraquinones which occur in teak (*Tectona grandis*) (Rudman, 1960;

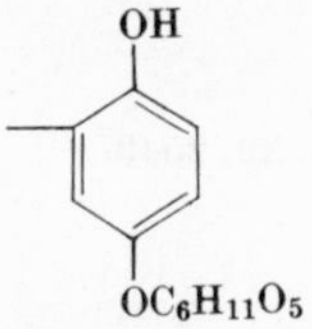

(LXXVIII) Homoarbutin

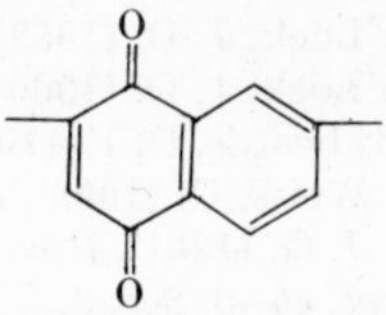

(LXXIX) Chimaphilin

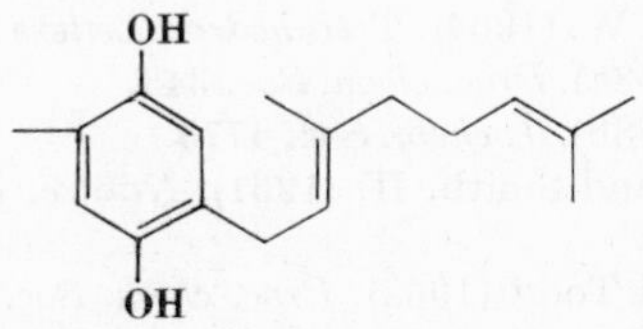

(LXXX) Pyrolatin

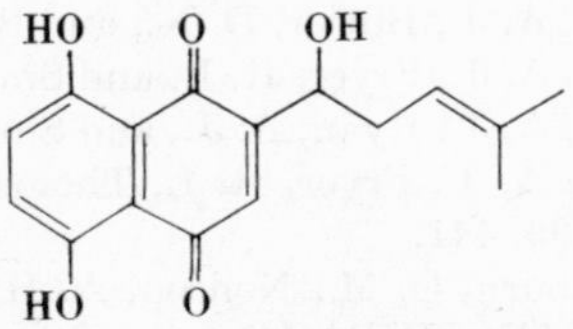

(LXXXI) Alkannin

Pavanaram and Row, 1957). The implication that a benzenoid ring in (LXXVII) originates from mevalonate, may be extended to chimaphilin (LXXIX), which is found with homoarbutin (LXXVIII) and pyrolatin (LXXX) in *Pyrola* spp., and alkannin (LXXXI).

11*

VIII. Miscellaneous Quinones

The pigments mentioned briefly under this heading are of great interest but bear no relationship to those already discussed. They are all Streptomycete metabolites of very unusual structure and are biologically active.

The mitomycins (LXXXII)* are a group of purple pigments produced by *S. verticillatus* (Lefemine *et al.*, 1962, *et seq.*) and streptonigrin is the

(LXXXII) Mitomycins

X = MeO or NH$_2$
Y = MeO or OH
Z = H or Me

(LXXXIII) Streptonigrin

(LXXXIV)

quinolinequinone (LXXXIII) elaborated by *S. flocculus* (Rao *et al.*, 1963). Woodward points out that the aminoquinone structure (LXXXIV) which is common to most of these pigments and to the actinomycins, can be correlated with their anti-cancer activity.

References

Allport, D. C., and Bu'Lock, J. D. (1958). *J. chem. Soc.* 4090.
Allport, D. C., and Bu'Lock, J. D. (1960). *J. chem. Soc.* 654.
ApSimon, J. W., and Edwards, O. E. (1961). *Canad. J. Chem.* **39**, 2543.
Batterham, T. J., and Weiss, U. (1963). *Proc. chem. Soc.* 89.
Bentley, R., and Keil, J. G. (1961). *Proc. chem. Soc.* 111.
Birch, A. J. (1962). *Proc. chem. Soc.* 3.
Birch, A. J., and Donovan, F. W. (1954). *Chem. & Ind.* 1047.
Birch, A. J., and Donovan, F. W. (1955). *Austral. J. Chem.* **8**, 529.
Birch, A. J., Butler, D. N., and Richards, R. W. (1964). *Tetrahedron Letters* 1853.
Birch, A. J., Fryer, R. I., and Smith, H. (1958a). *Proc. chem. Soc.* 343.
Birch, A. J., Ryan, A. J., and Smith, H. (1958b). *J. chem. Soc.* 4773.
Birch, A. J., Fryer, R. I., Thomson, P. J., and Smith, H. (1961). *Nature, Lond.* **190**, 441.
Blackburn, G. M., Neilson, A. H., and Lord Todd (1962). *Proc. chem. Soc.* 327; XIXth IUPAC Congress, Abstracts A, 310.
Bocks, S. M., Brown, B. R., and Todd, A. H. (1962). *Proc. chem. Soc.* 117.
Bohlmann, F., Lüders, W., and Plattner, W. (1961). *Arch. Pharm.* **294/66**, 521.
Bowie, J. H., Cooke, R. G., and Wilkin, P. E. (1962). *Austral. J. Chem.* **15**, 336.
Briggs, L. H. (1962). *In* "Recent Progress in the Chemistry of Natural and Synthetic Colouring Matters" (T. S. Gore, B. S. Joshi, S. V. Sunthankar and B. D. Tilak, eds.), p. 659, Academic Press, New York.

* Porfiromycin is N-methylmitomycin C.

Brockmann, H. (1957). *Proc. chem. Soc.* 304.

Brockmann, H. (1963). *In* "Progress in the Chemistry of Organic Natural Products" (L. Zechmeister, ed.), vol. 21, 121.

Brockmann, H. Jr., and Legrand, M. (1963). *Tetrahedron* 19, 395–400.

Brockmann, H., Brockmann, H. Jr., Gordon, J. J., Keller-Schlierlein, W., Lenk, W., Ollis, W. D., Prelog, V., and Sutherland, I. O. (1960). *Tetrahedron Letters* No. 8, 25.

Brockmann, H., Müller, W., and Van der Merve, K. (1962). *Naturwissenschaften* 49, 131.

Boross, L. (1963). *Acta chim. hung.* 35, 195.

Bu'Lock, J. D., and Smalley, H. M. (1961). *Proc. chem. Soc.* 209.

Castle, H., and Kubsch, F. (1949). *Arch. Biochem.* 23, 158.

Chi, J. J., Hsu, S. T., Hu, M., and Wang, S. (1947). *J. Chin. chem. Soc.* 15, 21.

Comin, J., Gonçalves de Lima, O., Grant, H. N., Jackman, L. M., Keller-Schierlein, W., and Prelog, V. (1962). *Helv. chim. acta* 46, 409.

Cooke, R. G., and Johnson, B. L. (1964). *Proc. Indian Acad. Sci.* (in the press).

Cosulich, D. B., Mowat, J. H., Broschard, R. W., Patrick, J. B., and Meyer, W. E. (1963). *Tetrahedron Letters* 453.

Edwards, O. E., Feniak, G., and Los, M. (1962). *Canad. J. Chem.* 40, 1540.

Ehrensvärd, G., and Gatenbeck, S. (1961). *Internat. Congr. pure appl. Chem.* (1959) vol. II, 99.

Eyton, W. B., Ollis, W. D., Sutherland, I. O., Jackman, L. M., Gottlieb, O. R., and Magalhaes, M. T. (1962). *Proc. chem. Soc.* 301. Marini-Bettolo, G. B., Casinovi, C. G., Gonçalves Da Lima, O., Dalia Maia, M. H., and D'Albuquerque, I. L. (1962). *Ann. Chim. (Roma)* 52, 1190. Rao, M. M., and Seshadri, T. R. (1963). *Tetrahedron Letters* 211. Dempsey, C. B., Donnelly, D. M. X., and Laidlaw, R. A. (1963). *Chem. & Ind.* 491. Sandermann, W., Dietrichs, H.-H., and Puth, M. (1960). *Holz Roh u. Werkstoff* 18, 63.

Gatenbeck, S. (1958). *Acta chem. scand.* 12, 1211.

Gatenbeck, S. (1960a). *Acta chem. scand.* 14, 296.

Gatenbeck, S. (1960b). *Svensk Kem. Tids.* 72, 188.

Gatenbeck, S. (1960c). *Acta chem. scand.* 14, 102.

Gatenbeck, S. (1962). *Acta chem. scand.* 16, 1053.

Grinev, A. N., Mezentsev, A. S., and Sibiryakova, D. V. (1963). *Zh. Obshch. Khim.* 33, 315. [*Chem. Abs.* 58, 13863.]

Grisebach, H. (1961). *In* "Chemistry of Natural Phenolic Compounds" (W. D. Ollis, ed.), p. 237. Pergamon Press, New York.

Hackeng, W. H. L., Copier, H., and Salemink, C. A. (1963). *Rev. trav. chim.* 82, 322.

Henriquez Ulloa, N. (1960). *Anal. Fac. Quim. Farm. Univ. Chile* 12, 113.

Jain, A. C., and Mathur, S. K., *Proc. Indian Acad. Sci.* in the press.

Just, G., Day, W. C., and Blank, F. (1963). *Canad. J. Chem.* 41, 74.

Kapil, R. S., and Dhar, M. M. (1961). *J. Sci. Ind. Res. (India)* 20B, 498.

Kikuchi, M. (1962). *Bot. Mag. Tokyo* 75, 158.

Kikuchi, M., and Nakahara, M. (1961). *Bot. Mag. Tokyo* 74, 463.

Kuyama, S. (1962). *J. Amer. chem. Soc.* 27, 939 and earlier papers.

Lefemine, D. V., Dann, M., Barbatschi, F., Hausmann, W. K., Zbinovsky, V., Monnikendam, P., Adams, J., and Bohonos, N. (1962). *J. Amer. chem. Soc.* 84, 3184. Webb, J. S., Cosulich, D. B., Mowat, J. H., Patrick, J. B., Broschard, R. W., Meyer, W. E., Williams, R. P., Wolf, C. F., Fulmor, W., Pidacks, C., and Lancaster, J. E. *J. Amer. chem. Soc.* 84, 3185, 3186. Tulinsky, A. *J. Amer. chem. Soc.* 84, 3188.

McMorris, T. C., and Anchel, M. (1963). *Tetrahedron Letters* 335.

Ollis, W. D., and Sutherland, I. O. (1961). *In* "Chemistry of Natural Phenolic Compounds" (W. D. Ollis, ed.), p. 237, Pergamon Press, New York.

Ollis, W. D., Sutherland, I. O., Codner, R. C., Gordon, J. J., and Miller, G. A. (1960). *Proc. chem. Soc.* 347.

Overeem, J. C. and Van der Kerk, G. J. M. (1964). *Rec. trav. chim.* **83**, 995, 1005.

Pavanaram, S. K., and Row, L. R. (1957). *J. Sci. Ind. Res.* (*India*) **16B**, 409.

Penas Goas, D. (1950). *Farmacognosia* **10**, 229.

Pettersson, G. (1963). *Acta chem. scand.* **17**, 1323.

Polonsky, J., and Lederer, E. (1959). *Bull. Soc. chim. Fr.* 1157. Kupchan, S. M., and Obasi, M. E. (1960). *J. Amer. pharm. Assoc.* **49**, 257. Inamoto, N., Masuda, S., Simamura, O., and Tsuyuki, T. (1961). *Bull. chem. Soc. Japan* **34**, 888. Freudenberg, K., and Sidhu, G. B. (1961). *Holzforschung* **15**, 33. Polonsky, J., Zylber, J., and Wijesekera (1962). *Bull. Soc. chim. Fr.* 1715.

Polonsky, J., Johnson, B. C., Cohen, P., and Lederer, E. (1963). *Bull. Soc. chim. Fr.* 1909.

Pusey, D. F. G., and Roberts, J. C. (1963). *J. chem. Soc.* 3542.

Rao, Ch. B., and Venkateswarlu, V. (1961). *J. org. Chem.* **26**, 4529.

Rao, K. V., Biemann, K., and Woodward, R. B. (1963). *J. Amer. chem. Soc.* **85**, 2532.

Read, G., and Vining, L. C. (1963). *Chem. & Ind.* 1239.

Read, G., Vining, L. C., and Haskins, R. H. (1962). *Canad. J. Chem.* **40**, 2357.

Rudman, P. (1960). *Chem. & Ind.* 1356.

Sandermann, W. (1962). *In* "Comparative Biochemistry" (M. Florkin and H. S. Mason, eds.), vol. IIIA, p. 959, Academic Press, New York.

Sandermann, W., and Dietrichs, H. H. (1957). *Holz. Roh. u. Werkstoff* **15**, 281.

Sandermann, W., and Simatupang, M. H. (1963). *Chem. Ber.* **96**, 2182.

Seshadri, T. R. (1957). *Curr. Sci.* **26**, 239.

Seshadri, T. R., and Thakur, R. S. (1960). *Curr. Sci.* **29**, 54.

Shibata, S. (1962). *In* "Recent Progress in the Chemistry of Natural and Synthetic Colouring Matters and Related Fields" (T. S. Gore, B. S. Joshi, S. V. Sunthankar and B. D. Tilak, eds.), p. 659, Academic Press, New York.

Shibata, S., and Ikekawa, T. (1963). *Chem. Pharm. Bull. Japan* **11**, 368.

Stout, G. H., Alden, R. A., Kraut, J., and High, D. F. (1962). *J. Amer. chem. Soc.* **84**, 2653.

Thomson, R. H. (1957). "Naturally Occurring Quinones," pp. 302, Butterworths, London.

Thomson, R. H. (1962). *In* "Comparative Biochemistry" (H. S. Mason and M. Florkin, eds.), vol. IIIA, Academic Press, New York.

Tomaselli, R. (1963). *Arch. Bot. Biogeog. Ital.* **39**, 4th Ser., vol. VIII, 1.

Van Rheede van Oudtshoorn, M. C. B. (1964). *Phytochem.* **3**, 383.

Yamazaki, M., Usui, T., and Shibata, S. (1963). *Chem. Pharm. Bull. Japan* **11**, 363.

Zavarin, E. (1958). *J. org. Chem.* **23**, 1198, 1264.

Chapter 12

MISCELLANEOUS PIGMENTS

R. H. Thomson

Department of Chemistry, University of Aberdeen, Scotland

I. Introduction

The major groups of plant pigments, discussed in the preceding chapters, by no means exhaust the range of chemical structures found in natural colouring matters. The aim of this chapter is to draw attention to the existence of a number of smaller groups. Most of these appear to be of little significance at present, and are of restricted distribution, but the number of plants so far examined is only a trifling percentage of the plant kingdom and the relative importance of minor groups, and exceptional pigments, may change as knowledge increases. Furthermore, it seems desirable that biochemists should be aware of the variety of plant pigmentation occurring outside the carotenoid-flavonoid-quinonoid-porphyrin domain.

It should be appreciated that the appearance of colour is often incidental, arising from a minor modification of a chromophore which normally absorbs only in the ultra-violet region. Aromatic ketones provide many examples: the parent compounds and their monohydroxy derivatives are colourless, but the introduction of additional hydroxyl groups shifts the long-wave absorption into the visible region. A variety

of simple phenolic ketones occur in plants, of which the fungal metabolite 2,6-dihydroxyacetophenone (I)* (*Daldinia concentrica*) and the
heartwood constituent musizin (II) (*Maesopsis eminii*) (Covell *et al.*,
1961) are yellow; more strikingly the trihydric phenol (III) (*Polyporus*

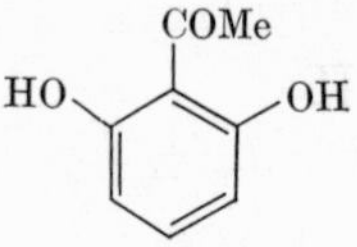

(I) 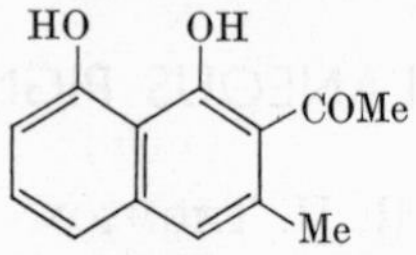   (II) Musizin 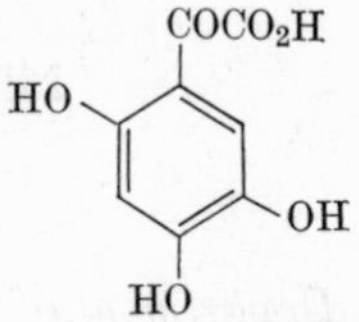   (III)

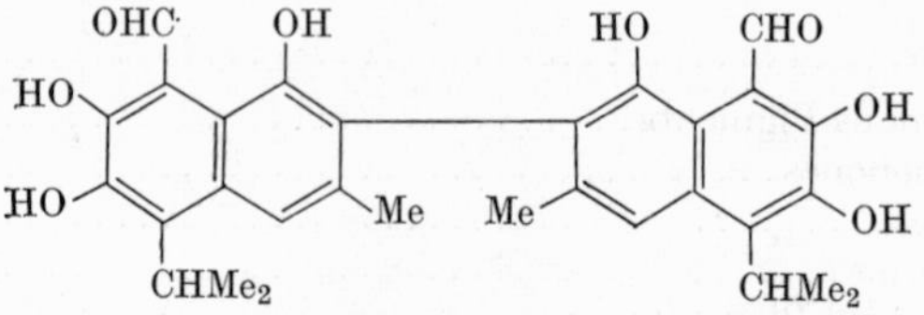

(IV) Gossypol

tumulosus) is bright red. A more complex example is gossypol (IV), the
yellow pigment from cottonseed (*Gossypium* spp.). The bathochromic
shift which results when a carbonyl group is conjugated with olefinic
double bonds contributes to the colour of the orange pigments curcumin (V), from the root of *Curcuma* spp., and sorbicillin (VI) (*Peni-*

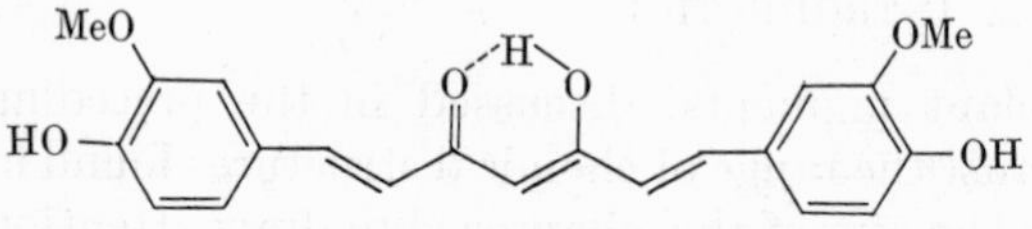

(V) Curcumin 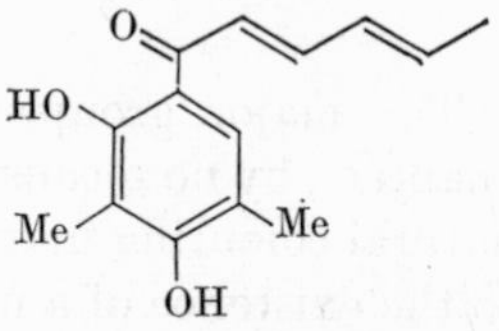   (VI) Sorbicillin

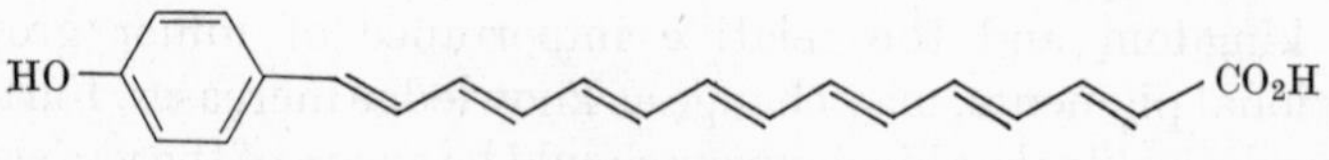

(VII) Cortisalin

cillium notatum). This type of unsaturated phenolic ketone is uncommon
whilst cortisalin (VII), the violet-red colouring matter found in the fruit
bodies of *Corticium salicinum*, is a unique phenolic polyene.

It should also be noted that compounds having little or no colour may
give rise to intense pigmentation if they occur *in vivo* in a modified form

* References to most of the pigments cited are given by Karrer (1958) and Miller (1961).
Individual references are given to more recent work.

as salts, quaternary bases or metal complexes (examples are the red
ferric complex pulcherrimin (VIII), isolated from cultures of *Candida
pulcherrima* (MacDonald, 1963) and the bright yellow isoquinoline
alkaloid berberine (IX) (*Berberis* spp.)), and furthermore, colourless

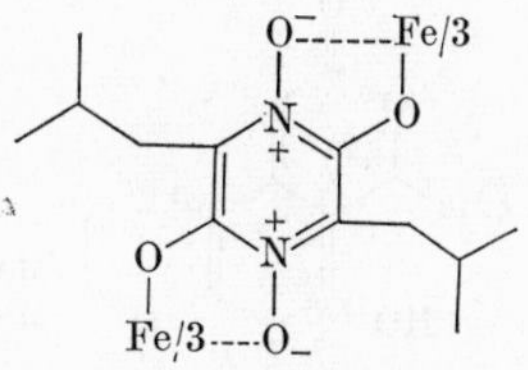

(VIII) Pulcherrimin 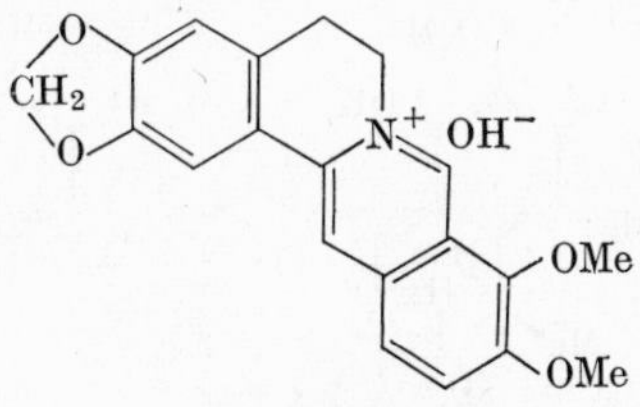   (IX) Berberine

compounds may yield coloured artefacts (notably azulenes) as a result of
natural oxidative processes.

It is convenient to divide these miscellaneous pigments into two
sections, nitrogenous and nitrogen-free. The latter are mainly of acetate
origin while the former are derived from amino-acids.

II. NON-NITROGENEOUS PIGMENTS

A. CYCLIC DIENONES

The dienone structure (X) which is present in the true quinones also
occurs in a number of miscellaneous, yellow to red, pigments, some of
which behave as methylene-quinones. Additional oxygen functions are
invariably attached to the dienone chromophore which may be part of a
more extensive system of conjugation.

In citrinin (XI) (Mehta and Whalley, 1963) and pulvilloric acid (XII)
(McOmie *et al.*, 1963), yellow pigments obtained from *Penicillium* spp.,
the conjugation terminates in a cyclic enol ether whereas in the orange

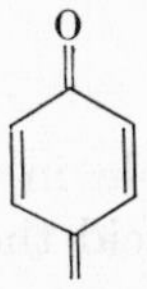

(X)

metabolite fuscin (XII) (*Oidiodendron fuscum*) it is linked to a lactone
grouping. Tracer studies (Birch *et al.*, 1958; Schwenk *et al.*, 1958) have
established that the carbon skeleton (and the methyl group at (a) of
citrinin) is constructed from five acetate units, the remaining carbon
atoms being derived from the C_1 pool. Fuscin also contains a penta-
acetate skeleton the pyran ring being formed from an isopentenyl group

introduced by mevalonate (A. J. Birch, P. Fitton and H. Smith, 1963, unpublished). Although fuscin has an asymmetric carbon atom it is not optically active; this may be a consequence of its tautomeric structure or alternatively, racemization may occur in the reduced form (the leuco

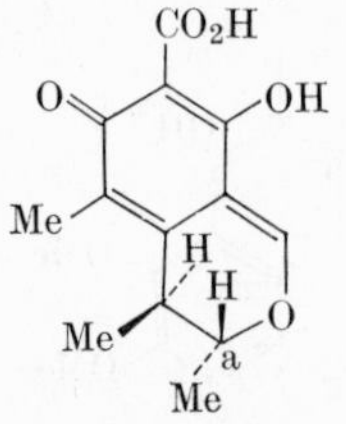

(XI) Citrinin 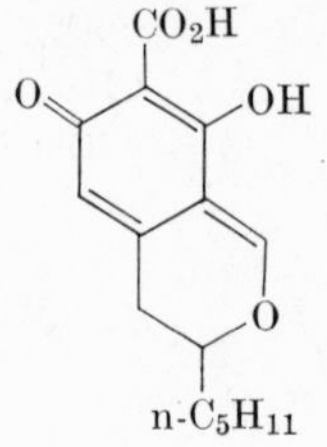   (XII) Pulvilloric acid 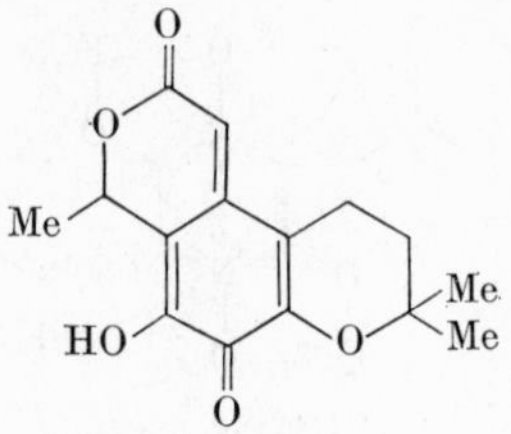   (XIII) Fuscin

compound is also present in cultures of *O. fuscum*) which contains a benzylic proton.

Mention must be made of a small group of red pigments having a cyclic dienone structure which strictly belongs to the flavonoid series. These are the anhydro-bases, typified by carajurin (XIV) from the leaves of

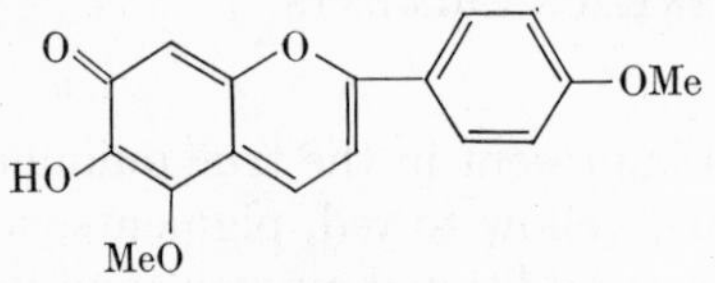

(XIV) Carajurin

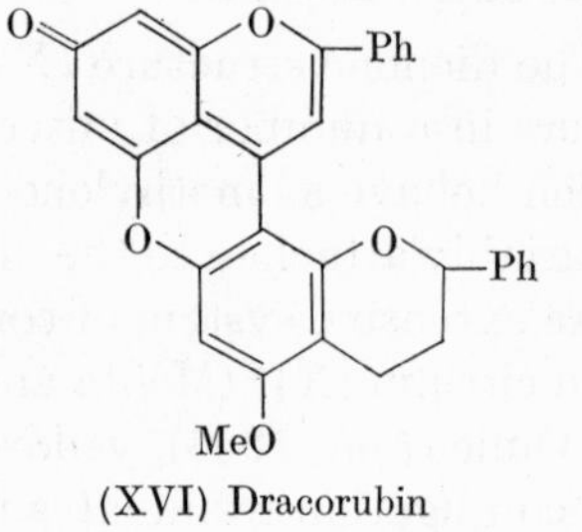

(XV)

(XVI) Dracorubin

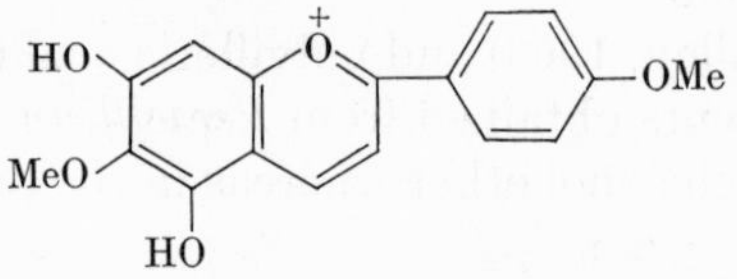

Bignonia chica, which are stable in the absence of substituents at position 3. On treatment with acid they are converted into flavylium salts (XV). Since anthocyanins are normally isolated from plant material by acid extraction it is conceivable that some may exist *in vivo* in the quinonoid anhydro-base form, possibly stabilized by chelation, or in other ways. Dracorubin (XVI), one of the pigments in "dragon's blood", a resin exuded by *Dracaeno draco* and other palm trees, is a more complex anhydro-base, and several others of incompletely defined structure are present in the "insoluble red" woods, sandalwood, barwood and camwood. It is of interest that brazilein (XVII), isolated from the "soluble red" woods of the *Caesalpinia* genus, has a similar quinonoid structure. However, it is an artefact formed by oxidation of a colourless precursor, brazilin.

Two other cyclic dienones, both solitary representatives of their particular type, illustrate the variety of structural environment in which this chromophore is found.* Pristimerin (XVIII) and its parent

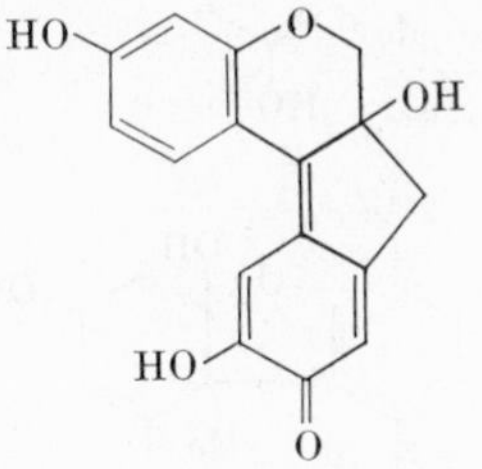

(XVII) Brazilein

acid, celastrol are orange-red triterpenes found in the root bark of *Pristimera* spp. and other Celastraceous plants (Johnson *et al.*, 1963), whilst usnic acid (XIX) is a yellow colouring matter widely distributed in lichens. The usnic acid molecule can be dissected into two C-methyl-phloracetophenone units and there is little doubt that these are linked by oxidative coupling *in vivo*. Tracer studies have not been attempted but an elegant laboratory synthesis of the racemic product, which almost

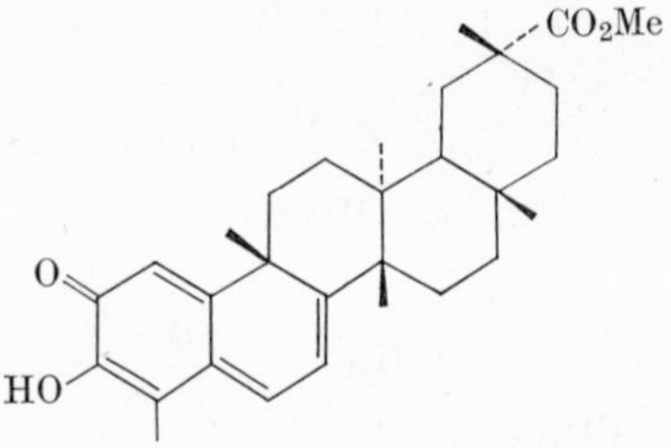

(XVIII) Pristimerin

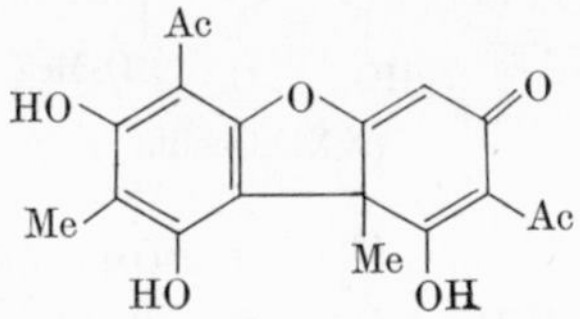

(XIX) Usnic acid

certainly follows the natural pathway, was effected by Barton and his colleagues (1956) by ferricyanide oxidation of C-methylphloraceto-phenone, and subsequent dehydration. The other dibenzofuran deriva-tives found in lichens are doubtless formed in the same way (Barton and Cohen, 1957) but the intermediate stages corresponding to (XX) undergo aromatization as they lack the blocking methyl group. The loss of the dienone structure results in colourless products, again illustrating the effect of minor structural changes on colour. In usnic acid the dienone chromophore is not conjugated with the benzenoid portion of the

* See also harunganin, p. 314.

molecule; a similar situation is found in the spirodienones, a few of which are known as fungal products. One or two of these show end absorption in the visible region and are yellow, e.g. geodin (XXI) and geodoxin

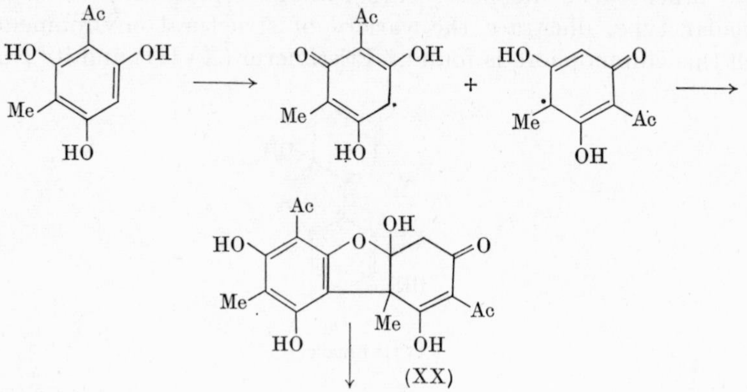

(XIX)

(XX)

(XXII), both metabolites of *Aspergillus terreus*, but on the other hand dehydrogriseofulvin (XXIII) (*Penicillium patulum*) and picrolichenic acid (XXIV) (from the lichen *Pertusaria amara*) have no colour. This is

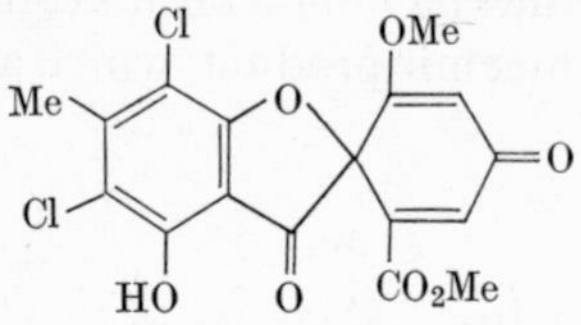

(XXI) Geodin

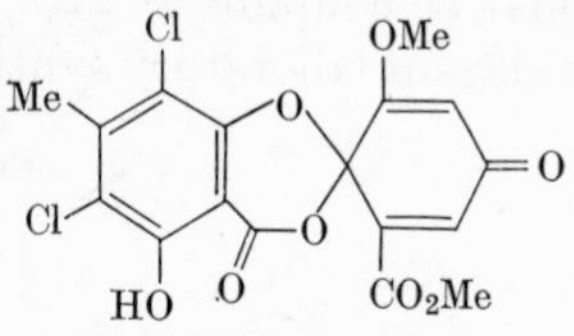

(XXII) Geodoxin

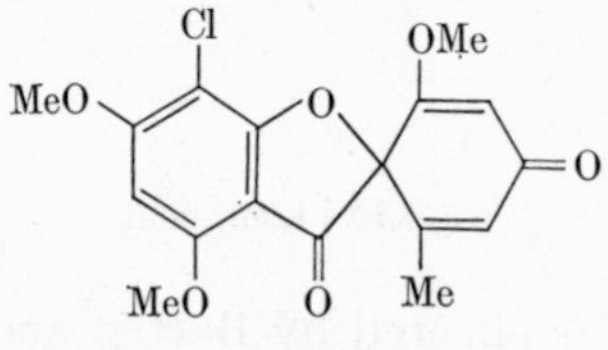

(XXIII) Dehydrogriseofulvin

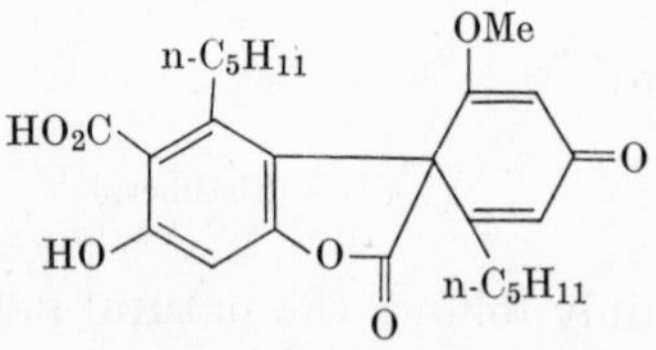

(XXIV) Picrolichenic acid

therefore a borderline group of pigments, of little consequence from the present viewpoint. Their biogenesis has been reviewed (Hassall and Scott, 1961).

Finally in this section, a very small group of colouring matters which are polyhydroxy derivatives of perinaphthenone, should be noted. One of these, haemocorin, occurs as a glycoside in the bulbous roots of *Haemodorum corymbosum* and yields, on hydrolysis, the purple-red aglycone (XXV). The others are *Penicillium* metabolites, several strains of *P. herquei* producing the brownish-yellow atrovenetin (XXVII) and the red pigments norherqueinone (XXVIII) and herqueinone (mono-methyl ether of XXVIII) (Narasimhachari and Vining, 1963; Paul *et al.*, 1963). The proposal of Barton and co-workers (1959) that the perinaphthenone system is evolved from a C_{14}-polyketide, as indicated (XXIX) (cf. anthraquinone biogenesis), has been supported by tracer studies on

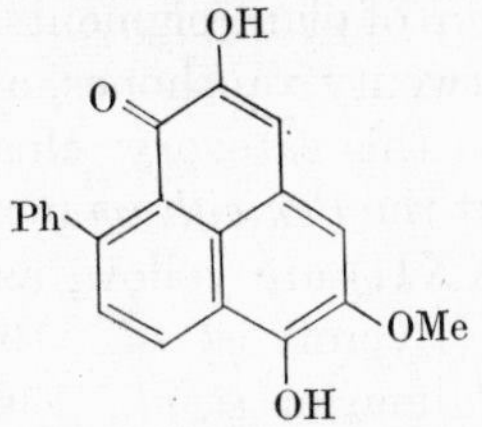

(XXV) Haemocorin aglycone

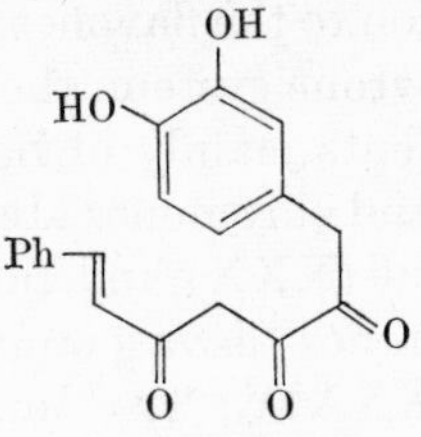

(XXVI)

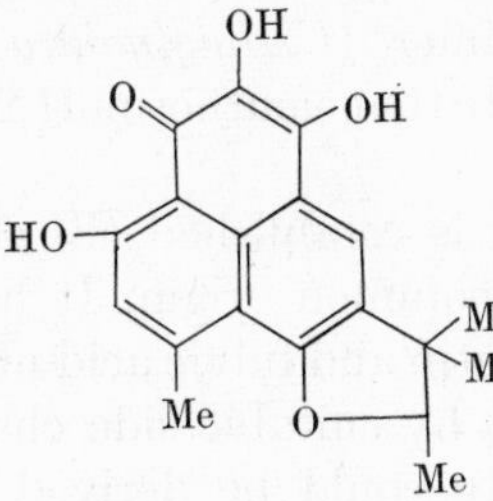

(XXVII) Atrovenetin

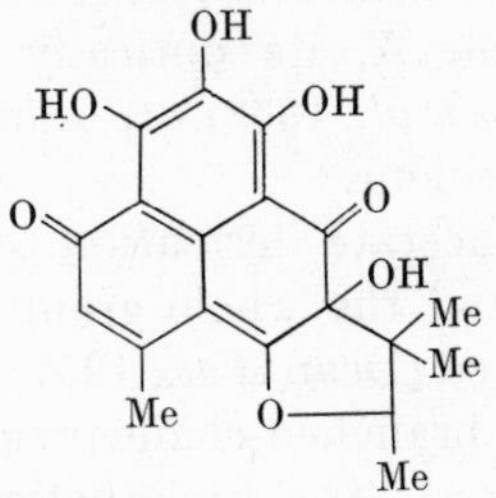

(XXVIII) Norherqueinone

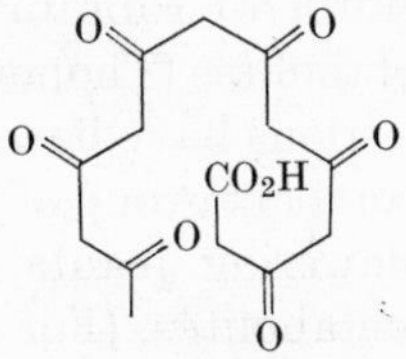

(XXIX)

norherqueinone (Thomas, 1961a) which also established that the di-hydrofuran ring is derived from mevalonate. The isoprenoid residue is unusual in that it is attached to the aromatic ring at the tertiary carbon atom. Presumably all the fungal perinaphthenones arise in the same way but some other mode of formation seems likely for haemocorin which has a different oxygenation pattern and a phenyl group directly attached to the perinaphthene skeleton. Thomas (1961a) suggests that haemocorin may be formed by cyclization of an intermediate (XXVI) derived from one acetate unit and two C_6–C_3 units originating from shikimic acid; two compounds of the type (XXVI) occur in *Curcuma longa* (e.g. V).

Both *P. atrovenetum* and *P. herquei* form characteristic blue-green nitrogenous pigments and Narasimhachari and Vining (1963) have suggested that these are formed by condensation of an amino-acid with a perinaphthane-1,2,3-trione, formed by oxidation, in the manner of ninhydrin.

B. γ-PYRONES

In addition to the flavones, the main group of plant pigments containing the γ-pyrone system, there are about twenty xanthones, and a few other pigments mainly of fungal origin, in this category. Most simple γ-pyrones and chromones are colourless but the *Penicillium* metabolites citromycetin (XXX) and fulvic acid (XXXII) are yellow, as are the naphthapyrones flavasperone (XXXV) (Bycroft *et al.*, 1962) and fonsecin (XXXIV; R = Me, R′ = H) (Galmarini *et al.*, 1962) from *Aspergillus* spp. Rubrofusarin (XXXIV; R = H, R′ = Me) (*Fusarium* spp.), nor-rubrofusarin (XXXIV; R = R′ = H) (*Cassia tora*) and ustilaginoidin A, its optically active 9,9′-dimer (*Ustilaginoidea virens*) (Shibata *et al.*, 1963), are orange-red, but note that eleutherinol (XXXVI) has no colour.

The acetate derivation of citromycetin is established (Birch *et al.*, 1958) and the whole group may have a common origin. It has been suggested (Dean *et al.*, 1957) that citromycetin and fulvic acid may arise from a branched-chain precursor (XXXI) by suitable side chain condensations. The hypothetical intermediate could be derived from a polyketo-acid (XXXIII) (Whalley, 1961) related to orsellinic acid, which itself is a possible progenitor of rubrofusarin, fonsecin, flavasperone, and a number of other metabolites (Thomas, 1961b). This is speculation, of course, and other suggestions have been made (see Money, 1963).

The xanthones form a compact group of yellow pigments which have a limited distribution in flowering plants (Bate-Smith and Harborne, 1963); a few are fungal metabolites. (For a review, see Roberts, 1961.) They all possess a hydroxyl group at C-1 and the majority have a phloroglucinol nucleus. Structural variation lies mainly in the hydroxylation pattern of the other benzene ring and the location of methyl and prenyl side chains. Representative examples are decussatin (XXXVII) (*Swertia decussata*), lichexanthone (XXXVIII) (*Parmelia formosana*), the only member of the group found in lichens, and mangostin (XXXIX) (*Garcinia mangostana*).

Inspection of formulae suggests that xanthones are biosynthesized from acetate as indicated by the β-polyketide (XL). No direct evidence is available but this view is supported by studies on the biogenesis of griseofulvin (McMaster *et al.*, 1960; Rhodes *et al.*, 1961) in cultures of *P. patulum*; these produce, *inter alia*, griseoxanthone C (XLII) which is

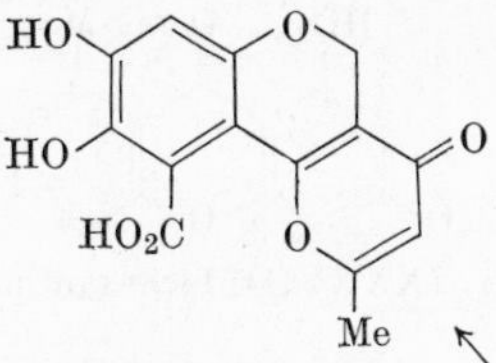

(XXX) Citromycetin

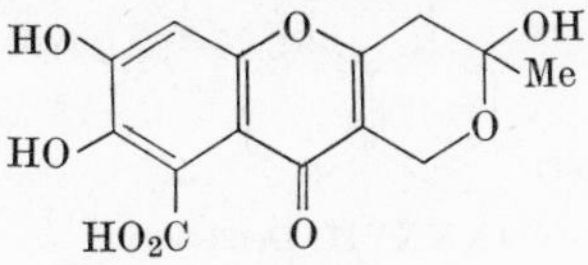

(XXXII) Fulvic acid

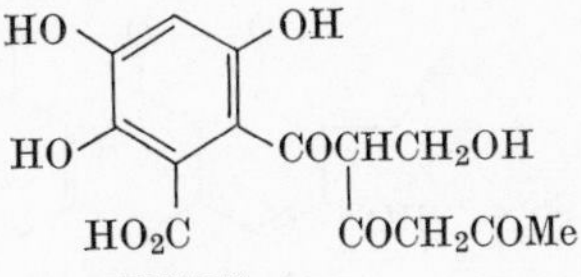

(XXXI)

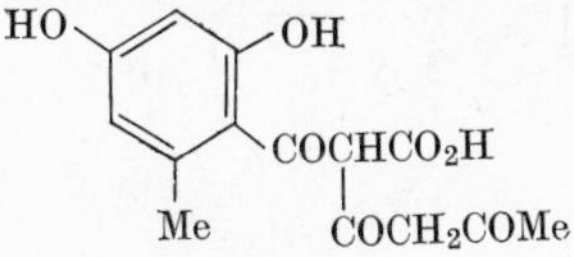

(XXXIII)

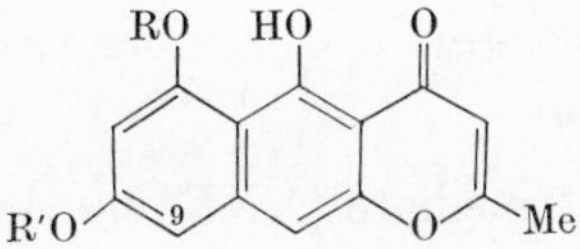

(XXXIV) Fonsecin (R = Me, R' = H)
Rubrofusarin (R = H, R' = Me)

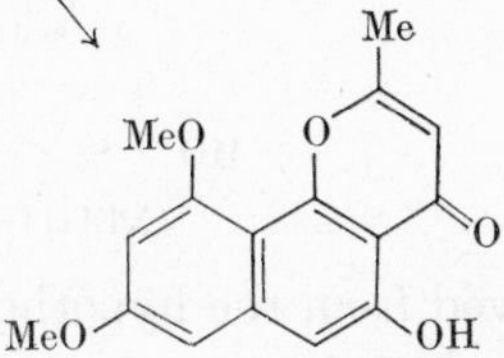

(XXXV) Flavasperone

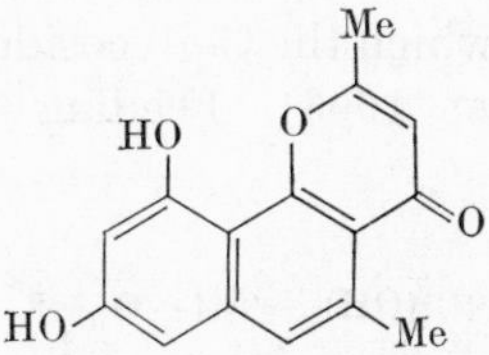

(XXXVI) Eleutherinol

intimately connected with a series of metabolites, some of proven acetate derivation. It was found that if chlorination (a stage in the formation of griseofulvin) was inhibited, the benzophenone (XLI) accumulated, and later griseoxanthone C (XLII) appeared. This implies that the xanthone arises from (XLI) a transformation easily effected in the laboratory. Thomas (1961b) has pointed out that the benzophenone (XLI) may also

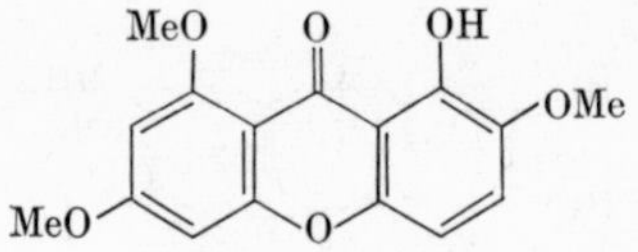

(XXXVII) Decussatin

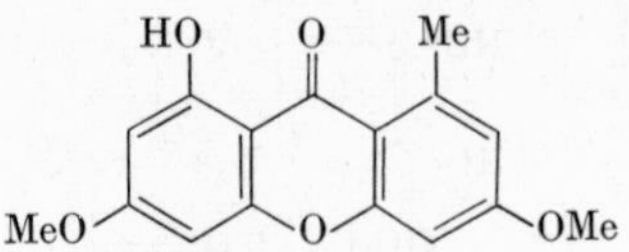

(XXXVIII) Lichexanthone

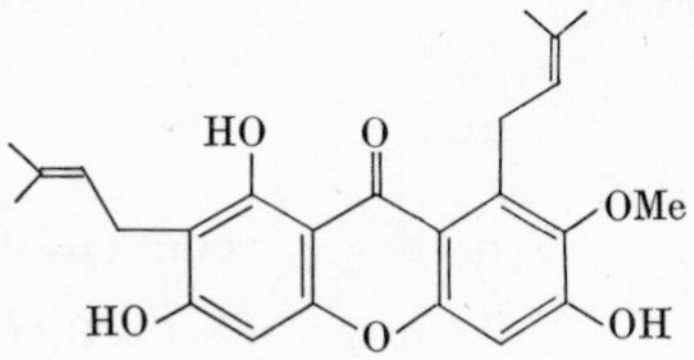

(XXXIX) Mangostin

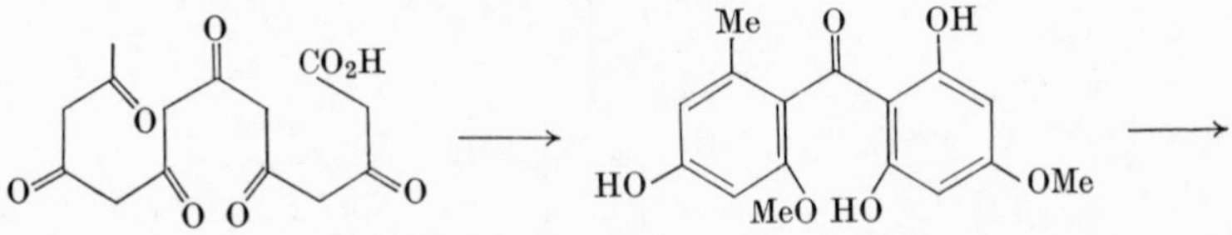

(XL) → (XLI) →

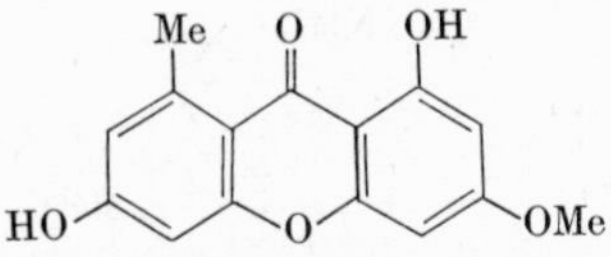

(XLII) Griseoxanthone

be derived from the hypothetical intermediate (XXX) by the appropriate condensations.

The pigment euxanthic acid (XLIII), a glucuronide of euxanthone, is found in the urine of cows fed on mango leaves (*Mangifera indica*); these contain mangiferin for which the C-glycoside structure (XLIV) has been suggested (cf. Haynes, 1963). Feeding experiments with rabbits

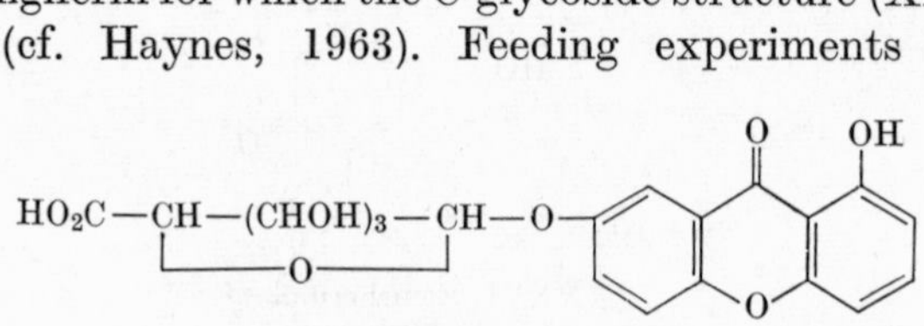

(XLIII) Euxanthic acid

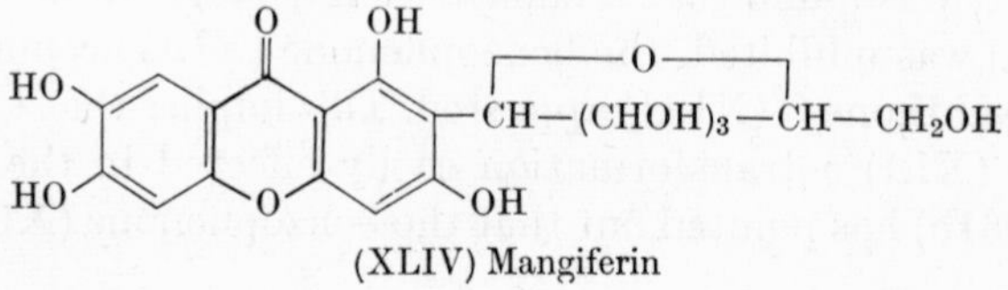

(XLIV) Mangiferin

(Wiechowski, 1923) have shown that mangiferin is converted into euxanthic acid in the animal body, a rare example of the biochemical reduction of a phenolic group.

C. SCLEROTIORINS*

This is a small group of yellow to red mould pigments (XLV to XLIX) elaborated by a limited number of *Monascus* and *Penicillium* spp. They are rather unusual in structure and may be regarded as extended pyrones,

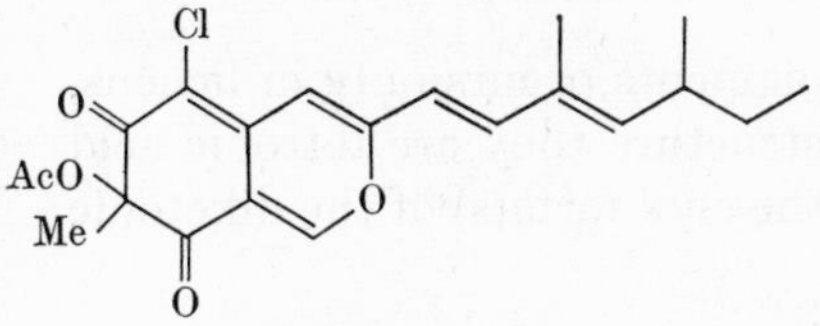

(XLV) Sclerotiorin

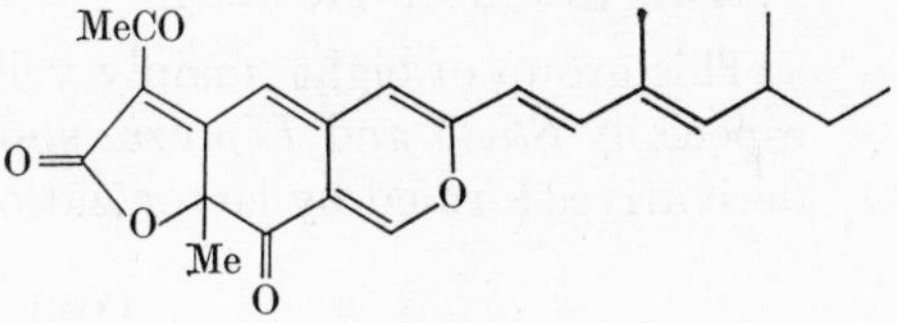

(XLVI) Rotiorin

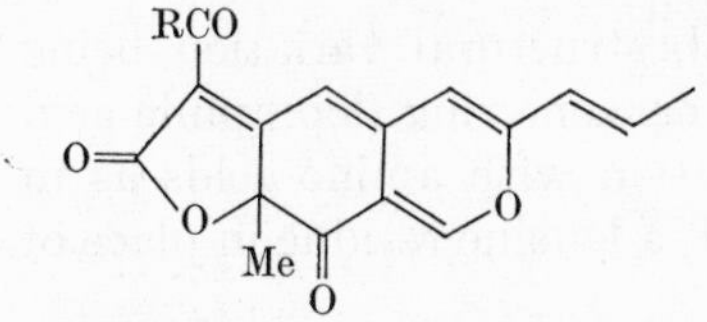

(XLVII) Rubropunctatin (R = n-C₅H₁₁)
(XLVIII) Monascorubin (R = n-C₇H₁₅)

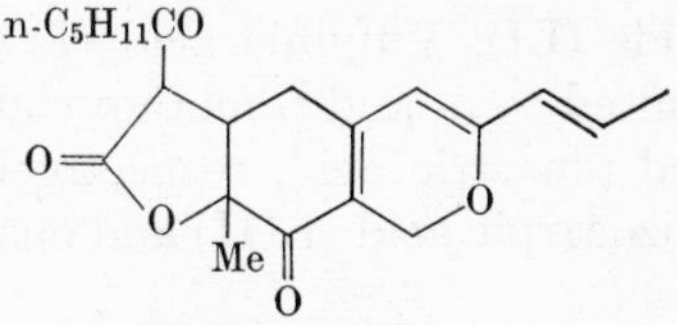

(XLIX) Monascin (Monascoflavin)

having certain features in common with some of the compounds already mentioned, notably citrinin (XI). (For a review see Whalley, 1963.)

Tracer studies with labelled acetate and formate (Birch *et al.*, 1958, 1962; Kurono *et al.*, 1963) lead to the conclusion that these pigments are

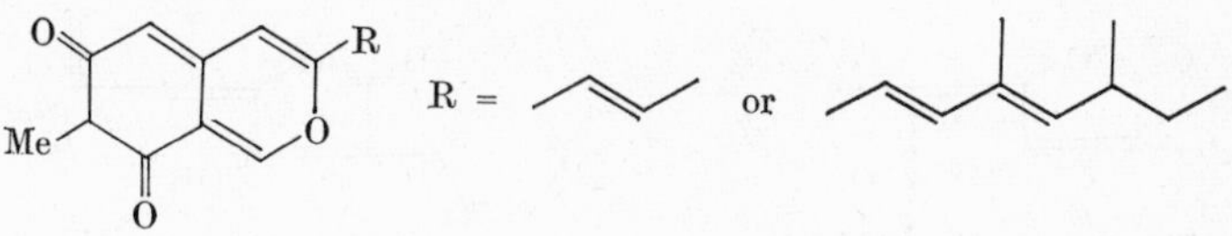

(L)

biosynthesized from two β-polyketide chains, the main chain forming an intermediate of type (L) from six (XLVII to XLIX) or eight (XLV and XLVI) C_2-units, the C-methyl group being introduced from the C_1 pool. Sclerotiorin is then formed by subsequent chlorination and oxidation, and introduction of the second "chain" (one acetate unit)

---

* These pigments were previously known as azaphilones, so-called on account of the ease with which most of them react with ammonia and amines to form nitrogenous compounds in which the cyclic oxygen is replaced by the group >NR (Powell *et al.*, 1956).

as an acetoxyl group. In rotiorin the second chain is an acetoacetate unit, the β-oxolactone system arising by aldol condensation and dehydration; the other pigments are similar except that the second chain is of greater length. Recent experiments (Whalley, 1963) on the biosynthesis of sclerotiorin and rotiorin using labelled malonate and butyrate have demonstrated that the main chain is formed by the acetate-malonate pathway and the β-oxolactone system is derived directly from two acetate units.

D. VULPINIC ACID PIGMENTS

This group of eight, mainly yellow, pigments occurs only in lichens, especially *Sticta* and *Lepraria* spp. In structure they are tetronic acid derivatives formed by lactonization of the enol form(s) of the diketonic

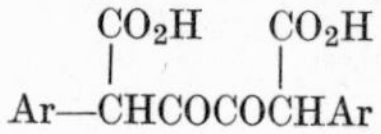

$$\begin{array}{cc} CO_2H & CO_2H \\ | & | \\ Ar\text{---}CHCOCOCHAr \end{array} \quad (LI)$$

acids (LI). Vulpinic acid (LII) is typical, structural variation being limited to *o*- and *p*-methoxylation of the benzene ring (leprapinic acid and pinastric acid, respectively), conjugation with amino-acids as in rhizocarpic acid (LIII) and epanorin (LIII, a leucine residue in place of

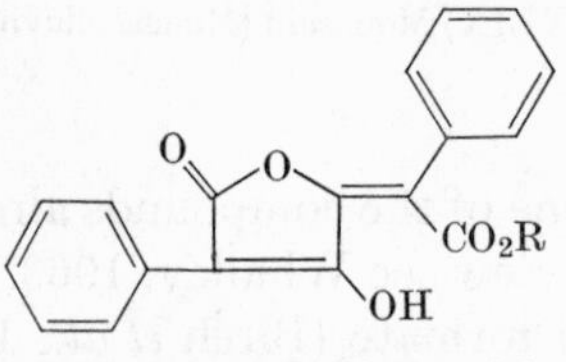

(LII) Vulpinic acid (R = Me)
Pulvic acid (R = H)

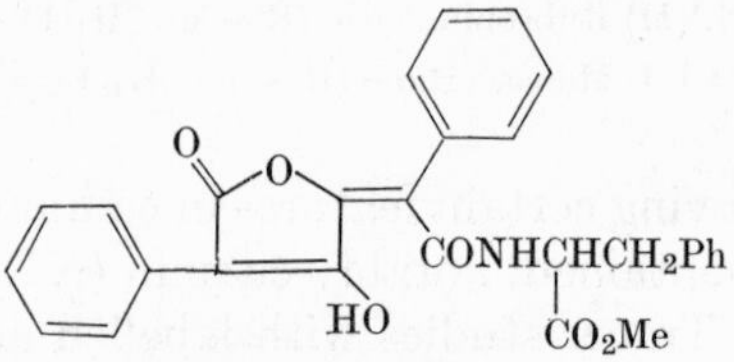

(LIII) Rhizocarpic acid

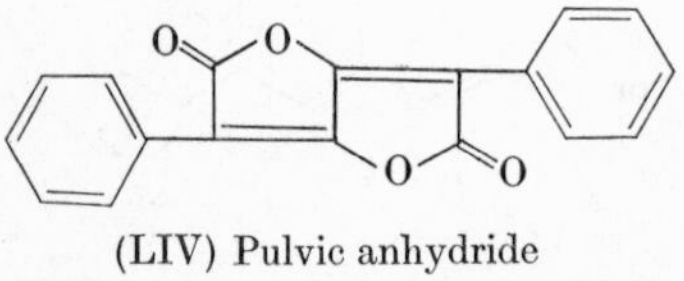

(LIV) Pulvic anhydride

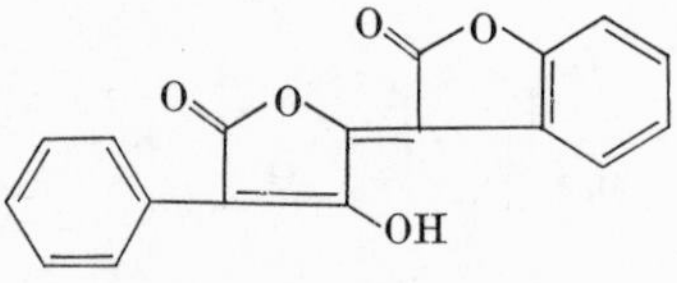

(LV) Calycin

phenylalanine), and the formation of dilactones. The ring system in pulvic anhydride (pulvinic dilactone) (LIV) is highly strained and yields vulpinic acid merely on boiling in methanol, whereas calycin (LV) is stable under these conditions (Åkermark, 1961).

The vulpinic acid pigments are chemically related to the terphenyl-quinones (p. 321). This was first demonstrated by Kögl *et al.* (1928) who oxidized atromentin to atromentic acid (4,4′-dihydroxypulvic acid) with hydrogen peroxide. Under the same conditions polyporic acid

(LVI) gives only a little pulvic anhydride, presumably by cyclization of the intermediate acid (LVII), better yields being obtained with lead tetra-acetate (Frank *et al.*, 1950). Polyporic acid is found in the lichens *Sticta coronata* and *S. colensoi*, together with pulvic anhydride and calycin. The biochemical significance of this is uncertain but it does suggest that the vulpinic acid pigments and the terphenylquinones have

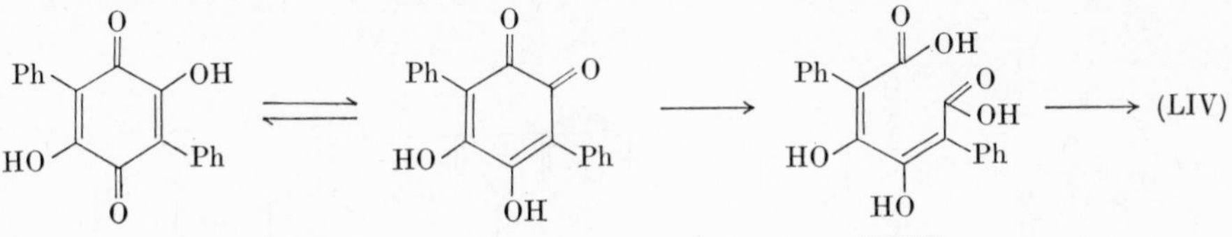

(LVI)   (LVII)

a common origin, and the latter, as we have seen (p. 323) appear to be derived from shikimic acid. In this connection the phenylalanine residue in rhizocarpic acid (LIII) is noteworthy.

III. NITROGENOUS PIGMENTS

The most important nitrogen-containing plant pigments have already been considered in earlier chapters but there are, in addition, a number of smaller groups, and a few scattered pigments which are not easily classified. Riboflavin, folic acid, and their relations occur widely but as these are adequately described elsewhere they need not be discussed here. The well known insect pigments, xanthopterin and erythropterin, have been found in bacterial cultures but scarcely warrant consideration as plant pigments.

Several Streptomycetes elaborate yellow pyrrolic compounds of

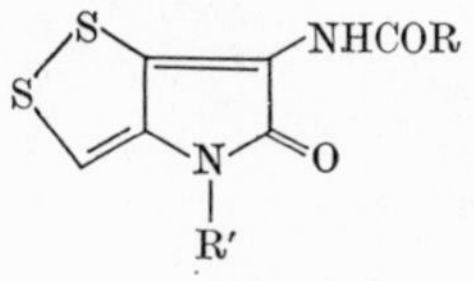

(LVIII) 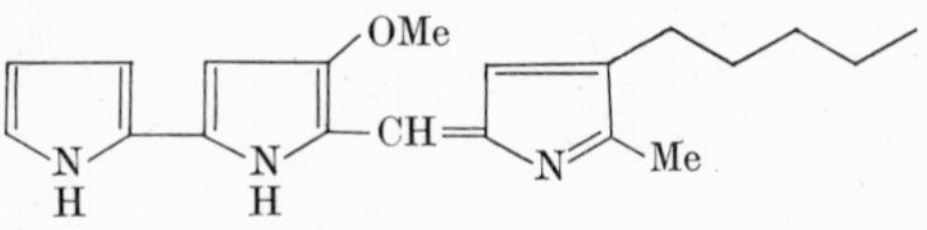   (LIX) Prodigiosin

Holomycin (R = Me; R′ = H)
Thiolutin (R = R′ = Me)
Aureothricin (R = Et, R′ = Me)
Isobutyropyrrothin (R = *i*-Pr, R′ = Me)

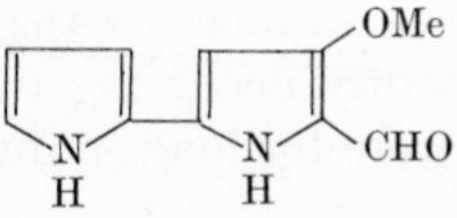

(LX)

unusual structure (LVIII) for which a glycine-cysteine derivation has been postulated (Miller, 1961). Prodigiosin (LIX), a red bacterial pigment (*Serratia marcescens*), is reminiscent of the bile pigments but two of the pyrrole rings are directly linked together as in the corrin nucleus. This link is evidently formed before the third pyrrole ring is attached since (LX), obtained from a mutant strain of *S. marcescens*, is an established precursor (Santer and Vogel, 1956; Rapoport and Holden, 1962).

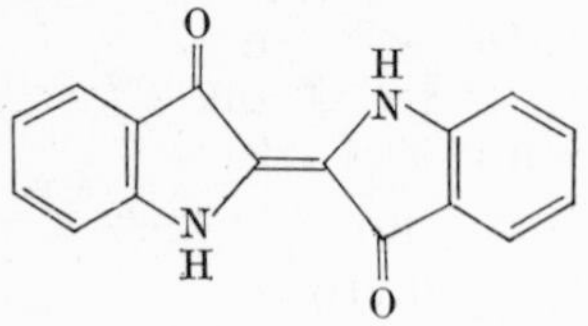

(LXI) Indigotin 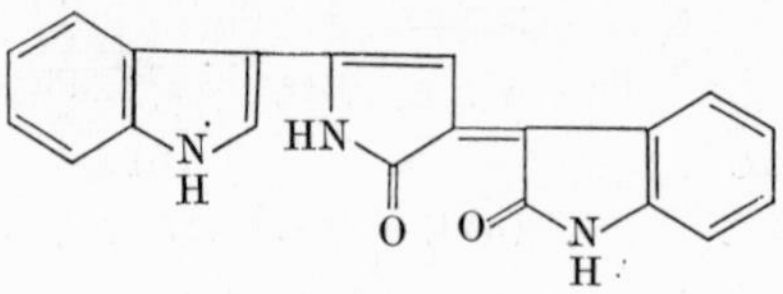   (LXII) Violacein

The formation of indigotin (LXI) in cultures of *Schizophyllum commune* is of interest (Miles *et al.*, 1956) as the indigo obtained from higher plants (*Indigofera* and other spp.) is an artefact formed by oxidative hydrolysis of indican. Another indole derivative is the violet-black pigment violacein (LXII) found in cultures of *Chromobacterium violaceum*. By using labelled intermediates DeMoss and Evans (1960) have shown that L-tryptophan can serve as the sole precursor, the central ring evidently arising from the side chains of two tryptophan molecules.

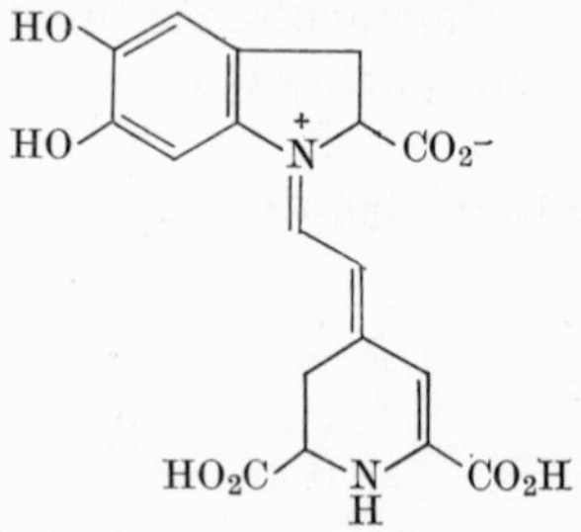

(LXIII) Betanidin

Finally, in this short survey of miscellaneous nitrogenous pigments attention must be drawn to two conspicuous groups of colouring matters which are incompletely characterized. These are the red-violet betacyanins* found in beetroot, bougainvillea leaf, and elsewhere, and the yellow betaxanthins present in most cactus flowers, about which little is known. The two frequently occur together producing intermediate shades. The betacyanins were for long confused with the anthocyanins,

* See also p. 232.

although it is now known that these two types are never found in the same plant, a fact of taxonomic importance. Dreiding (1961) and Mabry *et al.*, (1963) list over a hundred and fifty plants belonging to ten families of the order *Centrospermae* which contain betacyanins.

The most closely studied pigment is betanin which has been isolated in crystalline form from beetroot (*Beta vulgaris*) and from the pokeberry (*Phytolacca americana*). On hydrolysis it yields glucose and the aglycone betanidin (LXIII) (Wyler *et al.*, 1963) which partly isomerizes to iso-betanidin in the presence of acid, or of base in the absence of oxygen. Several other betacyanins (amarantin, phytolaccin, bougainvillein) appear to be glycosides of betanidin whilst *Lampranthus roseus* is pigmented by the aglycone itself. (For a general survey see Dreiding, 1961.) Nothing is known yet of the origin of these colouring matters.

A. PHENAZINES

About a dozen phenazine pigments have been isolated from bacteria, principally *Pseudomonas* and *Streptomyces* spp. Pyocyanine (LXIV), the blue colouring matter of pus, is the best known although the majority

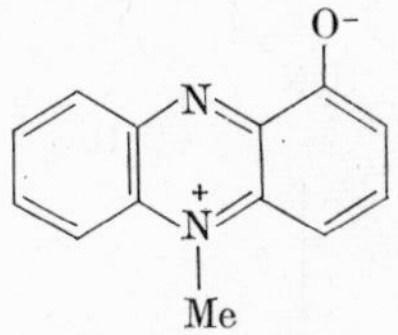

(LXIV) Pyocyanine

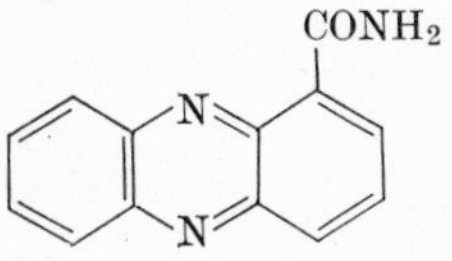

(LXV) Oxychlororaphine

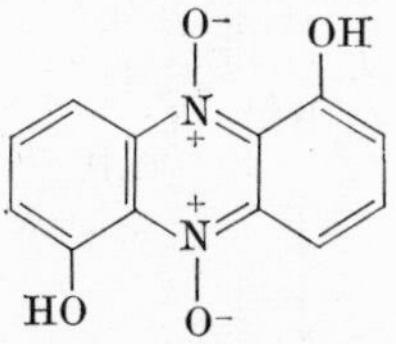

(LXVI) Iodinin

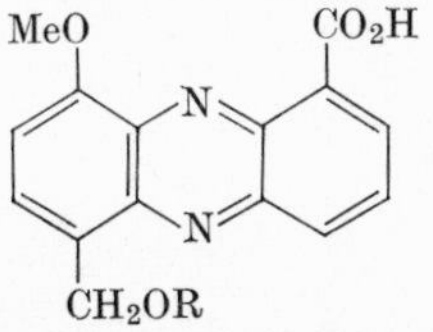

(LXVII) Griseolutein A (R = CO—CH$_2$OH)
Griseolutein B (R = CH—CH$_2$OH)
|
OH
Griseolutic acid (R = H)

are yellow. Chlororaphine, however, is a green molecular compound of phenazine-1-carboxamide (LXV) and its dihydro derivative in the ratio 3:1, and iodinin (LXVI) (*Chromobacterium iodinum*) is purple. The group includes quite simple derivatives such as phenazin-1-ol and phenazine-1-carboxylic acid, and an oxygen function or C$_1$ side chain at positions 1 and/or 6 is a common feature.

Little is known of the biogenesis of these pigments (Frank and DeMoss, 1959): *Ps. aeruginosa* produces phenazine-1-carboxylic acid and its amide, together with anthranilic acid (Takeda and Nakanishi, 1959), and the latter, isotopically labelled, has been incorporated (in trace amounts) into chlororaphine in cultures of *Ps. chlororaphis* (Carter and Richards, 1961). This has led to the suggestion that these pigments may be formed by the oxidative dimerization of appropriate amines and a

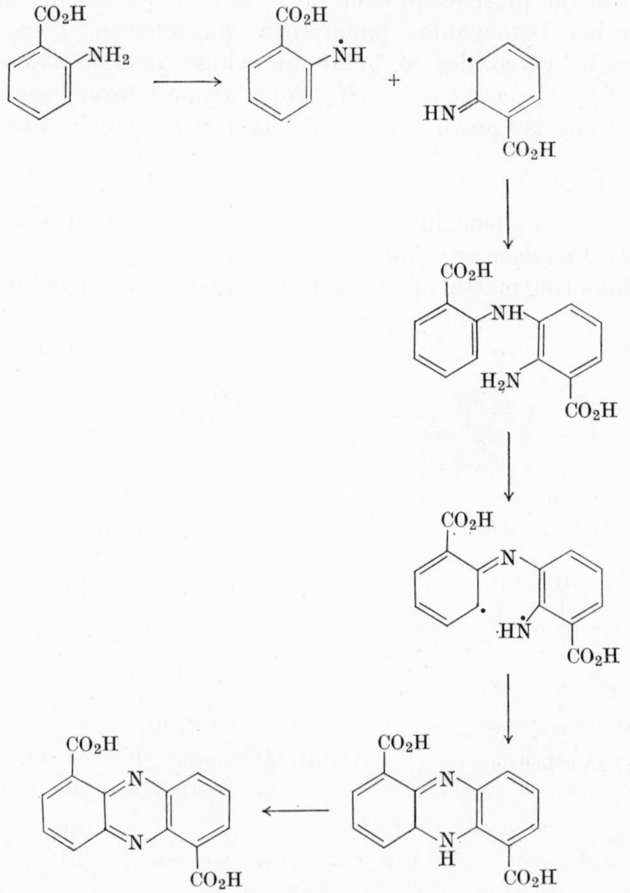

(LXVIII)

laboratory analogy has been provided by Morgan and Aubert (1962). Oxidation of anthranilic acid with manganese dioxide in benzene or chloroform gave phenazine-1,6-dicarboxylic acid (LXVIII) in 16% yield.

B. PHENOXAZONES

The phenoxazone chromophore is present in the actinomycins (LXX) (Brockmann, 1960), a group of bright red antibiotic chromopeptides produced by some twenty strains of *Streptomyces*, in the red cinnabarin

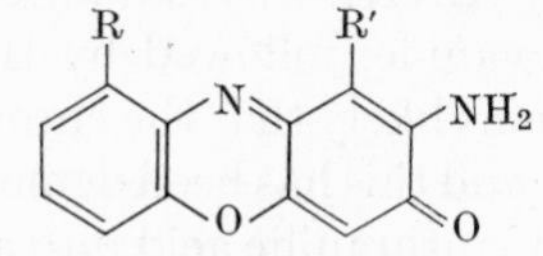

(LXIX)

Cinnabarin (R = CH₂OH, R' = CO₂H)
Cinnabarinic acid (R = R' = CO₂H)
Tramesanguin (R = CO₂H, R' = CHO)

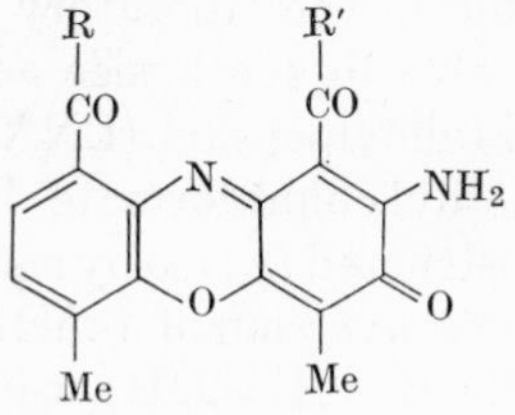

(LXX) Actinomycins

pigments (LXIX) isolated from the wood-rotting fungus *Coriolus sanguineus* (Cavill *et al.*, 1953; Gripenberg, 1963) and in the ommo-chromes which are confined to the animal kingdom (Butenandt and Schäfer, 1962). It is of interest that litmus and the orcein pigments

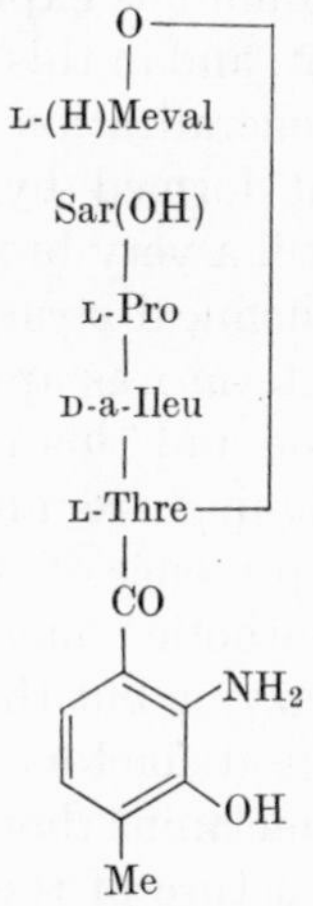

(LXXI) 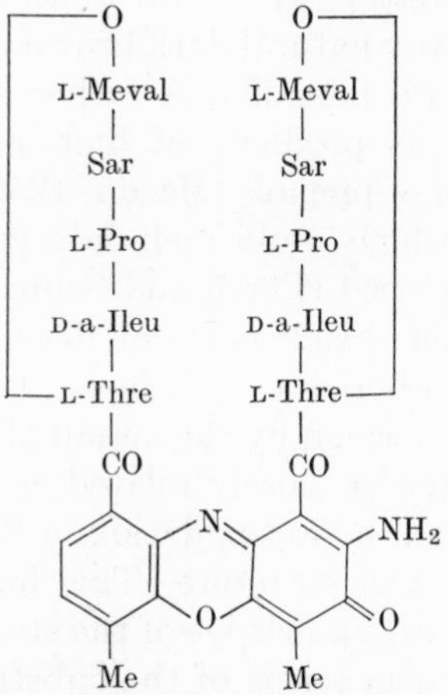   (LXXII) Actinomycin C₃

obtained from certain lichens by aerial oxidation in the presence of ammonia, also contain the phenoxazone nucleus (Musso, 1960).

There appear to be five principal actinomycins and numerous minor ones, all having a common chromophoric moiety actinocin (LXX; R = R' = OH). Thus the pigments differ only in the nature of the peptide chains (R and R' in LXX) each of which consists of five amino-acid residues (LXXII), and it is possible to modify these chains by addition of appropriate amino-acids to the culture medium.

It is well established that the insect pigments (ommochromes) are biosynthesized by oxidative condensation of 3-hydroxykynurenine, itself a product of tryptophan metabolism. Similar oxidations can be effected in the laboratory and indeed Brockmann and Lackner (1960) were able to synthesize actinomycin C_3 (LXXII) by oxidation of the anthraniloylpeptide (LXXI) with ferricyanide, followed by treatment with ethyl chloroformate. It therefore seems likely that the chromophore is constructed *in vivo* by a similar process and this has been demonstrated by the conversion of 4-methyl-3-hydroxy-anthranilic acid into actinocin (LXX; R = R' = OH) using a cell-free enzyme system obtained from *S. antibioticus*. Recent tracer experiments (Sivak *et al.*, 1962) show that labelled tryptophan is incorporated into the actinomycin chromophore, presumably via 3-hydroxyanthranilic acid. It was also shown that the methyl groups are derived from methionine although the stage at which methylation takes place during the biogenesis of the chromophore is not yet known.

C. MELANINS

The term melanin is often used loosely as an omnibus expression to describe any natural dark brown or black pigment, and in this sense has no chemical meaning. A rather less sweeping generalization describes melanins as products of high molecular weight formed by enzymic oxidation of phenols (Mason, 1959), but this is still a very broad classification which could include a great range of chemical structures. As originally used (Fürth and Schneider, 1902) the term was applied to a nitrogenous black pigment derived from tyrosine and this restriction will be adhered to (Thomas, 1955). Thus melanins are nitrogenous polymers formed by the action of oxygen, in the presence of tyrosinase, on tyrosine or closely related compounds. ("Synthetic" melanins can be obtained by autoxidation in the absence of enzyme but they do not have the same structure.) This definition is still unsatisfactory but as we have no real knowledge of the structure of plant melanins they can only be defined in terms of the substrate. As the structure of the polymer varies with the structure of the substrate it is customary, and indeed desirable, to speak of tyrosine-melanin, dopa-melanin etc., and the expressions catechol-melanin, dihydroxynaphthalene-melanin are useful in that it is clear that these are essentially nitrogen-free pigments.

As melanic pigmentation in animals, especially chordates, is of considerable importance, the subject has been extensively studied whereas the plant melanins which have less obvious functions have received little attention, and no work has been reported on their structure. The early stages in the biogenesis of tyrosine-melanin, which lead through a series of intermediates to 5,6-dihydroxyindole, are well known (Raper, 1927; Nicolaus, 1962), and it is generally accepted that the final stages involve the oxidative polymerization of indole-5,6-quinone (LXXIII). The details are still uncertain but from experimental work with model

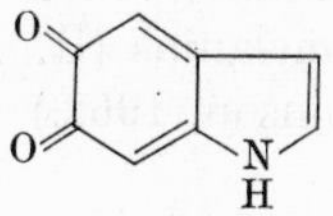

(LXXIII)

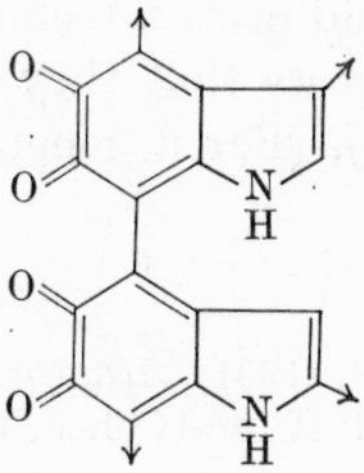

(LXXIV)

compounds, and degradative studies on animal melanins, it is clear that the latter are highly irregular polymers in which the indole units are probably linked mainly at positions 4 and 7 (as in the simplified structure LXXIV), but positions 2 and 3 are also involved; there appear to be pyrrole units in the chain arising from oxidative degradation (Piattelli *et al.*, 1963a), and the main chains are cross-linked. Native melanins are conjugated with protein.

The evidence that plant melanins have a similar structure is all presumptive, and is based chiefly on the co-existence of a tyrosine-tyrosinase or related system. It should be noted that black pigmentation may arise during normal development or it may only appear following injury, death or decay. Amongst higher plants it seems likely that the black pigments in *Vicia faba, Cytisus nigricans* and *Sarothamnus scoparius*, are melanins, the precursor being tyrosine or dopa, and Griffiths (1959) has shown that blackening of banana tissue is due to the oxidation of β-(3,4-dihydroxyphenyl)ethylamine. (Other examples are given by Thomas (1955).) Many microorganisms produce dark pigments and have the advantage that isolation of the colouring matter is relatively simple. Thus it is known that the black pigments formed by *Bacillus salmonicida* (Lloyd and Johnston, 1929) and the vibrio *Microspira tyrosinatica* (Larway and Evans, 1962), when grown in a medium containing tyrosine, show general melanin characteristics and contain nitrogen, and radioactive tyrosine has been incorporated into the black-brown pigment synthesized by *Streptomyces lavendulae* (Mencher and Heim, 1962). Unfortunately none of these plant pigments have been subjected to chemical degradation. Of the great majority of dark pigments found as markings on petals, in the spores of higher fungi, in senescent leaves and seedpods, and in the dead cells of bark and peri-carps, virtually nothing is known although in a few cases, *Aspergillus niger*, *Daldinia concentrica* and, recently, *Ustilago maydis* (Piattelli *et al.*, 1963b), it is established that they are non-nitrogenous polymers quite different from melanins in structure. The dark pigments in *Ustilago maydis* spores, and in sunflower and water melon seeds, yield catechol, and protocatechuic and salicyclic acids on fusion with potash, which suggests that they may be catechol-melanins (R. A. Nicolaus *et al.*, 1964). (For a general survey see Thomson, 1962.)

REFERENCES

Åkermark, B. (1961). *Acta chem. scand.* 15, 1695.
Barton, D. H. R., and Cohen, T. (1957). *In* "Festschrift Stoll", p. 911, Birkhäuser, Basel.
Barton, D. H. R., DeFlorin, A. M., and Edwards, O. E. (1956). *J. chem. Soc.* 530.
Barton, D. H. R., de Mayo, P., Morrison, G. A., and Raistrick, H. (1959). *Tetrahedron* 6, 48.
Bate-Smith, E. C., and Harborne, J. B. (1963). *Nature, Lond.* 198, 1307.
Birch, A. J., Fitton, P., Ryan, A. J., Smith, H., and Whalley, W. B. (1958). *J. chem. Soc.* 4576.
Birch, A. J., Cassera, A., Fitton, P., Holker, J. S. E., Smith, H., Thompson, G. A., and Whalley, W. B. (1962). *J. chem. Soc.* 3583.
Brockmann, H. (1960). *In* "Progress in the Chemistry of Organic Natural Products" (L. Zechmeister, ed.), 18, 1.
Brockmann, H., and Lackner, H. (1960). *Naturwissenschaften* 47, 230.
Butenandt, A., and Schäfer, W. (1962). *In* "Recent Progress in the Chemistry of Natural and Synthetic Colouring Matters and Related Fields" (T. S. Gore, B. S. Joshi, S. V. Sunthankar and B. D. Tilak, eds.), p. 659, Academic Press, New York.
Bycroft, B. W., Dobson, T. A., and Roberts, J. C. (1962). *J. chem. Soc.* 40.
Carter, R. E., and Richards, J. H. (1961). *J. Amer. chem. Soc.* 83, 495.
Cavill, G. W. K., Ralph, B. J., Tetaz, J. R., and Werner, R. L. (1953). *J. chem. Soc.* 525.
Covell, C. J., King, F. E., and Morgan, J. W. W. (1961). *J. chem. Soc.* 702.
Dean, F. M., Eade, R. A., Moubasher, R. A., and Robertson, A. (1957). *Nature, Lond.* 179, 366.
DeMoss, R. D., and Evans, N. R. (1960). *J. Bacteriol.* 79, 729.
Dreiding, A. S. (1961). *In* "Recent Developments in the Chemistry of Natural Phenolic Compounds" (W. D. Ollis, ed.), pp. 237, Pergamon Press, New York.
Frank, R. L., Clark, G. R., and Coker, J. N. (1950). *J. Amer. chem. Soc.* 72, 1824.
Frank, L. H., and DeMoss, R. D. (1959). *J. Bacteriol.* 77, 776.
Fürth, O. v., and Schneider, H. (1902). *Beitr. Chem. Physiol. Pathol.* 1, 229.
Galmarini, O. L., Stodola, F. H., Raper, K. B., and Fennell, D. I. (1962). *Nature, Lond.* 195, 502.
Griffiths, L. A. (1959). *Nature, Lond.* 184, 58.
Gripenberg, J. (1963). *Acta. chem. scand.* 17, 703 (and earlier papers).
Hassall, C. H., and Scott, A. I. (1961). *In* "Recent Developments in the Chemistry of Natural Phenolic Compounds" (W. D. Ollis, ed.), pp. 237, Pergamon Press, New York.

Haynes, L. J. (1963). *Adv. Carbohydrate Chemistry* **18**, 241.

Johnson, A. W., Juby, P. F., King, T. J., and Tam, S. W. (1963). *J. chem. Soc.* 2884 (and earlier papers).

Karrer, W. (1958). "Konstitution und Vorkommen der organischen Pflanzenstoffe," pp. 959, Birkhäuser, Basel.

Kögl, F., Becker, H., Detzel, A., and de Voss, G. (1928). *Liebigs Ann.* **465**, 211.

Kurono, M., Nakanishi, K., Shindo, K., and Tada, M. (1963). *Chem. Pharm. Bull., Japan* **11**, 359.

Larway, P., and Evans, W. C. (1962). *Biochem. J.* **85**, 22P.

Lloyd, B., and Johnston, A. (1929). *J. Roy. Tech. Coll.* (*Glasgow*) **2**, 346; Lloyd, B. (1929). *ibid.* **2**, 142.

Mabry, T. J., Taylor, A., and Turner, B. L. (1963). *Phytochem.* **2**, 61.

MacDonald, J. C. (1963). *Canad. J. Chem.* **41**, 165.

Mason, H. S. (1959). *In* "Pigment Cell Biology" (M. Gordon, ed.), Academic Press, New York.

McMaster, W. J., Scott, A. I., and Trippett, S. (1960). *J. chem. Soc.* 4628.

McOmie, J. F. W., Tute, M. S., Turner, A. B., and Bullimore, B. K. (1963). *Chem. & Ind.* 1689.

Mehta, P. P., and Whalley, W. B. (1963). *J. chem. Soc.* 3777.

Mencher, J. R., and Heim, A. H. (1962). *J. gen. Microbiol.* **28**, 665.

Miles, P. G., Lund, H., and Raper, J. R. (1956). *Arch. Biochem. Biophys.* **62**, 1.

Miller, M. W. (1961). "The Pfizer Handbook of Microbial Metabolites," pp. 772, McGraw-Hill, New York.

Money, T. (1963). *Nature, Lond.* **199**, 592.

Morgan, L. R., and Aubert, C. C. (1962). *J. org. Chem.* **27**, 4092.

Musso, H. (1960). *Planta Med.* **8**, 432.

Narasimhachari, N., and Vining, L. C. (1963). *Canad. J. Chem.* **41**, 641.

Nicolaus, R. A. (1962). *Rass. Med. Sper.* **9**, Suppl. 1, 1.

Nicolaus, R. A., Piatelli, M., and Fattorusso, E. (1964). *Tetrahedron* **20**, 1163.

Paul, I. C., Sim, G. A., and Morrison, G. A. (1963). *Proc. chem. Soc.* 352.

Piattelli, M., Fattorusso, E., Magno, S., and Nicolaus, R. A. (1963a). *Tetrahedron Letters* 997.

Piattelli, M., Fattorusso, E., Magno, S., and Nicolaus, R. A. (1963b). *Tetrahedron Letters* **19**, 2061.

Powell, A. D. G., Robertson, A., and Whalley, W. B. (1956). *Chem. Soc. Special Pub.* No. 5, 27.

Raper, H. S. (1927). *Biochem. J.* **21**, 89.

Rapoport, H., and Holden, K. G. (1962). *J. Amer. chem. Soc.* **84**, 635.

Rhodes, A., Boothroyd, B., McGonagle, M. P., and Somerfield, G. A. (1961). *Biochem. J.* **81**, 28.

Roberts, J. C. (1961). *Chem. Revs.* **61**, 591.

Santer, U. V., and Vogel, H. J. (1956). *Biochim. biophys. Acta* **19**, 578.

Schwenk, E., Alexander, G. J., Gold, A. M., and Stevens, D. F. (1958). *J. biol. Chem.* **233**, 1211.

Shibata, S., Ogihara, Y., and Ohta, A. (1963). *Chem. Pharm. Bull., Japan* **11**, 1179.

Sivak, A., Meloni, M. L., Nobili, F., and Katz, E. (1962). *Biochim. biophys. Acta,* **57**, 283.

Takeda, R., and Nakanishi, I. (1959). *Hakko Kogaku Zasshi* **38**, 9.

Thomas, M. (1955). *In* "Modern Methods of Plant Analysis" (K. Paech and M. W. Tracey, eds.), vol. 4, Springer, Berlin.

Thomas, R. (1961a). *Biochem. J.* **78**, 807.

Thomas, R. (1961b). *Biochem. J.* **78**, 748.

Thomson, R. H. (1962). *In* "Recent Progress in the Chemistry of Natural and Synthetic Colouring Matters and Related Fields" (T. S. Gore, B. S. Joshi, S. V. Sunthankar and B. D. Tilak, eds.), p. 99, Academic Press, New York.

Whalley, W. B. (1961). *In* "Recent Developments in the Chemistry of Natural Phenolic Compounds" (W. D. Ollis, ed.), p. 20, Pergamon, New York.

Whalley, W. B. (1963). *Pure appl. Chem.* **7**, 565.

Wiechowski, W. (1923). *Arch. exp. Path.* **97**, 462.

Wyler, H., Mabry, T. J., and Dreiding, A. S. (1963). *Helv. chim. acta.* **46, 1745.**

PART II: FUNCTION

Chapter 13

FUNCTION IN PHOTOSYNTHESIS

C. P. WHITTINGHAM

*Queen Mary College, London, England**

I. INTRODUCTION

Photosynthesis involves the photoreduction of carbon dioxide to an organic form such as carbohydrate. In green plants there is a concomitant liberation of oxygen from water.

$$CO_2 + H_2O \rightarrow [CHOH] + O_2 \ (\Delta F + 112 \text{ kcal}).$$

In photosynthetic bacteria in place of water much stronger reducing substances are used such as H_2, H_2S and H_2R where R is an organic residue.

$$CO_2 + 2H_2R \rightarrow CH_2O + H_2O + 2R$$

In this case the energy required for the reaction is considerably smaller.

The pigment which photosensitizes the reaction has been known since the time of Dutrochet to be chlorophyll in the case of green plants; in the bacteria it is bacteriochlorophyll or chloroviridin. Chlorophyll in organic solution has two absorption maxima in the visible region of the spectrum both at wavelengths shorter than 720 mμ. The absorption of bacteriochlorophyll *in vitro* extends into the infra red to 800 mμ. Excitation of either the blue or red absorption band of chlorophyll produces, after initial excitation to a short-lived state, the same common fluorescent state. This may return to the ground state either by the emission of

* Present address: *Department of Plant Phpsiology, Imperial College, London, England.*

fluorescence, by dissipating energy as heat, or by chemical reaction. Prior to any of these there is the possibility of transfer of energy by resonance from one pigment molecule to another. *In vitro* a non-fluorescent long-lived excited triplet stage has also been demonstrated (Livingstone, 1954). While in principle energy migration can also take place from this metastable state, it is likely to be small in comparison with migration from the fluorescent state.

Evidence for homogeneous energy migration can be obtained from observations of the depolarization of fluorescence. Unless all molecules in a pigment aggregate are arranged in parallel, energy transfer results in a change in the direction of the oscillating electric dipole responsible for the emission of fluorescence. After several transfers, parallelism between the electric vectors of the absorbed and of the emitted light will be lost. If excitation is produced by plane-polarized light, the light emitted in fluorescence will be polarized also; but if energy migration occurs, fluorescence will be more or less depolarized. This has been observed by Goodheer (1957) in the fluorescence of phycobilins, even when observed in molecular dispersion. This can be interpreted as evidence that a quantum absorbed by one of the pigment molecules attached to a given protein molecule in the chromoprotein migrates through other pigment molecules before it is emitted as fluorescence. A similar process with excitation quanta absorbed *in vivo* by chlorophyll may occur: but investigations are missing which would permit us to determine the extent of homogeneous energy migrations in the chlorophyll layers of photosynthesizing plant cells.

Energy migration can lead not only to depolarization, but also to quenching of fluorescence, if the energy quantum encounters centres in which the excitation energy is dissipated, either by conversion into heat, or by utilization in a photochemical reaction. The fluorescence yield of chlorophyll *a* in solution may be of the order of 30%. In the living cell it is 2–3%.

In addition to the different forms of excited molecule there are chemically different forms of chlorophyll in the ground state which may play a part in photosynthesis. In organic solution chlorophyll is reversibly bleached when illuminated in complete absence of oxygen. Chlorophyll dissolved in pyridine can be reduced in light by ascorbate or phenyl-hydrazine (Krasnovsky reaction).

$$\text{Chl } a + \text{ascorbate} \xrightarrow{h\nu} \text{Chl } a \cdot \text{H}_2(\text{eosinophyll}) + \text{dehydroascorbic acid.}$$

The reduced form of chlorophyll (eosinophyll) is a pink compound with absorption bands at 518 and 585 mμ. It exhibits no paramagnetic resonance and is not therefore a free radical. It has a strong negative redox potential since it can reduce riboflavin or other oxidants, e.g. saffranin, with redox potentials down to -0.30 V. The photoreduction of riboflavin by ascorbate which is photosensitized by chlorophyll involves a free energy change of $+9$ kcal/mole.

II. Photochemistry of Pigments *in vivo*

Microscopic studies of the photosynthetic green plant show that the pigments are concentrated in the chloroplast particles with an average concentration of 10^{-1} M corresponding to an average distance between molecules in the grana of the order of 50 Å. Theoretical studies of resonance transfer suggest that the probability of energy transfer within the lifetime of the fluorescent state should be high (Förster, 1959). This calculation assumes that chlorophyll is uniformly distributed throughout the granum of the chloroplast. Detailed studies (to be discussed later) of the absorption band in the red for chloroplasts or living cells show a complexity indicating the possible presence of more than one component. On extraction of the pigment a single absorption band is obtained indicating that the complexity *in vivo* may be due to combination of a single chromatophore with different molecules, e.g. a lipid or protein phase. In addition the chloroplast contains accessory pigments which are predominantly carotenoids in the green plant and phycobilins in the blue-green and red algae. The carotenoids are relatively lipophilic and the phycobilins hydrophilic compared with chlorophyll. This may indicate the existence of at least a two-phase system. In spite of this complexity it is probable that the mean separation of molecules of different pigments does not exceed the distance through which resonance transfer is likely to take place.

Chlorophyll is located probably on the interface between hydrophilic and hydrophobic layers, forming monomolecular (or bimolecular) layers. An excited chlorophyll molecule may, for example, transfer one electron to an "acceptor" molecule in the adjacent lipid layer and recover it from a protein layer. The two reaction products would then be in different phases and could undergo enzymatic stabilization, ultimately leading to their conversion into carbohydrate and molecular oxygen, without danger of immediate recombination. It has been suggested by Calvin (1959) that a separation of products could be based on an electron migration similar to that occurring in crystalline photoelectric conductors although the absorption curve *in vivo* gives little evidence that the bulk of the chlorophyll *in vivo* is crystalline. But minute amounts of regular crystalline pigment structure could occur.

In vitro neither carotenoids nor phycobilins show fluorescence. *In vivo* they are able to sensitize the fluorescence of chlorophyll. In the diatom

Nitzchia absorption of light quanta predominantly by the carotenoid fucoxanthin produced fluorescence of chlorophyll *a* with approximately the same yield as light absorbed by chlorophyll itself (Dutton *et al.*, 1943). Similarly the fluorescence of chlorophyll *a* may be sensitized by absorption by chlorophyll *b* in *Chlorella*. Similarly in the red and blue-green algae phycobilins have been shown to transfer their energy to chlorophyll. The transfer of energy takes place with high efficiency, but can occur only from a pigment absorbing at a shorter wavelength to one absorbing at a longer wavelength and not vice versa. Furthermore, in the red algae, efficiency of energy transfer from phycoerythrin to chlorophyll *a* depends on pretreatment (Brody, 1958). If the cells are preilluminated by light absorbed by phycoerythrin the efficiency of

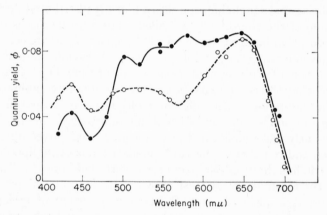

Fig. 1. Action spectra of photosynthesis in the red alga, *Porphyridium* after pre-illumination with green (●———●) or blue light (○– – –○). (After Brody and Emerson, 1959.)

transfer from phycoerythrin to chlorophyll is improved; whereas pre-illumination with light absorbed by chlorophyll decreases the apparent efficiency (compare Fig. 1).

The efficiency of excitation of photosynthesis by absorption by different pigments can also be seen from action spectra. The action spectrum shows the quantum yield of photosynthesis as a function of the wavelength of monochromatic light. The action spectrum can be compared with the absorption spectra for individual pigments isolated from the plant and the photosynthetic activity compared with the proportion of light at each wavelength absorbed by individual pigments (Fig. 2). Such comparisons have shown that, taken as a whole, the carotenoids of higher plants and green algae are only half as efficient as chlorophyll in producing photosynthesis (Emerson and Lewis, 1943). By contrast the carotenoid fucoxanthin in the brown algae and diatoms is almost as efficient as chlorophyll itself (Tanada, 1951). The phycobilin pigments are highly efficient in photosynthesis in the red and blue-green algae (Emerson and Lewis, 1942). One possible hypothesis is that all these pigments sensitize photosynthesis directly. A more attractive hypothesis, consistent with the observations of fluorescence discussed previously, is that light absorbed by pigments other than chlorophyll *a*

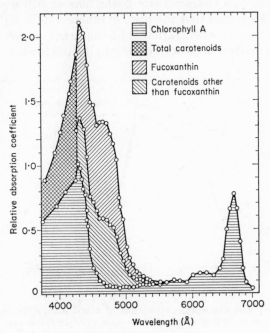

FIG. 2. The contribution of different pigments to the absorption spectrum of the diatom *Nitzchia closterium*. (After Dutton *et al.*, 1943.)

is transferred to this pigment which then alone sensitizes photosynthesis. In general terms we may postulate a transfer by resonance from various pigments to that pigment which shows absorption at the longest wavelength. In the early studies this was regarded as being chlorophyll *a*.

III. "ENHANCEMENT" EFFECTS

A detailed study of the action spectrum in the far red region of the visible spectrum gave evidence of further complexity. Emerson and Lewis (1943) observed that the quantum efficiency of photosynthesis in the green alga, *Chlorella*, decreased very rapidly in the region between 680 and 700 mμ where there was still appreciable absorption. The effect was even more striking in certain red algae where the quantum yield

12*

declined beyond 650 mμ although there was appreciable absorption at 680 mμ (Fig. 3). This suggested that a form of chlorophyll which absorbed in the far red was ineffective in photosynthesis.

Emerson and co-workers showed that far red absorption could be made effective if it was supplemented by simultaneous absorption at a shorter wavelength. The action spectrum for the increased rate of photosynthesis resulting from a second wavelength superimposed on a beam of light of 697 mμ showed two characteristic peaks, one at 650 mμ and one at 670 mμ. This suggested that the photosynthetic rate in light of 697 mμ is limited in some way whereas that at 650 mμ is not. At 650 mμ illumination results in excitation of both chlorophyll a and b, whereas at 697 mμ

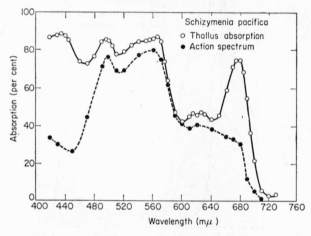

FIG. 3. Action and absorption spectrum of a red alga, *Schizymenia pacifica*. Absorption ○——○ , Photosynthesis ●– – –● . (After Haxo and Blinks, 1953.)

the absorption is largely due to chlorophyll a. Emerson concluded that the simultaneous excitation of chlorophyll b must improve the photosynthetic efficiency of the light absorbed in the far red by chlorophyll a (Emerson et al., 1957). At that time Emerson made no comment on the second peak in the enhancement action spectrum at 670 mμ.

An increased photosynthetic activity (enhancement effect) due to simultaneous illumination by two different wavelengths has now been found in a large number of organism (Haxo, 1960). In the red alga *Porphyridium*, Brody and Emerson (1959) showed a marked increase in activity of light absorbed in the far red when this was supplemented by light absorbed by phycocyanin. In *Chlorella* the action spectrum for the effectiveness of the second light showed two peaks, one at 480 mμ and one at 658 mμ, giving a curve resembling the absorption spectrum of chlorophyll b; in *Porphyra* the action spectrum showed a single peak at

550 mμ resembling the absorption spectrum of phycoerythrin. In the blue-green alga *Anacystis* maximum enhancement was obtained by illumination at 600 mμ; this implied phycocyanin. In the diatom *Navicula*, enhancement was obtained at 540 mμ and 645 mμ implicating fucoxanthin and chlorophyll c. It was observed that the enhancement effect resulted from excitation of a second pigment throughout its spectrum. For example, excitation in *Chlorella* of either the blue or the red absorption bands of chlorophyll b was equally effective for enhancement. The general conclusion was that it is necessary to have simultaneous excitation of both chlorophyll a and of some other pigment for efficient photosynthesis. In studies with monochromatic light, the relative inefficiency of absorption by chlorophyll a alone appears only at the far red end of the spectrum because this is the only region in the visible where chlorophyll a is the sole absorbing pigment. It is clear there is evidence suggesting the operation of two light reactions in photosynthesis, one resulting from absorption by chlorophyll a, the other from absorption by the accessory pigments.

Independent evidence of a different type supporting this general conclusion came from studies by Blinks (1960) on the short-term changes in rate consequent upon a change in the wavelength of incident light. Even although the intensity at two different wavelengths was adjusted to give equal steady state photosynthetic rates, a marked change in rate was observed immediately upon a change from one wavelength to another. For example in the green alga, *Ulva*, on changing the wavelength of light from 688 to 640 mμ an abrupt increase in oxygen evolution was observed. On return to 688 mμ there was a corresponding decrease. When in *Porphyridium* the activity resulting from light of wavelength 702 mμ was taken as a fixed reference rate, the action spectrum for the size of transient due to alternate illumination with light of a variable wavelength corresponded to the absorption spectrum of phycoerythrin. In *Ulva* an action spectrum obtained in a similar way corresponded to the absorption spectrum of chlorophyll b. Blinks chose to interpret these transients as due in part to differing changes in respiratory rate produced by light of different wavelengths. French and Fork (1961) have shown that a stimulation of respiration does take place as a consequence of illumination at certain wavelengths. They determined the action spectrum both for the effect on respiration immediately following illumination and for the enhancement effect on photosynthesis. The former gave an action spectrum similar to absorption of chlorophyll in the far red, whereas the latter resulted from absorption by accessory pigments.

The enhancement effect has been observed not only in photosynthesis but also in the photoreduction of quinone by *Chlorella* cells (Govindjee *et al.*, 1960b) and in the photoreduction of NADP by isolated spinach chloroplasts. Hence this effect is not mainly associated with the carbon dioxide-reducing phase of photosynthesis. Peaks at 650 and 670 mμ in the enhancement spectrum of quinone reduction in *Chlorella*, show that light absorbed by chlorophyll *a*, 670 mμ, as well as that absorbed by chlorophyll *b* can effectively supplement far-red light (> 680 mμ); light absorbed by chlorophyll *a* 680 mμ cannot do so.

Myers and French (1960) have shown that the enhancement effect observed with *Chlorella* illuminated with two wavelengths does not require that the two wavelengths be given simultaneously, but that these may be given alternately in periods of several seconds' duration. This suggested the formation of an intermediate common to the two reactions with a life of several seconds. Such a mechanism could also be used to explain the observations of Whittingham and Brown (1958) and Whittingham and Bishop (1961) who observed enhancement in oxygen production from a flash of several milliseconds duration by a preceding shorter flash. Maximum enhancement was observed, both in algal cells and in spinach chloroplasts reducing ferricyanide, when the flashes were separated by several seconds dark time.

Emerson made no comment on the second peak at 670 in the enhancement action spectrum observed by him. A peak (Govindjee and Rabinowitch, 1960) or shoulder (Myers and French, 1960) at 670 mμ in action spectra for the Emerson effect in *Chlorella*, was interpreted by the first-mentioned authors as an indication of the participation in the enhancement effect of a chlorophyll *a* type, with maximum absorption at 670 mμ. Emerson and Rabinowitch (1960) (cf. also Franck, 1958) proposed the following hypothesis. Two photochemical reactions occur in photosynthesis: one of these is caused by a non- or weakly-fluorescent chlorophyll *a*, the second by a fluorescent chlorophyll *a*. Excitation of the non-fluorescent chlorophyll *a* alone does not lead to photosynthesis. However, if both chlorophylls are excited simultaneously, the two reactions can co-operate, and lead to an enhanced photosynthesis. The so-called accessory pigments, e.g. chlorophyll *b* in *Chlorella*, and the phycobilins in red and blue-green algae, effect photosynthesis by transferring their excitation energy by resonance transfer to fluorescent chlorophyll *a* but not to the non-fluorescent form.

Franck (1958) suggested that the two kinds of chlorophyll involved in photosynthesis are a non-fluorescent form, in which the excited molecules in the S* singlet-state are instantaneously converted, via the nπ-state, into metastable molecules T; and a fluorescent kind, which permits the S*-state to survive long enough either to fluoresce, or to transfer its energy by resonance, through a sequence of chlorophyll molecules, to a molecule already in the T-state, raising it into an excited triplet state,

T*. The latter was postulated to be able to permit direct sensitization of an electron transfer from H_2O to CO_2 (as $R.COOH$) i.e. through 1·2 V.

Absorption on the long-wave side of the main absorption peak, > 690 mμ, is suggested in Franck's theory, to be due predominantly to $n\pi$ transitions in the non-fluorescent state. It therefore produces predominantly T-molecules, which alone cannot bring about photosynthesis. Absorption in the main band, 650 to 690 mμ, on the other hand, excites both types of chlorophyll. Depending on their ratio, it can either produce about equal numbers of S* and T-molecules, and thus ultimately, a large number of T*-molecules and a high yield of photosynthesis (as in *Chlorella*), or predominantly T-molecules, and thus a low yield of chlorophyll fluorescence and photosynthesis (as in *Porphyridium*). Finally, Rabinowitch has suggested that absorption at 640 to 650 mμ could excite predominantly the fluorescent species (in which the absorption on the short-wave side of the main peak is reinforced by the $n\pi$-transition), and thus give, in all cells, a high yield of fluorescence and of photosynthesis.

It is to be noted that under no condition is there danger of a shortage of molecules in the T-state, since even in the extreme case of exclusive excitation of fluorescent molecules, the transition S* $\to$ T is the most likely fate of each S*-molecule, unless enough T-molecules have accumulated for the transition S* + T $\to$ S + T* to be equally likely. Lavorel (1957), Vorobyova and Krasnovsky (1958), and Brody (1958) have suggested as an alternative hypothesis that the two forms of chlorophyll a might be monomeric and dimeric respectively.

IV. EXISTENCE OF PIGMENT FORMS *in vivo*

Brown and French (1959) made a detailed study of the absorption spectra *in vivo* of living plants by the use of a differential spectrophotometer. This instrument measures the first derivative of optical extinction as a function of wavelength. The observed spectra are then matched by adding together derivatives of normal probability curves showing a single absorption maximum. The absorption in the red region of the spectrum for the higher plant could be analysed in terms of the presence of at least three distinct forms of chlorophyll. These are characterized by the position of their absorption maxima and are referred to as Ca 673, Ca 683, Ca 695. On extracting the chlorophyll from these organisms the extract shows only a single peak due to chlorophyll a. The presence of chlorophyll b also results in a shoulder on the absorption curve *in vivo* at 650 mμ. The proportion of the different forms of pigment varies from organism to organism and may indeed vary according to the cultural conditions in any one organism. For example, the spectrum of *Euglena* is characterized by three components having maxima at 673, 683 and 695 mμ; as the culture ages, or if a culture is grown at lower light intensity, the 695 mμ component becomes more and more pronounced (French and Elliot, 1958). Again after exposure of chloroplast suspensions to high intensities of illumination the absorption spectrum shifts, suggesting that the 673 component is preferentially bleached compared with 683. Three forms of phycoerythrin have been observed in different organisms and phycocyanin also shows differences in different organism (Ó hEocha, 1960).

In the purple bacteria, three forms of bacteriochlorophyll (with absorption bands at 800, 850 and 890 mμ) appear *in vivo* but give rise to only one band (at about 770 mμ) upon extraction in methanol. The wider separation of these bands is in agreement with the generally greater influence of solvent on the position of the absorption bands of bacteriochlorophyll, compared with those of chlorophyll *a*. It remains to be seen whether distinct photochemical functions must be attributed to all these forms in bacteria as well as in algae.

The two photochemical reactions required for efficient photosynthesis have been called by French the long wave chlorophyll reaction and the accessory pigment reaction. French and Fork (1961) have suggested that chlorophyll *a* 683 and chlorophyll *a* 695 are both capable of a single photochemical step, referred to as the long wavelength chlorophyll reaction. The accessory pigment reaction can be affected by absorption by chlorophyll *a* 673 and chlorophyll *b* in *Chlorella*, by chlorophyll *b* in the green plant, by chlorophyll *c* and fucoxanthin in the brown algae and by phycoerythrin and phycocyanin in the red algae.

As pointed out by Duysens it should not be assumed that the action spectrum for enhancement corresponds to the action spectrum of a photochemical system. The quantum yield is not necessarily maximal at shorter wavelengths where the accessory pigments absorb. The action spectrum for one system should be observed as the action spectrum of photosynthesis against a background of intense light activating the other system and vice versa. French *et al.* (1960) measured the action spectrum for *Chlorella* against strong background light of 700 mμ and of 650 mμ. The two resulting action spectra crossed at 683 mμ, the wavelength which presumably results in equal excitation of both systems. Beyond 683 mμ the short wavelength system is relatively less excited; at shorter wavelengths the accessory system less excited.

V. Photochemical Reactions of Isolated Chloroplasts

The study of the photochemical reactions of photosynthesis received a great impetus when R. Hill showed that it was possible to demonstrate photochemical activity of chloroplasts outside the living plant. He isolated chloroplasts from higher plants and showed that if ferric salts were added and the system illuminated the ferric ions were reduced to ferrous ions and oxygen was evolved. It was suggested that the essential photochemical step was a "splitting" or photolysis of water molecules. The oxidized radical produced from water [OH]* gave rise to the evolution of oxygen and the reduced radical [H]* reacted with the ferric salt.

The view that the splitting of water was the primary event in the photochemical reaction of photosynthesis had been suggested by Van Niel on the basis of his studies of the photosynthetic bacteria. Van Niel distinguished two large groups, the Thiorhodaceae which require not only light energy and carbon dioxide to grow but in addition a reduced sulphur compound such as H_2S and the Athiorhodaceae which require in place of the sulphur compound an organic substance such as an alcohol. In no case in the photosynthetic bacteria was oxygen produced. Van Niel suggested that in these organisms the oxidized radical produced from the splitting of water did not give rise to oxygen as in the green plant but was disposed of necessarily by reaction with the added substance which thus became oxidized. This was in agreement with the observation that in the Thiorhodaceae sulphur was a product of photosynthesis, and in the Athiorhodaceae a ketone.

A number of hydrogen acceptors have been shown to be capable of stimulating oxygen production by illuminated chloroplasts. These include quinones which are reduced to hydroquinones and dyes such as dichlorphenolindophenol. At first it was not realized that during the preparation and isolation of the chloroplasts a soluble protein ferredoxin† was lost from the chloroplasts. When this was added back it was found that chloroplasts could reduce NADP in light with the simultaneous production of oxygen (Davenport, 1959).

Arnon and his colleagues showed later that if adenosine diphosphate, phosphate and magnesium ions are supplied, chloroplasts produce ATP in the light. For this phosphorylative activity, light is essential and oxygen is not; hence the process has been called photophosphorylation to distinguish it from the analogous reactions of mitochondria which require oxygen (oxidative phosphorylation). Arnon showed that when hydrogen acceptor and phosphate acceptors were added together both the rate of phosphorylation and of oxygen evolution increased above their separate independent individual rates. Under certain conditions the amount of reduced product (NADPH) was stoichiometrically equivalent to the amount of ATP produced. This suggested a "coupling" between the phosphorylative and the oxidoreductive reactions.

* [ ], square backets, indicate the radicals are probably in a combined form.
† Ferredoxin of chloroplasts is the same substance as the methemoglobin-reducing factor of Davenport et al. (1952), the NADP-reducing factor of Arnon et al. (1957) and the photosynthetic pyridine nucleotide reductase (PPNR) of San Pietro and Lang (1958).

In addition, a further phosphorylative activity of isolated chloroplasts was found when such substances as vitamin K or FMN (flavin mononucleotide) were added to the chloroplasts without any added hydrogen acceptor. Under these conditions the phosphorylative activity was greatly increased but the oxidoreductive activity diminished, demonstrating an alternative sequence of reactions resulting in the production of ATP as the sole product without any accumulation of reduced product. This was called cyclic photophosphorylation.

If the essential feature of photosynthesis is the photolysis of water, then during the transfer of hydrogen to an intermediate hydrogen acceptor phosphorylation must take place. The hydrogen acceptor normally reacts ultimately with carbon dioxide in the green plant or in isolated chloroplasts with added substances, e.g. ferric ions. However, in the presence of vitamin K it must be reoxidized reforming a water molecule and thus reversing the initial photolysis. There would then be no net oxidation-reduction reaction but if the reoxidation was coupled to phosphorylation, ATP could result as the sole product.

Later Arnon (1961a) compared the photochemical activity of chloroplasts isolated from higher plants and chromatophores isolated from bacteria. Not all the photochemical activities exhibited by chloroplasts isolated from green plants are shown by isolated bacterial chromatophores. For example, addition of NADP was found to have little effect on the photophosphorylative activity of chromatophores. One reaction shown to be common to both types of particle was the formation of ATP in the presence of vitamin K but absence of an external hydrogen acceptor—cyclic photophosphorylation. Arnon was then led to suggest that it is not necessary to regard the photochemical process as universally involving water splitting. He suggested that during excitation by light, chlorophyll loses an electron which is expelled with a high potential energy. This electron is returned to the chlorophyll molecule by a series of carriers of which vitamin K is one, and during this sequence of reactions a phosphate bond is formed.

Photosynthetic bacteria when supplied with hydrogen gas do not require light energy for the reduction of NADP, but if succinate or thiosulphate is the hydrogen donor additional energy must be provided by light for the reduction. In this case only some of the electrons ejected by light could return to chlorophyll and result in photophosphorylation, the remainder being used to reduce NADP. In the latter case some electrons must be restored to chlorophyll from the external hydrogen donor. This process in the case of thiosulphate and succinate is catalysed by cytochromes and is thought to be coupled to phosphorylation. Light energy is therefore used to give an electron from thiosulphate a potential which will enable it to reduce NADP. Alternatively the strongly reducing electron produced can be used in the photo-production of hydrogen gas or the photofixation of nitrogen gas. In agreement with these hypotheses both these processes are stimulated by addition of thiosulphate (Fig. 4).

There is good evidence for the occurrence of cytochromes peculiar to photosynthetic organisms, both in green plants, and bacteria. Since the photosynthetic bacteria include obligate anaerobes, a distinction between these cytochromes and those concerned in aerobic metabolism is apparent. Two cytochromes have been observed in

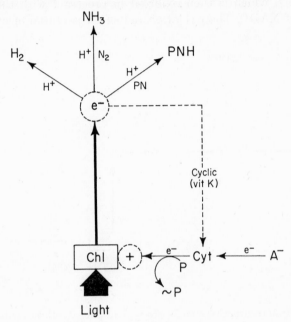

FIG. 4. Electron transport system in photosynthetic bacteria e.g. *Chromatium*. (After Arnon.)

leaves of higher plants, one of the *c* type, cytochrome *f*, and one of the *b* type, cytochrome b_6. Neither is oxidized by cytochrome oxidase. In *Rhodospirillum*, a facultative aerobic photosynthetic bacteria, a *c* type, and a *b* type have been observed. Both cytochrome *f* and the *Rhodospirillum c* type have redox potentials nearer to the oxygen electrode than *c* type. In *Chromatium*, an obligate anaerobic photosynthetic bacterium, four individual α-peaks have been observed and two of the cytochrome components have been extracted. Again components with the *c* type spectrum but a redox potential nearer to *b* type have been observed.

In green plants water is utilized as the electron donor to chlorophyll, presumably through cytochromes. This process is highly endergonic and requires a second light quantum for sensitization. This second light reaction will be called photochemical process 2. Thus photochemical process 1 sensitizes the transfer of electrons from some intermediate to a potential more negative than that of pyridine nucleotides. Process 2 produces this intermediate from water with the simultaneous production of oxygen. Hill and Bendall (1960) have suggested that cytochromes may act as intermediates. They proposed that cytochrome b_6 is reduced with the simultaneous oxidation of water in process 2, transferring its electron to cytochrome f, which is then oxidized in process 1 with the ultimate reduction of NADP. The oxidation reduction potential of cytochrome

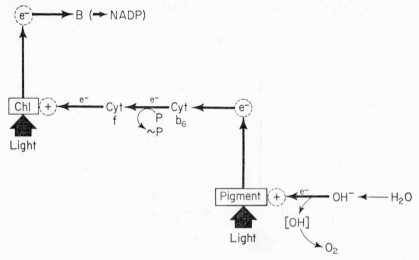

Fig. 5. Electron transport system in green plant photosynthesis. (After Arnon.)

b_6 is 0 V. and of cytochrome $f + 0.34$ V. They proposed a dark reaction between photochemical reactions 1 and 2 in which the electron transfer between cytochromes is coupled to phosphorylation (compare Fig. 5).

Katoh (1960) has reported a copper-containing protein, plastocyanin, which might also act as an intermediate between the two photochemical processes.

The two processes can be separated chemically. If DCMU* is added to isolated chloroplasts they lose the ability to evolve oxygen in light. They can, however, continue to reduce NADP in the light if a suitable electron donor is supplied, e.g. reduced 2,6-dichlorophenolindophenol. The dye can be maintained in the reduced form by the addition of substrate amounts of ascorbate. The reaction is accompanied by phosphorylation

* DCMU = dichlorphenyl-1,1-dimethylurea.

and it is presumed that the reduced dye supplies the electrons to cyto-chromes and hence to photochemical system 1. A comparison of the effectiveness of monochromatic light for NADP reduction in the absence and presence of 2,6-dichlorphenolindophenol and ascorbate suggests

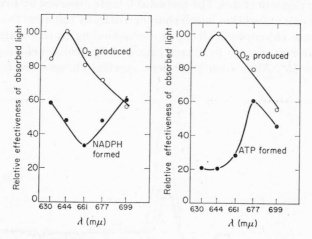

FIG. 6. *L.H.* Action spectra for oxygen evolution with indophenol dye as acceptor and for NAD reduction with ascorbate as electron donor by isolated chloroplasts.
R.H. Action spectra for oxygen evolution and ATP production in the presence of vitamin K under anaerobic conditions. (After Arnon, 1961b.)

that process 1 is activated preferentially by long wavelengths (Arnon *et al.*, 1961; Fig. 6). It is also process 1 which photocatalyses cyclic phosphorylation.

VI. Light-induced Absorption Changes

The difference spectrum of photosynthesis represents the difference between the absorption spectrum of photosynthesizing cells in light and dark. Absorption changes have been measured following a flash of light, notably by Witt and Kok and during steady illumination by Duysens. Characteristic changes at a number of wavelengths were observed (Fig. 7). A characteristic reduction in absorption occurs at 480 with a corres-ponding increase at 515 mμ. Duysens observed a marked reduction in absorption at 420 mμ and attributed this to oxidation of a cytochrome. In the red region decreased absorption was observed at 630, 650 and 703 mμ. Correlated with the change at 703 is also a change at 433. Kok and Hoch (1961) attribute this to the oxidation of a pigment which they have called P.700. The substance responsible for the 480 mμ and corres-ponding 515 mμ change is still unknown. It is tempting to assign all these absorption changes to changes in either pigment states or oxidation reduction states of carriers in the electron transport chain.

Witt has classified the changes into seven types. The changes at 700, 660, 420 and 520 mμ have been suggested by Witt to correspond to changes in pigment states. The metastable state observed by Livingstone *in vitro* has an absorption curve characteristically different from that of ground state chlorophyll. Changes corresponding to this state are not observed *in vivo* except after inactivation of algal cells or chloroplasts by heating to 65°. After such treatment spectral changes are observable

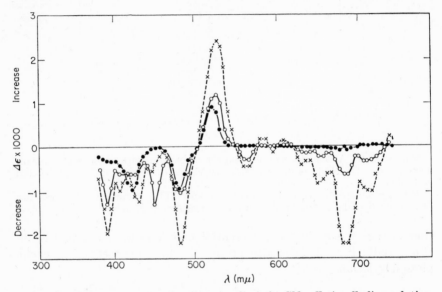

Fig. 7. Difference spectra for photosynthesis in *Chlorella* in alkaline solution. Actinic light intensity $3 \cdot 3 \times 10^{14}$ quanta/cm^2/sec ●———●, $1 \cdot 2 \times 10^{15}$ q/cm^2/sec ○———○, $3 \cdot 1 \times 10^{16}$ q/cm^2/sec ×‒‒‒×. (After Coleman and Rabinowitch, 1959.)

similar to those of the metastable state, which now persists since no photometabolism is possible. The increased absorption at 515 mμ correlated with a decrease at 420 mμ observed in living material also occurs in material lyophilized at $-160°$. Witt considers they represent a conversion of the chlorophyll ground state to an excited triplet state.

Kok was first to observe a marked decrease in absorption at 703 mμ accompanied by a decrease at 433 mμ. He attributes both of these to oxidation of a pigment called P.700. Witt has regarded them as resulting from a change of a form of chlorophyll concerned in photochemical process 1. These two changes remain conspicuous both in aged chloroplasts and in chloroplasts after extraction with petrol ether. Witt *et al.* (1961) showed that in a very short flash the decrease at 703 mμ occurred more rapidly than oxidation of cytochrome (see later) suggesting that P.700 oxidizes a cytochrome. The redox potential of the substance causing these changes is of the order of $+0.45$ V. and is relatively independent of pH between 4·0 and 11·0. The changes in absorption at 433 and 703 mμ showed a marked wavelength response corresponding to oxidation by actinic light of 710 mμ and to reduction by shorter actinic wavelengths. These absorption changes can still be observed in the presence of DCMU. Hence they are thought to be associated with photo-chemical process 1.

There has been considerable speculation (see preceding section) that cytochromes might act as electron carriers between the product of process 2 and the photoreactant of process 1. Their redox potentials would make them suitable carriers between substances concluded as having about zero potential (the product of process 2) and the reactant of process 1, say P.700. Cytochrome oxido-reduction is characterized by absorption changes near 405, 430 and 555 mμ. In green plants such changes have not been readily observed under normal conditions by Duysens or by Witt. Duysens has attributed a small change at 420 mμ to a cytochrome and assumes that the changes at 405 and 555 mμ which should have accompanied it were obscured by larger changes resulting from a change in state of another substance X. By exciting chloroplasts at low temperature ($-150°$C), or by using light of 720 mμ, changes in cytochrome absorption could be observed. Both these procedures might be expected to slow down the reduction of cytochromes thus allowing the oxidation to be more readily seen. Chance (unpublished) has reported observations with whole leaves at $77°$K, both of Swiss chard and spinach, where changes at 555 mμ were observed which he attributed to a cyto-chrome. Chance preferred to consider cytochrome as the photoreagent for process 1 and P.700 to be a secondary change induced by process 1 and not itself in the main electron chain. Bonner has observed that plastids isolated from etiolated mung bean leaves show an absorption change at 557 mμ which becomes less apparent when the leaf is green. Only in the fully green leaf do the changes at 518 mμ appear.

Duysens first showed changes characteristic of cytochromes in the red algae *Porphyridium*. In *Anacystis*, Duysens and Amesz (1962) and later Olson and Smillie (in press) observed light oxidation of cytochrome f by the development of a decreased absorption at 556 mμ. In *Euglena* similar changes have been observed for a cytochrome 552 mμ. Far red light resulted in an oxidation of the cytochrome, whereas shorter wave-lengths caused an initial oxidation followed by a slower reduction to a final steady state (Fig. 8). Cytochrome oxidation was more effective when chlorophyll a was excited rather than phycocyanin. When DCMU is added to stop reduction of the cytochrome, it is found that excitation of a pigment absorbing at 705 mμ is more effective than absorption by chlorophyll a at 690 mμ. This suggests that P.700 might be primarily concerned in cytochrome oxidation. Olson and Smillie showed that washed chloroplast fragments from *Euglena* lost much of the cytochrome 552. When such fragments were illuminated in tris buffer strong light caused gradual reduction of cytochrome b_6, but if the light intensity were appreciably lower a light-induced oxidation was found. Therefore the evidence suggests that several constituents such as P.700 or cytochrome

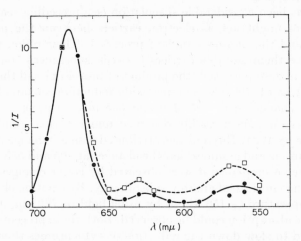

FIG. 8. Action spectra for cytochrome oxidation in *Porphyridium* for a small additional change in the steady state (●——●) and for the initial rate □– – –□ . The reciprocal of intensity to induce a given change is plotted against wavelength. (After Duysens, 1963.)

b_6 might be both oxidized by far red light and reduced by shorter wavelengths, thus occupying a flip-flop position between the two photochemical systems.

There remain the pair of characteristic absorption changes corresponding to a rise in absorption at 515 mμ and a decrease at 475 mμ. Witt has also reported that there is a corresponding change in the ultraviolet at 254 mμ. These changes are lost after extraction of chloroplasts with light petroleum but can be restored by the addition of plastoquinone. Plastoquinone *in vitro* does not show changes in absorption in the visible region of the spectrum upon oxidation. Therefore the changes in the visible are ascribed to a substance which may be related or reactive with plastoquinone. The change in the ultra-violet may be due to plastoquinone. By using flash techniques it has been possible to examine the kinetic behaviour and show that the 475 and 515 mμ changes are related to the presence of the same unknown compound X. When the action spectrum is determined for stimulation of the 515 mμ change it is found to have peaks in the red at 682 and 695 mμ characteristic of photochemical process 2 (Fig. 9). It therefore appears that the substance X is photo-reduced by process 2 and photo-oxidized by process 1, thus occupying a similar position to that suggested for cytochromes by Hill and Bendall.

Some other workers have argued that substance X may not be an essential constituent of the photosynthetic electron chain. Chance and Strehler (1957) have suggested that since a carotenoid-less mutant of

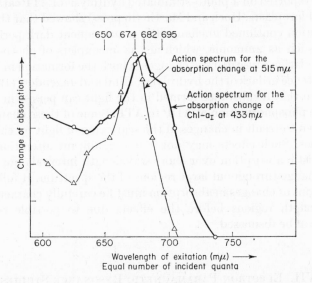

FIG. 9. Action spectra for production of absorption changes in spinach chloro-plast fragments.

The 515 mμ change was determined in presence of ferricyanide together with a small amount of indophenol dye; the 433 mμ change in the presence of phenazine methosulphate. (After Müller *et al.*, 1963.)

Chlamydomonas (which can photosynthesize) does not show the 515 mμ change carotenoids may be responsible. Witt has replied that one sub-stance undergoing change (i.e. plastoquinone) may influence the absorp-tion of another pigment (X) surrounding it in very high concentration. He suggests therefore that the changes at 475 and 515 mμ give evidence of a component, although they may not be due to a substance directly in the electron transport chain. It is clear that the change in absorption at any given wavelength, e.g. around 430 mμ, represents the net change resulting from changes in a number of constituents. It is known that the time course of the 520 mμ change is at least biphasic. It is not possible at the present time to attribute all these changes to unique isolatable compounds. It is, however, clear that these changes can be broadly separated into two categories, some of which are associated with photochemical process 1 and excited by far red light, others being associated with processes 1 and 2 and associated with shorter wavelength light.

The photoreduced form of chlorophyll observed by Krasnovsky shows a bleaching at 680 mμ and increase at 520 mμ. Presence of this intermediate would result in absorption changes, particularly at intensities above those which saturate photosynthesis. In 1960 Petrack and Lipmann reported on a photo-stimulated hydrolysis of ATP catalysed by spinach chloroplasts. Hoch and Martin (in press) showed that the hydrolytic reaction continued unchanged in a subsequent dark period. Substances, such as ammonia, which act as uncouplers of photosynthetic phosphorylation cause marked changes in both the formation in light and the persistence in dark of the hydrolysis. Hind and Jagendorf (1963) have also shown that a substance formed in the light can persist in the dark and cause phosphorylation of ADP to ATP. Some of these changes have been shown to result in changes in the scattering of light by chloroplast suspensions. Such effects may not cause significant alterations in the characteristic absorption over short wavelength intervals but rather a general change throughout large regions of the spectrum. It follows that observations of changes in absorption must be carefully characterized as to wavelength regions before the effects due to possible scattering changes can be dismissed.

VII. Electron Paramagnetic Resonance Studies

Electron paramagnetic resonance spectroscopy can be used to detect the formation of free radicals or other types of paramagnetic centres. Suspensions of algal cells and of isolated chloroplasts give an EPR signal characteristic of illumination. A study of the action spectrum shows that these signals result from excitation of the far red absorbing forms of chlorophyll (Allen *et al.*, 1961). Detailed examination of the light-dependent signal in *Chlorella* has shown it to consist of two components; one, a signal which rapidly decreased when the light is turned off and was excited by far red absorption and two, a signal which persists for a longer time after darkening which can also be excited with shorter wavelengths. Kok and Beinert (1962) have prepared a particulate preparation from red algae from which two-thirds of the chlorophyll have been removed by acetone but most of the P.700 remains. This preparation after dispersion by sonication shows a reversible absorption change in the light. A free radical signal was obtained of the same type as that resulting from illumination of whole chloroplasts. The signal was affected by light, ferricyanide and PMS* in a way correlated with changes in absorption at 700 mμ. It was therefore suggested that the light-dependent short EPR signal in photosynthetic material might be due to the photo-oxidized form of P.700. In *Anacystis* 713 mμ light stimulated the EPR signal to a much greater extent than 635 mμ light. This conclusion has been confirmed by studies of mutants of *Chlamydomonas reinhardii*. Mutant ac-141 studied by Levine and Smillie (1962) shows biochemical activity indicating that system 2 is blocked but system 1 is active; it also shows a fast EPR signal, but lacks the slow signal. The slow decaying signal has not yet been attributed to any particular constituent.

VIII. FLUORESCENCE STUDIES

As discussed earlier in this chapter quanta absorbed by phycobilins in red and blue-green algae are more efficient in exciting fluorescence of chlorophyll *a* than excitation of chlorophyll *a* itself. From this observation it was concluded that energy was transferred perferentially from the phycobilins to some part of chlorophyll *a*, say chlorophyll a^2, and not to another part of chlorophyll, say chlorophyll a^1, which is only weakly fluorescent or does not fluoresce at all. In *Porphyridium cruentum* actinic light of 680 and 430 mμ results in oxidation of cytochrome and hence must activate photochemical process 1 more than process 2. Since it gives relatively little fluorescence the weakly fluorescent form chlorophyll a^1 is to be associated with process 1. Addition of 560 light (which excites fluorescence with high efficiency) to illumination with 680 mμ light causes reduction of cytochrome, suggesting that the fluorescent form of chlorophyll a^2 is associated with process 2.

Govindjee *et al.* (1960a) investigated the effect on fluorescence in *Chlorella* of the addition of far red light to illumination with shorter wavelengths. They found that the total fluorescence from combined illumination with a far red and a red beam given together was smaller than the sum of the fluorescence intensities excited by the beams given separately. This is consistent with the mechanism just discussed. They claim that the fluorescence yield at both wavelengths was independent of intensity but Duysens and Sweers (1963) showed that the steady-state fluorescence yield increased with an increase in light intensity for light preferentially activating process 2. The latter authors observed marked changes in fluorescence intensity upon changing from a light which primarily activated process 2 to one primarily activating process 1 and

* PMS = phenazine methosulphate.

vice versa. They postulated that the decrease in fluorescence resulting from addition of light activating process 1, indicated that some reagent for process 1 called Q must quench the fluorescence of chlorophyll a^2 when oxidized but not when reduced. In *Porphyridium* absorption of only one quantum per 100 chlorophyll a^2 molecules restored fluorescence so that Q is present in concentration of about one hundredth that of chlorophyll (Fig. 10). In the presence of DCMU, even upon illumination

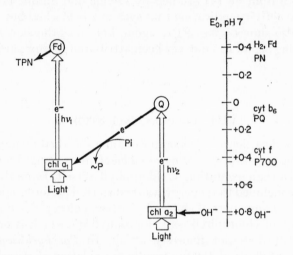

Fig. 10. Generalized diagram of two light reactions in photosynthesis. The oxidation reduction potentials (standard, pH 7) of some possible carriers is given on the right; Fd—ferredoxin, PN—pyridine nucleotide, PQ—plastoquinone, cyt—cytochromes, P.700. Q is the fluorescence quencher.

with weak light, chlorophyll a^2 fluorescence is not decreased by addition of light-activating system 1. Hence DCMU must inhibit the reoxidation of QH.

$$H_2O \rightarrow \{\text{fluorescent chlorophyll } a^2 \text{ (system 2)}\} \rightarrow Q \rightarrow$$
$$\text{cytochromes} \rightarrow \{\text{non-fluorescent chlorophyll } a^1 \text{ (system 1)}\} \rightarrow NADP$$

Duysens and Sweers suggest further that Q may be converted by a dark reaction into a form Q^1. This also is postulated to quench fluorescence but to be non-photoactive. The reverse reaction $Q^1 \rightarrow Q$ which takes place in light 2 (since Q is then converted to QH and hence Q^1 to Q) is considered to be slow. This indeed may be the slow reaction which has been observed in a number of induction phenomena referred to previously, and would mean that no slow reaction need be postulated in the main electron transport generally. Other possible slow dark reactions include a back reaction between NADPH and Q.

REFERENCES

Allen, M. B., Piette, L. H., and Murchio, J. C. (1961). *Biochem. Biophys. Res. Comm.* **4**, 271.

Arnon, D. I. (1961a). *Nature, Lond.* **190**, 601.

Arnon, D. I. (1961b). *Bull. Torrey Bot. Club* **88**, 215.

Arnon, D. I., Whatley, F. R., and Allen, M. B. (1957). *Nature, Lond.* **180**, 182.

Arnon, D. I., Losada, M., Whatley, F. R., Tsujimoto, H. Y., Hall, D. O., and Horton, A. A. (1961). *Proc. nat. Acad. Sci., Wash.* **47**, 1314.

Blinks, L. R. (1960). *In* "Comparative Biochemistry of Photoreactive Systems" (M. B. Allen, ed.), ch. 22, Academic Press, New York.

Brody, M. (1958). *Science* **128**, 838.

Brody, M., and Emerson, R. (1959). *J. gen. Physiol.* **43**, 251.

Brown, J. S., and French, C. S. (1959). *Plant Physiol.* **34**, 305.

Calvin, M. (1959). *In* "The Photochemical Apparatus", p. 160, Brookhaven Symposium in Biology.

Chance, B., and Strehler, B. (1957). *Plant Physiol.* **32**, 536.

Coleman, J. W., and Rabinowitch, E. I. (1959). *J. phys. Chem.* **63**, 30.

Davenport, H. E. (1959). *Biochem. J.* **73**, 45P.

Davenport, H. E., Hill, R., and Whatley, F. R. (1952). *Proc. roy. Soc. B* **139**, 346.

Dutton, H. J., Manning, W. M., and Duggar, B. M. (1943). *J. phys. Chem.* **47**, 308.

Duysens, L. N. M. (1956). *Annu. Rev. Plant Physiol.* **7**, 25.

Duysens, L. N. M. (1963). *Proc. roy. Soc. B* **157**, 301.

Duysens, L. N. M., and Amesz, J. (1962). *Biochim. biophys. Acta* **64**, 243.

Duysens, L. N. M., and Sweers, H. E. (1963). *In* "Microalgae and Photosynthetic Bacteria", a special edition of *Plant and Cell Physiol.*, 353.

Emerson, R., and Lewis, C. S. (1942). *J. gen. Physiol.* **25**, 579.

Emerson, R., and Lewis, C. S. (1943). *Amer. J. Bot.* **30**, 165.

Emerson, R., and Rabinowitch, E. (1960). *Plant Physiol.* **35**, 477.

Emerson, R., Chalmers, R. F., and Cederstrand, C. (1957). *Proc. nat. Acad. Sci. Wash.* **43**, 133.

Förster, T. (1959). *Disc. Faraday Soc.* **27**, 7.

Franck, J. (1958). *Proc. nat. Acad. Sci. Wash.* **44**, 941.

French, C. S., and Elliott, R. F. (1958). *Yearb. Carneg. Instn.* **57**, 278.

French, C. S., and Fork, D. C. (1961). International Biochemical Congress, Moscow.

French, C. S., Myers, J., and McLeod, G. C. (1960). "Symposium on Comparative Biochemistry," vol. 7, Academic Press, New York.

Goodheer, J. C. (1957). "Optical Properties and *in vivo* orientation of photosynthetic pigments." Ph.D. thesis, Utrecht.

Govindjee, R., and Rabinowitch, E. I. (1960). *Science* **132**, 355.

Govindjee, R., Ichimura, S., Cederstrand, C., and Rabinowitch, E. I. (1960a). *Arch. Biochem. Biophys.* **89**, 321.

Govindjee, R., Thomas, J. B., and Rabinowitch, E. I. (1960b). *Science* **132**, 421.

Haxo, F. T. (1960). *In* "Comparative Biochemistry of Photoreactive Systems" (M. B. Allen, ed.), ch. 21, Academic Press, New York.

Haxo, F. T., and Blinks, L. R. (1953). *J. gen. Physiol.* **73**, 389.

Hill, R., and Bendall, F. (1960). *Nature, Lond.* **186**, 136.

Hind, G., and Jagendorf, A. T. (1963). *Proc. nat. Acad. Sci., Wash.* **49**, 715.

Katoh, S. (1960). *Nature, Lond.* **186**, 533.

Kok, B., and Beinert, H. (1962). *Biochem. Biophys. Res. Comm.* **9**, 349.

Kok, B., and Hoch, G. (1961). *In* "Light and Life" (W. D. McElroy and B. Glass, eds.), p. 397, Johns Hopkins Press, Baltimore.

Krasnovsky, A. A. (1948). *C. R. Acad. Sci., U.R.S.S.* **60**, 421.

Lavorel, J. (1957). *Phys. Chem.* **61**, 1600.

Levine, R. P., and Smillie, R. M. (1962). *Proc. nat. Acad. Sci. Wash.* **48**, 417.

Livingstone, R. (1954). *Nature, Lond.* **173**, 485.

Müller, A., Fork, D. C., and Witt, H. T. (1963). *Z. Naturf.* **18B**, 142.

Myers, S., and French, C. S. (1960). *J. gen. Physiol.* **43**, 723.

Ó hEocha, C. (1960). *In* "Comparative Biochemistry of Photoreactive Systems" (M. B. Allen, ed.), ch. 12, Academic Press, New York.

Petrack, B., and Lipmann, F. (1961). *In* "Light and Life" (W. D. McElroy and B. Glass, eds.), p. 621, Johns Hopkins Press, Baltimore.

San Pietro, A., and Lang, H. M. (1958). *J. biol. Chem.* **231**, 211.

Tagawa, K., and Arnon, D. I. (1962). *Nature, Lond.* **195**, 537.

Tanada, T. (1951). *Amer. J. Bot.* **38**, 276.

Vorobyova, L. H., and Krasnovsky, A. A. (1958). *Biokhimiya* **23**, 760.

Whittingham, C. P., and Bishop, P. M. (1961). *Nature, Lond.* **192**, 426.

Whittingham, C. P., and Brown, A. H. (1958). *J. exp. Bot.* **9**, 311.

Witt, H. T., Müller, A., and Rumberg, B. (1961). *Nature, Lond.* **191**, 194.

Chapter 14

FUNCTIONS OF CAROTENOIDS OTHER THAN IN PHOTOSYNTHESIS

J. H. BURNETT

Department of Botany, The University of Newcastle upon Tyne, England

I. INTRODUCTION

This account is concerned with certain possible functions of carotenoids in plants, other than in photosynthesis. At the present time it seems to be more valuable to describe certain well-documented situations in some detail than to refer to all the possible suggestions which have been made. Many of these suggestions have been referred to in various recent comprehensive reviews by Goodwin (1952a, 1959).

It has been suggested that carotenoids are implicated in (a) photoresponses, such as those involved in phototropism in higher plants and fungi and phototaxis in motile algal cells and bacteria; (b) reproduction, especially in certain fungi; (c) the protection of cells from damage caused by the incidental absorption of visible light by other pigments, in bacteria and certain algae.

There has been a tendency to seek for a universal function for carotenoids in all plants, whether chlorophyllous or not; the protective function is the only one suggested so far that could conceivably meet such a requirement. With present knowledge however, there is no indisputable reason why carotenoids should have a single, universal function in all plants.

Whatever the cellular, metabolic function(s) of carotenoids may be it is clear that their presence in flowers, fruits and, to some extent, even in leaves, stems and roots of higher plants, subserves important, if incidental, roles in attracting or repelling animals during pollination and dispersal (whether of fruits or vegetative fragments). Once carotenoids have been formed in any organ of a plant they may affect visual stimulation in animals and, thereafter, selection may operate to perpetuate and increase the numbers of individuals forming such carotenoids, or vice versa. In terrestrial higher plants, at least, this may explain the apparently bewildering range of species-specific xanthophylls which are so frequently found in petals and fruits. An implication of this view is that such carotenoids are initially functionless, metabolic by-products whose perpetuation has been maintained through visual selection by animals. Such a view is a slightly more sophisticated version of that expressed nearly thirty years ago by Frey-Wyssling (1935).

It is difficult to suppose that this kind of explanation can account for the occurrence of the plastid carotenoids of terrestrial green plants, or the carotenoids of algae, fungi and bacteria, whether or not they are located in these organisms in specific organelles, e.g. plastids, eye-spots or submicroscopic chromatophores. The functional role of carotenoids in plastids and chromatophores in photosynthesis has been dealt with in the previous chapter. While carotenoids can function in such reactions it may be questioned whether this is their most important cellular function. Other possible functions will now be discussed.

II. PHOTOTROPISM AND PHOTOTAXIS

A. GENERAL OBSERVATIONS

The experimental evidence that carotenoids play some role in photoresponses, such as in phototropism and phototaxis, is inconclusive at present. The evidence is derived almost entirely from the comparison of the action spectrum of the photoresponse with the absorption spectrum of, usually, the major carotenoid component extracted from the organism or organ showing the response. If these spectra are, in the opinion of the investigator, reasonably congruent and, provided that no other compounds exist with absorption spectra which are at least as congruent, then it has been concluded that the carotenoid is the effective photoreceptive pigment involved in the response. It will readily be appreciated that this procedure is liable to a variety of experimental errors and that quite small errors may have a profound effect on interpretations made when the action and absorption spectra are compared.

Two kinds of experimental difficulties lie behind all attempts to investigate the role of carotenoids in photoresponses. The first is to obtain a sufficiently accurate and comprehensive action spectrum of the response; the second is to measure, or assess, the effective absorption spectrum of the carotenoid(s) in the intact organism. French (1959) has clearly described the difficulties inherent in the accurate measurement of action spectra in plants. Recently, it has been stated that "an action spectrum measured to a precision of 12% at 10 mμ wavelength intervals with a half-band width of 5 to 10 mμ is considered good work. The precision now ordinarily obtained in absorption spectroscopy is far greater than in action spectroscopy" (Smith and French, 1963). Very few measurements of the action spectra for phototropic responses have achieved this accuracy and none for phototaxis. The second problem is even more difficult to deal with in experiments and most measurements have been made, in fact, on extracted carotenoids. Measurements made on, more or less, intact cells are difficult to interpret. Such absorption spectra suffer interference by other pigments or absorbing systems in the cells, by scattering losses due to the nature of the material examined and possibly by distortion due to the many fluorescent substances which can occur in higher plants, at least (cf. R. H. Goodwin, 1953). A further source of error is that it may well be that in the living plant the carotenoids occur as carotenoid-protein complexes. This is suggested by the fact that, in higher plants, carotenoids are readily extracted after treatment with a polar solvent (which denatures proteins) but not after treatment with non-polar solvents and by the fact that absorption maxima *in vivo* are somewhat higher than in solvent extracts. Moreover, although it appears to be a special case at present, a unique β-carotene-protein has been identified with reasonable certainty in spinach leaves (Nishimura and Takamatsu, 1957). Shibata (1958) has also drawn attention to the fact that alterations can be brought about in absorption spectra if the carotenoids are present in the cells in a crystalline form, e.g. a peak at 515 mμ in the spectrum of β-carotene in carrot tissue which is not present when extracted in a solvent such as benzene.

It will now be convenient to consider these problems in more detail for phototropism in higher plants and fungi and for phototaxis in algae and flagellates.

B. PHOTOTROPISM IN HIGHER PLANTS

In two recent reviews, W. R. Briggs (1963, 1964) has suggested that there are at least four well-defined phototropic systems which have been effectively characterized for coleoptiles of grasses and that it is not clear whether these systems are necessarily the same as those found in dicotyledonous flowering plants. Moreover, the relationship of these types of growth curvature to the so-called "light-growth" reactions first described by Blaauw (1914, 1915, 1918) is not very clear. Even if carotenoids are implicated in any one system, therefore, they may, or may not, be implicated in any other system.

The system which has been studied most fully is Brigg's system I; positive curvatures towards a light source by the coleoptiles of oats (*Avena*) and maize (*Zea*), the extreme tip of the coleoptile being the most sensitive perceptive region. The most effective wave-lengths are in the blue and long ultra-violet so that the peaks of the action spectrum for *Avena* lie at 370, 425, 445 and 474 mμ, figures which have been determined with reasonable exactitude (Shropshire and Withrow, 1958; Thimann and Curry, 1960). Compared with the absorption spectrum of a direct hexane extract of some 500 lyophylized coleoptile tips, which had been freed from all internal leaf tissue, there was considerable similarity. Three of the peaks of the absorption spectrum of the extract were at somewhat shorter wave-lengths 422, 442, and 474 mμ but this could reflect the different absorptive properties of hexane-extracted carotenoids and carotenoid-proteins *in vivo*. The principal discrepancy was that the peak at 370 mμ in the action spectrum was replaced by a hollow in the absorption spectrum of the extract. Thimann and Curry have suggested that in the intact plant a *cis*-isomer of a carotene such as β-carotene could be present which has a peak at just under 350 mμ. This is a good deal shorter than that in the action spectrum at 370 mμ. Indeed, very few of the *cis*-isomers of the all-*trans*-carotenoids have peaks at wave-lengths as long as that found in the action spectrum. Moreover, it is necessary to account for the absence of a *cis*-isomer in the extract and this inevitably requires the development of further hypotheses which at present are unsubstantiated.

An alternative hypothesis to account for findings such as these was that developed by Galston (cf. review, 1959) who suggested that the photoreceptor molecule was riboflavin. The case for riboflavin was based largely upon the supposed metabolic interactions between indole acetic acid and riboflavin, the former being implicated as the effective hormone in bringing about the phototropic response. No clear implication of carotenoids with indole acetic acid metabolism are known. It is only fair to point out, however, that the role of indole acetic acid itself in phototropism is not entirely clear. The comparison of the absorption spectrum of riboflavin with the action spectrum of System I phototropism is no more satisfactory than when the comparison is made with carotenoids. It is true that in riboflavin there is a peak in the 340 mμ region, although it is higher relative to that at longer wave-lengths than with carotenoids. Moreover there is only a single peak in the 450 mμ region with riboflavin as compared with the clearly demonstrable double peak in this region of the action spectrum and in the absorption spectrum of the carotenoids. Finally riboflavin exhibits a relatively very high peak at 265 mμ, which is apparently quite without parallel in the action spectrum, although in neither of the best measured instances is the action spectrum extended into this region. Absorption in the 250–280 mμ region in intact material could, of course, be accounted for by purines, aromatic amino acids, nucleic acids, phytoene or other materials and the significance of action spectra in such regions is, therefore, open to question.*

The partial congruence of the absorption curves of carotenoids and riboflavin with the action spectrum of System I responses, has been held by Reinert (1953) to indicate an interaction of both types of compounds. In his view, riboflavin is the significant photoreceptor-molecule but the presence of carotenoids results in the "masking" and depression of part of the single peak at c. 450 mμ in the absorption curve of the riboflavin. This, therefore, appears as a double peak. His ingenious hypothesis has not stood up to rigorous quantitative considerations (Thimann and Curry, 1960) and it is evident that such a system, involving interference between two pigments one only of which is effective in photoresponse, can only result in an action spectrum showing relatively small modifications. Furthermore, the absolute amounts of riboflavin and carotenoid in the *Avena* coleoptile are known (Johnston, 1934; Bünning, 1955) and, in these circumstances, the "masking" of riboflavin by carotenoids as required by Reinert's hypothesis can be shown to be too small to account for the form of the action spectrum.

There is little other evidence to support either carotenoids or riboflavin as the photoreceptor molecule. Histochemical studies on the localization of carotenoids are equivocal (Bünning, 1937a, b; Lange, 1927). Comparisons between mutants with reduced or non-detectable carotenoid contents and normal plants in respect of their phototropic responses are equally equivocal. Carotene-less mutants of *Zea* and *Hordeum* (Galston, 1959) are said to show no reduction in phototropic sensitivity but in *Helianthus* a mutant said to be "probably containing excessively low levels of carotene" (Thimann and Curry, 1960) showed abnormally low phototropic sensitivity. This approach is, in any case, difficult since it seems to be generally agreed that photoreceptor molecules need only be present in very small concentrations to be quite effective.

To any worker outside the immediate cut and thrust of experimentation and argument on this particular topic, it does seem as if there is no unambiguous evidence in favour of carotenoids as the photoreceptor molecules in the positive phototropic response of coleoptile tips.

The situation for System I photoresponses in higher plants has been discussed in some detail. It is sufficient to indicate here that

*Galston (X Botanical Congress, August, 1964) claimed that riboflavin in lipid material gave an absorption spectrum most similar to the action spectrum. Thimann counterclaimed that *cis*-carotenes gave a higher degree of congruence.

13

consideration of the role of carotenoids as possible photoreceptor molecules in other systems of phototropic response at present is even less worthwhile. The experimental data have been determined less precisely and the nature of the photoreceptor is, therefore, even more obscure than for System I responses.

C. PHOTOTROPISM IN FUNGI

In mucoraceous fungi, e.g. *Mucor, Phycomyces, Pilobolus*, carotenoids, notably β-carotene, have been implicated in phototropic curvatures of the sporangia-bearing structures, or sporangiophores. A considerable number of mucoraceous fungi lack β-carotene (Hocking, 1963a) and some of these are known to be indifferent or only weakly responsive to light, e.g. *Rhizopus nigricans, R. sexualis; Pilobolus sphaerospora*. The situation is of some interest compared with that in higher plants, for these fungi differ in that their carotenoids are not apparently located in specific organelles and indole acetic acid is almost certainly not involved in the tropistic response. The optical system involved in perception at the highly transparent tips, or subjacent regions, of the very slender sporangiophores has also been a subject of discussion and controversy (Banbury, 1959) and the situation here is clearly very different from that in most higher plants. Heim (1947), on the basis of an histochemical examination of a considerable number of Ascomycetes and Basidiomycetes and a review of earlier literature, concluded that carotenoids might well be formed in "chondriocontes", which are homologized with mitochondria, although the pigments might later become dispersed in the cytoplasm, usually in association with lipid material. Little or nothing is known of the phototropic responses of such fungi. In the mucoraceous fungi the coloured carotenoids appear to be closely associated with lipid material which is dispersed more or less irregularly throughout the cell. Recently, however Hocking (1963b) has shown that up to 4% of the β-carotene in *Mucor hiemalis* is associated with protein, although 70–75% is associated with free lipid and 20–25% with bound lipids (defined according to Hawk *et al.*, 1951). The scattered and somewhat controversial literature on the possible role of indole acetic acid as a growth regulator in fungi has been summarized by Gruen (1959) and it may be concluded with some certainty that the hormones implicated in flowering plants are ineffective in fungi.

Phototropic curvatures have been studied especially in the sporangiophores of *Phycomyces* and *Pilobolus*. In the former, Banbury (1952) has provided good direct evidence that indole acetic acid is not involved in such responses. As in the higher plants there are various kinds of responses including positive and negative curvatures in visible light, negative curvatures in ultra-violet light and light-growth responses of various kinds. In 1959, Curry and Gruen provided a reasonably precise action spectrum using a balance method for the positive response, and ultra-violet light-induced negative, curvatures of the sporangiophore of *Phycomyces*. Peaks were found at 474 and 445 mμ and a lower one at 370 mμ. These peaks are in reasonable agreement with earlier and less precise measurements of Bünning (1937a, b) in *Pilobolus*; here the peaks were at 485, 445 and 360 mμ. Both sets of data are comparable to those in the System I data described for *Avena* coleoptiles. Delbrück and Shropshire (1960) reported similar maxima in the following year using single sporangiophores of *Phycomyces*, viz. 485, 455, 385 and 280 mμ, the last being almost seven times larger than that in the visible. However, they used an entirely different method and rejected that of Curry and Gruen as a method which had already been tested and rejected. They conclude, "In view of these criticisms, the contention of Curry and Gruen of a double peak in the blue, characteristic of the absorption of β-carotene, cannot be considered as substantiated by their measurements." The optical difficulties in making measurements, already referred to, are stressed by Delbrück and Shropshire and they give a particularly good discussion of the problem of screening pigments, including consideration of the effect of gallic acid found to be an important constituent of the vacuole (Dennison, 1959). They, themselves, draw no conclusions as to the nature of the photoreceptor pigments apart from rejecting β-carotene because of the peaks in the ultra-violet. Goodwin (1952b) has characterized the carotenoids in *Phycomyces* with great precision, 84% being β-carotene, while "carotene" (probably a mixture in which β-carotene predominates) was identified by Bünning in his work on *Pilobolus*. Carlile (1957) re-interpreted early data concerning the negative, ultra-violet induced curvatures and presented his results as an action spectrum with a single peak at 280 mμ, a result borne out by the later work of Curry and Gruen (1957, 1959). On the basis of this action spectrum Carlile suggests that the photoreceptor molecule is a riboflavin rather than carotenoid. This interpretation has been questioned on methodological grounds by Banbury (1958, 1959) who points out that there is an inherent error in using phototropic curvature as a measure of photodynamic effectiveness in a relatively transparent organ, for the value of the absorption coefficient changes with wavelength, so changing the gradient of the correlated photon absorption per unit volume. As with higher plants it seems, therefore, that insufficient data are available for a clear discrimination to be made between the carotenoids and the flavins.

In these, and other fungi, however, it has proved possible both to prepare strains with reduced carotenoids e.g. *Phycomyces* grown in the presence of diphenylamine (Goodwin, 1958), *Pilobolus* strains (Schneider,

1943; Paul, 1950 in Banbury, 1959) or mutants of *Neurospora* (Haxo, 1956). In these, phototropic responses still occur strongly although no precise measurements are available. It should be noted that in these fungal cultures the β-carotene is considerably reduced but, at the same time, there is some increase in the less saturated carotenoids, e.g. *Phycomyces*, diphenylamine treated/normal values in μg: β-carotene 25/586; phytofluence 80/15; ζ-carotene 47/5. It will be noted that there is an appreciable amount of β-carotene present in diphenylamine-treated cultures which may well be sufficient to mediate the photoresponse in a very slender organ like the sporangiophore where carotenoids tend to accumulate in the photo-sensitive tip.

Two other kinds of investigation, neither specifically concerned with phototropic response, have some bearing on the possible occurrence of flavins as photoreceptor molecules in *Phycomyces* and *Pilobolus*. In the former Carlile (1962) has shown that mepacrine has a marked depressant effect on growth (measured as dry weight) of illuminated cultures but not on dark cultures; diphenylamine had no such differential effect. He suggested that this indicates that there is an effective flavoprotein system which operates as a photoreceptor in illuminated cultures and which can be inhibited by mepacrine. Page (1956) studied the photo-induction of trophocysts (potential asexual reproductive structures) in *Pilobolus* and suggested that riboflavin was implicated as the photo-receptor because of the action spectrum of the effect and because lyxoflavin was found to inhibit the morphogenetic changes. Lyxoflavin operated as a specific, competitive inhibitor to riboflavin and its in-hibitory effect could be reversed by the supply of additional exogenous riboflavin to the cultures. Recently Hocking (1963b) has repeated and extended Carlile's experiments. Although he obtained similar results in static cultures of *Phycomyces* and *Mucor hiemalis*, he obtained entirely different results in shake cultures of these fungi. In particular, he found no differential effect of mepacrine on illuminated and dark cultures. He, therefore, suggested that the mepacrine effect was metabolically non-specific and was related to the cultural conditions. The specificity of inhibition of flavins by mepacrine had already been seriously questioned (Hemker and Hülsmann, 1960). Hocking also investigated the effect of adding lyxoflavin to the cultures and found no growth inhibition under the conditions of his experiments. Hocking has, therefore, cast some doubt on the role of riboflavin as a photoreceptor in these growth reactions and hence on Carlile's suggestion that they were allied to phototropic responses. None of the results obtained by Hocking could be interpreted as favouring an alternative view, that carotenoids were responsible for these photoresponses. His evidence, like so much in this field, is unfortunately negative.

D. PHOTOTAXIS IN ALGAE AND FLAGELLATES

Carotenoids have been implicated in the phototactic responses of several flagellates. The nature of the photoreceptor organelle is unknown in these organisms although it is believed to be near the base of the flagella (Halldal, 1958). Several possess a pigmented organelle, the stigma or so-called eye-spot, but it is now certain this plays a secondary role in the response. As long ago as 1878 Strasburger described phototaxis in motile algae and fungal zoospores including ones which lacked a stigma. Many dinoflagellates which lack a stigma show positive responses and, more recently, mutants have been obtained which lack a stigma yet show normal responses, e.g. a pyribenzamine-treated *Euglena* sp. (Gössel, 1957) or somewhat impaired but effective, responses, e.g. ultra-violet treated *Chlamydomonas* (Hartshorne, 1953). In general, forms which lack a stigma are less sensitive in their response to light and some forms show no response at all. Mast (1927) suggested that the pigments in the stigma screened the primary photoreceptor and the organism responded in such a way as to minimize this screening. If the stigma functions in this way then its pigments are of some importance to phototaxis and the action spectrum for such a response may be compounded from the absorptive effects of stigma and photoreceptor pigments; a situation similar to, but different from, that envisaged by Reinert (1953) and already referred to earlier (p. 385). Halldal (1958) pointed out that the action spectrum in colourless flagellates could be distorted and give little information. If a screening body, e.g. a stigma, is able to reduce the illumination on the photoreceptor by at least 10% then supposing Weber's law to hold, the cell will only react within the overlapping region of the action spectra of the screening body and of the photoreceptor where the cell absorbs 10% or more, of the light. In coloured organisms such as green algae there will be a wide range of overlap between cell pigments which will absorb at least 10% of the light over the whole visible spectrum, so that the effective action spectrum for phototaxis should not be distorted from this cause. Experiments in which an analogous form of screening was studied, that of cells by other cells, bore out Halldal's view.

The organisms studied with some precision have been green algae such as Volvocales like *Chlamydomonas*, *Platymonas* and colonial forms such as *Eudorina* and *Volvox* and gametes or zoospores, e.g. *Ulva*; euglenoids, both coloured and colourless forms of *Euglena*; dinoflagellates like *Peridinium*, *Gonyaulax* and *Prorocentrum* and colourless flagellates like *Chilomonas*.

Action spectra for positive and negative phototaxis, i.e. response towards and away from light, respectively, have in general, been found to be identical in shape, although most responding organisms do so at much lower intensities in the positive response. The outstanding case where a very different action spectrum was obtained for positive and negative response in *Euglena* (Bünning and Schneiderhöhn, 1956) has been severely criticized on technical grounds (Halldal, 1958). In *Euglena* maxima occur at 495 and 475 mμ and lesser peaks at 450 and 425 mμ (Bünning and Schneiderhöhn, 1956); less precise measurements (Wolken and Shin, 1958) gave a peak at 490 mμ and a lesser peak at 420 mμ. In the Volvocales, *Eudorina* and *Volvox* showed a peak at 492 mμ (Lunz, 1931) and more recently Halldal (1958) found a more or less identical peak at 493 mμ with a clear shoulder at 435 mμ for five species of the genera *Dunaliella*, *Stephanoptera* and *Platymonas*; *Ulva* gametes showed a rather flat-topped response between a lower shoulder at *c.* 435 mμ and a peak at 485 mμ. The dinoflagellates *Peridinium* and *Gonyaulax* gave a sharp peak at 475 mμ and *Prorocentrum* at 570 mμ (Halldal, 1958) and the colourless flagellate *Chilomonas* a peak in the ultra-violet at 366 mμ (Lunz, 1931). This last organism was, however, almost 10^3 times less sensitive than the photosynthetic organisms studied. Most recently of all, Halldal (1961) has studied phototaxis of *Platymonas* and extended the spectrum into the ultra-violet region. He finds the principal peak at 495 mμ declining to a shoulder at 450 mμ, a small peak at 405 mμ and larger peaks at 335 and 275 mμ.

Attempts have also been made to study the absorption spectra of intact cells and of the stigma itself. Gössel (1957) attempted to measure the absorption spectra of stigmata of achlorophyllous strains of *Euglena* and the green euglenoid *Phacus acuminatus*. She employed a monochromatic source and a special microspectrophotometer with a beam only $3\cdot2$ μ wide; the dimensions of the stigmata in the two genera were $2 \times 2\cdot9$ μ and $5\cdot7 \times 3\cdot2$ μ respectively. She compared absorption spectra taken in the region of the stigmata with those from other parts of the cell as a control. All the stigmata showed a flat maximum in the region of 460 mμ declining gradually to about 600/625 mμ; in a particularly clear example she believed she could recognize a major peak at 460 mμ and lesser peaks at 420 and 440 mμ. There is no direct information concerning the identity of the pigments of the stigma of any alga or flagellate. Astaxanthin, which occurs in green algae and euglenoids, with an absorption maximum at *c.* 500 mμ (in CS_2) is unlikely to be involved even in conjunction with β-carotene (Gössel, 1957). There is no evidence for supporting Krinsky and Goldsmith's (1960) suggestion that keto carotenoids, like euglenanone, are stigma pigments. So far as intact cells are concerned, their absorption spectra resemble their action spectra plus additional peaks caused by photosynthetic pigments (e.g. Halldal, 1958).

The interpretation of the action spectra for phototaxis is no more clear than for other light responses. Some observers have supposed that pigments like astaxanthin are involved in *Euglena* (Bünning and Schneiderhöhn, 1956) and, after some hesitation, Halldal (1958, 1961) has now claimed that in the Volvocales and *Ulva* gametes carotenoids are implicated. He bases this view on his most recent work and compares his action spectrum with that obtained by workers on phototropism in *Phycomyces* such as Curry and Gruen and Delbrück and Shropshire (cf. p. 387). He supposes that the peaks in the visible are due to carotenoids, and also that at 335 mμ but the absorption at 275 mμ is said to be due to aromatic amino acids in a protein combined with the pigment. He points out that Krinsky and Goldsmith (1960) have reported the presence of traces of ketocarotenoids in a *Euglena* sp., one of which should be capable of binding with a protein. Without precise knowledge of the carotenoids in motile cells of Chlorophyta it is not really profitable to speculate. However, it is of interest and perhaps significant that *Ulva* gametes contain considerable amounts of γ-carotene (Haxo and Clendenning, 1953) whose absorption peaks lie between about 430–495 mμ, in hexane (Goodwin, 1952a). It certainly does look as if the two alternative photoreceptor pigments, the flavins and, more doubtfully, the pterins can be excluded from these cases, if it be supposed that the action and absorption spectra of living cells are meaningful.

The flagellates are, however, at the present time not so readily interpreted. Of course carotenoid-protein complexes may be invoked for the dinoflagellates with accompanying shifts in the absorption spectra of the carotenoids; even so, other difficulties arise. Peridininin, and diadinoxanthin and dinoxanthin have been isolated from *Peridinium* spp., all with a maximum at around 470–480 mμ but, in each case, they also have at least one other maximum, a good deal higher in peridinin, much lower in the other two pigments (Goodwin, 1952a). This does not match the action curves with their single, remarkably sharp maxima. The action spectrum of the colourless flagellate *Chilomonas* may well represent a distorted spectrum caused by the interaction of a screening pigment and a photoreceptor described earlier in this section. Riboflavin seems to be ruled out by the very low sensitivity of the organism to light: nothing is known concerning its pigment or flavin content.

It may be concluded that there is here, as in other plant photoresponses, a dearth of adequate knowledge on which to judge whether or not carotenoids play a functional role. The mechanism of phototaxis is not understood, neither the perceptive mechanism, the transfer of the stimulus nor the response. Even so, it seems not wholly impossible that, somehow or other, carotenoids are involved in perception in the green algae, at least.

Incidentally, phototaxis in algae and flagellates is clearly not akin to that in the purple bacteria where the process is mediated through a photosynthetic mechanism (Clayton, 1959). Algae and flagellates are far more sensitive to light than these bacteria, e.g. the phototactic threshold for *Rhodospirillum* is of the order of 10^4 times higher than that for *Euglena* (Manten, 1948); in *Ulva* gametes the saturation intensity for photosynthesis is about 72,000 ft-c, that for phototaxis about 100 ft-c (Goodwin, 1959); and in *Chlamydomonas*, phototactic response can take place normally in the absence of CO_2 (Mayer and Poljakoff-Mayber, 1959).

III. REPRODUCTION

A. GENERAL OBSERVATIONS

Goodwin (1950) has drawn attention to the widespread occurrence and accumulation of carotenoids in reproductive structures of plants and animals. It has been argued already, in the introduction to this chapter, that the carotenoids subserve the passive function of making flowers, fruits and even perhaps certain vegetative parts of higher plants, attractive to animals, thereby promoting processes such as pollination and dispersal. There is no firm evidence in support of any metabolic role for carotenoids in the reproduction of higher plants, or indeed amongst terrestrial lower plants. The situation in the algae and fungi is still obscure. The remarkable claims of Moewus (Kuhn and Moewus, 1940) for the functional role of crocetin esters in *Chlamydomonas* species are now effectively disproved on theoretical (Philip and Haldane, 1939; Thimann, 1940) and practical grounds (Ryan, 1955; Hartmann, 1955; Renner, 1958) and are best left without further discussion. It is clear that light is nearly always involved in the initiation of the mating reaction, but the action spectrum appears to implicate photosynthesis and it need not be considered further here.

In the fungi, the notion that carotenoids are involved in reproduction must be attributed to Chodat and Schopfer (1927) who drew attention to the differential accumulation of "carotene" in the + and − mating types of *Mucor hiemalis* and concluded that it was an important sexual difference. (Blakeslee, 1904, had noted this difference but drawn no conclusions from it.) Since then mycologists have sporadically noted this and similar phenomena and the idea has grown up that carotene and sexuality are, in some way, related. There are certainly fungi which possess no carotenoids and many which only possess one predominantly, usually β-carotene or lycopene (Goodwin, 1952c). Presumably, therefore, carotenoids do not play any universal role in fungal reproduction. Moreover, Carlile (1956) has shown that in *Fusarium macrosporum* it was possible to obtain macrospores in the absence of carotenoids and vice versa, although both processes were the result of a photostimulus;

similarly in *Pyronema confluens* (Carlile and Friend, 1956) sexual reproduction was shown to be a light-stimulated process which could still take place in a mutant lacking carotenoids. It is, however, amongst the Phycomycetes that the supposed connection has been most strongly pressed and the rest of this section will consider them alone.

B. REPRODUCTION IN PHYCOMYCETES

Carotenoids are supposed to be involved in the reproduction of Zygomycetes e.g., *Mucor, Phycomyces*, and Blastocladiales, e.g. *Allomyces, Blastocladiella*. The kinds of role envisaged are two-fold. Firstly in sexual or mating-type dimorphism; secondly, in the progress of the sexual reproductive process.

Attention has already been drawn to Schopfer's claim (Chodat and Schopfer, 1927; Schopfer, 1927) that the + mating type of *Mucor hiemalis* contained a higher concentration of "carotene" than the − mating type. A similar claim was made for *Phycomyces* sp. by Burgeff (1924) and later by Schopfer (1943) and for other Mucorales by Satina and Blakeslee (1926). In *Allomyces*, Emerson and Fox (1940) noted the accumulation of γ-carotene in the male gametangium and gametes compared with the colourless, adjacent female gametangium. Similarly in *Blastocladiella variabilis* the gametophyte (haploid) generation bear either a colourless female gametangium or an orange-coloured male (Harder and Sörgel, 1938).

Exceptions can be found to nearly all these cases, either in the same, or in related, species. Thus both Price (1927) and Ling-Yong (1930) isolated large numbers of strains of *M. hiemalis* and showed that it was not always the + mating type that accumulated the most carotene. A similar reversal was also recorded in strains of *Phycomyces* sp. (Garton *et al.*, 1950, 1951). In the fungus *Blastocladiella emersonii* it was shown that orange plants could always be derived from swarmers from colourless plants, so that the presence of pigment appeared to be determined environmentally and not genotypically (Emerson, 1950). In this fungus the pigment is again γ-carotene (Cantino and Hyatt, 1953a). In both *Allomyces* and *Blastocladiella* it has proved possible to interfere with carotenoid synthesis. In the former the carotenoid content has been reduced to 5% of normal (although there was a concomitant increase of phytofluene and an unidentified carotenoid (Turian, 1952; Turian and Haxo, 1954)) by treatment with diphenylamine and, in addition, albino ultra-violet induced mutants have been isolated (Foley, 1958). In the latter, orange mutants have been isolated which virtually never produce colourless offspring (Cantino and Hyatt, 1953b). The suppressed *Allomyces* functioned normally and produced functional gametes, but the mutant form produced only female gametangia. This is thought by

13*

Foley to be significant since there is no doubt that the mutant form possesses far less carotenoid, if any, than the suppressed plants. It has also been thought significant that no coloured polyenes or colourless C_{40}-polyenes were detected in the sporophyte (Emerson and Fox, 1940; Turian and Haxo, 1954). The mutant *Blastocladiella*, like the normal pigmented plants, produces gametes which have never been seen to fuse either amongst themselves or with the presumed female gametes from colourless plants.

There seems to be no reason to suppose that reproductive dimorphism in the Zygomycetes is related to carotenoid content, but in the Blastocladiales the position is still obscure. In *Allomyces*, in particular, there does seem to be a strong correlation between maleness and accumulation of γ-carotene and, as in the albino mutant, the absence of carotenoid appears to be associated with an inability to develop male gametangia. The position in *Blastocladiella* is obscure and while far more is known of the general metabolism of this organism through the work of Cantino and his associates, it would seem wiser to search for a functional role for carotenoids in reproductive dimorphism in *Allomyces*, or possibly *B. variabilis*, at the present time. The metabolic role of the carotenoids in such dimorphic phenomena is unclear.

Evidence for some metabolic role for carotenoids, more or less specifically β-carotene, in reproduction has come largely from mucoraceous fungi. In his classic paper on heterothallism in 1904, Blakeslee commented upon the accumulation of yellow oil droplets in the progametangia and gametangia of many Mucoraceae. He also noted that the rare strains of *Phycomyces blakesleeanus* which were heterocaryotic for mating type, i.e. carried both + and − determining nuclei, developed an intense yellow colour which enabled them to be readily detected. Their vegetative growth was also impaired (Blakeslee, 1906). Some twenty years later Burgeff (1924) attempted to investigate the hormonal co-ordination of the reproductive processes by separating + and − mating types with a permeable membrane. He observed that the zone of reaction, induced by the diffusion of unknown hormones through the membrane, was intensely coloured as the result of yellow oil droplets developing in the reacting hyphae. This observation has been repeatedly observed by later workers in species of *Phycomyces* and *Mucor* (Köhler, 1935; Burnett, 1952; Plempel, 1957). Köhler, indeed, claimed that in *Mucor mucedo* carotene formation was essential for the mating reaction to proceed. An even more striking phenomenon which appeared to implicate carotenoids in reproduction was the observation that although + and − mating types of *Choanephora cucurbitarum* differ only slightly in their β-carotene content, mixtures of the two strains produce fifteen to twenty times as much as does either strain grown alone. This is true even if the two mating types are separated by a cellophane membrane; the effect is reciprocal and evidently mediated by one or more diffusable substances (Barnett *et al.*, 1956). Other members of this family, the Choanephoraceae, were shown to behave similarly in both intra-specific, and inter-specific crosses (Hesseltine and Anderson, 1957). It has been supposed for some time that the course of the mating reaction in all mucoraceous fungi was mediated through similar diffusible hormones (Blakeslee and Cartledge, 1927; Burnett, 1953b, 1956b) so that the results obtained in inter-specific crosses of Choanephoraceae were not wholly unexpected. Attempts have been made to see if this phenomenon occurs in other mucoraceous fungi. Reichel and Wallis (1958) found no stimulation of carotene formation in mixed mating-type cultures compared with production by mating types grown singly of *Phycomyces blakesleeanus* and this was also the case for β-carotene in *Mucor hiemalis* and *Phycomyces* spp. tested in various inter- and intra-specific combinations by Hocking (1963a). Indeed Hocking found no evidence for β-carotene formation at all in a number of species of the genera *Cunninghamella, Absidia, Rhizophus, Zygorrhynchus, Thamnidium, Conidiobolus* and *Pilobolus*. Carotenoid production at reproduction seems to be a phenomenon in *Mucor, Phycomyces* and Choanephoraceae and only in the latter group is there this notable increase of β-carotene throughout the mycelium when compatible mating types come together. It does seem, however, that there is an increased accumulation in the reacting region even in *Mucor* and *Phycomyces* although no net increase in amount in the reacting mycelia as a whole. In *Phycomyces blakesleeanus* an attempt was made (Burnett, 1956a) to investigate simultaneously the effect of modifying β-carotene synthesis and reproduction. No stoicheiometric relationship was found between the β-carotene content and zygote production and, indeed, diphenylamine cultures are still capable of producing zygotes (Goodwin, 1959). The only effect common to the two processes was the observation that pH 7·0 inhibited β-carotene synthesis and also zygote formation, although not that of gametangia and suspensors. This suggested that carotenoids might be implicated in the early stages of zygote formation. The only other observation bearing upon this point is that zinc-deficient cultures of *Rhizopus nigricans* result in the inhibition of zygote formation (Niethammer, 1938) and it is known that zinc deficiency can result in failure to form carotenoids in some fungi (Hawker, 1957). Although no β-carotene was found by Hocking in *R. nigricans* no investigation was made for the presence of any other carotenoids. It must be admitted that effects induced by factors such as abnormal pH or mineral deficiency are likely to be the result of a general disturbance of metabolism and it would be rash indeed to think of them as only affecting carotenoids. Thus the impairment of β-carotene synthesis and of zygote formation could readily be due to quite different immediate causes and the apparent correlation would then be spurious.

It does seem, however, as if an accumulation of β-carotene, in particular, is a concomitant of the reactions in the mating zone in certain mucoraceous fungi. This may merely represent an accumulation of metabolic products which tend to be produced whenever the general metabolic rate is increased and this latter certainly does seem to be the case (Burnett, 1953a). The accumulation of carotenoids would then be coincidental to the process of sexual reproduction and of no direct significance in the process. Although this is not yet proven it is probably the most plausible interpretation at the present time.

IV. PROTECTION

It now appears to be well established for bacteria, whether photosynthetic or not, that carotenoids can protect the cell from damage due to photo-oxidation catalysed by other light absorbing pigments such as chlorophylls, porphyrins, flavins, etc. Stanier and Cohen-Bazire (1957) suggested that this could be a general function of carotenoids in all plants which contain them.

In 1951, Swart-Füchtbauer and Rippel-Baldes showed that sunlight in the spectral region 366–405 mμ had a marked bactericidal effect. This suggested some form of pigment sensitized photo-oxidation, operative in the visible spectrum. The first evidence for such an effect was described for a mutant of the purple bacterium *Rhodopseudomonas spheroides* in 1955 and the situation has now been investigated in considerable detail in the mutant (Griffiths *et al.*, 1955; Griffiths and Stanier, 1956; Sistrom, *et al.*, 1956; Dworkin, 1958) and in normal cells in which carotenoid formation has been inhibited (Cohen-Bazire and Stanier, 1958; Fuller and Anderson, 1958; Dworkin, 1959).

In the mutant bacterial cell the normal coloured carotenes are replaced by the more highly saturated, colourless polyene phytoene; bacteriochlorophyll is also formed but in lesser amounts than in the normal cell. The cells can photosynthesize normally under the usual strictly anaerobic conditions but, if exposed to light under aerobic conditions the cells are rapidly killed and their bacteriochlorophyll destroyed. Normal cells are not killed by exposure to these conditions nor are mutant cells killed by exposure to aerobic conditions alone; indeed in both cases growth continues for at least 10–12 h and bacteriochlorophyll is synthesized by the former and not lost in the latter. Thus the death of the mutant is due to exposure both to light and oxygen. The bacteriochlorophyll absorbs light *in vivo* between 820 and 920 mμ. The mutant was exposed to light passed through a filter completely opaque to all wave-lengths shorter than 800 mμ and air introduced, once again cells were killed and the bacteriochlorophyll destroyed. There seems little doubt, therefore, that in this mutant the bacteriochlorophyll is the photosensitizing agent and, in the non-mutant cell, that protection is afforded by the normal carotenoids.

The protective action of the carotenoids in normal cells has been shown in *R. spheroides*, *Rhodospirillum rubrum* and *Chromatium* by interfering with carotenoid synthesis. Diphenylamine was added to cultures and as the carotenoids were depleted the characteristic lethal symptoms developed in light and aerobic conditions; removal of the diphenylamine restored synthesis of carotenoids and reduced the photosensitivity of the cells. In *Chromatium* a similar effect was observed using only the bacterial chromatophores. Chromatophores from the mutant had their photophosphorylative ability totally destroyed by an exposure of 10 min to light and air while those of normal cells retained 63% of their initial activity under the same conditions, and even after 30 min exposure still showed 42% activity. It is clear, therefore, that the phenomenon within the cell is intimately connected with the chromatophores in which both carotenoids and bacteriochlorophylls are located.

Investigations of this phenomenon have now been extended to non-photosynthetic bacteria such as *Corynebacterium poinsettiae* (Kunisawa and Stanier, 1958), *Sarcina lutea* (Mathews and Sistrom, 1959; Mathews, 1964) and *Mycobacterium* spp. (Mathews, 1963; Wright and Rilling, 1963). In all these cases it has been shown that the absence of carotenoids is associated with a lack of protection against lethal photodynamic action in the presence of a photosensitizer. In *Corynebacterium* lacking carotenoids, whether diphenylamine-treated normal cells or pigmentless mutants, cells were only killed on exposure to light in the presence of the exogenous, photosensitizing dye, toluidine blue. Similar photosensitized killing was known from *Serratia marescens* (Kaplan, 1956) and occurs in *Sarcina*. However, in this latter organism 99% of carotene-less mutant cells are killed in 2 h on exposing them to sunlight in the presence of oxygen without the addition of an exogenous photosensitizing pigment. Normal cells were unaffected by light whether in atmospheres of oxygen or nitrogen and even mutant cells were unaffected by light in an atmosphere of nitrogen. It has also been shown that the carotenoids in normal *Sarcina* cells are probably in the cell envelope, i.e. interposed between the light and the internal, unknown photosensitizing pigment (Mathews and Sistrom, 1960). Despite studies in this and other organisms, the nature of the cellular photosensitizing pigment(s) in non-photosynthetic bacteria are still unknown, although Wright and Rilling (1963) suggest that the photosensitizer absorbs in much the same spectral region as the carotenoids in their carotene-less *Mycobacterium* sp. If this is so then the

13**

system differs from that in photosynthetic bacteria or toluidene blue
mediated photo-killing, where the light is absorbed at a different wavelength from the carotenoids. In a system like this *Mycobacterium* the
light is presumably partitioned between the different pigments and the
carotenoids function as screening pigments, a situation analogous to
that already discussed in relation to algal phototaxis (p. 389).

There seems to be little doubt that carotenoids can and do function as
photochemical buffering agents in several bacteria. It now remains to
investigate the precise metabolic mechanisms involved. So far the only
kinds of experiments made to attack this problem have involved comparisons of the effect at normal and low (0–4° C) temperatures, but no
coherent information has, as yet, emerged from this work (Dworkin,
1959; Wright and Rilling, 1963; Mathews, 1964).

There is no convincing evidence that carotenoids function in this
manner in plants other than bacteria. Both Stanier and Cohen-Bazire
(1957) and Mathews and Sistrom (1959) have pointed out that the observation that carotenogenesis is frequently stimulated by light in fungi or
bacteria becomes intelligible, in an ecological sense, if this is an adaptive
process leading to protection from photosensitized photo-oxidation. It
is also a common observation that the water fern *Azolla filiculoides*
develops a deep red colour if exposed to high insolation. A similar
observation on the pondweed *Potamogeton fluitans* has been shown to
be due to the production of rhodoxanthin and this might be thought
to be a protective response (Ahrens, 1940).

There are available a number of carotene-less strains of algae and fungi
which should enable an analysis to be made similar to that in the bacteria.
Thus Claes (1954, 1956, 1957, 1958) isolated mutants of *Chlorella vulgaris*
which lacked the primary carotenoids but possessed phytoene, phytofluene etc., a situation analogous to that in the purple bacteria. Mutants
5/871, 5/515 and 9a are all killed by light under aerobic conditions, but
unfortunately these mutants are said to show greatly reduced chlorophyll
synthesis and, in the case of 9a, red light is ineffective in destroying the
pigments and killing the cells (Kandler and Schotz, 1956). It is known
from studies on the bleaching of chlorophyll in the related *C. pyrenoidosa*
that the speed and effectiveness of the breakdown is in part conditional
on the chlorophyll content, notably the chlorophyll *b* fraction which has
a stabilizing function (Allen, 1958). Thus the situation is not so clear cut
in the *Chlorella* mutants as in the purple bacteria and it seems possible
that a different interpretation is required, even although Claes and
Nakayama (1959) have shown that the aerobic destruction of chlorophyll
in vitro can only be alleviated by carotenoids with a conjugated chain
length at least equivalent to that in neurosporene, i.e. longer than in the
carotenoids of the light sensitive mutants. Similar difficulties arise in the

case of carotene-less mutants of *Chlamydomonas* such as that studied by Sager and Zalokar (1958). This *pale-green* mutant had less than 0·5% of the total carotenoid content of the normal plant and lacked phytoene and phytofluene. The chlorophyll content was only $\frac{1}{15}$ that of normal cells although, because of the reduction in carotenoids, the chlorophyll/carotenoid ratio was higher than in normal cells. The mutant can photosynthesize but dies in the light whether grown photosynthetically or heterotrophically. It is tempting to compare this situation with that in the purple bacteria, but the greater biochemical differences in this algal mutant and the structural modifications described in the lamellar membranes of the chloroplast render comparisons almost meaningless.

Many other carotene-less mutants of fungi and even of higher plants, e.g. *Helianthus annuus* (Wallace and Schwarting, 1954) are known, but there is no clear evidence that they suffer damage from light owing to the lack of protective carotenoids. At the present time, therefore, it seems wise to regard the protective action of carotenoids against photo-oxidation catalysed by other light-absorbing pigments as a phenomenon confined to certain bacteria. Nevertheless a careful and critical extension of this type of investigation, especially to fungi and algae, is most desirable.

V. CONCLUSIONS

Conclusions are best summarized concisely, since fairly full discussions have been given in each of the previous sections.

It is clear that a considerable research effort must be put into discovering the form in which carotenoids exist in living cells. Until this is known, interpretations of absorption or action spectra are virtually guess-work, however carefully the spectra have been measured.

Carotenoids may play a photoreceptor role in the System I phototropic curvatures of higher plants and in the positive curvatures of the sporangiophores of certain mucoraceous fungi. The evidence is equivocal and nothing is known of the metabolic steps in these postulated photo-perceptive processes. In the fungi, the optical situation is also still in need of clarification despite much recent work. Until this is done recognition of potential photoreceptor pigments will not be possible.

The case for the carotenoids acting as photoreceptors in the phototactic processes of certain Chlorophyta and euglenoids seems to be a little stronger than that for their involvement in phototropism. This is perhaps because less is known of the other possible photoreceptor molecules and of the metabolic pathways in photosactic processes, than their supposed equivalents in phototropism. It is most desirable to investigate with some urgency the problem of whether phototaxis really does involve interactions between screening and receptor pigments. Until a reasonable working hypothesis for phototaxis is available attempts to implicate carotenoids seem likely to make little progress.

In the fungi the most promising field for study would seem to lie in a more thorough examination of the situation in *Allomyces* in relation to sexual dimorphism and carotenoid accumulation and in the quite exceptional and, at present, inexplicable mutual stimulation of β-carotene synthesis in members of the Choanephoraceae. Whether additional studies will implicate carotenoids in fundamental metabolic processes is perhaps doubtful, but it is not really possible to predict anything with present knowledge. In such studies the use of mutants should greatly aid investigation, although the production of carotene-less mutants in fungi can be a long and unrewarding experience as studies in *Phycomyces* in this laboratory have shown.

Finally, it is at last possible to see reasonably clearly a fairly un-equivocal role for carotenoids in one group of organisms, the bacteria. The mechanism whereby carotenoids protect bacteria from photo-sensitized photo-oxidations has still to be elucidated but there seems no doubt at all now that these pigments can and do function in this way in bacteria. An extension of these studies to algae, especially Cyanophyta, and fungi is an urgent requirement and some of the latter might prove amenable to such studies, for example, *Rhodotorula* or spores of some of the carotenoid-containing ascomycetes and fungi imperfecti.

Carotenoids continue, and obviously will continue for some time, to astonish by their variety and to frustrate by their apparent lack of function. It is difficult to suppose that natural selection is so inefficient that this large group of compounds occurs passively and without func-tion in so many organisms. Yet is is, unfortunately, true that the last 30 years have shown very clearly that natural selection operates in diverse and unexpected ways: it seems likely that this applies to the biological functions of carotenoids.

REFERENCES

Ahrens, K. (1940). *Rodriguesia* 4, 167.
Allen, M. B. (1958). *Brookhaven Symp. Biol.* 11, 339.
Banbury, G. H. (1952). *J. exp. Bot.* 3, 77.
Banbury, G. H. (1958). *Nature, Lond.* 181, 358.
Banbury, G. H. (1959). *In* "Encyclopedia of Plant Physiology" (W. Ruhland, ed.), 17(1), 530, Springer, Berlin.
Barnett, H. L., Lilly, V. G., and Krause, R. F. (1956). *Science* 123, 141.
Blaauw, A. H. (1914). *Z. Bot.* 6, 641.
Blaauw, A. H. (1915). *Z. Bot.* 7, 465.
Blaauw, A. H. (1918). *Meded. LandbHoogesch., Wageningen* 15, 89.
Blakeslee, A. F. (1904). *Proc. Amer. Acad. Arts Sci.* 40, 203.

Blakeslee, A. F. (1906). *Ann. mycol., Berl.* 4, 1.

Blakeslee, A. F., and Cartledge, J. L. (1927). *Bot. Gaz.* 84, 51.

Briggs, W. R. (1963). *Annu. Rev. Pl. Physiol.* 14, 311.

Briggs, W. R. (1964). *In* "Photophysiology" (A. C. Giese, ed.), p. 223, Academic Press, New York and London.

Bünning, E. (1937a). *Planta* 26, 719.

Bünning, E. (1937b). *Planta* 27, 148.

Bünning, E. (1955). *Z. Bot.* 43, 167.

Bünning, E., and Schneiderhöhn, G. (1956). *Arch. Mikrobiol.* 24, 80.

Burgeff, H. (1924). *Bot. Abh., K. Goebel* 4, 1.

Burnett, J. H. (1952). D.Phil. Thesis. University of Oxford.

Burnett, J. H. (1953a). *New Phytol.* 52, 58.

Burnett, J. H. (1953b). *New Phytol.* 52, 86.

Burnett, J. H. (1956a). *New Phytol.* 55, 45.

Burnett, J. H. (1956b). *New Phytol.* 55, 50.

Cantino, E. C., and Hyatt, M. T. (1953a). *Antonie van Leeuwenhoek* 19, 25.

Cantino, E. C., and Hyatt, M. T. (1953b). *Amer. J. Bot.* 40, 688.

Carlile, M. J. (1956). *J. gen. Microbiol.* 14, 643.

Carlile, M. J. (1957). *Nature, Lond.* 180, 202.

Carlile, M. J. (1962). *J. gen. Microbiol.* 28, 161.

Carlile, M. J., and Friend, J. S. (1956). *Nature, Lond.* 178, 369.

Chodat, R., and Schopfer, W. H. (1927). *C. R. Soc. Phys. hist. nat., Genève* 44, 176.

Claes, H. (1954). *Z. Naturf.* 9b, 461.

Claes, H. (1956). *Z. Naturf.* 11b, 260.

Claes, H. (1957). *Z. Naturf.* 12b, 401.

Claes, H. (1958). *Z. Naturf.* 13b, 222.

Claes, H., and Nakayama, T. O. M. (1959). *Z. Naturf.* 14b, 746.

Clayton, R. K. (1959). *In* "Encyclopedia of Plant Physiology" (W. Ruhland, ed.), 17(1), 371, Springer, Berlin.

Cohen-Bazire, G., and Stanier, R. Y. (1958). *Nature, Lond.* 181, 250.

Curry, G. M., and Gruen, H. E. (1957). *Nature, Lond.* 179, 1028.

Curry, G. M., and Gruen, H. E. (1959). *Proc. nat. Acad. Sci., Wash.* 45, 797.

Delbrück, M., and Shropshire, W. (1960). *Plant Physiol.* 35, 194.

Dennison, D. S. (1959). *Nature, Lond.* 184, 2036.

Dworkin, M. (1958). *J. gen. Physiol.* 41, 1099.

Dworkin, M. (1959). *Nature, Lond.* 184, 1891.

Emerson, R. (1950). *Annu. Rev. Microbiol.* 4, 169.

Emerson, R., and Fox, D. L. (1940). *Proc. roy. Soc. B* 128, 275.

Foley, J. M. (1958). *Amer. J. Bot.* 45, 639.

French, C. S. (1959). *In* "Photoperiodism and Related Phenomena in Plants and Animals", p. 15, A.A.A.S., Washington, D.C.

Frey-Wyssling, A. (1935). "Die Stoffausscheidungen der höheren Pflanzen," Springer, Berlin.

Fuller, R. C., and Anderson, I. C. (1958). *Nature, Lond.* 181, 252.

Galston, A. W. (1959). *In* "Encyclopedia of Plant Physiology" (W. Ruhland, ed.), 17(1), 492, Springer, Berlin.

Garton, G. A., Goodwin, T. W., and Lijinsky, W. (1950). *Biochem. J.* 46, 35.

Garton, G. A., Goodwin, T. W., and Lijinsky, W. (1951). *Biochem. J.* 48, 154.

Goodwin, R. H. (1953). *Annu. Rev. Pl. Physiol.* 4, 283.

Goodwin, T. W. (1950). *Biol. Rev.* 25, 391.

Goodwin, T. W. (1952a). "The Comparative Biochemistry of Carotenoids," Chapman and Hall, London.

Goodwin, T. W. (1952b). *Biochem. J.* **50**, 550.

Goodwin, T. W. (1952c). *Bot. Rev.* **18**, 291.

Goodwin, T. W. (1958). *In* "Encyclopedia of Plant Physiology" (W. Ruhland, ed.), **10**, 186, Springer, Berlin.

Goodwin, T. W. (1959). *Adv. Enzymol.* **21**, 295.

Gössel, I. (1957). *Arch. Mikrobiol.* **27**, 288.

Griffiths, M., and Stanier, R. Y. (1956). *J. gen. Microbiol.* **14**, 698.

Griffiths, M., Sistrom, W. R., Cohen-Bazire, G., and Stanier, R. Y. (1955). *Nature, Lond.* **176**, 1211.

Gruen, H. (1959). *Annu. Rev. Pl. Physiol.* **10**, 405.

Halldal, P. (1958). *Physiol. Plant.* **11**, 118.

Halldal, P. (1961). *Physiol. Plant.* **14**, 133.

Hawk, P. B., Oser, B. L., and Summerson, W. H. (1951). "Practical Physiological Chemistry," Blakiston, New York.

Harder, R., and Sörgel, G. (1938). *Nachr. Ges. Wiss. Göttingen, Phys. Kl.*, N.F., 6, *Biol.* **3**, 119.

Hartmann, M. (1955). *Amer. Naturalist* **89**, 321.

Hartshorne, J. N. (1953). *New Phytol.* **52**, 292.

Haxo, F. (1956). *Fortschr. Chem. org. Naturst.* **12**, 169.

Haxo, F., and Clendenning, K. A. (1953). *Biol. Bull.* **105**, 103.

Hawker, L. E. (1957). "The Physiology of Reproduction in Fungi," Cambridge.

Heim, P. (1947). *Rev. Mycol. (Paris)* **12**, 104.

Hemker, H. C., and Hülsmann, W. C. (1960). *Biochem. biophys. Acta* **44**, 175.

Hesseltine, C. W., and Anderson, R. F. (1957). *Mycologia* **49**, 449.

Hocking, D. (1963a). *Nature, Lond.* **197**, 404.

Hocking, D. (1963b). Ph.D. Thesis. King's College, University of Durham.

Johnston, E. S. (1934). *Smithson misc. Coll.* **92**, 1.

Kandler, O., and Schotz, F. (1956). *Z. Naturf.* **11b**, 708.

Kaplan, R. W. (1956). *Arch. Mikrobiol.* **24**, 60.

Köhler, F. (1935). *Planta* **23**, 258.

Krinsky, N. I., and Goldsmith, T. H. (1960). *Arch. Biochem. Biophys.* **91**, 271.

Kuhn, R., and Moewus, F. (1940). *Ber. dtsch. chem. Ges.* **73**, 547.

Kunisawa, R., and Stanier, R. Y. (1958). *Arch. Mikrobiol.* **31**, 146.

Lange, S. (1927). *Jahrb. wiss. Bot.* **67**, 1.

Ling-Yong, M. (1930). *Rev. gen. Bot.* **42**, 618; 681.

Lunz, A. (1931). *Z. vergl. Physiol.* **14**, 68.

Manten, A. (1948). *Dissertation*. Utrecht, Holland.

Mast, S. O. (1927). *Z. vergl. Physiol.* **5**, 730.

Mathews, M. M. (1963). *Photochem. Photobiol.* **2**, 1.

Mathews, M. M. (1964). *Photochem. Photobiol.* **3**, 75.

Mathews, M. M., and Sistrom, W. R. (1959). *Nature, Lond.* **184**, 1892.

Mathews, M. M., and Sistrom, W. R. (1960). *Arch. Mikrobiol.* **35**, 139.

Mayer, A. M., and Poljakoff-Mayber, A. (1959). *Physiol. Plant.* **12**, 8.

Niethammer, A. (1938). *Arch. Mikrobiol.* **9**, 23.

Nishimura, M., and Takamatsu, K. (1957). *Nature, Lond.* **180**, 699.

Page, R. M. (1956). *Mycologia* **48**, 206.

Paul, H. L. (1950). *In* Banbury (1959).

Philip, U., and Haldane, J. B. S. (1939). *Nature, Lond.* **143**, 334.

Plempel, M. (1957). *Arch. Mikrobiol.* **26**, 151.

Price, B. (1927). *Bull. Soc. bot.*, Genève **19**, 1.

Reichel, L., and Wallis, M. (1958). *Naturwissenschaften* **45**, 130.

Reinert, J. (1953). *Z. Bot.* **41**, 103.

Renner, O. (1958). *Z. Naturf.* **13b**, 339.

Ryan, F. J. (1955). *Science* **122**, 470.

Sager, R., and Zalokar, M. (1958). *Nature, Lond.* **182**, 48.

Satina, S., and Blakeslee, A. F. (1926). *Proc. nat. Acad. Sci., Wash.* **12**, 191.

Schneider, R. (1943). *In* Banbury (1959).

Shibata, K. (1958). *J. Biochem., Tokyo* **45**, 599.

Schopfer, W. H. (1927). *Bull. Soc. bot., Genève* **20**, 149.

Schopfer, W. H. (1943). "Plants and Vitamins," Chronica–Botanica, Waltham, Mass.

Shropshire, W., and Withrow, R. B. (1958). *Plant Physiol.* **33**, 360.

Sistrom, W. R., Griffiths, M., and Stanier, R. Y. (1956). *J. cell. comp. Physiol.* **48**, 459.

Smith, J. H., and French, C. S. (1963). *Annu. Rev. Pl. Physiol.* **14**, 181.

Stanier, R. Y., and Cohen-Bazire, G. (1957). *In* "Microbial Ecology" (R. E. O. Williams and C. C. Spicer, eds.), p. 56, Cambridge University Press, London.

Strasburger, E. (1878). *Jena. Z. Naturw.* **12**, 551.

Swart-Füchtbauer, H., and Rippel-Baldes, A. (1951). *Arch. Mikrobiol.* **16**, 358.

Thimann, K. V. (1940). *Chron. Bot.* **6**, 31.

Thimann, K. V., and Curry, G. M. (1960). *In* "Comparative Biochemistry" (M. Florkin and H. S. Mason, eds.), vol. 1, p. 243, Academic Press, New York and London.

Turian, G. (1952). *Experientia* **8**, 302.

Turian, G., and Haxo, F. T. (1954). *Bot. Gaz.* **115**, 254.

Wallace, R. H., and Schwarting, A. E. (1954). *Plant Physiol.* **29**, 431.

Wolken, J. J., and Shin, E. (1958). *J. Protozool.* **5**, 39.

Wright, C. J., and Rilling, H. C. (1963). *Photochem. Photobiol.* **2**, 339.

Chapter 15

THE PHYSIOLOGICAL FUNCTIONS OF PHYTOCHROME

S. B. Hendricks and H. A. Borthwick

*Agricultural Research Service, U.S. Department of Agriculture,
Beltsville, Maryland, U.S.A.*

I. Introduction

Many physiological observations on plants gave the basis for isolation of phytochrome described in Chapter 7. Isolation of the pigment and the degree of understanding attained about its molecular properties are elements of knowledge aiding further physiological work. Both precedent and subsequent findings are the subjects of this chapter.

The physiological expressions of phytochrome action are manifold. The most striking ones are control of flowering (photoperiodism), elongation of structures (etiolation), germination of seeds and spores, formation of anthocyanins and carotenoids, display of crassulaecean metabolism, and induction of dormancies. In short, the entire plant is subject to compulsive change by phytochrome conversion.

In its general aspect phytochrome is a senser of two of the most important factors of a plant's environment, namely, light and temperature. The sensing of light is the more obvious and is turned to the unexpected end of aiding seasonal adaptation through measurement of night length as a seasonal variable. It also ensures survival of seeds for reproduction by conserving reserves for germination in ones covered with soil. Seedlings are ensured of a two-fold action, first to elongate until the surface of the ground is detected and then to grow with shortened internodes. Temperature-sensing is less expected for all reactions of a plant are sensitive to temperature change, but phytochrome action maintains a uniformity of response with changing temperature.

II. SOME EARLY OBSERVATIONS LEADING TO RECOGNITION OF PHYTOCHROME

The discovery in 1920 (Garner and Allard, 1920) of control of flowering in some plants by the length of the day or night (photoperiodism) attracted much attention to its prevalence and measurement of critical day lengths. There was some conjecture about the nature of the control which eventually led to two concepts: (a) an initial action of light can control flowering, and (b) a stimulus for flowering moves from the leaf to the differentiating meristem (Cajlachjan, 1937). Knowledge about phytochrome comes from (a). Garner and Allard (1920) established that extension of a normal day of high-light intensity by a period of some hours with light of low intensity (a few foot candles of illumination) was adequate for control of flowering. This was, in truth, a physiological discovery of a controlling pigment. An eventual finding was that flowering control could be attained by short interruptions of nights (Hamner and Bonner, 1938; Emsweller et al., 1941) with illumination of leaves, establishing them as a site of the pigment (Knott, 1926).

Red light falling on the leaves was early found to be highly effective in preventing flowering of plants requiring long nights for induction (Withrow and Withrow, 1940; Kleshnin, 1943). Action spectra expressing incident irradiance required at various wavelengths for suppression of flowering were measured and found to be closely the same for two such plant species, namely *Xanthium pensylvanicum* and *Glycine max* var. Biloxi (Parker et al., 1946) or cocklebur and soyabean. Reciprocity or dependence of response on energy rather than duration of irradiation was also found to hold over periods as great as 15 min for these two species. The maxima of action are in the red, and because they are so close to the absorption maxima of chlorophyll *a* and *b* the possibility of chlorophyll being the pigment was entertained despite the low effectiveness of blue radiation. The energy required at the red maximum for half suppression of flowering is about $1 \cdot 0 \times 10^{-9}$ Einsteins/cm^2 of leaf area. Saturation of response is attained with several fold this energy. Both energy magnitudes are very low in the sense of exciting only a small number of moles of a dilute receiving pigment.

While cocklebur and soyabean require long nights for flowering many other plants flower when nights are short. Action spectra for induction of flowering of two of these, namely, *Hordeum vulgare* var. Wintex and *Hyoscyamus niger* or barley and henbane, measured by interrupting long nights with light, are closely the same as the preceding ones (Borthwick *et al.*, 1948; Parker *et al.*, 1950). It follows that the same pigment is involved in the two types of plants even though the flowering response is opposite—suppression in one and induction in the other.

III. Essential Physiological Discoveries for Progress towards Separation of Phytochrome from Plants

The findings about control of flowering were neither very helpful for recognition of the effective pigment nor did they suggest an assay as a basis for isolation. At this stage in logical pursuit of the subject, two discoveries opened up other approaches. These were:

(a) The finding that many photoresponses of plants and seeds have closely the same action spectra with respect to the *absolute* energy requirement for a given degree of response.

(b) The photoaction is reversible (Borthwick *et al.*, 1952a, b).

An action spectrum for enhancement of leaf lengthening of etiolated pea (*Pisum sativum*) seedlings gave the first indication of (a) (Parker *et al.*, 1949). This was soon followed by a similar finding for the photorequirement for germination of lettuce seed (*Lactuca sativa*) (Borthwick *et al.*, 1952a). Recognition of a light requirement for response of these two types had preceded that of flowering control by many years. Indeed, it is likely that early man was aware of etiolation, and documentation came as early as 1832 (DeCandolle, 1832). Enhancement of seed germination by light was noted in 1861 (Caspary, 1861).

Measurement of light requirements for germination of lettuce seed (Flint and McAllister, 1935, 1937; Borthwick *et al.*, 1954) indicated induction in the red region of the spectrum and suppression at somewhat longer wavelengths. Action spectra show maximum effects near 660 mμ

for induction and 730 mμ for suppression (Fig. 1), with a minor action maximum in the region of 440 mμ. The action spectrum for induction is identical with that for suppression of cocklebur flowering.

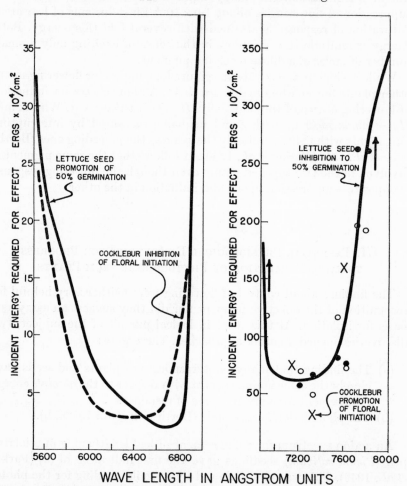

WAVE LENGTH IN ANGSTROM UNITS

FIG. 1. Action spectra for promotion (*left*) and inhibition (*right*) of lettuce seed (*Lactuca sativa* var. Grand Rapids) germination and promotion (*right*) and inhibition (*left, dotted line*) of flowering of cocklebur (*Xanthium saccharatum*) in the region of 5,600 to 8,000 Å. The dark and open circles are from two experiments with lettuce seed (Borthwick *et al.*, 1952a, 1954).

Consideration of the lettuce seed responses to light led to the idea that action in the region of 660 mμ might only potentiate germination and that the potentiated germination might be suppressed near 730 mμ. This interpretation was realized in a sequence of exposures to the two spectral regions (Fig. 2). Reversibility of light action implies two forms of a pigment and indicates that the photoactions are conversions of molecular configuration and not transfer of energy to other systems. The duality of the pigment action in seed germination indicated that flowering control (Fig. 1) and etiolation should also show reversibility of induction. The reversibility was found to be general and gave great security to the identity of the initial photochemical act controlling the varied responses. Induction of the following responses has been shown to be photoreversible: Seed germination (Borthwick *et al.*, 1952a); flowering

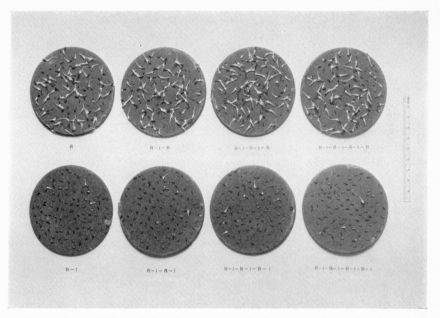

FIG. 2. Reversibility of the photoresponse for lettuce seed germination. Each lot of seed after inhibition in darkness received the indicated succession of irradiations (R = red radiation, I = far-red radiation) and then was returned to darkness for 2 days for development of germination.

(Borthwick *et al.*, 1952b); cuticle colouration (Piringer and Heinze, 1954); seed respiration (Hagen *et al.*, 1954); etiolation (Downs, 1955); fern spore germination (Mohr, 1956); anthocyanin synthesis (Siegelman and Hendricks, 1957; Mohr, 1957); plumular hook formation (Withrow *et al.*, 1957; Mohr and Noble, 1960); moss spore germination (Bauer and Mohr, 1959); chloroplast orientation in algae (Haupt, 1959); hair formation (Mohr, 1959a); stem stiffening (Mohr and Pichler, 1960); chlorophyll formation (Price and Klein, 1961); fern sporeling elongation (Laetsch and Briggs, 1962).

Other growth phenomena probably controlled by the reversible change in form of phytochrome have been observed either qualitatively or only for control by the absorption of red radiation. They include, without references being given, leaf abscission, philloidy of bracts, epinasty, flower development, formation of cleistogamous flowers, sex expression, rhizome formation, bulbing, gemmae formation, crassulacean metabolism, and dormancy of buds.

The photoreversibility led to the bichromatic photometric assay for phytochrome essential for isolation (Chapter 7). Recognition of a conversion of form explained the saturation with respect to radiant energy. The degree of physiological response is a function of the degree of phytochrome conversion, but the same function does not hold for control of all phenomena (Hendricks et al., 1956).

IV. INTRODUCTION TO PHYTOCHROME ACTION

A. P_{fr} AS THE PHYSIOLOGICALLY ACTIVE FORM OF PHYTOCHROME

A measurable effect on enlargement of etiolated pea leaves is observed with an energy of 1.0×10^{-14} Einsteins/cm^2 in the region of 660 mμ (Parker et al., 1949) adequate for conversion of only one part in 10^5 of the phytochrome. If phytochrome is placed in the P_{fr} form (abs. max. 730 mμ) little effect is observed with irradiation at 730 mμ having an energy of 1.0×10^{-12} Einsteins/cm^2. This hundred-fold dissymmetry of action from opposite directions of conversion led to the conclusions that P_{fr}, formed by red radiation, was the active form and probably amplified the red light effect by functioning as an enzyme. The isolation was based on this supposition of phytochrome being a protein which was immediately verified by denaturation after the successful assay and by eventual isolation (Chapter 7).

That P_{fr} is the active form is tenuous, because of symmetry of physiological arguments about activators and inhibitors, and awaits rigorous demonstration. Supporting evidence, however, is abundant for its being an activator. Seed lying covered in the ground can remain dormant for more than 80 years (Darlington and Steinbauer, 1961), with P_r present, and germinate a few days after its conversion by light into P_{fr}. Another supporting argument is that the potentiated germination of light-requiring seed can be reversed in some cases with decreasing effectiveness over a period of hours (Borthwick et al., 1954). P_{fr} is considered to be active over the period and the action is irreversible even though the pigment is eventually changed in form.

B. DARK REVERSION OF P_{fr} TO P_r in vivo

The reversion, and accordingly the inherent thermodynamic stability of P_r, was recognized by the fact that flowering of plants irradiated with red light as they entered the dark period was controlled by red light near the middle of the night. Reversion was clearly demonstrated by the photometric observations on living etiolated tissue (Chapter 7). The physiological work is much concerned with the times required for reversion of P_{fr} to P_r in darkness. This is involved in dependence of flowering on the length of the night (photoperiodism) as well as in other responses. The time for reversion varies from as little as 1 min to more than 24 h in different objects, which has implications about the nature of the reversion and about the substrate on which P_{fr} acts.

The dominant reversion of P_{fr} to P_r *in vivo* compared to the negligible reversion of the native protein *in vitro* (Chapter 7) is suggestive of coupling to enzymatic action. If such coupling exists it could be used as an assay in seeking the exact enzymatic reaction involved. This effect and the rates of conversion are discussed in the several sections.

C. A PRELIMINARY TO CONSIDERATION OF PHYSIOLOGICAL FUNCTION OF PHYTOCHROME

A deduction from the manifold responses is that P_{fr} is essential for life of higher plants. This follows from the diversity of the responses that are unlikely to have common metabolic pathways except in their more primitive steps. While the nature of a common enzymatic step will be considered in later sections, it would preferably be known for logical order before further consideration of the physiology. But the exact type is unknown and might not readily be found.

A second handicap for discussion of physiological functions of phytochrome is that action of P_{fr} is only one of many interconnected reactions in metabolic pathways. The plant display is a function of all the pathways, albeit possibly dominated by one. The photoreversibility, however, lends peculiar power for following the intricacies of physiological response by permitting use of a null-method. P_{fr} can be formed by a light beam reaching the point of action without disturbing intervening tissue and left for only a short time before reconversion to P_{fr} by far-red radiation.

A second photoreaction, or photoreactions, sometimes referred to as the "high energy reaction" or HER (Siegelman and Hendricks, 1957; Mohr, 1962) is also involved in many of the responses that have been mentioned. It is evident only after irradiation with much higher energies than required to change the form of phytochrome, usually more than a J/cm^2 of incident energy. The two reactions have sometimes been confused, particularly when irradiation is prolonged as is usually necessary for the HER. Operation of the two reactions in conjunction is well illustrated by anthocyanin synthesis (Siegelman and Hendricks, 1957) and by control of stem elongation (Mohr, 1957), as will later be treated in detail.

V. PHYTOCHROME CONTROL OF PLANT DEVELOPMENT

A. FLOWERING

Chenopodium rubrum is illustrative of plants requiring long nights to flower. Induction with low variability can be achieved as soon as the cotyledons expand (Cummings, 1959, 1962). Plants suitable for use on a spectrograph are shown in Fig. 3. The action spectrum for suppression of flowering by interruptions near the middle of 16-h nights (Kasperbauer

FIG. 3. A 12 × 12 cm box of soil with rows of *C. rubrum* seedlings ready for spectrographic irradiation.

et al., 1963, 1964) has a minimum energy requirement near 645 mμ (Fig. 4) which is displaced by about 15 mμ from the absorption minimum of P_r (Chapter 7) because of chlorophyll absorption.

If flower induction is first potentially suppressed by red light the action spectrum for re-promotion shows a minimum energy requirement in the far-red near 730 mμ (Fig. 5) corresponding to the absorption maximum of P_{fr}. Continued irradiation in this region, however, again potentially suppresses flowering as can be seen in the upper part of Fig. 5. These opposite responses to the same radiation arise from the overlap of absorbancies of P_{fr} and P_r in the far-red region (Chapter 7). Continued irradiation maintains a low but definite level of P_{fr} (possibly

1 to 2% of total P), favoured somewhat by a lower quantum efficiency for conversion relative to that of P_r. The maintenance of 1 to 2% P_{fr} by far-red radiation for 60 min is as effective in inhibiting flowering as 80% P_{fr} established in 1 min by red radiation. If both P_{fr} actions are terminated after 30 min, the first by stopping the far-red radiation and the second by giving 1 min of irradiance with far-red radiation of adequate intensity to establish the $P_{fr} \rightleftarrows P_r$ equilibrium at 730 mμ, the same

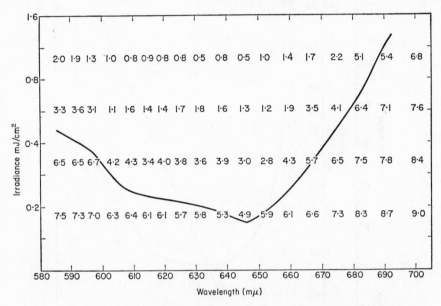

FIG. 4. Action spectrum for inhibition of flowering of *C. rubrum* in the region of 580 to 700 mμ. The curve shows irradiances required near the centres of five successive 16-h nights with 8-h days to reduce the average flowering stage from 9·0 (controls) to 5·0 (Kasperbauer *et al.*, 1963).

intermediate degree of flowering results (about 75%). It follows that only 1 to 2% of the P_{fr} is effective; consequently, most of the 80% P_{fr} is ineffective except to replace the effective part as it reverts to P_r. The effective part (1 to 2%) is interpreted as being effective because of association with the substrate upon which it acts. The substrate, accordingly, is limiting. Under these conditions P_{fr} is reverting to P_r at the rate of about 1% per min. The reversion is accordingly catalysed by the action on the substrate, which is itself changed by the catalytic (enzymatic) action of P_{fr}.

Long-night plants are inhibited in flowering by P_{fr} action; in other words, by the products of P_{fr} action. Short-night ones, such as barley and hyoscyamus, which are induced to flower by interruptions of long nights with red light, that is, by the presence of P_{fr}, are probably limited by P_{fr}-substrate combination. They, accordingly, either have a low total amount of phytochrome or a low rate of supply of substrate for action. While these features are well supported for the long night plants, much more work is needed on the short night ones, both to scrutinize the

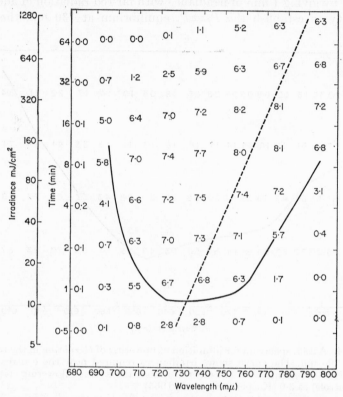

FIG. 5. Action spectrum for promotion and inhibition of flowering of *C. rubrum* in the region of 670 to 795 mμ. The solid curve gives the interpolated position of promotion from vegetative (stage 0) to flowering (stage 6). The dashed line indicates the energy required to reduce the flowering level to 7 as irradiation is continued (Kasperbauer *et al.*, 1963).

deductions and to differentiate between the alternatives that might be raised.

Pharbitis nil plants, which are like *C. rubrum* in requiring long nights to flower and which can also be induced as soon as the cotyledons unfold (Nakayama, 1958; Takimoto and Ikeda, 1959); show further aspects of the substrate supply for P_{fr} action. Plants growing on 2- to 8-h days with light of high intensity and 22- to 16-h nights, can be potentiated to flower by P_{fr} formation, that is, by red light (660 mμ), at the beginning of the long dark period. This action can be reversed by far-red radiation. The two action spectra (Nakayama *et al.*, 1960) are closely the same as found for *C. rubrum*, except that continued far-red radiation (730 mμ) for an hour does not inhibit flowering. The substrate for action accordingly must be relatively low in concentration.

The action of red light on *P. nil* 6 to 10 h after the beginning of the dark period is opposite to that at the beginning, that is, flowering is inhibited. Moreover, far-red irradiation for several minutes (about 20 μw/cm^2) is essentially without effect either by itself or following several minutes red irradiation adequate to give a high percentage conversion to P_{fr}. If continued for more than 20 min, however, it acts, as in *C. rubrum*, to inhibit flowering. Conversion of phytochrome into P_{fr} in a few seconds, followed within a half minute by intense far-red irradiation for a few seconds, however, promotes flowering (H. Fredericq, 1963, personal communication). Accordingly, P_{fr} action and reversion must have been completed in less than a minute from a high per cent level of P_{fr}. This indicates that the substrate for P_{fr} action is present in excess since P_{fr} effectiveness is proportional to its percentage formation (Hendricks *et al.*, 1956).

Chrysanthemum morifolium varieties require long nights to flower. If 16-h nights are interrupted near their midpoints with intense irradiances with red light for the order of a minute, flowering is inhibited. Sunlight or intense incandescent light, each of which has approximately equal red and far-red components, however, is ineffective over periods of many minutes. The red-light potentiated action is reversible with decreasing effectiveness for about one hour, and far-red radiation over the same period also inhibits flowering. If the intermediate levels of P_{fr} given by sunlight or incandescent radiation are re-established at $\frac{1}{2}$-h intervals for 2 to 4 h they, too, are effective in preventing flowering (Borthwick and Cathey, 1962; Cathey and Borthwick, 1962). Accordingly, substrate for P_{fr} action is limiting at any given time but is formed in adequate total amounts over periods of several hours for prevention of flowering by P_{fr} action and reversion of P_{fr} to P_r.

P. nil, *Kalanchoe blossfeldiana* (Fredericq, 1964) and *Xanthium pensylvanicum*, which are all long-night plants, give further information about substrate formation for P_{fr} action. When grown on 2-h days and 22-h nights, flowering is inhibited by far-red light (giving P_{fr}) at the beginning of darkness, as noted earlier, or for as much as 6 h after the beginning. In the first instance red light reverses the potentiated effect if given any time during the first 4 to 6 h of darkness. This indicates that the substrate for P_{fr} action is very low during the first hours of darkness under these conditions. As the intensity of the light is raised from 500 to 2,000 f.c. illuminance or the light period increased from 2 to 8 h, the period in darkness over which the reversal of P_{fr} has an effect decreases. This is evidence that the substrate begins to form from the start of the light period, but about 6 h in darkness is required for it to be adequate for one reversal, at moderate intensities, of the P_{fr} present. The substrate, accordingly, is an eventual, but not an immediate, product of a photo-reaction and its amount is dependent upon the radiant energy.

To recapitulate: the products of P_{fr} action are required for control of flowering. Reversion of P_{fr} depends upon its action and reflects the concentration of the substrate upon which it acts. The substrate is a result of a photochemical reaction starting some 6 to 8 h before the time of enzymatic action of P_{fr}.

B. FORMATION OF ANTHOCYANIN

Information about the substrate for P_{fr} action has been obtained from observations on anthocyanin formation (see e.g. Table I). Cyanidin is produced by seedlings of *Brassica oleracea* var. Red Acre in readily assayable amounts by a few hours of irradiation at high intensity in the regions of 400 to 600 mμ, followed by red radiation for a few minutes to establish P_{fr} and holding in darkness for 24 h (Siegelman and Hendricks, 1957). Some cyanidin is formed in darkness and

TABLE I

Reversibility of Anthocyanin Formation induced by
50 mW/cm^2 Irradiation in the Region of 420 to 500 mμ
(3 h) with Successive Exposures to Far-red (3 min,
0·8 mW/cm^2 700 to 800 mμ), and Red Radiation (1
min, 0·6 mW/cm^2 600 to 670 mμ), followed by 24 h
in Darkness (Wheatland milo)

| Exposures | | Anthocyanin |
Far-red number	Red number	Relative amounts
0	0	106
1	0	48
1	1	106
27	26	45
27	27	109
42	41	49
42	42	103

shortly (minutes) after the start of irradiation the amount eventually formed in 24 h increases linearly with irradiance (Fig. 6). This is an important observation interpreted as indicating that dark reactions, in part, supply substrate for P_{fr} enzymatic action. With the supply partially met, the induction period shown for substrate formation by most other tissues is absent. Both the immediate and eventual linear dependencies show that the energy of radiation is used for eventual substrate formation and not indirectly for enzyme production.

The action spectrum (high energy reaction—HER) for induction of anthocyanin formation in *B. oleracea* seedlings is shown in Fig. 7 in the region of 600 to 800 mμ. The action maximum is near 690 mμ. After the HER induction, anthocyanin formation depends on the presence of P_{fr}. The action maxima for the reversible change of phytochrome are near

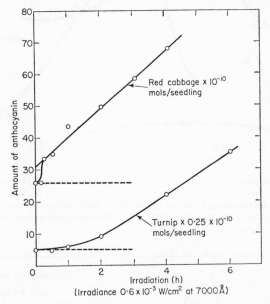

Fig. 6. Variation in anthocyanin synthesis in red cabbage and turnip seedlings with irradiance. The seedlings were extracted for analysis 24 h after the beginning of irradiation. Dashed lines indicated anthocyanin level in darkness (Siegelman and Hendricks, 1957).

660 and 720 to 740 mμ, respectively, as was observed for the photoconversion $P_r \rightleftarrows P_{fr}$ displayed for control of flowering, seed germination, and also *in vitro* (Chapter 8).

The action spectrum (HER) for initiation of cyanidin production in Wheatland milo, which does not produce anthocyanin in darkness, is shown in Fig. 8. In the experiment as reported by Downs and Siegelman (1963), P_{fr} was not re-established after high energy irradiation in the region of 700 to 800 mμ. When it is re-established, anthocyanin production is still absent, indicating essential lack of action except in the region of 400 to 600 mμ with a pronounced peak near 460 to 470 mμ. The anthocyanin production after irradiation (HER) followed by establishing P_{fr} (5 min of red radiation) and holding for 24 h in darkness for completion

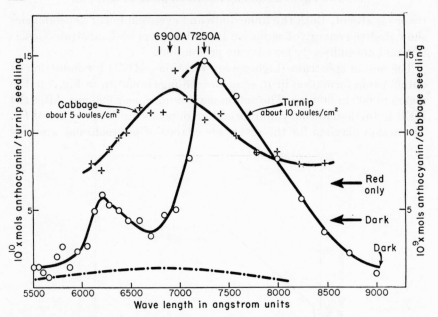

FIG. 7. Action spectra in the region of 5,500 to 9,000 Å for anthocyanin synthesis in red cabbage and turnip seedlings. The heavy arrows indicate anthocyanin synthesis after darkness and a short exposure of red cabbage seedlings to red light. Seedlings were held in darkness for 16 to 24 h after irradiation and prior to analysis (Siegelman and Hendricks, 1957).

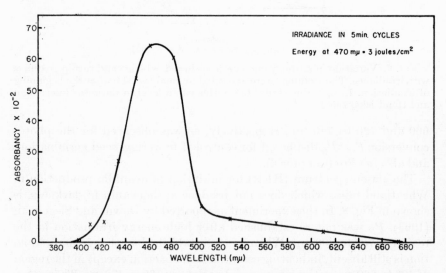

FIG. 8. Action spectrum for the high energy photoreaction (HER) for anthocyanin synthesis in dark-grown seedlings of *Sorghum vulgare* cv Wheatland milo (Downs and Siegelman, 1963).

of synthesis is not immediately linearly dependent on irradiance but has an induction period of as much as 6 h depending on intensity. If red radiation given at the end of the HER with moderate intensity is followed after increasing times in darkness by far-red radiation (Fig. 9) to remove P_{fr}, the effect of anthocyanin formation decreases to zero by the sixth hour. A period of hours then is required for the product of the HER to be moderately effective as the substrate for P_{fr} enzymatic action. An interval of this magnitude is generally found at moderate HER intensities. It implies a period for intermediate reactions, which is the same as the one found for flowering control in *P. nil*, *K. blossfeldiana*, and *X. pensylvanicum* as previously discussed.

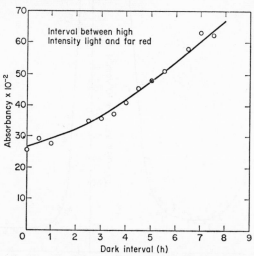

FIG. 9. Loss of far-red inhibition of anthocyanin synthesis in seedlings of Wheatland milo when successively longer dark periods intervene between the high energy photoreaction (HER) and exposure to far-red radiation (Downs and Siegelman, 1963).

Action spectra at high energies for anthocyanin synthesis in a number of other plants differ from the one shown in Fig. 10 and from each other. In general, however, lower yields of anthocyanin are obtained per J/cm^2 of radiant energy, necessitating longer irradiations for examination. Action maxima are present in the region 600 to 800 mμ, but the positions of these maxima are not the same; thus, apple, 640 to 660 mμ (Siegelman and Hendricks, 1958a), turnip, 720 mμ (Siegelman and Hendricks, 1957), and mustard, 720 mμ (Mohr, 1957). A maximum for action is also found in the region of 440 to 470 mμ.

Further information is obtained from anthocyanin synthesis in the apple skin (sub-epidermal cells). Reddening, that is, cyanidin glycoside formation, is dependent on irradiation in genetically suited fruits. The green skins of mature apples can be removed and used for experiments. An action spectrum with high energy, HER, has maxima in the region of 460 and 640 to 660 mμ. If skins are irradiated as follows (1) 16 h high intensity fluorescent, 24 h darkness, 24 h high intensity fluorescent, 24 h darkness, and (2) the same as (1) except 24 h low intensity red radiation instead of the first 24 h of darkness (to give P_{fr}), more anthocyanin is formed in (2) than in (1). Phytochrome, then, is effective as an enzyme in the P_{fr} form.

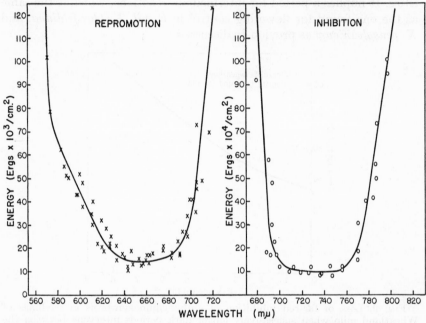

Fig. 10. Action spectra for phytochrome control of anthocyanin synthesis in seedlings of Wheatland milo after induction of synthesis by the HER.

Apple skins floating on sugar solutions in darkness have a typical apple odour which is absent when they are irradiated at high intensity. This superficial and seemingly trivial observation affords an approach to the biochemistry of P_{fr} action. The effect of irradiation on acetaldehyde and ethanol production is shown in Fig. 11 (Siegelman and Hendricks, 1958b). Apparently the substrate for the high intensity reaction (HER), if not utilized in that reaction, forms ethanol and acetaldehyde in apple skin. The probable substrate for this reaction, accordingly, is pyruvate or very close to pyruvate in derivation.

Acyl compounds are probably in part the precursors of flavonoid compounds as suggested by Birch (1957) and Geissman (1962). Acetate has been shown to be incorporated in the A ring, that is, the phloroglucinol ring, of anthocyanins (Watkins *et al.*, 1957; Grisebach, 1957; Geissman and Swain, 1957). Grisebach found by degradation studies with ^{14}C as a tracer that the A ring of cyanidin is derived from head to tail linkage of 3 acetate units (see Chapter 17 for full details). The HER reaction is accordingly interpreted as the producer of acyl groups for synthesis of the A ring. It is of interest that the methoxy 3,3-dimethyl derivative of the triketo form of cinnamoylphlorglucinol has been isolated from a fern (Nilsson, 1959).

The course of reactions in anthocyanin synthesis with the approximate

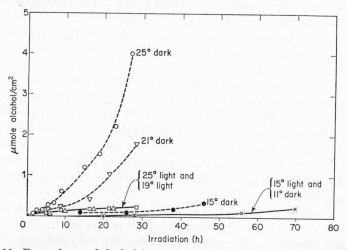

FIG. 11. Dependence of alcohol formation in apple skin (var. Arkansas) floating on 0·3 M sucrose on duration of irradiation or darkness at various temperatures.

times in hours required to reach steady-state rates on the basis of the preceding considerations are, schematically:

Sucrose or glucose $\xrightarrow{0·5}$ pyruvate $\xrightarrow{1}$ active acetate $\xrightarrow{\text{HER limited}}$ first product of radiation $\xrightarrow{4}$ intermediate reactions (including head to tail active condensation) $\xrightarrow{P_{fr} \text{ limited}}$ product of P_{fr} enzymatic action $\xrightarrow{6 \text{ to } 8}$ dark reactions leading to final cyanidin (Siegelman and Hendricks, 1958a).

To recapitulate: Presence of P_{fr} is required for anthocyanin synthesis in many tissues. The HER reaction in anthocyanin synthesis controls the supply of acyl groups to form the substrate for P_{fr} enzymatic reaction which follows the HER reaction by 4 to 6 h and precedes appearance of anthocyanin by about 6 h.

C. CONTROL OF SEED GERMINATION

A light requirement has been demonstrated for seeds of many species and varieties of plants (Kinzel, 1913–1926; Evenari, 1956). This requirement whenever tested in detail has been found to involve P_{fr} enzymatic action (Borthwick and Hendricks, 1961). A similar requirement has been demonstrated for germination of spores of the moss *Funaria hygrometrica* (Bauer and Mohr, 1959) and the fern *Dryopteris filix-mas* (Mohr, 1956).

Phytochrome has been observed by differential spectrophotometry in the cotyledons of kidney bean, squash, soyabean, peanut, and avocado seed. Light-responsive lettuce and many other seed are sensitive within less than 30 min after being wetted. It appears that phytochrome is present in the dry seed and, in fact, potentiated suppression of germination has been effected by irradiation of dry seed (Nyman, 1963).

Action spectra for control of *Lactuca sativa* var. Grand Rapids seed germination are shown in Fig. 1 (p. 408) (Borthwick *et al.*, 1954). The relative actions for germination of many seeds showing a light response have closely the same wavelength dependence. When measured with full knowledge of phytochrome control, they are the same as for control of flowering and anthocyanin formation in various plants but differ in energies required for a given action (such as 25% of the maximum effect). Equal actions are attained for *L. sativa* with less energy in the red and more in the far-red than for *Lepidium virginicum* (Toole *et al.*, 1955). These differences cannot be explained by screening of the incident radiation. They rather indicate a requirement for a lower per cent conversion of P_r to P_{fr} for a given germination in *L. sativa* than in *L. virginicum* seed.

Lactuca sativa var. Grand Rapids and *L. virginicum* seed potentiated to germinate by red light (P_{fr} formation) are reversible by far-red with decreasing effectiveness for about 12 h after the red irradiation. This is evidence both of variation between individual seed, some passing the point of control after 1 h while others require various times up to 12 h, and of slow formation of the substrate for P_{fr} action from the reserves of the seed. Seed of *L. sativa* irradiated with red light and held in darkness for 24 h at 30° fail to germinate upon returning to a favourable temperature for germination but respond to a second red irradiation (demonstrating viability). This again indicates that P_r is the thermodynamically stable form of phytochrome.

Many varieties of lettuce, Great Lakes for instance, and tomato seed that germinate in darkness can be induced to require red radiation by holding for 24 h or more under far-red radiation or at a temperature too high for germination. Action spectra under irradiances at two energy levels are shown for germination of seeds of *L. sativa* var. Great Lakes in Fig. 12 (Hendricks *et al.*, 1959). Similar results have been obtained for seeds of *Lamium amplexicaule*. These effects are interpreted as indicating either that low levels of P_{fr} maintained by far-red radiation drain off the substrate for P_{fr} action without establishing an adequate product level for germination, or that P_{fr} is being slowly formed *de novo* and far-red radiation is required for its elimination (perhaps less likely). These action spectra can readily be confused with the HER but, in reality, are more closely similar to suppression of flowering in *C. rubrum* (Fig. 5, p. 414) and other plants. Energies needed for appreciable percentage suppression are only of the order of several-fold (much less than the HER) that required for photoreversion of 90% P_{fr} to P_r.

Seeds of bromeliads, *Whitrockia superba* and *Bilbergia elegans*, (Downs, 1964) require light for germination. After irradiation they can be inhibited by far-red radiation to about 30% germination. A low irradiation of the dark-imbibed seed with far-red induces the same percentage and continued far-red leads to full germination. This is evidence of an

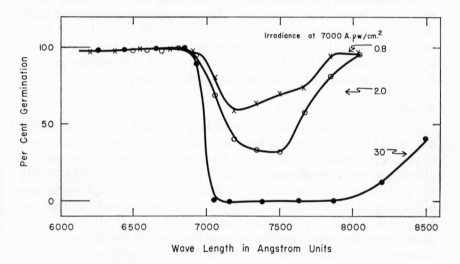

FIG. 12. Action spectrum for germination of *Lactuca sativa* var. Great Lakes seed under continuous irradiation in various wavelength regions.

appreciable incident level of substrate and of a high continued rate of supply. It also suggests that the eventual P_{fr} level reached in a stored seed in darkness is far below the stage to which the $P_{fr} \rightleftarrows P_r$ photochemical steady state can be driven by far-red radiation. Freshly harvested seed usually contain inhibitors of germination which assures a period, often of months, after maturing during which P_{fr} could revert to a low level without causing germination.

Many kinds of seed require repeated establishment of P_{fr} at high levels for germination. This behaviour has been considered to be similar to the photoperiodic or time-dependent features of flowering (Wareing and Black, 1957; Vaartaja, 1956; Isikawa *et al.*, 1961). In non-succulent plants the periodicity is an eventual result of the need for photosynthesis, with the HER yielding the substrate supply for P_{fr} action. The substrate supply in seed derives from the seed reserves but more than one full activation of the phytochrome is needed in some seeds to give a product level adequate for germination. An example is afforded by seed of *Paulownia tomentosa* (H. A. Borthwick and V. K. Toole, 1963, unpublished observations) for which light is obligatory for germination. Imbibed seed fail to germinate after a red irradiation unless exposed a second time after about 24 h. During the 24-h period the final effect can be reduced by photoreversion of P_{fr} to P_r. Continuous P_{fr} irradiation for 48 h yields the same result but has the misleading appearance of the HER.

To recapitulate: Evidence for a requirement for the presence of P_{fr} has been obtained from the action of light on germination of many kinds of seed. Some seed require several activations of phytochrome to P_{fr} for germination. Others are suppressed in germination by continued low levels of P_{fr} attained with far-red radiation, which utilizes substrates for P_{fr} action but at a rate inadequate for germination.

D. CONTROL OF ETIOLATION

Dark-grown seedlings usually have long internodes and small leaves lacking chlorophyll. Dicotyledons often form a plumular hook and leaves of monocotyledons remain rolled. Internode lengths and leaf sizes of plants growing on usual days and nights are influenced by light intensity and by the state of phytochrome during darkness. The displays are ones depending on cell number, elongation, and plastid formation. They are controlled both by P_{fr} enzymatic action and by the HER in much the same way as for the previously discussed phenomena. The photoreactions involved can be differentiated by the energies required for a given action, reversibility or its absence, and by detailed action spectra at appropriate times. Much of the information, however, is qualitative.

Suppression of internode lengthening by red light of low intensity was recognized by Vogt (1915) and was studied in detail by Trumpf (1924) and Lange (1929). It was the basis for suppressing lengthening in Avena seedlings in phototropic assays for auxin.

Action spectra for enhancement of the leaf enlargement and suppression of elongation of the first internode in dark-grown *Pisum sativum* seedlings show action maxima in the region of 650 mμ and near 400 mμ for the former (Parker *et al.*, 1949). Half saturation of the low energy effect at 650 mμ is attained with an irradiance of about 1 mJ/cm^2. The effects are partly reversed with far-red radiation (to the order of 90%), but a detailed action spectrum has not been obtained for the reversal. In these and other dark-grown seedlings potentiated action by very weak red radiation is incompletely reversed by far-red, indicating that the dark equilibrium $P_{fr}\rightleftarrows P_r$ is at a lower P_{fr} level than the photochemical equilibrium attained with 740 mμ radiation. As irradiation is continued, lack of reversibility arises from the effect of the HER.

The enzymatic action of P_{fr} and the HER have been shown for hypocotyl elongation, anthocyanin formation (Mohr, 1957), hair formation, and leaf enlargement (Mohr, 1959a) of *Sinapis alba* L. The HER action maxima are observed in these instances near 440 and 725 mμ, with the latter being about two-fold more effective than the first at equal energy. The P_{fr} enzymatic action is seen as a degree of red, far-red reversibility after the high-energy photoreaction. It also takes place during the HER photoreaction if the irradiation is over a period of many hours as is often required for pronounced effects. The scheme for the combined effects given by Mohr (1956) is similar in the order of photoreactions to one advanced for anthocyanin synthesis (Siegelman and Hendricks, 1958b), but shows the HER as an enzymatic action. This difference might be a manner of speaking if it is understood that a product is formed from a substrate, with an efficiency of probably less than 1·0 for each absorbed quantum, as is required by the eventual linear dependence on energy. The P_{fr} enzymatic action probably has a turnover of the order of 10^4 to 10^6 before P_{fr} reverts to P_r.

Opening of the plumular hook of *Phaseolus vulgaris* var. Black Valentine (Withrow *et al.*, 1957) with low-energy irradiation shows a maximum effectiveness under irradiation near 660 mμ and for reversal at 710 to 730 mμ. A flattened peak of effectiveness for pigment photoconversion is observed in solutions of phytochrome that are partly denatured (Chapter 8). The phytochrome content of etiolated seedling shoots is higher than is found in other plant parts. Part of the phytochrome is denatured in the plant upon standing at room temperature in light. The failure of complete reversal as energy is increased in the region of 710 to 730 mμ might arise for the reasons discussed under control of etiolation in *Pisum sativum* with the better evidence for a low steady-state level for P_{fr}.

Light-induced change in the plumular hook of *L. sativa* var. Grand Rapids seedlings (Mohr and Noble, 1960) differs from that of *Phaseolus vulgaris*. The hook is essentially absent in seedlings grown from seed exposed to red light to promote germination. It is present in many completely dark-grown seedlings (Downs, 1964), but is induced by many hours (10 to 20 h) of irradiation with low-intensity red, and equally by 6 irradiations of 4 min each at 2-h intervals. Far-red irradiation at low intensities for 4 min at hourly intervals for 3 h also led to hook formation but to a somewhat lesser degree (127° instead of 144° from the shoot apex). This similar effect indicates that the response is saturated by maintaining about 1% of the phytochrome as P_{fr}, as arises from overlap

14

of absorptions of P_r and P_{fr} in the far-red region. The substrate for P_{fr} action is accordingly very limited in the seedling held in darkness.

Continued irradiation (12 h) of *L. sativa* seedlings with high energies in the region of 700 to 800 mμ (far-red) or 400 to 480 mμ (blue) after formation of the hook causes it to open. The action spectrum is similar to that of the HER responses in *S. alba* with peaks of effectiveness near 450 and 725 mμ (Fig. 13). Evidently the supply of substrate for P_{fr} enzymatic action is enhanced and the limiting reaction in its production is the high-energy photochemical one.

Very low red irradiation adequate to change only a small percentage of phytochrome to P_{fr} causes a stiffening of *S. alba* seedlings (described

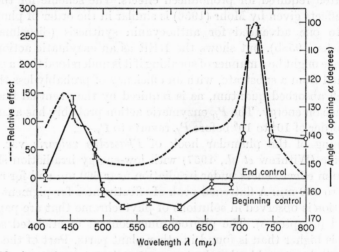

FIG. 13. An action spectrum (solid curve) for opening of the plumular hook, induced by red radiation of *Lactuca sativa* var. Grand Rapids. The dotted curve is the HER for enlargement of *Sinapis alba* cotyledons (after Mohr and Noble, 1960).

as negative geotropism) (Mohr and Pichler, 1960). This stiffening is very evident in seedlings of *Phaseolus vulgaris* var. Red Kidney following a short exposure to red radiation, leading to only slight suppression of stem lengthening.

Action spectra have not been measured for control of internode elongation of plants growing under usual day and night conditions. A reversible action of phytochrome, however, has been observed with *P. vulgaris* var. Red Kidney (Downs *et al.*, 1957). If plants are irradiated in the far-red at the end of a series of 8-h days of moderate illumination (1,000 f.c.) the forming internodes are relatively long compared with those receiving red radiation as the night started. The effect is reversible by low-energy red irradiation with decreasing effectiveness through a

16-h night. In this case, the plants must have reached a steady state with respect to the HER photoreaction during the day and the eventual products of its action arrived at the point of P_{fr} action in decreasing amounts with increased time in darkness. The substrate for P_{fr} action must have been limiting over a period of many hours in darkness.

Stem elongation of many woody and herbaceous plants is strikingly

Fig. 14. Slash pine (*Pinus elliotii*) grown on 8-h days with sunlight extended by low intensity incandescent filament radiation for 0, 6, and 8 h (*left to right*).

affected by day length and by extension of day length with red or far-red light of low intensity. Most of the observations are qualitative and were made on plants under usual growing conditions in a glasshouse with extension in neighbouring chambers (Borthwick, 1957; Piringer *et al.*, 1961; Cathey and Piringer, 1961). An example is the growth of *Pinus elliotii* on a basic 8-h day extended for 4 to 8 hours with radiation of low intensity (Fig. 14) which ensures a moderate percentage of phytochrome

14*

being present as P_{fr}. The plants do not grow on the 8-h day, but if P_{fr} is maintained for 8 additional hours growth is continuous. Similar results are obtained with young deciduous trees, *Catalpa* and *Acer rubrum*. A dormancy is induced in the terminal buds of the main and lateral axes by the absence of P_{fr} during many hours.

Effects on *Petunia hybrida* growing on 8-h days extended for 8 h with radiation of low intensity from incandescent filament lamps are shown in Fig. 15. The effect here is to induce growth of lateral buds which, too, is a result of a degree of inhibition of growth of the main axis. *Glycine*

Fig. 15. *Petunia hybrida* var. Ballerina grown for sixty-four 8-h days with sunlight extended by low intensity filament radiation for 0, 1, 2, 4, 6, and 8 h (*left to right*).

max growing under fluorescent radiation (low far-red) shows similar branching on normal days which is suppressed by addition of incandescent filament radiation which leads to predominant P_r in some parts of a leaf because of the filtering action of chlorophyll between 600 and 700 mμ.

Plants growing under radiation sources in limited spectral regions such as blue, green, red, and far-red display internode lengthening and flowering responses apparently arising from both the low energy and high energy (HER) blue, far-red actions (van der Veen and Meijer, 1959). An example is stem lengths of *Mirabilis jalapa* which are short when growth is with combinations of 8 h blue light + far-red, 8 h of other colours, and 8 h of darkness as contrasted with combinations including 8 h of red light. Blue and red radiations have opposite effects, with far-red giving effects similar to blue. Similar effects on flowering are induced in *Salvia occidentalis*. It is very difficult, however, in such displays to disentangle the effects of the HER, P_{fr} enzymatic action, and reduced photosynthesis.

To recapitulate: Control of lengthening of stems and leaves depends upon P_{fr}. The control by P_{fr} is determined by the concentration of the substrate upon which it acts. The substrate concentration is determined by the HER antecedent to the low-energy formation of P_{fr} or is supplied by reserves in dark-grown seedlings. The action of the HER is determined by the level of its substrate produced by photosynthesis.

VI. The HER Photoreaction

Evidence has been given in the preceding sections for a high-energy photoreaction (HER) prior to the photoreactions establishing P_{fr} as an enzyme. The HER was first appreciated as a dependence of plant growth on light quality (Pfeffer, 1904) or intensity as beneath the canopy of a forest. Much attention was turned to adjustment of light quality as artificially lighted rooms came into use for plant growth. The growth effects are very pronounced, particularly on elongation (van der Veen and Meijer, 1959), but analysis of causation cannot be pressed very far on the basis of such observations. Need for a light period preceding the dark period in photoperiodism was widely appreciated. The light period was generally considered to fulfil the requirements for photosynthesis.

Features of the HER are: (1) Physiological response in a particular wave band, often after an induction period, depends linearly on the radiant energy (Fig. 6, p. 417); (2) action maxima measured in terms of physiological response for a given incident energy per unit wave band are always found between 440 and 470 mμ and usually in the region of 640 to 730 mμ (Fig. 7, p. 418, 8, p. 418, 13, p. 426); (3) variations of wavelengths of maxima in both the 440 to 470 mμ and the 640 to 730 mμ regions are far outside the experimental error.

The HER and P_{fr} establishment for enzyme action have been confounded because the former must be followed by the latter and the P_{fr} must often be preceded by the HER for display of the physiological response used for assay. Both are accomplished in the region of 400 to 700 mμ, but if an action maximum for HER is in the region of 700 to 800 mμ, the phytochrome simultaneously is driven chiefly to P_r and blocks or greatly reduces the response. This difficulty is very serious if long times of exposure (> 8 h) are used as is often the case and sometimes is necessary. If irradiation periods of not more than 4 h are used for the

HER, phytochrome can be established in the P_{fr} form at the end of irradiation and maintained by repeated exposures without serious loss of potentiated action. Mohr (1962) and his students have advanced much evidence for the HER and have usually disentangled it from the simultaneous action of P_{fr} as controlled by low energy.

Absorption of chlorophyll as a screening pigment in the red and blue regions of the spectrum and other plant pigments in the blue is another distorting influence on the HER and phytochrome conversion. The amounts of chlorophyll in normal green leaves of seedlings, if fully effective for screening, could reduce the transmitted intensity of radiation more than ten-fold in the region of 640 to 690 mμ. Screening in green leaves in many cases does not have a marked effect on displacement of the action maximum for P_r conversion to P_{fr} as measured physiologically (Fig. 1). The displacement is from 660 mμ to about 640 mμ in *C. rubrum* (Fig. 4, p. 413) and about the same in other green plants. The incident energy, however, is reduced several fold more in these leaves at 660 mμ than at 640 mμ before reaching the region of action. This broadens the peak for P_r conversion to P_{fr} in green plants compared with solutions. Radiation of equal intensity throughout the 600 to 800 mμ region (as is approximately valid for sunlight) incident on leaves can reduce the P_{fr} percentage of total phytochrome present at steady state from about 80% characteristic of solutions to 20%.

Two suggestions have been advanced for the HER action spectra. The first (Siegelman and Hendricks, 1957) considers the photoreceptor to have maximum effectiveness for excitation in the 440 to 470 and 640 to 730 mμ regions. This is seemingly straightforward but does not account for the great variation in the positions of the maxima. It is equally straightforward to interpret the variability among the peaks either as arising from effects discussed in the previous paragraph or as evidence for a multiplicity of photoreceptors, each with its distinctive maximum. While these interpretations are probably broad enough not to be wrong, they are of limited value. The second suggestion (Hendricks *et al.*, 1959) is that phytochrome is the photoreceptor for the HER. At first sight this seems unreasonable (Mohr, 1962). In its support is the fact that the peak at 440 to 470 mμ is in a region where both P_r and P_{fr} have moderate absorbancies and the peak at 640 to 730 mμ is where either one or the other forms of phytochrome has a high absorbancy. But the possibility cannot be maintained in view of the finding that the latter peak is absent for anthocyanin synthesis in Wheatland milo (Downs and Siegelman, 1963) and that the peaks at 440 to 470 mμ are considerably to the long wavelength side of the minor absorption maxima of P'_r and P_{fr}.

A more likely possibility is that the effective HER photoresponsive system is the photosynthetic one involving either or both system 1 or system 2 (Hill and Bendall, 1960). The enhancement spectrum for photosynthesis by *Chlorella pyrenoidosa* (Myers and Graham, 1963) is shown in Fig. 16. In most of the objects for which the HER action

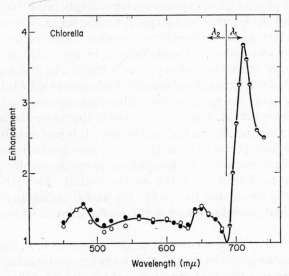

FIG. 16. Photosynthetic enhancement spectrum of *Chlorella pyrenoidoisa*. Enhancements are shown for the long wavelength (λ_1) and short wavelength (λ_2) components. Each component is shown as observed in the presence of the other (after Myers and Graham, 1963).

spectra have been measured the photosynthetic system is in the process of formation and is poorly organized. The effectiveness of coupling between systems 1 and 2 and the degree of involvement of the 705 mμ enhancement maximum in electron transfer with another system would probably be altered from that in normal green plants. Protochlorophyll is the only non-reversible pigment with an absorption maximum of the order of magnitude of the P_{fr} absorbancy seen in crude protein preparations from some etiolated tissues (maize) in the region of 640 to 730 mμ. Carotenoid proteins and cytochromes have been observed at this stage of purification, which serves as an indication of sensitivity. The discussion is left at this juncture because none of the HER action spectra has been measured suitably for testing the possibilities of simultaneous action in the spectral regions for photosynthesis.

VII. The Manner of Phytochrome Action

Factors mentioned in the preceding sections as indicating something about the reaction catalysed by P_{fr} are considered further. The diversity of the physiological expressions are indicative of their having some reaction in common, which must be a simple one. Flowering, anthocyanin formation, and elongation of structures display evidence of dependence on both the HER and the low energy photoreaction for formation of P_{fr}. The various physiological expressions accordingly must share these two reactions and the intermediate steps. A finding for anthocyanin production should be equally applicable to flowering and structure elongation.

Formation of ethanol and acetaldehyde in apple skin as alternative products to the A ring of anthocyanins is the key to understanding the reactions involved. Ethanol and acetaldehyde appear quickly in darkness, while many hours are required for anthocyanin appearance (Siegelman and Hendricks, 1958b). The common step of the many displays must be very close to ethanol formation, and because it is probably formed from pyruvate a first postulation is that pyruvate is the initial common substrate. Many metabolic pathways from pyruvate involve production, transfer, or modification of the acetyl radical. The HER reaction accordingly is considered to involve the acetyl radical in all cases, but whether oxidation-reduction or acyl transfer is involved is open at this time.

P_{fr} produced in the low energy transformation from P_r then is apparently an enzyme involved in one of the steps for combination of the three acetyl groups required for formation of the A ring of anthocyanins. It is improbable that common pathways would go to much more elaborate compounds. A reasonable possibility is that P_{fr} is involved in acyl transfer or modification, the acyl itself being derived from acetyl.

Acyl transfer or production is generally mediated by CoASH (reduced coenzyme A), often accompanied by oxidation, and involves other sulphur-containing groups in co-factors or the enzyme. For example (Walker and Beevers, 1955),

$$CH_3COCOOH + NAD^+ + CoASH \rightarrow CH_3COSCoA + NADH + CO_2 + H^+$$

with thiamine pyrophosphate, Mg^{++}, and α-lipoic acid as co-factors, which is known to occur in most plants. The course of phytochrome denaturation is of interest in this regard. P_{fr} is far more sensitive than P_r to denaturation by urea, p-chloromercuribenzoate, and N-ethyl maleimide (Chapter 8). In the photoconversion of P_r to P_{fr} an SH group is unmasked and could be playing a role in imparting enzymatic activity to P_{fr} since it is in the neighbourhood of the chromophore, the transformation of which leads to enzymatic activity.

The HER is not involved in germination control of light-sensitive seed and P_{fr} control of growth of etiolated seedlings. Most of these responses require transformation of P_r to P_{fr} and, in some, maintenance of P_{fr} by repeated transformations by the low energy photoreaction. The latter has been confused with the HER. How is the common chain of substrate supply avoided in these instances? The answer is afforded by an observation on the germination of *Digitalis purpurea* seed by Grohne (1952). The first detected change in the germination process was the appearance of starch in the oil droplet near the micropilar end in the neighbourhood of the radicle tip. The course of fatty acid degradation is known to involve freeing of the acid in seed by lipase action with degradation by β-oxidation mediated by formation of acyl CoA and of acetyl CoA with accompanying NADH. This process, then, is an alternative method for supplying the product of the HER. Later, in the developing seedling the HER becomes predominant in supplying the substrate for P_{fr} action.

In this dependence on lipid utilization, buried seeds in darkness with phytochrome in the P_r form can block the fat utilization for respiration and thus conserve reserves for viability over decades.

To recapitulate the last two sections: The HER is considered to be a first or early step in the production of acetyl groups. The phytochrome enzymatic reaction is a later step in the condensation of such groups to polyacyl groups such as the A ring of anthocyanins.

VIII. GENERAL RÉSUMÉ

A first purpose was to illustrate the manifold aspects of plant growth and development controlled by the change in form of phytochrome. This development rests on demonstration of multiple physiological expressions associated with phytochrome conversion. The clear-cut recognition of a high energy reaction (HER), often antecedent to P_{fr} action, is secure enough for future elaboration.

A second purpose was to place the phytochrome and HER actions and the physiological displays in relation to metabolic pathways. This was based on alternative anthocyanin and ethanol formation in apple fruit subepidermal tissue. Evidence is advanced that the HER acts near pyruvate and the suggestion is made that the photoresponse arises from the chlorophyll systems. The P_{fr} enzymatic action is considered to take part in formation of polyacyl compounds. The HER is bypassed in seed germination and low energy etiolation responses by supply of substrates for P_{fr} action from metabolic reserves, which are probably lipids in the case of seed germination. The enzymatic reaction catalysed by P_{fr} and the exact nature of the HER remain to be discovered.

Possible third and fourth objectives of understanding were hardly mentioned. The third is the identity of the specific compounds which produce the physiological displays. Reasonable knowledge exists only for anthocyanin formation. Determination of flowering has been discussed at length in the physiological literature. A diffusible compound influencing flowering results from P_{fr} action but the nature of this compound is unknown. Attention could also be turned to phytochrome control of axis elongation which also must involve diffusible compounds. Its consideration is quickly involved with auxin and gibberellin actions.

The fourth objective is central to physiological display but nothing is known of its nature. This is the manner in which specific diffusible compounds achieve physiological control.

REFERENCES

Bauer, L., and Mohr, H. (1959). *Planta* 54, 68–73.

Birch, A. J. (1957). *Fortschr. Chem. org. Naturst.* 14, 186–216.

Borthwick, H. A. (1957). *Ohio J. Sci.* 57, 357–364.

Borthwick, H. A., and Cathey, H. M. (1962). *Bot. Gaz.* 123, 155–162.

Borthwick, H. A., and Hendricks, S. B. (1961). *In* "Handbuch der Pflanzen-physiologie" (W. Ruhland, ed.), vol. XVI, pp. 299–330, Springer-Verlag, Berlin.

Borthwick, H. A., Hendricks, S. B., and Parker, M. W. (1948). *Bot. Gaz.* 110, 103–118.

Borthwick, H. A., Hendricks, S. B., Parker, M. W., Toole, E. H., and Toole, V. K. (1952a). *Proc. nat. Acad. Sci., Wash.* 38, 662–666.

Borthwick, H. A., Hendricks, S. B., and Parker, M. W. (1952b). *Proc. nat. Acad. Sci., Wash.* 38, 929–934.

Borthwick, H. A., Hendricks, S. B., Toole, E. H., and Toole, V. K. (1954). *Bot. Gaz.* 115, 205–225.

Cajlachjan, M. C. (1937). "On the Hormonal Theory of Plant Development," 200 pp., Izvest. Akad. Nauk. S.S.S.R., Moskva.

Caspary, R. (1861). *Schr. phys.-ökon. Ges. Königb.* 1, 66–91.

Cathey, H. M., and Borthwick, H. A. (1962). *Flor. Rev.* 131, 3391.

Cathey, H. M., and Piringer, A. A. (1961). *Proc. Amer. Soc. hort. Sci.* 77, 608–619.

Cumming, B. G. (1959). *Nature, Lond.* 184, 1044–1045.

Cumming, B. G. (1962). *Canad. J. Bot.* 41, 901–926.

Darlington, H. T., and Steinbauer, G. P. (1961). *Amer. J. Bot.* 48, 321–325.

DeCandolle, A. P. (1832). *Physiol. Végét.* 3, 1078.

Downs, R. J. (1955). *Plant Physiol.* 30, 468–472.

Downs, R. J. (1964). *Phyton* 21, 1–6.

Downs, R. J., and Siegelman, H. W. (1963). *Plant Physiol.* 38, 25–30.

Downs, R. J., Hendricks, S. B., and Borthwick, H. A. (1957). *Bot. Gaz.* 118, 199–208.

Emsweller, S. L., Stewart, N. W., and Byrnes, J. W. (1941). *Bull. Chrysanth. Soc. Amer.* 9, 19–20.

Evenari, M. (1956). *In* "Radiation Biology" (A. Hollaender, ed.), vol. 3, pp. 519–549, McGraw Hill, New York.

Flint, L. H., and McAlister, E. D. (1935). *Smithson. Misc. Coll.* 94, 1–11.

Flint, L. H., and McAlister, E. D. (1937). *Smithson. Misc. Coll.* 96, 1–7.

Fredericq, H. (1964). *Plant Physiol.* (In press).

Garner, W. W., and Allard, H. A. (1920). *J. agric. Res.* 18, 553–606.

Geissman, T. A. (1962). "The Chemistry of Flavonoid Compounds," 666 pp., Macmillan Co., New York.

Geissman, T. A., and Swain, T. (1957). *Chem. Ind.* 984.

Grisebach, H. (1957). *Z. Naturf.* 126, 227–231.

Grohne, U. (1952). *Biol. Zbl.* **71**, 10–42.

Hagen, C. E., Borthwick, H. A., and Hendricks, S. B. (1954). *Bot. Gaz.* **116**, 360–364.

Hamner, K. C., and Bonner, J. (1938). *Bot. Gaz.* **100**, 388–431.

Haupt, W. (1959). *Planta* **53**, 484–501.

Hendricks, S. B., Borthwick, H. A., and Downs, R. J. (1956). *Proc. nat. Acad. Sci., Wash.* **42**, 19–26.

Hendricks, S. B., Toole, E. H., Toole, V. K., and Borthwick, H. A. (1959). *Bot. Gaz.* **121**, 1–8.

Hill, R., and Bendall, F. (1960). *Nature, Lond.* **186**, 136–137.

Isikawa, S., Fujii, T., and Yokohama, Y. (1961). *Bot. Mag., Tokyo* **74**, 14–18.

Kasperbauer, M. J., Borthwick, H. A., and Hendricks, S. B. (1963). *Bot. Gaz.* (In press).

Kasperbauer, M. J., Borthwick, H. A., and Hendricks, S. B. (1964). *Bot. Gaz.* (In press).

Kinzel, W. (1913–1926). "Frost und Licht als beeinflussende Kräfte bei der Samenkeimung," (E. Ulmer, ed.), Lupwidsberg.

Kleshnin, A. F. (1943). *C. R. Acad. Sci., U.R.S.S.* **40**, 208–211.

Knott, J. E. (1926). *Proc. Amer. Soc. hort. Sci.* **23**, 67–70.

Laetsch, W. M., and Briggs, W. R. (1962). *Plant Physiol.* **37**, 142–148.

Lange, S. (1929). *Jb. wiss. Bot.* **71**, 1–25.

Mohr, H. (1956). *Planta* **46**, 534–551.

Mohr, H. (1957). *Planta* **49**, 389–405.

Mohr, H. (1959a). *Planta* **53**, 109–124.

Mohr, H. (1959b). *Planta* **53**, 219–245.

Mohr, H. (1962). *Ann. Rev. Pl. Physiol.* **13**, 465–488.

Mohr, H., and Noble, A. (1960). *Planta* **55**, 327–340.

Mohr, H., and Pichler, I. (1960). *Planta* **55**, 57–66.

Myers, J., and Graham, J. (1963). *Plant Physiol.* **38**, 105–116.

Nakayama, S. (1958). *Ecol. Rev.* **14**, 325–326.

Nakayama, S., Borthwick, H. A., and Hendricks, S. B. (1960). *Bot. Gaz.* **121**, 237–243.

Nilsson, M. (1959). *Acta chem. scand.* **13**, 750.

Nyman, B. (1963). *Studia Forstelia Suecica* **2**, 1–164.

Parker, M. W., Hendricks, S. B., Borthwick, H. A., and Scully, N. J. (1946). *Bot. Gaz.* **108**, 1–26.

Parker, M. W., Hendricks, S. B., Borthwick, H. A., and Went, F. W. (1949). *Amer. J. Bot.* **36**, 194–204.

Parker, M. W., Hendricks, S. B., and Borthwick, H. A. (1950). *Botan. Gaz.* **111**, 242–252.

Pfeffer, W. (1904). "Pflanzenphysiologie," Bd. 11, Kraftwechsel, 2 Aufl., Vol. 2, 117, Wilhelm Engelmann, Leipzig.

Piringer, A. A., and Heinze, P. H. (1954). *Plant Physiol.* **29**, 467–472.

Piringer, A. A., Downs, R. J., and Borthwick, H. A. (1961). *Proc. Amer. Soc. hort. Sci.* **77**, 202–210.

Price, L., and Klein, W. H. (1961). *Plant Physiol.* **36**, 733–735.

Siegelman, H. W., and Hendricks, S. B. (1957). *Plant Physiol.* **32**, 393–398.

Siegelman, H. W., and Hendricks, S. B. (1958a). *Plant Physiol.* **33**, 185–190.

Siegelman, H. W., and Hendricks, S. B. (1958b). *Plant Physiol.* **33**, 409–413.

Takimoto, A., and Ikeda, K. (1959). *Bot. Mag., Tokyo* **72**, 181–189.

Toole, E. H., Toole, V. K., Borthwick, H. A., and Hendricks, S. B. (1955). *Plant Physiol.* **30**, 15–21.

Trumpf, C. (1924). *Bot. Arch.* **5**, 381–410.

Vaartaja, O. (1956). *Canad. J. Bot.* **34**, 377–388.

van der Veen, R., and Meijer, G. (1959). "Light and Plant Growth," 159 pp., Macmillan, New York.

Vogt, E. (1915). *Zbl. Bot.* **7**, 193–271.

Walker, P. F., and Beevers, H. (1955). *Biochem. J.* **62**, 120.

Wareing, P. F., and Black, M. (1957). *In* "The Physiology of Forest Trees" (K. V. Thimann, ed.), pp. 539–556.

Watkin, J. E., Underhill, E. W., and Neish, A. C. (1957). *Canad. J. Biochem. Physiol.* **35**, 229–237.

Withrow, R. B., and Withrow, A. P. (1940). *Plant Physiol.* **15**, 609–624.

Withrow, R. B., Klein, W. H., and Elstad, V. (1957). *Plant Physiol.* **32**, 453–462.

PART III: METABOLISM IN SENESCENT AND STORED TISSUE

Chapter 16

PIGMENT CHANGES IN SENESCENT AND STORED TISSUE

C. O. CHICHESTER and T. O. M. NAKAYAMA*

Department of Food Science and Technology,
University of California, Davis, California, U.S.A.

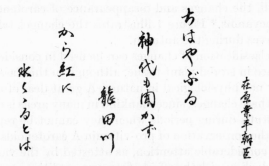

The hills are aflame with autumnal tints.
The riverside of the famous Tatsutagawa river is also
   beautiful covered with scarlet-tinged leaves.
The clear blue water of the Tatsutagawa river looks as
   if the water be dyed crimson (the waters below
   caught the crimson glow of the maple leaves
   above).
This is the first that I have heard that the water of
   the river was dyed beautiful red.

Narihira Arihara (12th Century)

* The authors would like to acknowledge the support given by N.S.F. Grant GB 558
and N.I.H. Grant GM 8869.

I. Introduction

This section reviews the chemical changes of pigmented compounds during the senescence and/or storage of plant materials. Both the production of autumn colours in vegetation and the fading of the colour of dried carrot tissue are appropriate to the discussion.

To set the stage for discussion it would not be remiss to define "senescence." The inevitable onset of senescence in all living things is axiomatic, and generally encompasses changes occurring between maturity and death. The cycle of life and death, witnessed annually in the temperate zones by the display of autumnal colours by vegetation, is a well-known phenomenon and has been investigated for a long time. The transformation is exemplified by a green leaf which turns yellow, red, and finally brown. Variations from this general case are commonplace. It will be expedient to view the changes in senescence in terms of the disappearance of chlorophyll, the changes and disappearance of carotenoids, and the fate of anthocyanins.* Figure 1 illustrates the changes taking place in raspberry leaves during the autumn.

The same classification of changes can be used in considering changes that take place in stored plant tissue, although in this case the changes are generally not physiological in nature. A great deal of attention has been paid to these changes, since mankind in many areas is dependent on storing foodstuffs during periods when they cannot be replenished. As an example, the conservation of pro-vitamin A carotenoids in foodstuffs has received considerable attention, as attested by the vast number of publications dealing with the effect of storage conditions on the retention of carotene. An almost equivalent number of investigations have centred on the appearance of produce, dealing with retention of the green colour in vegetables and the red colour in fruits.

One can consider storage to be of two classes: In the first, the plant material is so treated that physiological processes are halted or slowed, such as by blanching, drying, etc. In the second, the environment of storage is so controlled as to reduce the rate at which senescence progresses. Examples of this are the cool storage of fruits, roots, and vegetables.

Tracing to its ultimate end (the reverse of photosynthesis) the degradation (either physiological or nonphysiological) of the complex polyfunctional molecules found in small amounts in plant tissue is a formidable problem, reflecting as it does so many environmental conditions affecting both physiological and chemical degradations. Indeed, the difference in colouration between identical plants in different environments is well known. Considerations of biochemical inter-

* Changes in colourless flavonoid compounds are not considered in this chapter.

mediates in degradation are necessarily limited to those compounds which can be recognized by virtue of structural relationships to be derived from the parent compounds. It may well be that the production of ethylene is concurrent with the disappearance of chlorophyll in many tissues. It is difficult to assume that the proposed conversion is more than

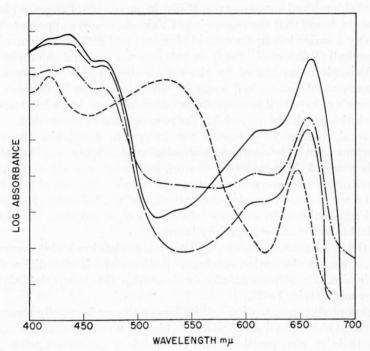

FIG. 1. Absorption spectra of extracts of raspberry leaves at four stages of senescence.

———————— green mature stage
— • — yellow stage
— — completely senescent stage
– – – – senescent stage—acidified with HCl

a fortuitous coincidence. Until such time as specific labelling of chlorophyll carbons can be accomplished *in vivo* and the ethylene identified as arising from these specifically labelled carbons, little other than a casual relationship can be assumed. This is not the case, however, when compounds containing pyrrole rings are produced during the disappearance of chlorophyll, since the structural relationship in this case is obvious.

Biochemical factors relating to senescence in general are omitted herein, and the reader is referred to a recent review by Varner (1961).

II. Chlorophyll

All green plant materials can be characterized as undergoing a loss in colour upon senescence, processing, or storage. In no case is there a net increase in chlorophyll content.

Valencia oranges might be thought to be an exception to the general case of chlorophyll loss; however, Miller, in measuring changes in plastid pigments, found that the regreening of Valencia oranges appears to take place by a major loss in carotenoid pigments and little or no increase in chlorophyll (Miller *et al.*, 1940). In this case the residual chlorophyll of the Valencia is unmasked by the loss of the secondary pigment. In comparisons of chlorophyll losses by several varieties of oranges, the Valencia's chlorophyll content did not decrease to as low a level as that of varieties which did not exhibit the phenomenon of regreening.

Several chlorophyll pigments are known to exist, but the most important from a chemical and technological standpoint are the chlorophylls *a* and *b*. The majority of work on the changes of chlorophyll concentration is concerned with these pigments, although chlorophylls *c* and *d* are of importance in marine flora, and the bacterial chlorophyll in microorganisms. In any case, the results cited are more than likely applicable to the other chlorophyll forms.

In the living systems, chlorophyll probably exists in a highly organized state, since the absorption spectrum of chlorophyll *in vitro* differs from that *in vivo*. It is estimated that only about 5% exists in an oriented state (Sauer and Calvin, 1962).

Chlorophyll concentration and its loss or change is usually measured in isolated chlorophyll preparations, which by necessity must be moved from their *in vivo* position. The methodology concerned with their measurement is mild, and, consequently, any changes determined on the chemical constituents are more than likely directly applicable to those occurring within the chloroplasts.

The presence of chlorophylls *a* and *b* in the leaves of higher plants has focused attention on their comparative biochemistry. Their behaviour during senescence has been investigated numerous times, and it appears that chlorophyll *a* generally tends to be destroyed at a faster rate (Seybold, 1943; Jeffrey and Griffith, 1947; Wolf and Wolf, 1955). Wolf (1956), in a comparative study of the leaves of twenty-five species of trees, showed that chlorophyll *a* averaged 69·4% of the chlorophylls in green leaves and 56·2% in yellow leaves. This is contrary to the previously held view that the ratio remained constant during the fading of autumn leaves (see Goodwin, 1952).

In view of the fact that the two forms are intimately associated in the chloroplasts, a physiological selection appears unlikely; rather, a difference of chemical reactivity can be involved. In the *in vitro* conversion of chlorophylls *a* and *b* into their respective pheophytins the rate of conversion of *a* exceeds that of *b* by five times (Schanderl *et al.*, 1963). Rate constants are not readily available for individual destruction, but the situation is probably similar, with the rate of loss for *a* being higher than that for *b*.

This difference in reactivity had been noticed in the making of silage, where the chlorophylls differed in their resistance to destruction by acids (Egle, 1944), and similar results with drying plant materials have suggested that acids normally present in leaves are important for the destruction of chlorophyll. The first manifestation of acid modification of chlorophyll should be pheophytin formation, and this is often found in leaf extracts although it is not known whether it is incidental to the extraction. Pheophytin formation during processing and storage is, however, an observed fact (Stoll and Wiedemann, 1933; Willstätter and Stoll, 1913). Thus far, this reaction is now known to be catalysed enzymatically.

Pheophytin *a* is normally found adsorbed on a sugar column below chlorophyll *a* and below chlorophyll *a'*. Pheophytin *b*, which is more strongly adsorbed, is adsorbed above chlorophyll *a* but below chlorophylls *b* and *b'* (Strain, 1958).

If the pheophytins *a* and *b* are heated in propanol, they are converted into pheophytins *a'* and *b'*, which are less strongly adsorbed than the initial pheophytins. At this stage the *a'* and *b'* derivatives are reconvertible to pheophytins *a* and *b*.

The ultimate fate of the chlorophyll during senescence remains unresolved. It appears that a rapid cleavage into small fragments must occur, because no large, obviously derived compounds are observed (Seybold, 1943). Goodwin (1958), however, has reported that the remaining chlorophylls, although chromatographically similar to chlorophylls *a* and *b*, were spectroscopically distinct, with red maxima in light petroleum at 652 mμ and 635 mμ, respectively, instead of at 662 and 644 mμ.

When plant materials are heated, such as may occur during blanching, isomeric chlorophylls *a* and *b* are formed. Strain (1958) has called these chlorophyll *a'* and chlorophyll *b'*, respectively. The isomers are separable from the parent compounds on sugar columns; they will undergo the phase test, as will the parent compounds. *In vitro* the same reactions occur at room temperature—in a few hours, or rapidly if alkali is added. These isomerization products are reconvertible to an equilibrium mixture of the parent compounds by treatment with additional alkali or by heating in normal propanol.

Freed *et al.* (1954) suggested that *a'* and *b'* are isomeric with the original chlorophyll, and that a third derivative of chlorophyll b, chlorophyll b'', is also an isomer of b and b'. They ascribe the three isomers to the three molecular structures which may be written for chlorophyll, with magnesium bonded to three different pairs of pyrrole nitrogen atoms. These must then exist as tautomers rather than as resonant hybrids. On this basis the magnesium is not free to move, but, rather, a potential barrier exists between the three forms, preventing their easy interconversion. This explanation could certainly explain the reversibility of the conversion of b' to b and a' to a. Strain later pointed out, however, that b'' and a'' are probably not isomers but rather non-reconvertible allomerized chlorophylls. He suggests that, because of the method of preparation, a'' and b'' are oxidation products of the original isomeric a' and b'. He cites as an additional argument that, if a, a', and a'' have the magnesium atom bound to different pairs of pyrrole nitrogen atoms, the three pigments should yield but one magnesium-free porphyrin. That is not the case, however, since three have been reported (Strain and Manning, 1942; Strain, 1955). It would thus appear that there exist a number of chlorophyll-like products which are separable from chlorophyll on chromatographic analysis and differ slightly in absorption spectra, but undergo all the chemical tests for native chlorophylls. Some of these must be isomers, and others the initial oxidation product of chlorophyll. Their structures have not yet been clarified, and additional investigation is needed to determine their relation to the parent compounds and their position in any oxidation scheme, either *in vivo* or *in vitro*. If they are not isomeric compounds, they may correspond to the first oxidation products of the chlorophylls.

A different picture is presented by the modification of chlorophylls to chlorophyllides (the removal of the phytol group) by the enzyme chlorophyllase. This enzyme, which was discovered by Willstätter and Stoll, is intimately associated with chlorophyll, and its development also is influenced by light, but this far no physiological role has clearly been assigned to this enzyme (Willstätter and Stoll, 1910; Holden, 1961, 1963, and Chapter 17). Suggestions have been made that the first step in the enzymatic breakdown of chlorophyll *in vivo* may be removal of the phytol group. It is probable, however, that the enzyme may be present in a chlorophyll-lipoprotein complex, and thus unable to exert its activity *in vivo* (Ardao and Vennesland, 1960; Sudyina, 1963). Maximum activity is obtained when the enzyme is solubilized. Preliminary extraction with solvents makes the preparation of chlorophyllase soluble; however, optimum solvent concentration appears to include 40–50% acetone (Holden, 1961).

The over-all ultimate fate of the chlorophyll molecule would appear to be oxidation. The oxidative destruction may be influenced by enzymes, heat, or light, as well as by numerous other factors. In green tissue macerated in such a manner that the oxidative enzyme systems are not destroyed, the chlorophylls are oxidized at a rate that permits the isolation of partly altered derivatives. These derivatives are readily separated chromatographically from the parent compounds, although their spectroscopic properties are similar. They invariably show a green-phase test, as opposed to the yellow-phase test of the parent chlorophyll. This phase test has long been used for detection of the allomerization of chlorophylls. The nonenzymatic oxidation of chlorophylls a and b results initially in the formation of allomerized derivatives (Aronoff, 1953). Strain (1958) separated these derivatives chromatographically and showed that the main allomerized derivative of chlorophyll a exhibits a spectral absorption maximum at wavelengths about 20 mμ shorter than those of chlorophyll a. Another oxidation product obtained was identical to the product obtained from enzymatic oxidation of chlorophyll a. Chlorophyll b yields in methanol an allomerization product which is slightly more strongly adsorbed than chlorophyll b and exhibits spectral absorption maxima of wavelengths about 10 mμ shorter. A second oxidation product exhibited identical absorption properties but different chromatographic properties, and was identical with the products of the enzymatic oxidation of chlorophyll b.

Traces of other pigments were also found. Nonenzymatic destruction of chlorophyll can be enhanced by light; thus, in a system exposed to oxygen and red light the destruction of chlorophyll proceeds in a straightforward manner (Aronoff and Mackinney, 1943; Pepkowitz, 1943). Whether this occurs in vivo requires investigation. In numerous studies dealing with losses of pigment during the growing of hay, the influence of light has been shown to be an additional accelerating factor (Rabinowitch, 1956; Braverman, 1963).

Figure 2 indicates schematically several pathways for initial destruction of the chlorophylls.

Beyond the formation of the oxidized chlorophylls, the next step in the nonenzymatic breakdown of the pigment is probably concerned with oxygen attack on the isocyclic carbon C-10. It is presumed that the process involves the oxidation of C-10 to hydroxy, followed by a breaking of the ring to form a variety of purpurins and chlorins. These materials are found in moderate quantities in dried plant materials (Aronoff, 1953). The exact pathway of oxidation is not known in vivo, and is only guessed at in vitro. The formation of pheophorbides and/or purpurins causes a considerable change in the colour of plant material. The further oxidation of these derivatives occurs through complete scission of the isocyclic ring, followed by oxidation of the tetrapyrrole (Aronoff, 1953). Seybold (1943) suggests that in plant materials the reactions between chlorophyll and materials of low molecular weight is comparatively rapid. He was unable to identify high-molecular-weight components and presumed that a rapid and extensive cleavage of the chlorophyll results, forming colourless low-molecular-weight compounds not easily identifiable by spectroscopic or chromatographic means.

There have been extensive investigations of the loss of chlorophyll or changes in chlorophyll in food materials. The vast majority of these studies shed no light on the fate of the chlorophyll molecule, but merely confirm that there is a net reduction influenced by temperature, pH, light, oxygen tension, etc. It is interesting, however, to note that the

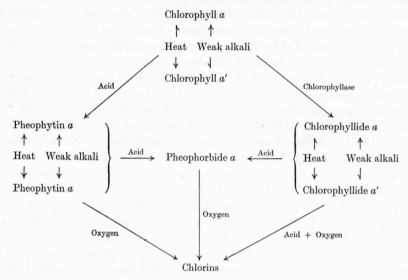

FIG. 2. Pathways for the initial degradation of chlorophyll *a*.

mechanism of regreening of vegetables is due to the chelation of metallic ions to an oxidation product of chlorophyll (Schanderl *et al.*, 1964). This occurs in a number of green vegetables where the copper or zinc content is substantial, such as peas. The vegetable, after preservation, fades to the typical pheophytin colour, and upon standing reassumes the typical green chlorophyll colouration, which is due to the chelation of free copper with the oxidation products of chlorophyll.

III. CAROTENOIDS

Carotenoid stability in plant materials, either living or stored, varies widely. As an example, in macerated green leaves half of the carotenoids are lost in 20 min (Friend and Nakayama, 1959). In the corona of narcissus (which contains the highest concentration of carotenoids known), the formation and loss of the carotenoids occurs in only a few days (Booth, 1957, 1963). In contrast, only half the carotenoids in stored corn was lost at 7° C in 3 years (Quackenbush, 1963). In green tissue, particularly *in vivo*, the carotenoids may be subject to enzymatic breakdown through the lipoxidase system, which in turn is catalysed by the presence of the chlorophyll (Blain and Styles, 1959). In contrast, nonphotosynthetic tissue, such as in corn, is almost wholly dependent upon direct oxidation by molecular oxygen (Quackenbush, 1963). This difference, however, does not completely explain the difference in stability encountered in various tissues. One can contrast narcissus with corn, both of which are non-green tissues. Obviously these pigments are complexed with protein or other substances. Thus the stability and physical characteristics differ with the association. The isolated compound, or pure compound, is very sensitive to direct oxidation, enzymatic conversion, and light. In all cases its stability is very much lower than that of the complexed material.

Light, particularly of the shorter wavelengths, is effective in increasing the rate of breakdown of carotenoids. Table I indicates the loss in carotenoid under different lighting conditions (Stahl *et al.*, 1957).

TABLE I

β-Carotene Losses in Drying Hay[a]

Lighting condition	Time (h)	Per cent loss
Intense sunlight	48	70
Shade	48	36
Diffuse sunlight indoors (through glass)	48	44
Diffuse sunlight indoors after steaming	48	0
Direct sunlight after steaming	—	40
Ultra-violet light after steaming	48	40

[a] Stahl, *et al.* (1957).

A great deal of reported work concerns the net loss of carotenoids, or rather, a decrease in absorption at 450 mμ. Even work which considers the mechanism of oxidation of carotenoids does not normally distinguish among the various classes of pigments, such as the epoxides, xanthophylls, and acyclic and alicyclic carotenoids. A mechanism which must assuredly differ with the functional groups attached to the carotenoid molecule makes difficult any discussion of the qualitative changes in carotenoids undergoing oxidation or destruction. As an example, β-carotene is usually used to study the coupled oxidation of lipoxidase and linoleate, whereas in studies on the stability of vitamin A precursors in hay, absorption at 450 mμ is usually taken as a measure of the remaining carotenoid (Crosby and Sumner, 1945; Blain et al., 1953; Orth and Koch, 1963).

The formation of autumn "carotene-xanthophylls" has been of historical interest since the observations of Berzelius (1837). The formation and consequent esterification of xanthophylls was studied by Kuhn and Brockmann (1932), who showed their carotene-like behaviour to be due to esterification. The original supposition was made that the hydrocarbon carotenoids were converted into the xanthophylls, which remained as the chlorophyll decreased. This would then account for the increasing yellow and red colours in the leaves. It has, however, been established that this is not the case. In all cases there is a decrease in total carotenoids; however, the hydrocarbons in general decrease more rapidly. As a consequence, the percentage of the xanthophylls increases during this period of carotenoid loss (Goodwin, 1958; Karrer and Walker, 1934; Nagel, 1939). Additionally, a reaction that appears to be quite general is the esterification of the xanthophylls. As the leaves age and the total carotenoid content decreases, the relative abundance of esterified xanthophylls increases. In contrast to the original photosynthetic tissue, which contains only a minute fraction of esterified xanthophylls, the autumn leaf, in its latter stages of development, consists almost entirely of esters of lutein and violaxanthin. These, in turn, are lost in the final fading process. It is interesting to note that the relative loss in carotenoids or their esterification may either precede, occur simultaneously, or follow the decrease in chlorophyll, depending upon the species. Obviously, then, there is no direct interaction between chlorophyll changes and xanthophyll changes.

In ripening fruits of the Rosaceae family it is evident that the development of ripe colour (carotenoids) does not begin until the chlorophyll has already dropped to a very low level. In the ripening fruit the formation of carotenoids appears subsequent to the decrease in chlorophyll. During this period of active carotenoid formation [^{14}C]mevalonic acid will be readily incorporated into carotenes and xanthophylls. However, as the fruit approaches maturity, the tendency for the xanthophylls to be labelled becomes less, and at complete maturity there is little or no labelling of xanthophylls. Thus the composition of the carotenoids of a fruit at any time subsequent to full maturity is a reflection of the relative stabilities of the various carotenoids involved, and these may be influenced by the presence of different function groups (T. Katayama, T. O. M. Nakayama and C. O. Chichester, 1964, unpublished observations).

It has been postulated that the initial breakdown of carotenoids occurs through formation of epoxides (Zechmeister et al., 1943; Fishwick, 1962).

Evidence for this is not very substantial; however, it has been shown that epoxy-carotenoids appear in both fruit and autumn leaves successively after the decrease in β-carotene and neoxanthin (T. Katayama, T. O. M. Nakayama, M. Yamaguchi and C. O. Chichester, 1964, unpublished observations; Goodwin, 1958). Glover demonstrated a stepwise oxidation of β-carotene, initiated at the ionone rings (Glover, 1960). In contrast to this, epoxides are formed in fruit simultaneously with the appearance of the xanthophylls and the hydrocarbon carotenoids. At maximum maturity of fruit the epoxides decrease and there is a net appearance of xanthophylls. The pathway of hydrocarbons → xanthophylls → epoxides cannot be substantiated as a general mechanism for the degradation of carotenoids in all tissues.

The open-chain carotenoids (the acyclic carotenoids), exemplified by lycopene, ζ-carotene, phytoene, etc., are an interesting case in relative stabilities. Lycopene is relatively stable in the tomato fruit, persisting under the most adverse conditions. In contrast, lycopene as a pigment has an extremely low stability (A. Lukton, 1963, personal communication), the isolated pigment being far less stable than β-carotene. In a comparison of the storage stability of two varieties of carrots, respectively containing β-carotene and lycopene, no major difference was found in loss of carotenoids. The loss of pigments of both, however, was accelerated by storage in light (Katayama et al., loc. cit.).

In seaweed post-mortem, it has been shown that the increase in zeaxanthin exactly matches the decrease in violaxanthin, indicating that there is a net conversion of the epoxy- to the hydroxy pigment. In the same material there was no change or interconversion of β-carotene and fucoxanthin to either violaxanthin or zeaxanthin (Braarud and Sörensen, 1956). The pathway for either the breakdown or the interconversion of carotenoids cannot at present be developed into a single scheme which fits all plant tissue.

In fruits or vegetables which contain the poly-cis-isomer of a carotenoid, heating and/or storage will on occasion cause a deepening in colour. Such isomeric changes are characteristic of the tangerine tomato and of rutabaga (Brassica rutabaga) (Joyce, 1953, 1954; G. Mackinney, 1960, personal communication).

In highly acid fruit it is possible to obtain isomerization in vivo by injuring the tissue. Singleton, in analysing changes occurring during the ripening of pineapple, found a considerable increase in the cis-isomers of carotenoids (Singleton et al., 1961; Gortner and Singleton, 1961). Handling, processing, or severe handling releases sufficient fruit acids to cause rapid isomerization. Processed fruit has, in general, isomerized completely. Citrus juices undergo the same type of transformation in that, upon the release of acids by tissue injury, a very rapid isomerization occurs. In addition, in stored fruit juices violaxanthin decreases rapidly. The carotenoid epoxides, which constitute almost half of the total carotenoids, do not completely decompose by conversion to the difuranoid pigments. The darkening of stored orange juice cannot, however, be attributed to the formation of *cis*-isomers, since these also decrease in concentration with time (Curl and Bailey, 1956). Similar changes take place in other acid fruits upon ripening, storage, or handling.

In the intact leaf it has been shown that carotenoid bleaching is associated with both mitochondrial and chloroplast fractions. Although the reaction is oxidative in nature, one does not need to postulate the same mechanisms for its enzymatic destruction as have been considered in fat-oxidizing systems (Friend and Nakayama, 1959; Friend, 1961). The destruction of carotenoids in intact chloroplasts is dependent upon oxygen and can be prevented by heat. β-Carotene is destroyed most rapidly, followed by violaxanthin, and then xanthophyll. Studies of the bleaching of the carotenoid crocin by chloroplasts showed maximum activity between pH 7 and 8, whereas that of the mitochondria was maximum between pH 4 and 5 (Friend and Mayer, 1960). Friend, from differences found in inhibition studies, suggests that the main carotenoid bleaching action of chloroplasts may not be due to a lipoxidase. The products that result from oxidation in the leaf system are similar to those found in fatty acid oxidation systems (Friend, 1958). This would argue somewhat against the initial assumption that the two systems are not necessarily the same. Additional work is required in this area.

The majority of work on enzymatically catalysed oxidation of the carotenes has been concerned with the lipoxidase systems, and the majority of these with purified soya lipoxidase. Without considering the mechanism of the destruction, it would appear that carotenoids act as antioxidants in a fat-oxidizing system, and as a consequence are themselves attacked as a secondary substrate. The oxidation of fatty acids such as linoleic acid is catalysed by the presence of iron porphyrin compounds (which in themselves may act as an autocatalyst for fatty acid oxidation). The end products of the enzyme-catalysed oxidation appear to be long-chain aldehydes, the apo-carotenals (Blain, 1963). On this basis it would appear that carotene undergoes a form of β-oxidation. Some of the apocarotenals have been isolated from the oxidation of β-carotene with chemical methods of degradation (Glover and Redfearn, 1954). In the lipoxidase system, in addition to the apocarotenals which are formed there also appears to be the formation of a series of epoxy derivatives involving the oxidation of a terminal ring. Winterstein isolated a series of carotenoid aldehydes such as apo-2'-carotenal, apo-6-lycopenal, and β-apo-10'-carotenal (Winterstein *et al.*,

1960). In considering this Isler suggests that the isolation of these components confirms the theory that carotenals can be oxidized *in vivo* by
attack of β-oxidation, leading to C-20 aldehydes (Isler *et al.*, 1962). There
is no reason that this should not be continued to below C-20, and may
indicate one pathway for the destruction of carotenoids *in vivo*.

In vitro degradation of carotenoids has invariably involved their
oxidation. Carotenes in the absence of oxygen are remarkably stable
products. If β-carotene, as representative of the carotenoids in general,
is placed under strong oxidizing conditions, such as one would expect in
stored tissue, both volatile and nonvolatile products are produced
(Karrer and Jucker, 1950). Initially it was suggested that a major volatile
product of the breakdown of β-carotene was β-ionone, resulting from
the liberation of one of the terminal rings of the molecule (Tomkins
et al., 1944). Investigations in several laboratories have indicated that,
under the mild oxidizing conditions found in stored carrots, no ionone
can be detected by gas chromatographic means in the volatiles which
appear after storage (Land, 1962; J. P. Clarey, 1962, unpublished
observations). Detected instead are products such as acetaldehyde,
2-methyl-propanol, butanol, diacetyl, and pentanol. These appear to
result from complete oxidation of the molecule, and little or no selectivity
is shown for retention of the ionone ring. It is interesting to note that the
volatiles always contain aliphatic hydrocarbons. These could result from
the oxidation of primary products. If a free radical oxidation mechanism
is involved, the normal complexity of the oxidation products could
explain the presence of such compounds. The recombination of acetyl
and formyl radicals could yield products such as diacetyl and glyoxal.
All the volatile oxidation products can arise from the breakdown of
peroxides of β-carotene and secondary oxidation of these products.
Upon the oxidation of β-ionone in a manner similar to that of the carotenes, the volatile products produced are similar in nature except that
they do not contain some of the longer-chain aliphatic hydrocarbons.

The non-volatile components produced by the oxidation of carotenes
have generally been found to be epoxy carotenoids, epoxy aldehydic
carotenoids, apo-carotenals, and possibly furanoids (5,8-epoxy carotenals). It would thus seem that non-catalysed aerobic oxidation of the
carotenoids yields products similar in nature to those found in enzymatic
oxidation of carotenoids. Further, oxidation and re-oxidation would
seem to occur from the ends of the molecule rather than through an
initial scission in the chain (Fishwick, 1962; Mackinney and Wilson,
1959).

Carotenoids are relatively stable to radiation damage in the absence of
solvents. Studies by Lukton and Mackinney have shown that ionizing
radiation will rapidly decolourize and solubilize β-carotene, whereas

dried films or solid β-carotene are stable in the absence of oxygen. Products resulting from destruction by ionizing radiation appear to be shorter compounds with shorter chromophoric groups. Most of the isolable compounds appeared to be hydrocarbon in nature and to result from random scission of the parent molecule. The stability in the dry state and their rapid destruction when solubilized would suggest a free radical mechanism involving the solvent (Lukton and Mackinney, 1956).

IV. FLAVONOIDS

The flavonoid pigments, primarily the anthocyanins, differ significantly in stability from the chlorophylls and carotenoids. In the majority of bases, in both senescent tissue and stored tissue, they are more stable and do not show the quantitative decreases displayed by the others. Goodwin (1958), in a study of the changes occurring in autumn leaves, found no decrease in their anthocyanin content despite an almost complete loss of chlorophyll. In fruit tissue, after their initial formation, the anthocyanins are generally more persistent than other classes of pigments. Since anthocyanins as a pigment class are not fat-soluble, their characteristics are markedly different from those of the chlorophylls and carotenoids. They are found in the cytoplasm of the tissue rather than in the chloroplast or other lipoid bodies.

The pigmented flavonoids must of necessity differ significantly in stability, but little or no information upon their individual stability in plant tissue is available. In particular there is a dearth of information on their rates of breakdown and mechanism of colour loss. This lack is probably due to the reaction products of the breakdown. Very little is known about the chemistry of the condensed products, and, in common with the naturally occurring tannin-like polyphenolic materials, such as humic acids and lignins, no method has been developed for their isolation (Hathway, 1962).

The loss of anthocyanin colourations in fruit tissue, and possibly in plant tissue, is mediated in general by two sets of enzymes—the glucosidases and the polyphenol oxidases. The glucosidase (anthocyanase) was first established as an enzyme present in *Aspergillus* and was found to decolourize anthocyanins in berry juices (Huang, 1955, 1956a). It was shown that the enzyme was capable of splitting the sugar, or sugars, from the anthocyanin pigment. The aglucone moiety is less stable than the glucoside, and consequently fades rapidly (Nordström, 1956). It was later established that enzymes capable of decolourizing the anthocyanins are present in many fruits and plant tissues (Sakamura and Obata, 1963; Forsyth and Quesnel, 1957; Peng and Markakis, 1963; Bayer and Wegmann, 1957; Jurgensmeier and Bopp, 1960, 1961; Van Buren *et al.*,

1960; Wagenknecht *et al.*, 1960). It is interesting to note that some of the glucoses which have been isolated are specific for a particular sugar moiety whereas others apparently are not specific and are capable of splitting all the glucosidic linkages (Forsyth and Quesnel, 1957; Huang, 1956b).

The reasons that the aglucone of the anthocyanidin is lower in stability than the glucoside are not yet understood. Two possibilities have been suggested. Huang (1956a) suggested that the anthocyanidin can exist as a ketonic form, which is more susceptible to oxidative breakdown. Sondheimer (1953) suggested that the glucoside exists in equilibrium with its colourless pseudo-base. The equilibrium to the pseudo-base containing a hydroxyl at position 2 would be favoured by loss of the glucoside attachment. This, in turn, would open the way for an oxidative attack, with subsequent splitting of the molecule. In any case, the aglucone is susceptible to enzymatic attack whereas the glucoside is fairly resistant to attack by phenol oxidase systems (Baruah and Swain, 1959). As further evidence of this, the anthocyanins are persistent in systems where there are active phenol oxidases (Rohan, 1956).

The decrease in stability of the aglucones of the anthocyanin is substantiated by observations with sulphur dioxide used as a decolouring agent. Sulphur dioxide in moderate concentrations will reversibly decolourize solutions of anthocyanins. Upon the addition of acid and removal of the bisulfite ion, there is at least a partial restoration of colour. Jurd (personal communication, 1964) suggested that the site of attack of the sulphur dioxide is position 2 of the anthocyanin, which would lend substantiation to the observations of Sondheimer and Huang as to the susceptibility of these pigments to a splitting attack.

The enzymes concerned with the aerobic alteration of anthocyanins can be termed a phenolase complex, and are further classified into cresolases and catecholases, representing mono- and diphenol activity. Many appear to be dependent phenolases and require catechol, chlorogenic acid, or other compounds containing orthophenolic groups for maximum activity. In contrast to the animal enzymes, the plant complex is active toward a wide range of mono- and diphenolic substrates. The products are orthophenones, which undergo further oxidative changes; however, the result perhaps encountered more frequently is polymerization with a variety of substrates. The oxidation of orthodiphenols is often required to maintain enzymatic hydroxylation of monophenols, although the reaction can be sustained by other reducing substances. Thus, a decolourizing enzyme in the egg-plant, *Solanum melongena* L., does not act on pelargonidin glucoside, but the addition of chlorogenic acid makes decolourization of the pigment possible (Sakamura and Obata, 1963). The mechanism of such a reaction was reviewed by Mason (1957).

In plant tissues where enzymatic systems have been inactivated, the anthocyanins may still be destroyed by oxidation. Sondheimer and Kertesz (1952, 1953) suggested that the breakdown of anthocyanins by the addition of hydrogen peroxide occurred through the addition of a carbonium ion. Karrer and deMeuron (1932) obtained malvone from malvidin chloride in the presence of hydrogen peroxide. On the basis of the proposed structure of malvone, it was assumed that position 2 of the flavyllium salt was the site of hydrogen peroxide addition. The importance of the peroxide in the general degradation of anthocyanins in natural products is somewhat difficult to assess. It has been suggested that peroxide may be generated in fruit products by the breakdown of ascorbic acid and other substances. It is also possible that ascorbic acid itself induced the destruction of anthocyanin pigments (Swain, 1962; Sondheimer and Kertesz, 1953). The addition of copper increased the rate of destruction. In contrast to this, Lamb and Sreerangachar (1940) firmly established that peroxidase did not take part in the oxidation of polyphenols during fermentation. Thus it would seem that, in the non-enzymatic breakdown, peroxides generated from other substrates can react directly with the anthocyanin, causing a loss in colour. In natural systems the peroxides generated are either insufficient, or are utilized selectively by other substrates rather than by the anthocyanins.

The non-enzymatic loss of colour in anthocyanin-containing tissues can occur in either the presence or absence of oxygen. The stability is considerably lower in tissues than in pure solutions. Whether this is due to the presence of compounds such as ascorbic acid, or to other oxidizing materials, is not known. In the presence of oxygen, however, the colour changes rapidly. The non-enzymatic changes which have been observed contrast with those of other pigment groups in that they normally produce a brown product rather than merely fading. It has been suggested that this arises from the polymerization of the oxidized polyphenols (Meschter, 1953). Whether this is the case or not has not been proven, since it has been extremely difficult to isolate distinct breakdown products of the compounds (Lukton et al., 1956).

Hathway (1962) suggests that the autoxidation of flavonoids proceeds through quinone polymerization, and notes that the 3',4'-hydroxy groups cause hydrogen peroxide accumulation. The 5,7-dihydroxy and 5,7-dihydroxy-3',4'-dimethoxyflavenes lack such vicinal hydroxide groups and are unaffected by autoxidation.

The ability of the anthocyanin or polyphenolic compounds to chelate metals is responsible for changes in the colour of stored food materials (Harper, 1957). A dark discolouration of asparagus is caused by an iron-rutin complex (Dame et al., 1957, 1959). In asparagus, the rutin in solution chelates with the ferrous ion released in a tin container, and when the can is opened the ferrous ion oxidizes to form the darkly coloured ferric complex. Tin, on the other hand, in complexing with rutin, is responsible for the yellow colouration normally observed.

In other fruit tissues the presence of metallic compounds such as might be introduced during processing or canning can markedly influence the colour of the final product. This has been shown to account at least partly for a brown discolouration of canned freestone peaches (Luh et al., 1962).

The destruction of anthocyanins in red wine by gamma radiation appears to be linearly related to the dose, so treatment with ^{60}Co radiation would give the wine the appearance of having been aged (less red). There does not appear to be a polymerization of the breakdown product, resulting in brown polymers, in contrast to the normal non-enzymatic breakdown of anthocyanins (Singleton, 1963).

REFERENCES

Ardao, C., and Vennesland, B. (1960). *Plant Physiol.* **35**, 368.
Aronoff, S. (1953). *Advanc. Fd. Res.* **4**, 133.
Aronoff, S., and Mackinney, G. (1943). *J. Amer. chem. Soc.* **65**, 956.
Baruah, P., and Swain, T. (1959). *J. Sci. Fd. Agric.* **10**, 125.
Bayer, E., and Wegmann, K. (1957). *Z. Naturf.* **12b**, 37.
Berzelius, J. J. (1937). *Liebigs Ann.* **21–22**, 257.
Blain, J. A. (1963). *In* "Carotine und Carotinoide", Dr. Dietrich Steinkopff Verlag, Darmstadt.
Blain, J. A., and Styles, E. C. C. (1959). *Nature, Lond.* **184**, 1141.
Blain, J. A., Hawthorn, J., and Todd, J. P. (1953). *J. Sci. Fd. Agric.* **4**, 580.
Booth, V. H. (1957). *Biochem. J.* **65**, 660.
Booth, V. H. (1963). *Biochem. J.* **87**, 238.
Braarud, T., and Sörensen, N. A. (1956). "Second International Seaweed Symposium," Pergamon Press, London.
Braverman, J. B. S. (1963). "The Biochemistry of Foods," Elsevier, Amsterdam.
Crosby, E. L., and Sumner, J. B. (1945). *Arch. Biochem.* **8**, 259.
Curl, A. L., and Bailey, G. F. (1956). *J. Agric. Fd. Chem.* **4**, 156.
Dame, C. Jr., Chichester, C. O., and Marsh, G. L. (1957). *Food Res.* **22**, 658, 673; (1959). *Food Res.* **24**, 20, 28.
Egle, K. (1944). *Botan. Arch.* **44**, 93. [Quoted in Wolf, F. T. (1956).]
Fishwick, M. J. (1962). Absts. First Int. Cong. Food Sci. Tech.
Forsyth, W. G. C., and Quesnel, V. C. (1957). *Biochem. J.* **65**, 177.
Freed, S., Sancier, K. M., and Sporer, A. H. (1954). *J. Amer. chem. Soc.* **76**, 6006.
Friend, J. S. (1958). *Chem. Ind.* 597.
Friend, J. S. (1961). *S.C.I. Monograph No. II*, 160.
Friend, J. S., and Mayer, A. M. (1960). *Biochim. biophys. Acta* **41**, 422.
Friend, J. S., and Nakayama, T. O. M. (1959). *Nature, Lond.* **184**, 66.
Glover, J. (1960). *Vitam. & Horm.* **18**, 371.
Glover, J., and Redfearn, E. R. (1954). *Biochem. J.* **58**, xvl.
Goodwin, T. W. (1952). "Comparative Biochemistry of the Carotenoids," Chapman and Hall, London.

Goodwin, T. W. (1958). *Biochem. J.* **68**, 503.

Gortner, W. A., and Singleton, V. L. (1961). *Food Sci.* **26**, 53.

Harper, K. A. (1957). *Food Pres. Quart.* **17**, 68.

Hathway, D. E. (1962). *In* "Wood Extractives" (W. E. Hillis, ed.), Academic Press, New York.

Holden, M. (1961). *Biochem. J.* **78**, 359.

Holden, M. (1963). *Photochem. and Photobiol.* **2**, 175.

Huang, H. T. (1955). *J. Agric. Food Chem.* **3**, 141.

Huang, H. T. (1956a). *J. Amer. chem. Soc.* **78**, 2390.

Huang, H. T. (1956b). *Nature, Lond.* **177**, 39.

Isler, O., Rüegg, R., and Schudel, P. (1962). *In* "Recent Progress in the Chemistry of Natural and Synthetic Colouring Matters and Related Fields" (T. S. Gore, B. S. Joshi, S. V. Sunthankar, B. D. Tilak, eds.), Academic Press, New York.

Jeffrey, R. N., and Griffith, R. B. (1947). *Plant Physiol.* **22**, 34.

Joyce, A. E. (1953). *Proc. Symp.* Colour in Foods, National Academy of Sciences.

Joyce, A. E. (1954). *Nature, Lond.* **173**, 311.

Jurd, L. J. (1964). *J. Food Sci.* **29**, 10.

Jurgensmeier, H. L., and Bopp, M. (1960). *Planta* **55**, 80.

Jurgensmeier, H. L., and Bopp, M. (1961). *Planta* **56**, 233.

Karrer, P., and deMeuron, G. (1932). *Helv. chim. acta* **15**, 507.

Karrer, P., and Jucker, E. (1950). "Carotenoids," Elsevier, Amsterdam.

Karrer, P., and Walker, O. (1934). *Helv. chim. acta* **17**, 43.

Kuhn, R., and Brockmann, H. (1932). *Hoppe-Seyl. Z.* **206**, 41.

Lamb, J., and Sreerangachar, H. B. (1940). *Biochem. J.* **34**, 1472.

Land, D. G. (1962). *Absts.* First Int. Cong. Food Sci. Tech.

Luh, B. S., Chichester, C. O., Leonard, S. J. (1962). Second Int. Cong. Food Sci. Technol., London.

Lukton, A., and Mackinney, G. (1956). *Food Technol.* **10**, 630.

Lukton, A., Chichester, C. O., and Mackinney, G. (1956). *Food Technol.* **10**, 427.

Mackinney, G., and Wilson, L. G. (1959). *Quartermaster Food Cont. Inst. Activities Rept. No. 11 v. 4-327*, 1.

Mason, H. S. (1957). *Advanc. Enzymol.* **19**, 79.

Meschter, E. E. (1953). *J. Agric. Fd. Chem.* **1**, 574.

Miller, E. V., Winston, J. R., and Schomer, H. A. (1940). *J. agric. Res.* **60**, 259.

Nagel, W. (1939). *Botan. Arch.* **40**, 1.

Nordström, C. G. (1956). *Acta chem. scand.* **10**, 1491.

Orth, A., and Koch, G. (1963). *In* "Carotine and Carotinoide", p. 362, Dr. Dietrich Steinkopff Verlag, Darmstadt.

Peng, C. Y., and Markakis, P. (1963). *Nature, Lond.* **199**, 597.

Pepkowitz, L. (1943). *J. biol. Chem.* **149**, 465.

Quackenbush, F. W. (1963). *Cereal Chem.* **40**, 266.

Rabinowitch, E. I. (1956). "Photosynthesis," Interscience, New York.

Rohan, T. (1956). Quart. Rept. W. Afr. Cacao Res. Inst. No. 42, [quoted in Swain, T. (1962). *In* "The Chemistry of Flavonoid Compounds" (T. A. Geissman, ed.), The Macmillan Company, New York.]

Sakamura, S., and Obata, Y. (1963). *Agric. Biol. Chem.* **27** (2), 121.

Sauer, K., and Calvin, M. (1962). *J. mol. Biol.* **4**, 451.

Schanderl, S. H., Marsh, G., and Chichester, C. O. (1963). *J. org. Chem.* **27**, 3865.

Schanderl, S. H., Marsh, G., and Chichester, C. O. (1964). *Food Sci.* (In press).

Seybold, A. (1943). *Botan. Arch.* **44**, 551.

Singleton, V. L. (1963). *Food Technol.* **17** (6), 112.

Singleton, V. L., Gortner, W. A., and Young, H. Y. (1961). *J. Fd. Sci.* **26**, 49.

Sondheimer, E. (1953). *J. Amer. chem. Soc.* **75**, 1507.

Sondheimer, E., and Kertesz, Z. I. (1952). *Food Res.* **17**, 288.

Sondheimer, E., and Kertesz, Z. I. (1953). *Food Res.* **18**, 475.

Stahl, W., Steger, H., Kasdorff, K., and Pueschel, F. (1957). *Z. Tieren. Futtermittelkunde* **12**, 333.

Stoll, A., and Wiedemann, E. (1933). *Helv. chim. acta* **16**, 183.

Strain, H. H. (1955). *J. Amer. chem. Soc.* **77**, 5195.

Strain, H. H. (1958). Chloroplast Pigments and Chromatographic Analysis, Thirty-second Annual Priestley Lectures, Pennsylvania State University, University Park, Pennsylvania.

Strain, H. H., and Manning, W. M. (1942). *J. biol. Chem.* **146**, 275.

Sudyina, E. G. (1963). *Photochem. and Photobiol.* **2**, 181.

Swain, T. (1962). *In* "The Chemistry of Flavonoid Compounds" (T. A. Geissman, ed.), The MacMillan Company, New York.

Tomkins, R. G., Mapson, L. W., Allen, R. J. L., Wager, H. G., and Barker, J. (1944). *J. Soc. Chem. Ind.* **63**, 225.

Van Buren, J. P., Scheiner, D. M., and Wagenknecht, A. C. (1960). *Nature, Lond.* **185**, 165.

Varner, J. E. (1961). *Ann. Rev. Pl. Physiol.* **12**, 245.

Wagenknecht, A. C., Scheiner, D. M., and Van Buren, V. P. (1960). *Food Technol.* **14**, 47.

Willstätter, R., and Stoll, A. (1910). *Liebigs Ann.* **378**, 18.

Willstätter, R., and Stoll, A. (1913). *In* "Untersuchen über Chlorophyll", Julius Springer, Berlin.

Winterstein, A., Studer, A., and Rüegg, R. (1960). *Chem. Ber.* **93**, 2951.

Wolf, F. A., and Wolf, F. T. (1955). *Agron. J.* **47**, 351.

Wolf, F. T. (1956). *Amer. J. Bot.* **43**, 714.

Zechmeister, L., LeRosen, A. L., Schroeder, W. A., Polgár, A., and Pauling, L. (1943). *J. Amer. chem. Soc.* **65**, 1940.

PART IV: ANALYTICAL METHODS

Chapter 17

CHLOROPHYLLS

Margaret Holden

*Department of Biochemistry, Rothamsted Experimental Station,
Harpenden, Herts, England*

The chapter in "Modern Methods of Plant Analysis," Chlorophylls:
Analysis in Plant Materials, by Smith and Benitez (1955) was an excellent
review of the literature on methods of determining chlorophyll up to
about ten years ago. Since then a great many papers on various aspects
of chlorophyll metabolism have been published and there has been
considerable interest not only by biochemists and plant physiologists,
but also by food technologists, marine biologists and others in methods
for separating and determining chlorophylls. Wide use has been made of

15   461

column and paper chromatography for separating and purifying chlorophylls and their derivatives. Spectrophotometric methods for estimating chlorophylls and their breakdown products in extracts of plant tissues have been improved. Methods have been developed for measuring the absorption spectra of the pigments *in vivo*. In this chapter an attempt has been made to review the more recent literature as thoroughly as possible and for references to older methods the review by Smith and Benitez should be consulted.

I. PREPARATION OF MATERIALS

A. SAMPLING AND EXPRESSION OF RESULTS

It is not difficult to sample cultures of bacteria and unicellular algae for pigment determinations, but shortage of material is likely to be the problem with some of these organisms. Multicellular organisms present various problems owing to variability of development, except when plants are grown under the most carefully controlled conditions, and the uneven distribution of pigments in different organs and even in the same organ. Unless the sampling is done properly it is useless to spend time and effort on doing chlorophyll determinations with great accuracy. Various ways have been suggested for overcoming sampling difficulties. One of these is to number the leaves as they appear on each plant and take leaves from a known position. Friend (1961) measured the effect of temperature and light intensity on the rate of accumulation and maximal chlorophyll content in wheat. At each sampling he took leaves from the same position on four plants from three separate pots. For large leaves samples can be taken with a cork borer through a pile of randomly arranged leaves. Bukatsch and Rudolph (1963) who were interested in measuring diurnal fluctuations in chlorophyll content have discussed methods of error calculation.

Chlorophyll content can be expressed on the basis of wet weight, dry weight, or leaf area or alternatively on an absolute basis per plant, leaf or cell (Bruinsma, 1963). It is often important to express it both in relative and absolute terms or the significance of changes may be obscured. This is seen in the results of Wheeler and Humphries (1963) on the effect of applying gibberellic acid to potato plants. The total amount of chlorophyll per leaf was increased, but the amount per unit area decreased.

B. COLLECTION AND STORAGE

Although it is preferable when possible to use freshly picked plant material for chlorophyll determinations, it is frequently necessary to store it before analysis. The leaves of some species, e.g. sugar beet, can be kept in a polythene bag in the dark at 0° for several days without any trace of chlorophyll breakdown but in others, e.g. grasses, the chlorophyll deteriorates rapidly.

Friend (1960) kept wheat leaf samples, cut into 1 cm lengths, in acetone containing a little sodium carbonate at below 0°. Wickliff and Aronoff (1962) recommended storage in liquid nitrogen. Storage at $-20°$ to $-30°$ is adequate for most material that cannot be analysed at once.

Unicellular algae in phytoplankton are usually collected by filtration and the filters stored until the chlorophyll can be determined. Humphrey (1961) considered that filtration was better than centrifugation because under some conditions centrifuging did not retain all the plankton. The algae when collected should not be washed because of the danger of cytolysis.

Many chlorophyll determinations have been made on material which has been dried in air at temperatures between 40° and 70°. Stoll and Wiedemann (1959) used dried nettle leaves for preparing pure chlorophylls a and b. Drying in air as a preliminary to chlorophyll extraction is not recommended as there may be considerable loss of chlorophyll owing to conversion into pheophytin, pheophorbides and other brown compounds of unknown nature. In addition, the pigments are much more difficult to extract than from fresh material. If for any reason the tissue must be dried, drying *in vacuo* at 70° is rather better than in air and if the amount is reasonably small, freeze-drying (lyophilization) is a possible alternative.

C. EXTRACTION OF PIGMENTS

A good extraction procedure should result in little or no change in the pigments being extracted. A great variety of methods have been used but a few essential details must be mentioned. Bruinsma (1963) has dealt fully with some of these in connection with the extraction of chlorophylls a and b. Some workers have immersed material in boiling water to kill it before extraction with an organic solvent. This causes isomerization of chlorophylls a and b with the formation of chlorophylls a' and b' (Strain, 1954). Boiling also causes the breakdown of chlorophylls to pheophytins, particuarly if the tissue is rather acid. However, when extracting protochlorophyll(ide) from etiolated tissues heat treatment is a necessary preliminary in order to inactivate the transforming mechanism. Before heat treatment it is essential to work in total darkness or with a green safe-light, as exposure of the plants for less than a second to weak daylight will bring about reduction of the proto-pigment. Koski and Smith (1948) dipped leaves into water at 90° for 5 min and Kaler and Shlyk (1962) steamed them for 2 min. After heat treatment grinding and extraction can be done in dim light.

Acetone and methanol are the most frequently used solvents for breaking the linkage between pigments and protein and bringing the chlorophylls into solution; there seems to be little to choose between them. Steeman-Nielsen (1961), however, found methanol better than acetone for extracting pigments from *Chlorella*. Acetone has been preferred by some workers because of the possibility of allomerization in methanol, but as aqueous solvents are always used this is not very likely to occur in extracts stored for short periods. Strain (1958) used a mixture of methanol and petroleum ether (2:1). An acetone-methanol mixture (7:2) has been used for extracting bacteriochlorophyll (Cohen-Bazire *et al.*, 1957). Wickliff and Aronoff (1962) extracted chlorophyll from leaf tissue with hot 80% ethanol, but extraction with cold solvents appears to be preferable. S. W. Jeffrey (personal communication) found that with certain diatoms which had very high chlorophyllase activity it was necessary to freeze at −80° and extract with acetone at −20° to −30° or much of the chlorophyll *a* was converted into chlorophyllide. Pigments are not readily extracted from all species of algae, but if the cells are first allowed to swell in water extraction takes place easily (Jeffrey, 1961).

Tissues of multicellular plants are ground with solvent in a mortar or high speed macerator. When ground in a mortar an abrasive such as quartz sand is usually added. In the Official Method of Analysis of the A.O.A.C. (1960) the tissue is ground before the solvent is added. With seedlings of many legumes and some cereals, which have high lipoxidase activity, this could lead to quite large losses of chlorophyll as unidentified, colourless breakdown products (M. Holden, unpublished). It therefore appears essential to have a high concentration of solvent present before starting to macerate. A final concentration of at least 80% acetone or 90% methanol is necessary to ensure efficient extraction of the pigments and to prevent chlorophyllase action. For small amounts of tissue the amount of water in it is often neglected when calculating the amount of solvent to be added, but if the extraction is done on a large scale this must be taken into account since many leaves have 90% of their weight as water.

Grinding and filtering should be done quickly and in dim light. Substances such as $CaCO_3$, $MgCO_3$, $NaHCO_3$, Na_2CO_3 and dimethyl-aniline are usually added to prevent pheophytin formation during maceration and this is recommended, particularly for leaves known to be acid, since pheophytin will interfere in the subsequent determination of chlorophyll. The solvent extract is best separated from the solids by filtration through a sintered glass filter, and the residue is washed with more solvent on the filter. Filtration by suction through a thick filter paper on a buchner funnel is also satisfactory. To obtain completely clear extracts it is sometimes necessary to filter through a layer of kieselguhr. Some tissues may have to be ground a second time to obtain complete extraction of the pigments.

Extracts should be analysed as soon as possible after being made, but if they have to be stored they must be kept in the cold and dark.

After the pigments have been extracted chlorophyll can be determined by various methods based on colorimetry, spectrophotometry, fluorimetry and estimation of magnesium (Smith and Benitez, 1955).

II. METHODS OF DETERMINATION

A. COLORIMETRIC AND SPECTROPHOTOMETRIC METHODS

1. *Chlorophylls* a *and* b

Colorimetric methods have now been largely superseded by spectrophotometric methods and are not discussed in detail here. If a colorimetric method is needed the A.O.A.C. method of analysis for total chlorophyll (1960) is a useful one and describes how to calibrate a photoelectric colorimeter to obtain absolute results for chlorophyll content.

The absorption can be measured in 80% acetone (Arnon, 1949; Bruinsma, 1963) or after the pigments have been transferred to diethyl ether (A.O.A.C. spectrophotometric method for total chlorophyll, 1960). Alternatively, the pigments may be separated by column or paper chromatography (see below) before measuring the absorption. This is useful when degradation products are present.

The spectrophotometric determination of chlorophyll is dependent on the Lambert–Beer law and various equations have been derived for determining the concentration of total chlorophyll and of chlorophylls a and b in a mixture. The optical density at definite wavelengths of a known thickness of solution is measured and the specific absorption coefficients of the pure pigments at these wavelengths must be known. The specific absorption coefficient α is D/dC where D is the optical density, d the length of the light path in cm and C is the concentration of the pigment in g/l. Arnon (1949) gave the following equations, which have been widely used, for 80% acetone extracts with optical density measurements at 663 mμ and 645 mμ in a 1-cm cell using the specific absorption coefficients given by Mackinney (1941).

$$\text{Total chlorophyll (mg/l)} = 20{\cdot}2D_{645} + 8{\cdot}02D_{663}$$
$$\text{Chlorophyll } a \text{ (mg/l)} = 12{\cdot}7D_{663} - 2{\cdot}69D_{645}$$
$$\text{Chlorophyll } b \text{ (mg/l)} = 22{\cdot}9D_{645} - 4{\cdot}68D_{663}$$

Maclachlan and Zalik (1963) modified the values and gave the following equations for calculating the chlorophyll content on a fresh weight basis:

$$\text{Chlorophyll } a \text{ (mg/g)} = \frac{12 \cdot 3D_{663} - 0 \cdot 86D_{645}}{d \times 1000 \times W} V$$

$$\text{Chlorophyll } b \text{ (mg/g)} = \frac{19 \cdot 3D_{645} - 3 \cdot 6D_{663}}{d \times 1000 \times W} V$$

where V = volume in ml, d = length of light path in cm, W = fresh weight in g.

The quantitative absorption curves of chlorophylls a and b in 80% acetone intersect at 652 mμ. Bruinsma (1961, 1963) found the specific absorption coefficient at this point was 36·0. The total amount of chlorophyll can be determined by measuring the optical density at this wavelength and calculating the concentration in mg/l from $1000D_{652}/36$ or $27 \cdot 8D_{652}$. A measurement made at 652 mμ provides a good check on those made at the peaks of the chlorophyll curves and gives information about the presence of pheophytin and other breakdown products.

From the specific absorption coefficients given by Mackinney (1941) for chlorophylls a and b in methanol, equations similar to those used for 80% acetone solutions have been derived.

$$\text{Total chlorophyll (mg/l)} = 25 \cdot 5D_{650} + 4 \cdot 0D_{665}$$
$$\text{Chlorophyll } a \text{ (mg/l)} \quad = 16 \cdot 5D_{665} - 8 \cdot 3D_{650}$$
$$\text{Chlorophyll } b \text{ (mg/l)} \quad = 33 \cdot 8D_{650} - 12 \cdot 5D_{665}$$

For transfer of the pigments to ether, water and ether are added to a known volume of the acetone extract in a separating funnel and shaken very gently to avoid the formation of an emulsion. The ether layer is washed carefully with several lots of water to remove acetone and then diluted to a known volume with ether. A portion of this solution is dried with anhydrous Na_2SO_4 and then diluted to give a solution with an optical density between 0·2 and 0·8 at 660 mμ.

When the absorption is measured in diethyl ether the most frequently used equations are those of Comar and Zscheile (1942):

$$\text{Total chlorophyll (mg/l)} = 7 \cdot 12D_{660} + 16 \cdot 8D_{642 \cdot 5}$$
$$\text{Chlorophyll } a \text{ (mg/l)} \quad = 9 \cdot 93D_{660} - 0 \cdot 78D_{642 \cdot 5}$$
$$\text{Chlorophyll } b \text{ (mg/l)} \quad = 17 \cdot 6D_{642 \cdot 5} - 2 \cdot 81D_{660}$$

Smith and Benitez (1955) modified the equations on the basis of their own determinations of the wavelengths of the maxima and the specific absorption coefficients.

$$\text{Chlorophyll } a \text{ (mg/l)} = 10 \cdot 1D_{662} - 1 \cdot 01D_{644}$$
$$\text{Chlorophyll } b \text{ (mg/l)} = 16 \cdot 4D_{644} - 2 \cdot 57D_{662}$$

At 600 mμ both chlorophyll a and chlorophyll b in diethyl ether have an absorption coefficient of 9·95. A single measurement at this wavelength will give the combined chlorophyll a and b content according to the equation:

$$\text{Total chlorophyll (mg/l)} = \frac{1000}{9·95}D_{600} \quad \text{or} \quad 100·5D_{600}$$

Values obtained by this calculation sometimes do not agree particularly well with those calculated from absorption measurements at longer wavelengths. This could be due to absorption by other pigments but from the data of Smith, Benitez and Koski given in the appendix of French's review (1960) the curves actually intersect at 602 mμ and the absorption coefficient is 11·0.

The spectrophotometric determination of chlorophylls a and b in a mixture assumes that neither pigment influences the specific absorption of the other. Van Norman (1957) investigated the effect of varying the ratio of chlorophylls a and b and compared the expected values for absorption derived from the spectra of purified pigments and the actual values obtained. He found that when the two pigments were present in proportions approximately the same as in leaves there was reasonable agreement between expected and measured values, but that when one pigment was about five times as concentrated as the other the method was less reliable. When ether solutions of chlorophylls a and b were mixed in the ratio 5:1 and 1:5 the measured maxima for both pigments were shifted towards longer wavelengths. Absorption readings near the maximum are probably not greatly in error, but for those of the minor component on the steep part of the curve a shift of 2 mμ could have a marked effect on the observed values. It appears that where the ratio of the pigments varies much from normal, spectrophotometric analysis should be used with caution.

2. *Chlorophylls* a *and* c

Chlorophylls a and c in a mixture can be measured by making use of the specific absorption coefficient for chlorophyll c at 630 mμ which is 15·8 both in ether and 100% acetone (19·5 in 90% acetone) as determined by Jeffrey (1963). The absorption of chlorophyll c at 662 mμ is negligible.

3. *Chlorophylls* a *and* d

Smith and Benitez (1955) gave equations for determining chlorophylls a and d in a mixture using specific absorption coefficients for chlorophyll d of 11·3 at 663 mμ and 110·4 at 688 mμ.

4. *Chlorophyll and Protochlorophyll*

Koski (1950), Withrow *et al.* (1953) and Maclachlan and Zalik (1963) have given slightly different equations for determining the amount of chlorophyll and protochlorophyll in etiolated seedlings, greening in the light based on the specific absorption coefficients for protochlorophyll determined by Koski and Smith (1948).

5. *Bacteriochlorophyll*

Bacteriochlorophyll has frequently been determined by the method of van Niel and Arnold (1938). Because of the instability of the chlorophyll in organic solvents in the light it is converted into its pheophytin. In the original method the optical density at $667 \cdot 5$ mμ was measured but Lascelles (1956) modified it and took the reading at 750 mμ where maximum absorption occurs.

Cohen-Bazire *et al.* (1957) determined bacteriochlorophyll without conversion to pheophytin. The optical density of a methanolic extract of a green mutant of *Rhodopseudomonas spheroides* was measured at 775 mμ and the amount of chlorophyll expressed as mg/100 ml culture solution calculated from $D_{775} \times 2 \cdot 58$ when a 5-ml sample was taken. For acetone-methanol extracts of *R. rubrum* and of wild type *R. spheroides* the factor $2 \cdot 19$ was used instead of $2 \cdot 58$.

The same authors also gave a method for estimating bacteriochlorophyll in intact cells which can be used for following changes in the relative intensities of chlorophyll peaks during growth or for measuring chlorophyll synthesis. A light scattering curve for aerobically grown un-pigmented cells which have the same absorption at 680 mμ as the pigmented cells was used to correct for light scattering at the *in vivo* bacteriochlorophyll peaks, 805, 855 and 875 mμ.

6. *Porphyrins*

Cooper (1963) has described a spectrophotometric method for determining magnesium protoporphyrin monomethyl ester and coproporphyrinogen (or coproporphyrin) in a mixture. Samples of the extract were diluted with ethanol and KOH to give final concentrations of 50% v/v and $0 \cdot 02$ N respectively. After centrifuging to remove precipitated salts the optical density was measured at 418 mμ for the ester and 394 mμ for coproporphyrin (the coproporphyrinogen having been rapidly oxidized in the solvent). The optical densities at each wavelength were corrected for the absorption contributed by the compound with its peak at the other wavelength.

7. *Methods for Determining Chlorophyll as Pheophytin and for Measuring the Relative Amounts of both Substances when Present Together*

Food technologists are interested in determining the relative and absolute amounts of chlorophylls and pheophytins in canned and frozen green vegetables. Mackinney and Weast (1940) used a method based on the quantitative conversion of chlorophyll into pheophytin by treatment with oxalic acid. The optical density of aqueous acetone extracts was measured both before and after conversion at wavelengths where the maximum increase of the optical density occurred (535 mμ) and at a point of intersection of the pheophytin and chlorophyll curves (560 mμ) where there was no change. Several recent papers have described modifications of this method (Dietrich, 1958; Sweeney and Martin, 1958, 1961).

Sweeney and Martin (1958) calculated the percentage retention of chlorophyll in the following way. The total chlorophyll plus pheophytin (C + P) was found by dividing the optical density at 556 mμ by the specific absorption constant at that wavelength. The concentration of chlorophyll retained (Cr) was calculated from the average values obtained by dividing the changes in optical density at 535, 642·5 and 660 mμ by the corresponding specific absorption constants for the changes in optical density at these wavelengths.

$$\% \text{ retention of chlorophyll} = \frac{Cr}{C+P} \times 100$$

Sweeney and Martin (1961) also separated chlorophylls in extracts of cooked and uncooked frozen vegetables on powdered sugar columns and converted the eluted pigments into pheophytins for spectrophotometric measurement. Vernon (1960) developed Sweeney and Martins' (1958) method so that total chlorophyll, total pheophytin, chlorophylls a and b, pheophytins a and b and percentage retention of chlorophylls could all be determined in 80% acetone extracts of green vegetables. A number of equations were derived for doing this based on his own determination of specific absorption coefficients and changes in the values at several wavelengths. An acetone extract of plant tissue was prepared and two samples taken, one for a control and the other for conversion to pheophytin. Saturated oxalic acid in 80% acetone was added to the conversion sample and an equal volume of 80% acetone to the control. Both samples were kept in the dark at room temperature for 3 h and their optical densities were then read at 536, 558, 645, 649, 655, 662, 665, 666, 667 and 700 mμ. The reading at 700 mμ was a check on the optical clarity of the solution. The values at 649 and 665 mμ were used if chlorophyll concentration could be calculated directly assuming no conversion to pheophytin. The concentration of the pheophytins after conversion with oxalic acid was given by the following equations using the optical density readings at 666 and 655 mμ.

Total pheophytin (mg/l) $= 6·75 D_{666} + 26·03 D_{655}$
Pheophytin a (mg/l) $\quad = 20·15 D_{666} - 5·87 D_{655}$
Pheophytin b (mg/l) $\quad = 31·90 D_{655} - 13·40 D_{666}$

15*

Other equations were given making use of the absorption readings at 666 and 536 mμ. Two sets of equations were derived for determining the percentage of chlorophyll a, chlorophyll b and total chlorophyll. One set depended on the optical density reading at 655 mμ which tends to be inaccurate as it is on the steep part of the curve. The other set was based on the reading at 536 mμ and the equations were as follows:

$$\% \text{ chlorophyll } a = \frac{Ca \text{ present} \times 100}{\text{total } Ca \text{ with no conversion}}$$

$$= \frac{(25 \cdot 38 \Delta D_{662} + 3 \cdot 64 \Delta D_{645})100}{22 \cdot 31 D_{666} - 17 \cdot 90 D_{536}}$$

$$\% \text{ chlorophyll } b = \frac{Cb \text{ present} \times 100}{\text{total } Cb \text{ with no conversion}}$$

$$= \frac{(30 \cdot 38 \Delta D_{645} - 6 \cdot 58 \Delta D_{662})100}{97 \cdot 40 D_{536} - 22 \cdot 6 D_{666}}$$

$$\% \text{ total chlorophyll} = \frac{C \text{ present} \times 100}{\text{total } C \text{ with no conversion}}$$

$$= \frac{(18 \cdot 80 \Delta D_{662} + 34 \cdot 02 \Delta D_{645})100}{79 \cdot 5 D_{536} - 0 \cdot 29 D_{666}}$$

(ΔD = the change in the optical density at a given wavelength).

Tan and Francis (1962) chromatographed extracts of processed spinach and obtained pheophytins a and b in separate fractions and another fraction containing chlorophylls a and b. The chlorophyll concentrations were calculated from the equations of Comar and Zscheile (1942) modified for acetone extracts. Pheophytin a concentration in mg/l was given by $17 \cdot 6 D_{667 \cdot 5}$ and pheophytin b by $31 \cdot 4 D_{655}$.

Jones *et al.* (1963a) have developed a rather elaborate method for determining chlorophylls, chlorophyllides, pheophytins and pheophorbides in processed plant material and derived a set of sixteen equations for calculating the concentrations of the various pigments in diethyl ether. These workers found in some tissues a considerable amount of pheophorbides (Jones *et al.*, 1963b) which would have been missed if the method of Tan and Francis (1962) had been used, because in this the pigments are transferred from an acetone extract into petroleum ether and pheophorbides would have been left in the aqueous acetone. However, fractionation by chromatography as in this method, with modifications to include pheophorbide separation, would appear to be a useful preliminary and make the calculations easier.

Wickliff and Aronoff (1962) determined chlorophylls colorimetrically and spectrophotometrically in aqueous ethanol extracts of plant tissues by conversion into pheophytins with HCl. The specific absorption coefficients for pheophytins in 80% ethanol were determined. When these were applied to plant extracts abnormal, and in fact incorrect, ratios of chlorophyll a to b were obtained. "Operational" absorption coefficients were therefore calculated by quantitative transfer of pigments into ether from samples of extracts and spectrophotometry in that solvent. They recommend that these operational coefficients should be determined for each different system used. The difference between the observed and the calculated spectra of pheophytins a and b appears to be due to co-pigmentation of pheophytin a with another substance and may actually be due to polymerization.

Wilson and Nutting (1963) used a column of an ion-exchange resin, Dowex 50W–X4 in the H$^+$ form, for removing magnesium from chlorophylls to convert them into pheophytins, which were then separated from each other on the same resin. Material that could cause breakdown of pheophytins was also removed and the pheophytins obtained were more stable than those made by conversion with acids. This technique formed the basis of a method for the quantitative determination of chlorophylls. The pheophytins were eluted separately from the column and the absorption was measured at 667 and 409 mμ for pheophytin a in 85% acetone and at 654 and 436 mμ for pheophytin b in 100% acetone. Tetracyanoethylene was added to remove the absorption due to carotenoids which would interfere with measurements at the shorter wavelength maxima (Wilson et al., 1962).

8. Determination of Chlorophylls in Phytoplankton and Sediments

There are a number of papers in journals which are not readily accessible which are concerned with the determination of pigments in phytoplankton. Chlorophyll determinations have been used as a measure of the standing crop of phytoplankton and also as a basis for calculating the amount of organic matter produced in a given space during a definite period. Most marine and fresh water biologists have determined chlorophyll by methods based on that of Richards and Thompson (1952). In this method the concentration of chlorophyll a in mg/l is given by the equation $15 \cdot 6 D_{665} - 2 \cdot 0 D_{645} - 0 \cdot 8 D_{630}$. Talling and Driver (1961) have pointed out that the figure for the specific absorption coefficient of chlorophyll a in the Richards–Thompson method was taken from Zscheile (1934) and is at least 20% lower than other more recently published figures. This means that chlorophyll determinations will be about 25% too high.

Humphrey (1961) has tabulated details of the various modifications of the Richards–Thompson method and has critically examined the calculations used for estimating chlorophylls a, b and c. He concluded that the method gives good results for chlorophyll *a* (though this is doubtful if the wrong specific absorption coefficient is being used), but that the results for chlorophyll *b* are only semi-quantitative and the position is obscure with regard to chlorophyll *c*. Now that pure chlorophyll *c* has been obtained and its specific absorption coefficient determined the position can be improved. The most satisfactory method for determining chlorophylls in phytoplankton would appear to be to separate them chromatographically and estimate them individually. However, this might be too laborious for routine determinations and revised equations for direct spectrophotometric measurements for the different pigments present together would improve results.

Vallentyne (1955) and Vallentyne and Craston (1957) determined sedimentary chlorophyll degradation products (SCDP) in surface muds from lakes, by extracting mud samples with 90% acetone containing 0·5% dimethylaniline and measuring the optical density at 667 mμ. One unit is the amount of "chlorophyll" which dissolved in 10 ml of solvent gives an optical density reading of 0·10 in a 1-cm cell. The SCDP values were found to be decreased by about 10% when the dimethylaniline was omitted and by about 20% if magnesium carbonate was substituted for dimethylaniline.

Gorham (1959) and Fogg and Belcher (1961) measured chlorophyll derivatives in woodland soils and lake sediments by a similar method.

B. FLUORIMETRY

Goodwin (1947) described a fluorimetric method for determining chlorophyll concentration, but fluorimetry has not been so widely used as spectrophotometry although it is actually a much more sensitive method. Virgin has, however, used fluorescence measurements extensively for determining the concentration of chlorophyll in intact leaves (1954, 1955a), in leaf extracts (1955b) and in eluates from paper chromatograms (1960, 1961a). Details of the techniques used are given in these and other papers of the same series and also by French (1955), and French *et al.* (1956). Virgin (1956) discussed some of the problems encountered in studying chlorophyll fluorescence *in vivo*.

C. MAGNESIUM DETERMINATION

Deleano and Dick (1934) were the first to suggest that chlorophyll concentration could be measured by determining magnesium in solvent extracts in which inorganic salts were insoluble. Koski and Smith (1948) used the Titan Yellow colorimetric method for magnesium determinations and this is described in detail by Smith and Benitez (1955). Various other methods have recently been used. Vernon (1960) used a modification of the method of Robinson and Rathbun (1959). Magnesium is liberated from chlorophyll by acidification and is titrated with EDTA and Eriochrome Black T in a solution buffered at pH 10·4. Conti and Vishniac (1960) used a spectrophotometric method described by Mann and Yoe (1956) for determining magnesium in a purified preparation of *Chlorobium* chlorophyll-650.

A solution of the purified chlorophyll was evaporated in a platinum dish and ashed with sulphuric acid. The ash was transferred to a volumetric flask with a small volume of water and the dish rinsed with 95% ethanol. After making the solution slightly acid to phenolphthalein, 5 ml of a solution of 1-azo-2-hydroxy-3-(2,4-dimethylcarboxanilido)-naphthalene-1'-(2-hydroxybenzene-5-sulphonate) 0·15 mg/ml in 95% ethanol was added together with 0·5 ml of 0·08 M sodium borate solution and made up to 25 ml with 95% ethanol. After 1 h the absorption at 510 mμ was measured and the magnesium content calculated from a standard curve. The method is suitable for amounts of Mg between 0·5 and 10 μg.

Falk (1958) used both colorimetric (Titan Yellow) and complexometric (EDTA + Eriochrome Black T) methods for determining magnesium in preparations of chlorophylls *a* and *b*. Jeffrey (1963) determined the magnesium content of ashed preparations of chlorophyll *c* by atomic absorption spectroscopy; Jones (1963b) also used this method for pigments of *Rhodopseudomonas*.

D. NON-DESTRUCTIVE METHODS FOR ESTIMATING THE CHLOROPHYLL CONTENT OF LEAVES

It would frequently be convenient to be able to determine the chlorophyll content of a particular leaf without having to destroy it; serial determinations could then be made and sampling errors would be eliminated. Benedict and Swidler (1961) described a method they had used for leaves of soya and of Valencia orange. They measured the percentage reflectance of light of wavelength 625 mμ with a colorimeter fitted with a reflectance attachment. A quantitative relationship was found between the chlorophyll content (determined by the A.O.A.C. method) and the reflectance of light, except when the chlorophyll content was very high. The method seems useful for determining the chlorophyll content of chlorotic leaves, provided that proper precautions are taken such as avoiding veins and always using the same region of the leaf. With leaves in which the chlorophyll content approaches a maximum the increases may not be proportionately shown by decreased reflectance.

Virgin (1961b) determined the chlorophyll content of intact etiolated leaves greening in the light by measuring the light absorption of the leaves placed in a special sample-holder in a spectrophotometer. To overcome differences in thickness of the leaves and light scattering phenomena, a standard curve was plotted for absorption values of leaves in the holder against the chlorophyll content determined on extracts of leaves which had been treated in the same way.

III. Absorption Spectra of Chlorophyll in Leaves and Suspensions of Algal and Bacterial Cells

The problems encountered in measuring the absorption spectra of chlorophyll pigments *in vivo* have been discussed by French (1960) and Murchio and Allen (1962). Light scattering phenomena cause some of the difficulties and attempts have been made to overcome them by using opal glass plates (Shibata *et al.*, 1954) or an integrating sphere attachment (Madsen, 1963) in a spectrophotometer.

French and his associates at the Carnegie Institution (French and Elliott, 1958; Brown and French, 1959; Brown, 1963) have investigated the absorption properties of leaves and algae using a specially designed derivative spectrophotometer. This instrument measures the first derivative or slope of the absorption band. The light, after passing through a monochromator and vibrating slit up to 3 mμ wide, is directed by a rotating mirror alternately through the sample and a reference position. With a suitable electronic arrangement the change in absorption over this 3 mμ range is detected and recorded. Positive and negative peaks of derivative absorption spectra correspond to inflection points on the integral absorption band. The absorption maximum is shown by the point at which the zero line is crossed by the derivative spectrum going from positive to negative. Overlapping absorption bands which are fairly close together can be detected by derivative spectrophotometry. Two chlorophyll *a* absorption bands with maxima at 670 mμ and 683 mμ have been detected in all plant material examined. Frei (1962) measured derivative spectra of algal suspensions cooled to $-180°$.

IV. Methods of Separation

A. SEPARATION BY PARTITION BETWEEN SOLVENTS

Early work on the separation of plant pigments was nearly all based on differential solubility in various solvents. The chlorophylls themselves can now be separated from each other and from carotenoid pigments by better methods, but useful separation of chlorophyll derivatives is achieved by partition between polar and non-polar solvents and between ether and aqueous HCl solutions. Separation of phytylated and un-phytylated chlorophylls can be obtained by shaking an aqueous acetone solution with light petroleum. The phytylated pigments pass into the petroleum layer while the unphytylated pigments remain in the acetone.

This separation is made use of in methods for determining chlorophyllase activity (p. 484). It has also been used in this laboratory and elsewhere for measuring the amount of phytylated pigment in etiolated seedlings greening in the light.

Hughes and Holt (1962) have described a method (liquid–liquid partition chromatography) for purifying various porphyrins and chlorophyll derivatives on a preparative scale, by distribution between HCl and ether on Celite (diatomaceous earth) columns.

Dry Celite was packed into a tube and before use was treated with an aqueous solution of HCl saturated with ether to remove any iron impurity. "Acid-saturated" ether solution was then percolated through until aqueous and ether layers were seen in the receiving flask. After the column had been allowed to drain the top was covered with filter paper and the pigments put on dissolved in a suitable solvent. The chromatogram was then developed with ether. The pigments were recovered by elution or by extruding the column and washing out the individual bands with acetone containing dilute aqueous HCl.

Perkins and Roberts (1962) used this method as an alternative to icing sugar columns for purifying pheophorbides a and b and pyropheophorbides a and b.

B. COLUMN CHROMATOGRAPHY

Separation of plant pigments by column chromatography is a well-established procedure and a variety of adsorbents have been used for the purpose. These include inorganic adsorbents such as aluminium oxide and magnesia, polysaccharides such as inulin, starch and cellulose, powdered sugar and polyethylene. Inorganic adsorbents, which may be suitable for separating other pigments, are not usually recommended for chlorophylls as they frequently cause decomposition. However, Glemser and Rieck (1958) described the use of iron oxide, either as a gel or as haematite (α-Fe_2O_3), for separating chlorophylls a and b and obtained good preparations. Jeffrey (1963) used neutral aluminium oxide for the final stage of purification of chlorophyll c.

1. Cellulose and Starch

Duranton et al. (1958), Laborie (1963), Angapindu et al. (1958) and Anderson et al. (1960) used cellulose powder columns for separating chlorophylls and carotenoids. Anderson et al. packed the cellulose as a slurry in light petroleum under slight pressure. The column was developed first with light petroleum and then with 1% isopropanol in light petroleum when the bands of chlorophylls a and b had begun to travel down. Angapindu et al. considered that cellulose was better than powdered sugar as an adsorbent because cellulose columns percolated faster and their carrying capacity was greater. In this laboratory quicker and better separation of chlorophylls a and b, following chromatography on polyethylene (p. 478), was obtained by chromatographing on Whatman crystalline cellulose powder than on icing sugar.

Jeffrey (1963) used cellulose powder for the initial separation of chlorophyll c from extracts of *Sargassum flavicans*. The pigments were separated with 0·5% n-propanol in light petroleum and the carotene, chlorophyll a and xanthophylls were washed through leaving chlorophyll c in a band at the top of the column. Lipids were removed from the chlorophyll by chromatographing on a silicic acid column. The silicic acid was mixed with Hyflosupercel (5:2 w/w) and packed into a tube as a slurry in chloroform. The chlorophyll c was not adsorbed and was washed through with 5% methanol in chloroform.

Kaplan and Silberman (1959) purified bacteriochlorophyll and one of the *Chlorobium* chlorophylls on cellulose powder columns using solvents saturated with H_2S to maintain a reducing environment. For bacteriochlorophyll the chromatogram was developed with 20% benzene in light petroleum. For the *Chlorobium* chlorophyll the developing solvent was light petroleum and the chlorophyll was eluted with 2% isopropanol in light petroleum.

Hager (1957) used starch columns with a rather complicated solvent mixture consisting of petrol (b.p. 100–140°) 60:benzene 35:chloroform 1·25:acetone 0·55:isopropanol 0·06.

2. *Sugar*

Powdered sugar is probably the most widely used adsorbent for separating chlorophylls. Strain and Sato (1956) found that the pigment bands were better defined on sugar columns than on cellulose. Confectioner's sugar containing 3% starch has been found satisfactory by many workers and icing sugar containing about 1·5% of calcium phosphate gives equally good results. Strain (1958) gave detailed instructions for preparing sugar columns. He found that it was not necessary to dry or sieve the sugar before use, but others have recommended both drying and sieving. Small amounts of sugar are tightly pressed with a glass or plastic tamper into a vertically held glass tube, which has either a sintered glass plate or is plugged with cotton wool at the tapered base, until the column is the required length. 50 g of sugar in a tube 2·5 cm in diameter gives a column about 15 cm high and this will take about 5 mg of chlorophylls $a + b$ without being overloaded. The tube is then attached to a suction flask and a small volume of a light petroleum solution of the pigments is drawn into the top of the dry adsorbent. The chromatogram is usually developed with 0·5% n-propanol in petroleum ether but benzene–light petroleum mixtures have also been used (Stoll and

Wiedemann, 1959; Sweeney and Martin, 1958). Smith and Benitez (1955) used light petroleum alone. Alternatively, the column can be developed and eluted with solutions of acetone in light petroleum, starting with 5% acetone and finishing with 25% (Sweeney and Martin, 1961).

The carotenes move fastest on the column and can be washed right away. Chlorophyll a moves ahead of lutein and zeaxanthin followed by chlorophyll b and two other xanthophylls. Pheophytin a, if present, runs ahead of chlorophyll a and pheophytin b between the chlorophylls. Chlorophyllides are strongly adsorbed at the top of the column. The separated chlorophylls can either be eluted from the column or the column can be sucked dry and the bands dug out with a long handled spatula or the sugar can be extruded from the tube with compressed air, the bands cut out and the pigments dissolved in ether.

Strain (1958) was able to separate on sugar columns the chlorophyll isomers which are formed by boiling leaves before extraction of the pigments. He also separated the oxidation products formed on incubating barley leaves with acetone and those which arise on allomerization of chlorophyll in methanol.

Stanier and Smith (1960) used sugar for preparing *Chlorobium* chlorophylls 650 and 660 from different strains of *Chlorobium thiosulfatofilum*. For chlorophyll-650 the column was developed with 40% ether in light petroleum and for chlorophyll-660 the developing solvent was 50% ether in light petroleum.

Perkins and Roberts (1962) used sugar columns when purifying chlorophylls, pheophytins and pheophorbides for specific activity determinations. The solvent for developing chromatograms was 0·5% isopropanol in light petroleum for chlorophylls and pheophytins and a mixture of light petroleum 69·5:chloroform 30:isopropanol 0·5 for pheophorbides and pyropheophorbides. Acetone extracts of spruce needles contained ether-soluble compounds which prevented chlorophylls being adsorbed by the sugar and actually developed the chromatograms.

Tan and Francis (1962) used columns consisting of 70% confectioner's sugar and 30% corn starch (Melojel) for separating chlorophylls from pheophytins for quantitative determination in extracts of processed spinach. The adsorbent was dried before being made into a slurry with light petroleum, which was poured into a tube and compacted by applying slight pressure. A layer of anhydrous Na_2SO_4 was put on the top of the adsorbent and a light petroleum extract of the pigments added. Carotenes were washed from the column with light petroleum. Pheophytin a was eluted with 2% acetone in light petroleum, pheophytin b with 3% acetone in light petroleum and the chlorophylls with acetone.

3. *Polyethylene*

Anderson *et al.* (1960) and Anderson and Calvin (1962) described the use of powdered polyethylene for separating chlorophyll from other pigments in extracts from leaves and algae. This adsorbent has one very obvious advantage over all others that have been used because crude acetone extracts of plant tissues can be chromatographed without further treatment, such as precipitation of the chlorophylls on to talc or their transfer to light petroleum.

Jones (1963a) used polyethylene for separating the pigments of *Rhodopseudomonas spheroides* and (1963b) for preparing vinylpheoporphyrin a_5 monomethyl ester from the cotyledons of dark-grown bean seedlings. Mathewson *et al.* (1963) used it for preparing the pheophorbides of the *Chlorobium* chlorophylls.

The Dow Chemical Co. (UK) Ltd. kindly made a sample of powdered polyethylene (Experimental resin QX 2187) available for the method to be tested, and the following account refers to the use of this preparation.

A glass tube (2·5 cm diameter) with a sintered glass plate (porosity 1) was dry packed with 40 g powdered polyethylene in 2-cm lots well pressed down giving a column 24 cm high. The column was washed with 70% aqueous acetone and then attached to a water pump and slight pressure applied while 36 ml of a crude aqueous acetone extract containing about 15 mg chlorophyll was added. The extract was prepared by grinding leaves of *Phaseolus vulgaris* with acetone in a top drive macerator, 10 g leaf/40 ml acetone. With the water in the leaves the resulting extract has an acetone concentration of just over 80%. This concentration is too high for the pigments to be adsorbed in a narrow band, so the extract was diluted with water 1 ml/5 ml crude extract. If the extract is diluted with too much water the pigments stick tightly and are very difficult to move. After the extract had been drawn into the top of the column, 70% acetone was added to develop the chromatogram, slight suction being applied throughout. Three (or four) xanthophyll bands separated out and moved down the column ahead of the chlorophylls. When the last of these bands was about 5 cm from the bottom of the column the eluant was changed to 80% acetone. The chlorophylls then moved down and separated from each other, though there was no clear zone between them. Chlorophyll *b* moved ahead of chlorophyll *a*, whereas on sugar and cellulose columns the order is reversed. Any pheophytin present moved behind the chlorophylls. Carotenes remained on the column and could be eluted with light petroleum. If pheophorbides or chlorophyllides are present they are eluted before chlorophyll *b*.

After thorough washing with acetone and drying at room temperature the polyethylene could be re-used without further treatment.

Anderson and Calvin (1962) used either sugar or a polyethylene preparation with a lower melt index for separating chlorophylls a and b after removal of the carotenes and xanthophylls, and as mentioned earlier cellulose is also very useful for this purpose. Preparations of chlorophyll a made by chromatography on polyethylene followed by cellulose were deep blue in colour and the ratio between the heights of the blue and red absorption bands was 1·25 compared with 1·31 (Smith and Benitez, 1955) and 1·19 (Anderson and Calvin, 1962). Chlorophyll a could be crystallized from 90% acetone and chlorophyll b from 90% ethanol.

Perkins and Roberts (1964) found that one of the xanthophylls in wheat leaf extracts was not separated from the chlorophylls on a polyethylene column but was readily removed during the subsequent chromatography on a sugar column. It seems possible that either this xanthophyll may not be present in extracts of all species, or that it is only adsorbed on some samples of polyethylene.

C. PAPER CHROMATOGRAPHY

1. *Chlorophylls, Pheophytins, Chlorophyllides and Pheophorbides*

Of the many papers which have been published on the separation of chlorophylls by paper chromatography comparatively few had appeared at the time Smith and Benitez (1955) wrote their review. Šesták (1959) reviewed the literature up to 1958 and listed over fifty papers. Some papers are primarily concerned with the separation of chlorophylls a and b for quantitative determinations e.g. Sapozhnikov *et al.* (1959), while others also describe the separation of derivatives such as pheophytins, pheophorbides and chlorophyllides (Sironval, 1954; Hager, 1957; Holden, 1962). A very wide variety of solvent systems have been used and it is almost impossible to recommend a particular one, because results vary from one laboratory to another. Small variations in the running conditions markedly affect the results, and Rf values do not mean very much. It is more satisfactory to use a reference compound and relate the positions of the other compounds to this. Some of the factors affecting the mobility of individual pigments are: the degree of saturation of the tank with solvent, the type of paper used and whether it is equilibrated with solvent, and the amount of pigment applied. With impregnated papers, as used by Strain (1953) and Angapindu *et al.* (1958), the amount of substance in the paper may also influence the position of the spots.

In this laboratory (Holden, 1962) excellent separation of chlorophylls a and b could always be obtained with a mixture of light petroleum 4:benzene 1:acetone 0·5 as the running solvent in a tank which was well saturated with solvent and with the paper (Whatman No. 1 or 3MM) equilibrated with the solvent mixture. The temperature at which the chromatograms were run was $20° \pm 2°$ and with a higher or lower temperature it is probably necessary to alter the proportions of the solvent mixture. Anderson et al. (1960) used two-dimensional chromatography on Whatman 3MM paper with toluene as the first solvent and light petroleum 100:isopropanol 2·5 as the second. The separation took about 3 h and there was a loss of up to 30% of individual pigments. They found that centrifugally accelerated chromatography (McDonald et al., 1957) using a chromatofuge (Labline Inc. Chicago) with light petroleum 100:isopropanol 2·5 as the solvent gave more satisfactory results. The chromatogram was developed in 10 min and there was only 5–10% loss of pigments.

Jeffrey (1961) separated the chlorophylls and carotenoids of marine algae by two-dimensional chromatography using a modification of the method of Lind et al. (1953). Ascending chromatograms were run on Whatman 3MM paper using 20–30 μg pigment. The first solvent was 4% propanol in light petroleum and the second was 30% chloroform in light petroleum. The chromatograms were developed for about 30 min with each solvent. The composition of the solvent mixtures was critical for good resolution of the pigments and it was necessary to make up the mixtures daily. For quantitative determinations the chlorophyll spots were eluted with acetone and the optical density measured.

With both ascending and descending chromatograms a certain amount of tailing of the spots always occurs; radial chromatograms have better definition. Angapindu et al. (1958) developed the method of radial chromatography, first used for plastid pigments by Brown (1939), as they found it gave better results than either ascending, descending, or horizontal development on paper strips. With Whatman No. 1 or 3MM paper and 0·5–1% n-propanol in light petroleum well defined rings were formed, usually separated by colourless zones. Angapindu et al. also used reversed phase chromatography and tried several systems (Strain, 1953; Nunez, 1954) the most satisfactory of which was Whatman No. 4 paper impregnated with medicinal white paraffin and irrigated with methanol.

On unimpregnated paper the order of the pigments starting from the solvent front is carotenes, monohydroxy xanthophylls, chlorophyll a, chlorophyll b, dihydroxy xanthophylls. With reversed phase chromatography on paper the order is xanthophylls, chlorophyll b, chlorophyll a, carotenes, i.e. the same as on a polyethylene column.

A recent method of Jensen and Aasmundrud (1963) for characterizing algal and bacterial chlorophylls also makes use of radial chromatography on impregnated papers. Sucrose-impregnated paper was used (Sporer et al., 1954) with 0·5% butanol in light petroleum as the solvent and gave good separation of the algal chlorophylls, including 2-desvinyl-2-formyl chlorophyll *a* (chlorophyll *d*). They could also be separated on calcium carbonate paper (Schleicher and Schüll, No. 996) with light petroleum containing 5% acetone and 1% butanol, and on this paper the pigment zones were more sharply defined. The *Chlorobium* chlorophylls were not separated from each other on either type of paper, but were well separated from bacteriochlorophyll. Pheophytins except those of the *Chlorobium* chlorophylls were well separated on aluminium oxide-impregnated paper (Schleicher and Schüll No. 667) with 10% acetone in light petroleum as the solvent. Algal pheophytins could also be separated satisfactorily on sucrose and calcium carbonate papers. On papers impregnated with sucrose, calcium carbonate or aluminium oxide the pigments run in the same order as on unimpregnated paper.

Hendrickson *et al.* (1957) used radial chromatography for the analysis of mixtures of chlorophyll derivatives. They devised suitable apparatus and with it worked out constants relating the movement of the chlorophyll derivatives to the movement of solvents. Data for rhodochlorin dimethyl ester and purpurin 18a monomethyl ester were statistically analysed and preliminary results for a number of other derivatives were given.

Wolff and Price (1957) used paper chromatography for studying pigments in etiolated leaves after irradiation. They tried several solvent systems on sucrose impregnated paper and found that protochlorophyllide and chlorophyllide remained at the origin while chlorophyll *a* moved away. Virgin (1960, 1961a) separated phytylated from unphytylated pigments by ascending chromatography using a mixture of light petroleum 85:acetone 15. Protochlorophyll, protochlorophyllide and chlorophyllide all remained at, or near, the origin with this solvent. Loeffler (1955) separated protochlorophyllide from both protochlorophyll and chlorophyll using two-dimensional ascending chromatography. A mixture of light petroleum, ether and ethanol (30:10:0·5) was used for the first run. To determine which of the compounds contained magnesium the chromatogram was then run with an ether-ethanol solution of 1,5 diphenyl carbohydrazide. This reagent decomposed the magnesium-containing organic compounds and formed red spots where they had been. It also carried the organic residues on the solvent front and out of the chromatogram.

2. Porphyrins

Solvent systems for the paper chromatographic separation of porphyrins are given by Granick (1961). Rf values for various porphyrins are listed using 2,6 lutidine 10:0·05 N-NH$_4$OH 7 and acetone 30:light petroleum 70:acetic acid 0·1.

3. Imides

Gray et al. (1961) separated imides, which are degradation products of porphyrins, by chromatography on Whatman No. 2 paper with a mixture of ethanol 16:water 3:ammonia (0·88) 1 as the running solvent. The paper was treated with chlorine and then immersed in a saturated solution of o-tolidine in 2 N acetic acid to which an equal volume of 0·05 N-KI had been added. The imides appeared as blue spots. Morley et al. (1959) used gas-liquid partition chromatography for separation and identification of imides.

D. THIN-LAYER CHROMATOGRAPHY

Detailed information about this recently developed technique is given by Truter (1963), Randerath (1963) and Stahl (1963). Hager and Bertenrath (1962) used a mixture of kieselguhr, silica gel, calcium carbonate and calcium hydroxide in a solution of ascorbic acid for making the layer. An acetone extract was streaked on the plate and the pigments were separated by ascending chromatography with a solvent mixture of light petroleum (b.p. 100–140°), isopropanol and water (100:10:0·25). The chlorophylls were eluted with acetone.

Egger (1962) has applied reversed-phase thin-layer chromatography to the separation of chlorophylls and other plastid pigments. Kieselguhr layers were impregnated with a vegetable oil dissolved in light petroleum and the solvent evaporated off before use. A mixture of methanol, acetone and water (20:4:3) was used as an ascending solvent and the separation took place in less than 40 min. The separated pigments were eluted with N,N-dimethylformamide from which the fatty oil could be selectively extracted with light petroleum.

V. MISCELLANEOUS TESTS

Smith and Benitez (1955) described methods for doing the Phase Test and determining the Hydrochloric Acid Number of chlorophylls and their derivatives. These are discussed in Chapter 1.

VI. CHLOROPHYLLASE

The enzyme chlorophyllase (chlorophyll-chlorophyllido-hydrolase 3.1.1.14) was discovered by Willstätter and Stoll (1910) over fifty years ago but soluble enzyme preparations have only recently been obtained (Holden, 1961; Klein and Vishniac, 1961; Shimizu and Tamaki, 1962). In vivo the enzyme may be responsible for the final stage of chlorophyll biosynthesis, that is the attachment of the phytyl side chain to chlorophyllide (Sud'ina, 1963). *In vitro* it catalyses the removal of phytol from chlorophylls *a* and *b* and pheophytins *a* and *b*; bacteriochlorophyll is also a substrate (Fischer *et al.*, 1938). Klein and Vishniac (1961) reported that *Chlorobium* chlorophyll-650 was hydrolysed by rye chlorophyllase. If this observation is confirmed it will be of considerable interest, as the *Chlorobium* chlorophylls do not contain phytol but a C_{15} alcohol, farnesol (Rapoport and Hanlow, 1961).

When the reaction takes place in aqueous acetone, or ether saturated with water, the phytyl group is replaced by hydrogen, chlorophyllides or pheophorbides being formed. In aqueous methanol or ethanol transesterification takes place with replacement of the phytyl group by methyl or ethyl, giving esters of chlorophyllides and pheophorbides.

Fischer and Lambrecht (1938) found that purpurin-7-trimethyl ester and mesopurpurin-18-monomethyl ester were also hydrolysed by a crude preparation of the enzyme. Shimizu and Tamaki (1963) have recently been able to phytylate chlorophyllide and pheophorbide *in vitro* using a purified preparation of tobacco leaf chlorophyllase.

A. PREPARATION OF CHLOROPHYLLASE FROM SUGAR-BEET LEAVES

The method used in this laboratory is as follows.

Washed, de-ribbed leaves are macerated in ice-cold acetone (100 g leaf/400 ml solvent) and the suspension filtered on a buchner funnel. The solid portion is washed thoroughly with acetone, dried at room temperature and then milled finely. This powder retains its activity for many months if stored at 0°. The acetone-dried powder is extracted successively with ethanol, ethanol-ether (3:1) and ether and the enzyme is then soluble in a slightly alkaline solution such as 0·02 M sodium citrate (8 ml/g powder). The extract is centrifuged to remove insoluble material and the enzyme is precipitated with acetone at 0°. The precipitate obtained between 0 and 45% acetone is discarded as most of the activity is precipitated by increasing the acetone concentration from 45 to 60%. This fraction is dialysed overnight against a solution of disodium hydrogen phosphate (0·02 M adjusted to pH 7) which also contains cysteine hydrochloride 0·02% w/v. Any precipitate which forms is discarded and the solution is passed through a column of DEAE-cellulose (Whatman DE 50) suspended in the same phosphate solution. The enzyme is not adsorbed but leaves behind most of the brown pigment which was present and some inactive protein. The enzyme is again precipitated with acetone; it now comes down with 30% acetone, a much lower concentration than it did when precipitated from the crude extract. The precipitate is dissolved in a small volume of water and the solution passed through a column of cellulose phosphate (Whatman P 40) suspended in water. All chlorophyllase activity is adsorbed and it is eluted with 0·2 M phosphate solution pH 7. The final preparation contains about 10% of the original activity and is 500-600 fold purified.

B. METHODS OF DETERMINING CHLOROPHYLLASE ACTIVITY

Willstätter and Stoll (1910) suggested several methods for determining chlorophyllase activity, all using chlorophyll as the substrate. Chlorophyll was used by Mayer (1930), Weast and Mackinney (1940), Ardao and Vennesland (1960) and Holden (1961). Pheophytin, however, can also be used (Gage and Aronoff, 1956; Klein and Vishniac, 1961) and has the advantage that it, and the pheophorbide formed, are more light-stable than chlorophyll and chlorophyllide. But in this laboratory it has been found less satisfactory than chlorophyll, as pheophorbide is more soluble than chlorophyllide in light petroleum containing acetone. Most methods which have been used recently for estimating chlorophyllase are based on the partition of chlorophyll and chlorophyllide (or pheophytin and pheophorbide) between aqueous acetone and light petroleum. With chlorophyll as substrate the reaction will go to completion and eventually no green pigment is extracted into the light petroleum. With pheophytin under similar conditions a small amount of brown pigment can always be transferred however long the incubation is continued.

Chlorophyllase activity is usually determined with a high concentration of acetone or methanol present. The enzyme is remarkably stable in organic solvents, though less so when purified than in insoluble preparations. Holden (1961) used aqueous acetone extracts of bean leaves as the substrate when doing large numbers of chlorophyllase determinations. A better substrate is the mixture of chlorophylls a and b, free from xanthophylls and carotenes, which is eluted from a column of polyethylene with 80% acetone (p. 478). For determining the activity of both soluble and insoluble preparations the chlorophyll solution is diluted with sodium citrate solution so that the final concentration of acetone is 40% and the citrate 0·04 M and the pH about 7·7. After incubation at room temperature in the dark for 1 h or less, half the incubate is shaken twice with light petroleum to remove unsplit chlorophyll. The acetone layer is diluted with acetone to a suitable volume for measuring the optical density at 660 mμ. This is compared with the optical density of the other half of the incubate, that has not been extracted with light petroleum, similarly diluted. Enzyme activity is expressed as a percentage of the substrate split in a given time.

Klein and Vishniac (1961) used an aqueous system for chlorophyllase determinations as they were able to make pheophytin soluble with the detergent Triton X-100. The substrate was prepared by adding 2 ml of an ether solution of the pigment to 98 ml of 0·08 M potassium phosphate buffer pH 7·5, which was 0·2% with respect to the detergent. The assay mixture contained 0·5 ml of buffer-substrate (39·5 μg pheophytin *a*), 0·4 ml of the same phosphate buffer and 0·1 ml of enzyme solution. After incubating at 30°, 2 ml acetone and 3 ml light petroleum were added, the mixture shaken, the layers separated by centrifugation, the volumes of the two phases recorded and their optical densities measured. The degree of hydrolysis was calculated from both the decrease in optical density of the petroleum ether layer (disappearance of substrate) and from the increase of the aqueous acetone layer (appearance of product). A similar method can be used with "solubilized" chlorophyll instead of pheophytin.

Although the chlorophyllase methods described above are simpler and quicker than other possible methods they are not always applicable, as for example when bacteriochlorophyll, which is insoluble in light petroleum, is used as the substrate. Instead of shaking with light petroleum, the pigments are transferred to diethyl ether after incubation and the ether is shaken with 0·02 N-KOH which extracts chlorophyllide. The degree of hydrolysis can be determined by comparing the optical density of the ether solution with an identical sample which has been treated in the same way but without addition of enzyme.

REFERENCES

Anderson, A. F. H., and Calvin, M. (1962). *Nature, Lond.* **194**, 285.
Anderson, J. M., Blass, V. and Calvin, M. (1960). *In* "Comparative Biochemistry of Photoreactive Systems" (M. B. Allen, ed.), p. 15, Academic Press, New York.
Angapindu, A., Silberman, H., Tantivatana, P., and Kaplan, I. R. (1958). *Arch. Biochem. Biophys.* **75**, 56.
Ardao, C., and Vennesland, B. (1960). *Plant Physiol.* **35**, 368.
Arnon, D. I. (1949). *Plant Physiol.* **24**, 1.
Benedict, H. M., and Swidler, R. (1961). *Science* **133**, 2015.
Brown, J. S. (1963). *Photochem. Photobiol.* **2**, 159.
Brown, J. S., and French, C. S. (1959). *Plant Physiol.* **34**, 305.
Brown, W. G. (1939). *Nature, Lond.* **143**, 377.
Bruinsma, J. (1961). *Biochim. biophys. Acta* **52**, 576.
Bruinsma, J. (1963). *Photochem. Photobiol.* **2**, 241.
Bukatsch, F., and Rudolph, E. (1963). *Photochem. Photobiol.* **2**, 191.
Cohen-Bazire, G., Sistrom, W. R., and Stanier, R. Y. (1957). *J. cell. comp. Physiol.* **49**, 25.
Comar, C. L., and Zscheile, F. P. (1942). *Plant Physiol.* **17**, 198.
Conti, S. F., and Vishniac, W. (1960). *Nature, Lond.* **188**, 489.
Cooper, R. (1963). *Biochem. J.* **89**, 100.
Deleano, N. T., and Dick, J. (1934). *Biochem. Z.* **268**, 317.
Dietrich, W. C. (1958). *Food Technol.* **12**, 428.
Duranton, J., Galmiche, J. M., and Roux, E. (1958). *C. R. Acad. Sci., Paris* **246**, 992.

Egger, K. (1962). *Planta* **58**, 664.

Falk, H. (1958). *Planta* **51**, 49.

Fischer, H., and Lambrecht, R. (1938). *Hoppe-Seyl. Z.* **253**, 253.

Fischer, H., Lambrecht, R., and Mittenzwei, H. (1938). *Hoppe-Seyl. Z.* **253**, 1.

Fogg, G. E., and Belcher, J. H. (1961). *New Phytol.* **60**, 129.

Frei, Y. F. (1962). *Biochim. biophys. Acta* **55**, 82.

French, C. S. (1955). *In* "The Luminescence of Biological Systems" (F. H. Johnson, ed.), p. 51, A.A.A.S. Washington, D.C.

French, C. S. (1960). *In* "Encyclopaedia of Plant Physiology", vol. **5**, p. 252, Springer-Verlag, Berlin-Göttingen-Heidelberg.

French, C. S., and Elliott, R. F. (1958). *Yearb. Carneg. Instn.* **57**, 278.

French, C. S., Smith, J. H. C., Virgin, H. I., and Airth, R. L. (1956). *Plant Physiol.* **31**, 369.

Friend, D. J. C. (1960). *Physiol. Plant.* **13**, 776.

Friend, D. J. C. (1961). *Canad. J. Bot.* **39**, 51.

Gage, R. S., and Aronoff, S. (1956). *Plant Physiol.* **31**, 477.

Glemser, O., and Rieck, G. (1958). *Naturwissenschaften* **45**, 569.

Goodwin, R. H. (1947). *Industr. Engng. Chem. (Anal. Ed.)* **19**, 789.

Gorham, E. (1959). *Soil Sci.* **87**, 258.

Granick, S. (1961). *J. biol. Chem.* **236**, 1168.

Gray, C. H., and Kulczycka, A., and Nicholson, D. C. (1961). *J. chem. Soc.* p. 2268.

Hager, A. (1957). *Planta* **48**, 592.

Hager, A., and Bertenrath, T. (1962). *Planta* **58**, 564.

Hendrickson, M. J., Berueffy, R. R., and McIntyre, A. R. (1957). *Anal. Chem.* **29**, 1810.

Holden, M. (1961). *Biochem. J.* **78**, 359.

Holden, M. (1962). *Biochim. biophys. Acta* **56**, 378.

Hughes, D. W., and Holt, A. S. (1962). *Canad. J. Chem.* **40**, 171.

Humphrey, G. F. (1961). U.S. Atomic Energy Commission. TID 7633 p. 121.

Jeffrey, S. W. (1961). *Biochem. J.* **80**, 336.

Jeffrey, S. W. (1963). *Biochem. J.* **86**, 313.

Jensen, A., and Aasmundrud, O. (1963). *Acta chem. scand.* **17**, 907.

Jones, I. D., White, R. C., and Gibbs, E. (1963a). *J. Fd. Sci.* **28**, 431.

Jones, I. D., White, R. C., and Gibbs, E. (1963b). *J. Fd. Sci.* **28**, 437.

Jones, O. T. G. (1963a). *Biochem. J.* **88**, 335.

Jones, O. T. G. (1963b). *Biochem. J.* **89**, 182.

Kaler, V. L., and Shlyk, A. A. (1962). *Biokhimiya* **27**, 599.

Kaplan, I. R., and Silberman, H. (1959). *Arch. Biochem. Biophys.* **80**, 114.

Klein, A., and Vishniac, W. (1961). *J. biol. Chem.* **236**, 2544.

Koski, V. M. (1950). *Arch. Biochem.* **29**, 339.

Koski, V. M., and Smith, J. H. C. (1948). *J. Amer. chem. Soc.* **70**, 3558.

Laborie, M. E. (1963). *Ann. Physiol. Vég.* **5**, 89.

Lascelles, J. (1956). *Biochem. J.* **62**, 78.

Lind, E. F., Lane, H. C., and Gleason, L. S. (1953). *Plant Physiol.* **28**, 325.

Loeffler, J. E. (1955). *Yearb. Carneg. Instn.* **54**, 159.

McDonald, H. J., Bermes, E. W., and Shepherd, H. G. (1957). *Chromatog. Methods* **1**, 1.

Mackinney, G. (1941). *J. biol. Chem.* **140**, 315.

Mackinney, G., and Weast, C. A. (1940). *Industr. Engng. Chem.* **32**, 392.

Maclachlan, S., and Zalik, S. (1963). *Canad. J. Bot.* **41**, 1053.

Madsen, A. (1963). *Photochem. Photobiol.* **2**, 93.

Mann, C. K., and Yoe, J. H. (1956). *Anal. Chem.* **28**, 202.

Mathewson, J. W., Richards, W. R., and Rapoport, H. (1963). *J. Amer. chem. Soc.* **85**, 364.

Mayer, H. (1930). *Planta* **11**, 294.

Morley, H. V., Cooper, F. P., and Holt, A. S. (1959). *Chem. & Ind.* p. 1018.

Murchio, J. C., and Allen, M. B. (1962). *Photochem. Photobiol.* **1**, 259.

Nunez, G. (1954). *Bull. Soc. Chim. biol.* **36**, 411.

Official Methods of Analysis, 9th Edn. (1960). Association of Official Agricultural Chemists, Washington, D.C.

Perkins, H. J., and Roberts, D. W. A. (1962). *Biochim. biophys. Acta* **58**, 486.

Randerath, K. (1963). "Thin-layer Chromatography," Academic Press, New York.

Rapoport, H., and Hanlow, H. P. (1961). *Biochem. biophys. Res. Comm.* **6**, 134.

Richards, F. A., and Thompson, T. G. (1952). *J. Marine Res.* **11**, 156.

Robinson, H. M. C., and Rathbun, J. C. (1959). *Canad. J. Biochem. Physiol.* **37**, 225.

Sapozhnikov, D. I., Maevskaya, A. N., and Popova, I. A. (1959). *Fiziol. Rast.* **6**, 376.

Šesták, Z. (1959). *Chromatographic Reviews* **1**, 193.

Shibata, K., Benson, A. A., and Calvin, M. (1954). *Biochim. biophys. Acta* **15**, 464.

Shimizu, S., and Tamaki, E. (1962). *Botan. Mag., Tokyo* **75**, 480.

Shimizu, S., and Tamaki, E. (1963). *Arch. Biochem. Biophys.* **102**, 152.

Sironval, C. (1954). *Physiol. Plant* **7**, 523.

Smith, J. H. C., and Benitez, A. (1955). *In* "Modern Methods of Plant Analysis" (K. Paech and M. V. Tracey, eds.), vol. 4, p. 142, Springer-Verlag, Berlin.

Sporer, A. H., Freed, S., and Sancier, K. M. (1954). *Science* **119**, 68.

Stahl, E. (Ed.) (1963). "Thin-layer Chromatography, A Laboratory Handbook." Academic Press, New York.

Stanier, R. Y., and Smith, J. H. C. (1960). *Biochim. biophys. Acta* **41**, 478.

Steeman-Nielsen, E. (1961). *Physiol. Plant.* **14**, 868.

Stoll, A., and Wiedemann, E. (1959). *Helv. chim. acta* **42**, 679.

Strain, H. H. (1953). *J. phys. Chem.* **57**, 638.

Strain, H. H. (1954). *Agric. Fd. Chem.* **2**, 1222.

Strain, H. H. (1958). "Chloroplast pigments and chromatographic analysis" 32nd Annual Priestley Lectures, Penn. State Univ., Univ. Park, Pa.

Strain, H. H., and Sato, T. R. (1956). U.S. Atomic Energy Commission TID 7512 p. 175.

Sud'ina, E. G. (1963). *Photochem. Photobiol.* **2**, 181.

Sweeney, J. P., and Martin, M. E. (1958). *Food Res.* **23**, 635.

Sweeney, J. P., and Martin, M. E. (1961). *Food Technol.* **15**, 263.

Talling, J. F., and Driver, D. (1961). U.S. Atomic Energy Commission TID 7633 p. 142.

Tan, C. T., and Francis, F. J. (1962). *J. Fd Sci.* **27**, 232.

Truter, E. V. (1963). "Thin Film Chromatography," Cleaver-Hume Press, London.

Vallentyne, J. R. (1955). *Canad. J. Bot.* **33**, 304.

Vallentyne, J. R., and Craston, D. F. (1957). *Canad. J. Bot.* **35**, 35.

Van Niel, C. B., and Arnold, W. (1938). *Enzymologia* **5**, 244.

Van Norman, R. W. (1957). *Utah Acad. Sci. Proc.* **34**, 39.

Vernon, L. P. (1960). *Anal. Chem.* **32**, 1144.

Virgin, H. I. (1954). *Physiol. Plant.* **7**, 560.

Virgin, H. I. (1955a). *Physiol. Plant.* **8**, 389.

Virgin, H. I. (1955b). *Physiol. Plant.* **8**, 630.

Virgin, H. I. (1956). *Physiol. Plant.* **9**, 674.

Virgin, H. I. (1960). *Physiol. Plant.* **13**, 155.

Virgin, H. I. (1961a). *Physiol. Plant.* **14**, 384.

Virgin, H. I. (1961b). *Physiol. Plant.* **14**, 439.

Weast, C. A., and Mackinney, G. (1940). *J. biol. Chem.* **133**, 551.

Wheeler, A. W., and Humphries, E. C. (1963). *J. exp. Bot.* **14**, 132.

Wickliff, J. L., and Aronoff, S. (1962). *Plant Physiol.* **37**, 584.

Willstätter, R., and Stoll, A. (1910). *Liebigs Ann.* **378**, 18, *quoted in* "Investigations on Chlorophyll" (1928). Transl. by Schertz, F. M., and Merz, A. R., Science Press Printing Co., Lancaster, Pa.

Wilson, J. R., and Nutting, M-D. (1963). *Anal. Chem.* **35**, 144.

Wilson, J. R., Nutting, M-D, and Bailey, G. F. (1962). *Anal. Chem.* **34**, 1331.

Withrow, R. B., Klein, W. H., Price, L., and Elstad, V. (1953). *Plant Physiol.* **28**, 1.

Wolff, J. B., and Price, L. (1957). *Arch. Biochem. Biophys.* **72**, 293.

Zscheile, F. P. (1934). *J. phys. Chem.* **38**, 95.

Chapter 18

ANALYSIS OF CAROTENOID PIGMENTS

B. H. DAVIES

Department of Biochemistry and Agricultural Biochemistry, University College of Wales, Aberystwyth, Wales

I. CAROTENOID NOMENCLATURE

Carotenoids are tetraterpenes, having 8 isoprene units, which arise through the "tail-to-tail" condensation of two identical 20-C units. It is the series of conjugated olefinic bonds that constitutes the chromophoric group of a carotenoid, which may be red, orange or yellow. Although cyclization is not as extensive as in the triterpenes (e.g. sterols), carotenoids may be cyclized. Typical of "cyclic carotenoids" is β-carotene (I) which contains two β-ionone residues in its molecule. In

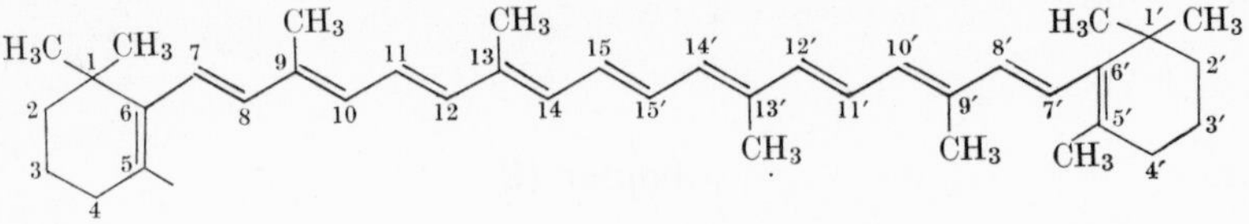

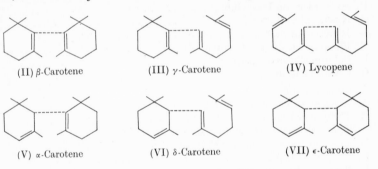

(I)

a molecule containing only one β-ionone unit, the ticked numerals are allocated to that half of the molecule *not* containing this residue.

Carotenoids can be subdivided into two main groups:

    A. Hydrocarbons, which are called "carotenes", and
    B. Oxygen-containing derivatives, which are called "xanthophylls".

A. CAROTENES

The structures of those carotenes which may be considered as "parent hydrocarbons" are indicated below (II–VII). Three compounds are mentioned in later sections although they are not strictly carotenoids, since they are colourless. These are lycopersene, phytoene and phytofluene, which are hydrocarbons related to lycopene.

(II) β-Carotene   (III) γ-Carotene   (IV) Lycopene

(V) α-Carotene   (VI) δ-Carotene   (VII) ε-Carotene

B. XANTHOPHYLLS

The oxygen in xanthophylls can occur as hydroxy-, methoxy-, epoxy-, carboxy- or keto- (oxo-) groupings. Most substituents are in the positions 1 to 6 and 1' to 6', although the 5,8-epoxides (VIII) are the main exceptions to this generalization (cf. 5,6-epoxides, IX).

In most structures (as in β-carotene), the link between the ring systems and the aliphatic chain joining the rings (i.e. the bond between C-6 and

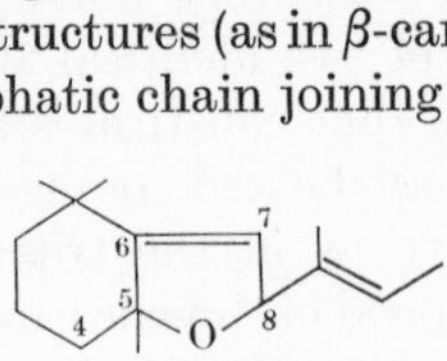

(VIII) 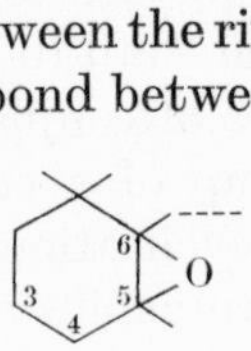   (IX)

C-7) is a single bond, and the compounds have the normal (cyclohexenyl) structure. When a double bond forms this link, a *retro* (cyclohexylidene) structure is obtained, as in *retro-β*-carotene (X).

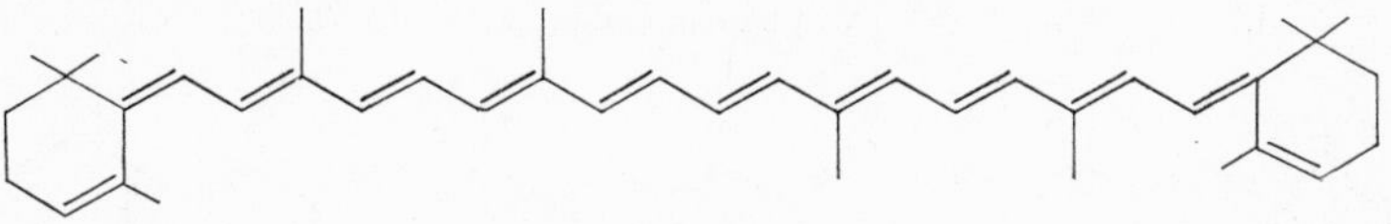

(X) *Retro-β*-carotene

c. *Cis-trans* ISOMERS

A glance at the structure of any carotenoid will reveal the considerable possibilities for *cis-trans* isomerization. This phenomenon has been reviewed in detail by Zechmeister (1960), whose work has revealed the presence of many *cis*-isomers in nature, although the predominant form of a pigment is generally the all-*trans* form. These isomers are discussed in Section III, D.

D. SPECIFIC STRUCTURES

The structures of carotenoids with somewhat special structures are indicated in Formulae XI–XIX; other carotenoids of known structure which can be related to the "parent" hydrocarbons II–VII are listed in Table I. In this, as in other tables, bacterial carotenoids have been listed in addition to plant carotenoids.

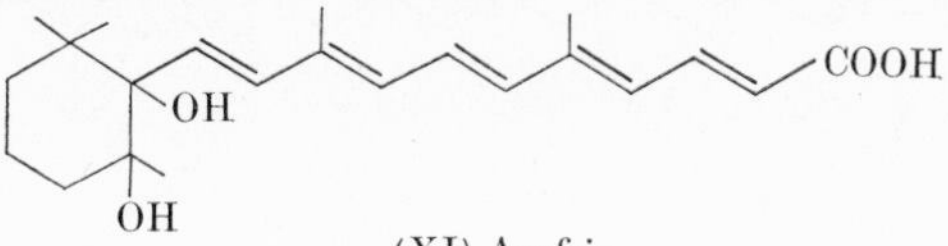

(XI) Azafrin

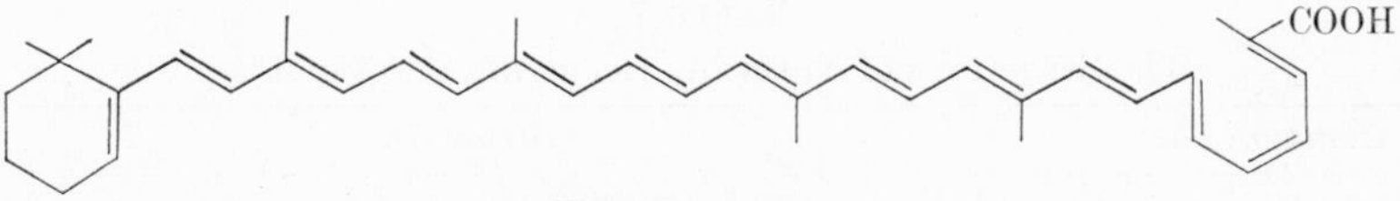

(XII) Torularhodin

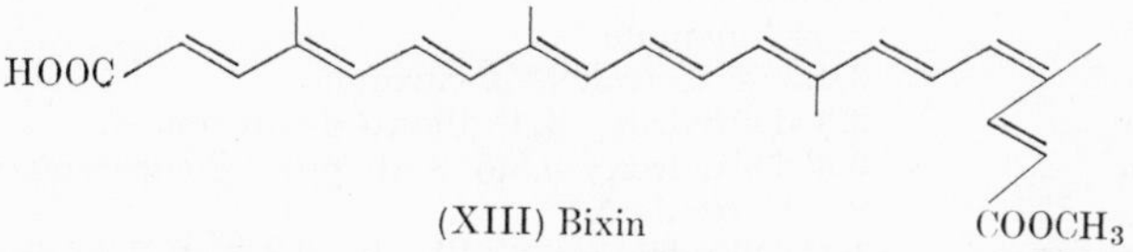

(XIII) Bixin

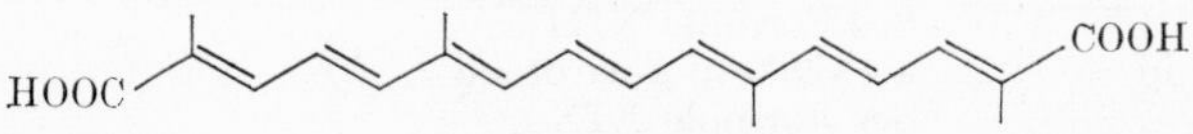

(XIV) Crocetin

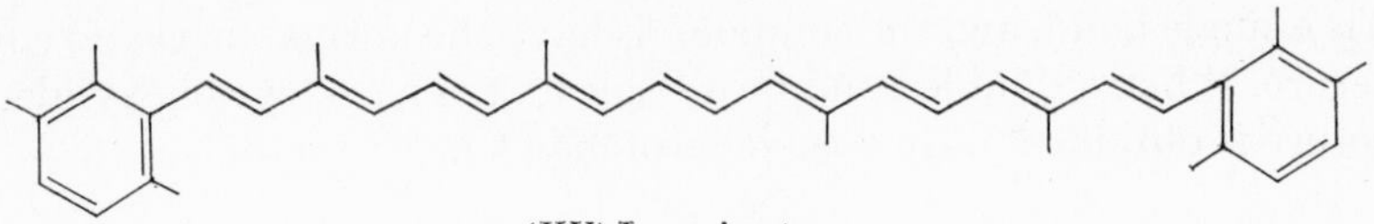

(XV) Isorenieratene

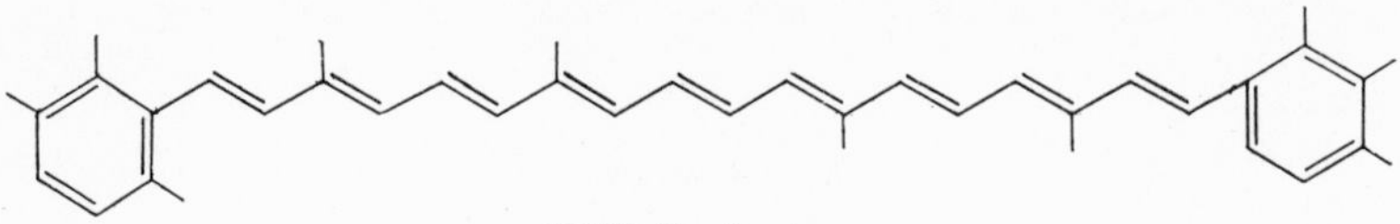

(XVI) Renieratene

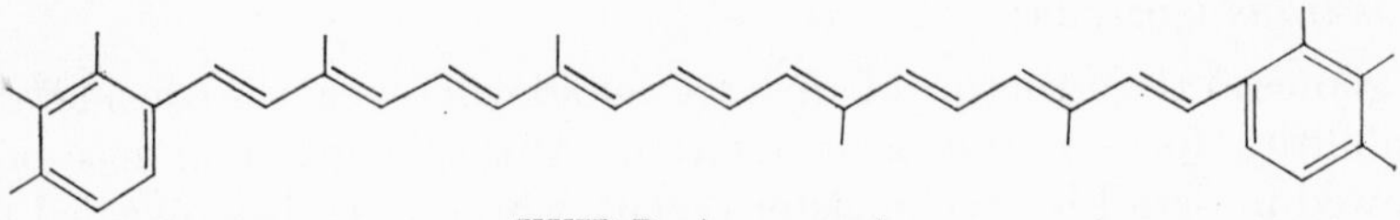

(XVII) Renierapurpurin

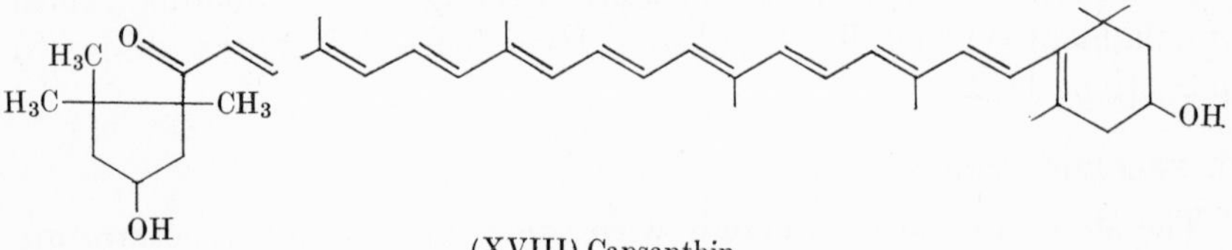

(XVIII) Capsanthin

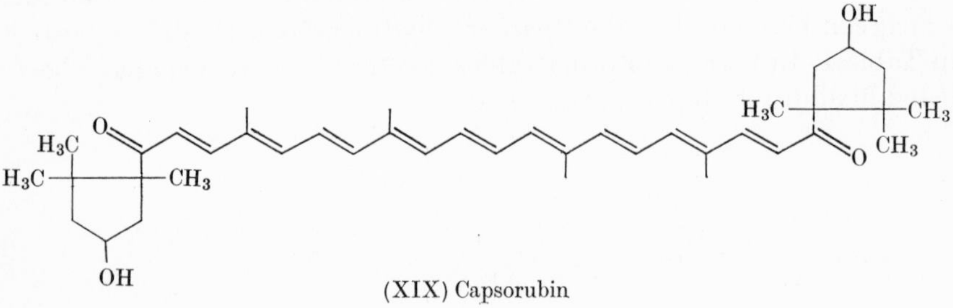

(XIX) Capsorubin

TABLE I

The Structures of Naturally Occurring Carotenoids

Common name	Structure
Anhydrorhodovibrin	1-Methoxy-2-hydro-3,4-dehydrolycopene
Antheraxanthin	3,3′-Dihydroxy-5,6-epoxy-β-carotene
Aphanicin	Unknown
Aphanin	= Echinenone
Astacene	3,4,3′,4′-Tetraketo-β-carotene
Astaxanthin	3,3′-Dihydroxy-4,4′-diketo-β-carotene
Auroxanthin	3,3′-Dihydroxy-5,8,5′,8′-diepoxy-β-carotene
Azafrin	See Formula XI
α-Bacterioruberin	1,1′-Dihydroxy-2,2′-dihydro-3,4,3′,4′-dehydrolycopene
Bixin	See Formula XIII
Canthaxanthin	4,4′-Diketo-β-carotene
Capsorubin	See Formula XIX
Capsanthin	See Formula XVIII

Common name	Structure
ζ-Carotene	7,8,7′,8′-Tetrahydrolycopene
Celaxanthin	3-Hydroxy-3′,4′-dehydro-γ-carotene
Chloroxanthin	1-Hydroxy-1,2,7′,8′-tetrahydrolycopene
Chrysanthemaxanthin	3,3′-Dihydroxy-5,8-epoxy-α-carotene
Citroxanthin	5,8-Epoxy-β-carotene
Corynexanthin	Unknown
Crocetin	See Formula XIV
Cryptochrome	3-Hydroxy-5,8,5′,8′-diepoxy-β-carotene
Cryptoflavin	3-Hydroxy-5,8-epoxy-β-carotene
Cryptoxanthin	3-Hydroxy-β-carotene
α-Cryptoxanthin	3′-Hydroxy-α-carotene
Diadinoxanthin	Unknown; closely related to lutein; a 5,6-epoxide
Diatoxanthin	Unknown; closely related to zeaxanthin
Dinoxanthin	Unknown
Echinenone	4-Keto-β-carotene
Eschscholtzxanthin	3,3′-Dihydroxy-retro-β-carotene
Euglenanone	= Canthaxanthin?
Flavochrome	5,8-Epoxy-α-carotene
Flavoxanthin	Stereoisomer of chrysanthemaxanthin?
Foliachrome	Unknown; 5,8-epoxide
Foliaxanthin	Unknown; 5,6-epoxide
Fucoxanthin	Unknown; contains C=C=C group
Gazaniaxanthin	3-Hydroxy-1′,2′-dihydro-γ-carotene
Helenien	Lutein dipalmitate
Hydroxyechinenone	3-Hydroxy-4-keto-α-carotene
Hydroxy P 481	= Rhodovibrin
Hydroxy R	1′,2′-Dihydro-1′-hydroxy-spheroidenone
Hydroxyspirilloxanthin	1-Methoxy-1′-hydroxy-1,2,1′,2′-tetrahydro-3,3′,4,4′-dehydrolycopene
Hydroxy Y	7′,8′-Dihydrorhodovibrin
Isocryptoxanthin	4-Hydroxy-β-carotene
Isolutein	3,3′-Dihydroxy-5,6-epoxy-α-carotene
Isorenieratene	See Formula XV
Isozeaxanthin	4,4′-Dihydroxy-β-carotene
Leprotene	Unknown
Lutein	3,3′-Dihydroxy-α-carotene
Luteoxanthin	3,3′-Dihydroxy-5,6-epoxy-5′,8′-epoxy-β-carotene
Lycophyll	3,3′-Dihydroxylycopene
Lycoxanthin	3-Hydroxylycopene
Monodemethyl spirilloxanthin	= Hydroxyspirilloxanthin
Mutatochrome	= Citroxanthin
Mutatoxanthin	3,3′-Dihydroxy-5,8-epoxy-β-carotene
Myxoxanthin	= Echinenone
Myxoxanthophyll	Unknown
Neoxanthin	3,3′,5′(or 6′)-Trihydroxy-6′(or 5′)-hydro-5,6-epoxy-β-carotene
Neurosporene	7,8-Dihydrolycopene
Ocillaxanthin	Unknown
P 481	= Anhydrorhodovibrin
P 518	2-Ketospirilloxanthin
Peridinin	Unknown; = Sulcatoxanthin

TABLE I—cont.

Common name	Structure
Persicachrome	Unknown
Persicaxanthin	Unknown
Physalien	Zeaxanthin dipalmitate
Phytoene	7,8,11,12,7′,8′,11′,12′-Octahydrolycopene
Phytofluene	7,8,11,12,7′,8′-Hexahydrolycopene
Physoxanthin	A *Cis*-isomer of cryptoxanthin
Pigment R	= Spheroidenone
Pigment Y	= Spheroidene
Prolycopene	Poly *cis*-lycopene
Renierapurpurin	See Formula XVII
Renieratene	See Formula XVI
Rhodopin	1-Hydroxy-1,2-dihydrolycopene
Rhodovibrin	1-Methoxy-1′-hydroxy-1,2,1′,2′-tetrahydro-3,4-dehydrolycopene
Rhodoviolascin	= Spirilloxanthin
Rhodoxanthin	3,3′-Diketo-*retro*-β-carotene
R, Pigment	= Spheroidenone
Rubichrome	3-Hydroxy-5,8-epoxy-γ-carotene
Rubixanthin	3-Hydroxy-γ-carotene
Sarcinaxanthin	Unknown
Sinensiachrome	Unknown
Sinensiaxanthin	Unknown
Siphonaxanthin	Unknown
Spheroidene	1-Methoxy-1,2,7′,8′-tetrahydro-3,4-dehydrolycopene
Spheroidenone	1-Methoxy-2-keto-7′,8′-dihydro-3,4-dehydrolycopene
Spirilloxanthin	1,1′-Dimethoxy-1,2,1′,2′-tetrahydro-3,4,3′,4′-dehydrolycopene
Sulcatoxanthin	Unknown; = peridinin
Taraxanthin	Unknown
Torularhodin	See Formula XII
Torulene	3′,4′-Dehydro-γ-carotene
Trollein	Unknown
Trollichrome	3,3′,6′-Trihydroxy-5,8-epoxy-α-carotene
Trollixanthin	3,3′,6′-Trihydroxy-5,6-epoxy-α-carotene
Valenciachrome	Unknown
Valenciaxanthin	Unknown
Violaxanthin	3,3′-Dihydroxy-5,6,5′,6′-diepoxy-β-carotene
Y, Pigment	See Spheroidene
α-Zeacarotene	7′,8′-Dihydro-δ-carotene
β-Zeacarotene	7′,8′-Dihydro-γ-carotene
Zeaxanthin	3,3′-Dihydroxy-β-carotene
Zeinoxanthin	3-Hydroxy-α-carotene

II. ISOLATION OF CAROTENOIDS

A. EXTRACTION OF CAROTENOIDS FROM TISSUES

Since carotenoids occur in such a variety of types of living organisms, no one method of extraction can be said to be completely satisfactory as a standard technique to meet all needs. The methods to be discussed have, in the hands of various workers, proved suitable for the extraction of carotenoids from specific sources, and can be considered as adaptable or interchangeable as circumstances demand.

Tissues should be as fresh as possible and undamaged. If it is not possible to use them immediately, they should be stored below $-10°C$ until required.

Since fresh tissues contain a high percentage of water, and the carotenoids are lipid-soluble, the organic solvent used for extraction must be miscible with water if it is required to extract the fresh tissues directly. After preliminary extraction with such a solvent (e.g. acetone, methanol, ethanol) the tissue is sufficiently dehydrated to permit the use of water-immiscible solvents such as diethyl ether or benzene in subsequent extractions, if this is required. An alternative approach is to dehydrate the tissue by grinding with anhydrous sodium sulphate prior to direct extraction with ether.

1. *Green Tissues of Higher Plants* (See Goodwin, 1955)

a. Method 1. In this method (the best for most purposes), leaves are extracted for 1–2 min with acetone in a suitable electric blendor; the solvent is filtered off on a sintered glass funnel under reduced pressure (filter pump) and the residue returned to the blendor for further extraction. The process is repeated until all the pigment is extracted (usually 2–3 times). The combined extracts are concentrated under reduced pressure to about a fifth of their volume (this step may be omitted if the extract is not too bulky), diluted with an equal volume of diethyl ether (freshly distilled over reduced iron to remove peroxides) and then diluted with water until two layers are formed, the pigmented material being in the upper (ether) phase. Any emulsion formed at this stage can usually be resolved by the addition of a few ml of ethanol or a few g of sodium chloride (see Section II, B). The lower aqueous phase is run off, and re-extracted with ether to remove any remaining lipid-soluble material and then discarded. The ether solutions are bulked and washed with water to remove traces of acetone, distilled to a small volume under reduced pressure and dried by standing over anhydrous sodium sulphate for at least 1 h. Any water remaining appears when the solution is taken down to dryness in a small conical flask on a hot-water bath under a stream of nitrogen, and can be removed by adding 2–5 ml absolute ethanol and distilling this off in the same way. The residue is the total lipid fraction.

b. Method 2. The leaves are quickly cut up and ground in a mortar to a fine powder with anhydrous sodium sulphate and acid-washed silver sand (it is a common fault to use too little sodium sulphate). The powder is now transferred to a deep-walled sintered glass funnel, freshly distilled diethyl ether added and the mixture stirred for 1–2 min. The ether is filtered off and the process repeated with successive portions of ether until all the pigment is extracted. The bulked ether solutions are then washed with water and treated as in (1) above to obtain the total lipid fraction.

If it is not possible to proceed immediately with subsequent operations, the lipid fraction should be kept in the dark under nitrogen at 0° C or below. The dangers of leaving carotenoids in solutions, in the light, in warm conditions or in the presence of air, cannot be over-emphasized because of the possibility of *cis-trans* isomerization and oxidation. For this reason, the A.O.A.C. method (1952) of extracting carotenoids, which involves prolonged refluxing, cannot be recommended for detailed work.

2. *Roots, Flowers and Fruit*

The best general method for dealing with these tissues is to cut them into pieces of a suitable size and grind them with anhydrous sodium sulphate and acid-washed silver sand. The dry powder can then be extracted with freshly distilled ether as described on p. 495. Some soft berries and most flower petals can also be extracted by other methods (see p. 495).

3. *Algae*

The cell mass of a culture of a unicellular alga is collected by centrifugation. Reduction to a dry powder followed by extraction of the pigments is not always satisfactory (Goodwin, 1955). Hodgkiss *et al.* (1954) suggested an alternative method which combines the stages of extraction and saponification. Aqueous potassium hydroxide (1 ml of 60% w/v) and then ethanol (10 ml) are added to the cell mass in a centrifuge tube; the tube is then placed in a water-bath at 40–50° and the mixture carefully stirred and ground with a flattened glass rod. After 5 min, the mixture is centrifuged and the supernatant decanted. The procedure is repeated twice with ethanol (10 ml), when all the pigments are extracted. The pigments are transferred to ether by adding an equal volume of this solvent and then water until two phases are separated. The ether solution is then treated as described in Section II, B.

Very few algae respond at all well to attempts at direct treatment with acetone followed by ether, and either methanol or ethanol is usually necessary to achieve satisfactory extractions. Goodwin (1955) suggested that an effective preliminary procedure with marine diatoms is to disrupt the cells by placing them in distilled water.

The seaweeds are probably the tissues from which it is most difficult to extract carotenoids. Most of this difficulty is due to the presence of the characteristic seaweed polysaccharides which cause the tissues to agglutinate in a sticky mass. One method which apparently overcomes this is to cut the fresh seaweed into suitably sized pieces and to soak these overnight in industrial alcohol. The solid material is then filtered off and exhaustively extracted with acetone in an electric blendor; all the pigmented solutions, including the industrial alcohol, are bulked and the pigments transferred to ether by the usual methods (see p. 495).

An alternative method is to freeze the seaweed at −15° and to feed portions of it into an ice grinder. The pieces are then freeze-dried and powdered by grinding. The dry powder is readily extracted with ethanol. The total lipid fraction is extracted from this ethanolic solution by adding an equal volume of freshly distilled ether and then water until two layers are formed. The ether phase is then treated as described on p. 495.

4. *Fungi*

The following method has been found suitable for *Neurospora crassa* (Davies *et al.*, 1963a), *Phycomyces blakesleeanus* and *Rhizophlyctis rosea* (Davies, 1961b). The cultures are filtered through muslin in a Buchner funnel, washed thoroughly with water and pressed as dry as possible. The mycelium is cut into small pieces and ground under acetone with washed silver sand. The mixture is filtered through a sintered glass funnel and the residue re-extracted until the filtrate is colourless. The acetone extract is mixed with half its volume of ether, and water is added until the ether layer separates. The aqueous phase is extracted to completion with ether, and then the ether solutions are bulked, washed with water and dried over anhydrous sodium sulphate for at least an hour. After filtering off the sodium sulphate, the ether is distilled away under reduced pressure to leave the lipid residue. This is then saponified. An alternative method is to cover the mycelium with acetone and to add solid carbon dioxide until the mycelium is sufficiently frozen to allow it to be ground easily (E. C. Grob and A. Boschetti, personal communication).

Carotenoid formation in some fungi appears to be enhanced by the presence in the culture medium of a detergent such as Tween 80 (e.g. *N. crassa*). Although washing the mycelia prior to extraction removes most of the detergent, the extraction of such mycelia is often made difficult by the formation of emulsions, so that it is difficult to extract the acetone with ether. These emulsions can usually be resolved by the addition of ethanol or sodium chloride.

The sodium sulphate–solvent technique (p. 495) has been used successfully for many fungi (see Garton *et al.*, 1951), but other species (e.g. *Lycogola epidendron*, Lederer, 1938) require more polar solvents. A method for qualitatively screening yeasts for carotenoids has been described by Mrak *et al.* (1949), but the individual pigments undergo some considerable change in the course of this treatment (Peterson *et al.*, 1954). The use of mechanical methods to disrupt *Rhodotorula* cells in order to facilitate extraction has been described by Simpson *et al.* (1964). For volumes of more than 500 ml a colloid mill was used to disrupt the cells prior to extraction, but for smaller volumes, a modified French press was used according to the method of French and Milner (1955) at a pressure of 25,000 p.s.i. (Simpson *et al.*, 1963).

B. SAPONIFICATION PROCEDURE

This step is generally necessary in carotenoid analysis to remove unwanted lipid material. It is especially useful in the purification of carotenoids from photosynthetic organisms, since it also removes the chlorophylls. Instances in which the saponification procedure is avoided include the examination of material for carotenoid esters, and the analysis of extracts containing alkali-labile carotenoids such as astaxanthin and fucoxanthin.

Sufficient absolute ethanol is added to the total lipid to dissolve it completely, and then 60% (w/v) aqueous potassium hydroxide is added, 1 ml to every 10 ml of ethanolic solution. There are two alternative methods for the subsequent treatment.

1. The alkaline mixture is boiled for 5–10 min in the dark on a steam bath under a constant stream of nitrogen, and is then cooled. This method is time-saving and is therefore often more convenient.

2. The alkaline mixture is left in the dark at room temperature under nitrogen for about 12 h (overnight). This method has the advantage that the carotenoids, which are to a certain extent thermolabile, are not subjected to heat.

Subsequent operations are the same whether method (1) or (2) is used. The cold alkaline solution is diluted with 3 volumes of water, and freshly distilled diethyl ether is added (1 volume to 3 of the alkaline water/ ethanol phase). The mixture is shaken firmly, but not too vigorously, in a separating funnel and allowed to stand until two phases appear, the carotenoids being in the upper (ether) phase. Should separation not occur, the addition of absolute ethanol, or a few g of solid sodium chloride, should resolve the offending emulsion. The extraction with ether is repeated twice and the three extracts (the third is usually colourless) are bulked. The ether solution is then washed free of alkali by shaking gently with its own volume of water. After the two phases have separated, the water is discarded and the washing repeated until the washings are no longer alkaline to an alcoholic solution of phenolphthalein. The ether extract is dried by shaking it with powdered anhydrous sodium sulphate (5–10 g per 100 ml extract) and leaving it to stand over the drying agent for at least 1 h. If the sodium sulphate has been previously heated to 105° and allowed to cool in a desiccator, the length of time required for drying may be reduced to 15 min. The sodium sulphate is filtered off on a sintered glass funnel, and washed free of pigment with fresh dry ether. The ether solution is concentrated by distillation, preferably in the dark and under reduced pressure, and is then transferred to a small conical flask and blown down to dryness with a stream of nitrogen on a hot-water bath. The residue is the unsaponifiable fraction containing the carotenoids.

C. XANTHOPHYLL ESTERS

In most normal analyses, it is sufficient to identify the actual carotenoids present in a tissue, but in certain cases, as in the study of the pigment changes occurring in leaves during autumn necrosis, it may be necessary to determine whether or not the xanthophylls are esterified with fatty acids (Goodwin, 1958). Under circumstances such as these, it is impossible to include the saponification step in the analytical procedure until after the isolation of individual pigments by column chromatography. When a pigment has been isolated, it is possible to identify an ester by a marked increase in adsorption affinity after saponification. A further test is based on the fact that while hydroxylated carotenoids are hypophasic in the light petroleum—95% methanol system, the esters are epiphasic. As well as forming the free xanthophyll, saponification releases the esterifying fatty acid as its potassium (or sodium) salt. The methyl salts of the fatty acids may be prepared and identified by gas-liquid chromatography (Eichenberger and Grob, 1963).

Another instance in which it is inadvisable to remove the saponifiable components by alkali treatment of the lipid extract at an early stage in the procedure, is when the extract is suspected of containing astaxanthin (3,3'-dihydroxy-4,4'-dioxo-β-carotene). This compound is converted by alkalis into astacene (3,3',4,4'-tetraoxo-β-carotene). It is again necessary in these cases to isolate the carotenoid esters rather than the free xanthophylls by column chromatography.

D. REMOVAL OF STEROLS

In most instances, the unsaponifiable fraction may contain comparatively large amounts of sterol, most of which precipitates out when a light petroleum solution of the fraction is kept overnight at −10°. Most sterols with the 3β-hydroxy substituent can be precipitated completely as their digitonides; but certain sterols, particuarly those with 4-*gem* dimethyl groups (e.g. lanosterol) are only partly precipitated by this procedure.

The unsaponifiable material is dissolved in 95% ethanol to a concentration of 30 mg per 100 ml. For every 6 ml of this solution, 5 ml of a solution of digitonin in 90% ethanol is used. This is boiled and immediately added to the boiling solution of the unsaponifiable material in a centrifuge tube. Boiling is continued until the white precipitate of digitonides appears (Windaus, 1909). Completion of precipitation will occur overnight at 4°C, and then the mixture is centrifuged and the supernatant retained. The digitonides are washed free from pigments with small quantities of pre-cooled ether. The pigmented solutions are bulked and extracted with ether, a satisfactory phase separation being achieved by the addition of water. The ether solution, after washing and drying, is distilled to leave the sterol-free, unsaponifiable material.

For most qualitative and quantitative analyses, the removal of sterols is not essential, and in view of the thermolability of the carotenoids, is not advisable. It is essential, however, in studies where sterol contamination must be avoided, such as those in which the radioactivity of a particular carotenoid is being determined.

E. PHASE SEPARATION OF CAROTENOIDS

When a solution of the unsaponifiable material in light petroleum is shaken with an equal volume of 90% methanol, all the xanthophylls containing 2 or more free hydroxy- or keto- groups are extracted into the methanolic hypophase. The carotenes, their epoxides, mono-keto- or monohydroxy- derivatives, or xanthophylls with their hydroxy groups esterified or methylated remain in the epiphase (upper light petroleum phase). The extraction with 90% methanol is repeated until no further pigments are extracted (usually 2 or 3 times).

The epiphase can now be treated with an equal volume of 95% methanol, when the monohydroxy- and monoketo- carotenoids are extracted. The epoxides presumably remain with the carotenes in the epiphase (Goodwin, 1955). It is important to wash the epiphase free from methanol before drying if the fraction is to undergo subsequent chromatography. The pigments present in the methanolic phases are recovered by adding an equal volume of diethyl ether and then water until two layers are formed. The ether is washed free from methanol and dried prior to distillation.

When phase separation is being used as a qualitative technique (see also Section III, E) it is important not to miss traces of xanthophylls present in the methanol layer. Re-extraction into a small volume of ether will reveal the presence of traces which might have been missed in the methanol.

If phase separation is used on lipid extracts which have not been saponified, it is important to remember that xanthophyll esters (of e.g.

astaxanthin) remain in the epiphase, and that chlorophylls will appear in the hypophase.

The method of phase separation described above is suitable for a preliminary differentiation between carotenes and xanthophylls. The technique can, however, be adjusted to meet particular requirements. For instance, Willstätter and Page (see Zechmeister and Cholnoky, 1943) extracted a 1:1 mixture of light petroleum and ether with 70% (v/v) methanol to separate lutein and fucoxanthin, and Kuhn and Winterstein (1931) used a very similar method for the resolution of a mixture of lutein and violaxanthin. The great advances in chromatographic techniques during the past 20 years have made these techniques obsolete.

The method of phase separation may also be used in a more elegant form for the identification of carotenoids and the investigation of functional groups. This is described later in Section III, E.

F. COLUMN CHROMATOGRAPHY

The most important technique of all in the separation, purification and isolation of carotenoids is that of column chromatography. Indeed, ever since the classical separation of carotene from chlorophylls by Tswett (1903), and the development of column chromatography as we know it today by Kuhn's carotenoid school (Kuhn and Lederer, 1931; Kuhn et al., 1931), the column separation of carotenoids has provided one of the best examples of this technique. This is still the only satisfactory technique for the separation, purification and isolation of large quantities of carotenoids, but in more recent years, its usefulness as a means of identifying carotenoids by co-chromatography with authentic samples has been overshadowed by the advent of such techniques as paper and thin-layer chromatography. These techniques, involving the separation of carotenoids in filter paper impregnated with an adsorbent, or on thin layers of adsorbent supported on glass plates have as their advantages small sample size and rapidity of separation. Thus at the present time, whilst thin-layer and paper chromatography have their use in qualitative analysis and identification of carotenoids, their small sample size prohibits their use in most preparative work, a need for which column chromatography is better suited.

Three basic methods of column chromatography are available for the separation of carotenoids, namely the zone chromatogram, the stepwise elution chromatogram, and the gradient elution chromatogram.

1. *Zone Chromatogram*

In this case, the carotenoid mixture (unsaponifiable fraction) is applied to the top of the column in a non-polar solvent (such as light petroleum)

16*

and a suitable (usually more polar, depending on the nature of the carotenoids) solvent is run through the column until the zones are separated over the length of the column. The column is extracted and the appropriate coloured zones cut out and eluted with a polar solvent. This method has been used successfully by Strain (1958) for the separation of chloroplast pigments on sucrose (icing sugar) using 0·5% n-propanol in light petroleum as the developing solvent. Goodwin (1955) recommended this technique for the separation of xanthophylls.

2. *Stepwise Elution Chromatogram*

In this method the sample mixture is applied to the top of the column in a non-polar solvent such as light petroleum and the column is eluted in turn with solvents of increasing polarity (e.g. 1%, 2%, 4%, 8% etc. diethyl ether in light petroleum). The pigments are sequentially eluted from the main band at the top of the column and are collected in the eluate. Goodwin (1955) considers this more suitable for carotenes than xanthophylls.

3. *Gradient Elution Chromatogram*

Adsorption chromatography depends for its effectiveness on the distribution of solutes between the adsorbent and the mobile solution. This can be shown by considering the separation of two compounds, A and B.

Fraction of solute A in liquid phase $\quad = \alpha$
Fraction of solute A in adsorbed state $= 1 - \alpha$
Fraction of solute B in liquid phase $\quad = \beta$
Fraction of solute B in adsorbed state $= 1 - \beta$

The two distribution ratios are $\alpha/1 - \alpha$ and $\beta/1 - \beta$. When these differ it is easy to resolve the compounds A and B.

e.g. If $\quad \beta \to 1\cdot0 \qquad \beta/1 - \beta \to \infty$
and $\alpha \to 0 \qquad \alpha/1 - \alpha \to 0$

Under these circumstances, B is mostly in the liquid phase, and flows through the column, leaving A on the adsorbent.

The ratio $\alpha/1 - \alpha$ is not always constant, since it is influenced by the concentration and the presence of other substances. If $\alpha/1 - \alpha$ increases with concentration, the band on the column and the elution curve have sharp leading edges. If, on the other hand, $\alpha/1 - \alpha$ decreases with concentration (e.g. β-carotene), there is a general spreading of the zone. In most cases, the carotenoid isotherm increases with concentration, so there is some tailing. This means that stepwise elution is not always effective for carotenoid separation, since substances which trail on the column will be eluted partly with one solvent, and partly with the next.

If the polarity of the eluting solvent is increased not in a stepwise manner, but continually, the trailing can be diminished to give sharper bands. Even substances with a constant adsorption isotherm can be better separated in this way, since the adsorbability of the compound is

TABLE II

Adsorbents for Column Chromatography
(Listed in increasing order of polarity)

Starch	MgO
Sucrose	Ca(OH)$_2$
CaCO$_3$	CaO
Ca$_3$(PO$_4$)$_2$	Silicic acid (activated)
ZnCO$_3$	Al$_2$O$_3$ (activated)
MgCO$_3$	Kieselguhr
Al$_2$O$_3$ (deactivated)	

greater at the front of the band than at the rear. This gives a sharper, less Gaussian, elution band. The variation of the gradient in gradient elution tends to improve the separation, and it has been shown that the best gradient is one with a small upward curve (Lederer and Lederer, 1957).

This type of chromatography is carried out in practice by filling the column from a reservoir, and replenishing the reservoir not with the

TABLE III

Solvents for Column Chromatography
(Listed in increasing order of polarity)

Light petroleum (b.p. 40–60°)	Ethyl acetate
Light petroleum (b.p. 60–80°)	Ethanol
Cyclohexane	Methanol
Diethyl ether	Pyridine
Acetone	Ethanol/acetic acid (9:1 v/v)
Benzene	

same solvent, but with a more polar one. This gives a positive gradient with a slight downward curve. An upward curve is produced by replenishing the second solvent reservoir with a third, even more polar, solvent. This is best operated in a closed, pressurized system, with efficient mixing at each addition stage. A typical solvent system would

TABLE IV

Carotenoids of Known Structure, in Order of Increasing Polarity, together with the Functional Groups that Contribute Towards Adsorption Affinity

Carotenoid	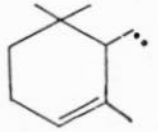 $^aF_6'$	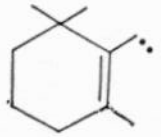	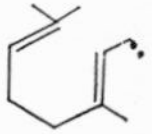	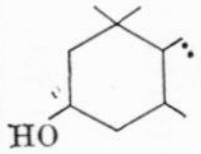	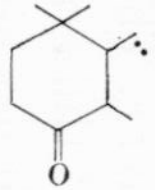 HO	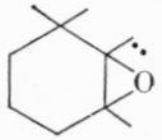 =O	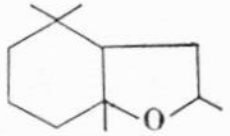 epoxide	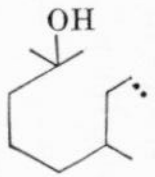 —O (lactone)	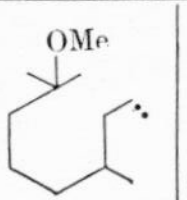 OH	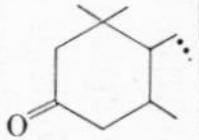 OMe	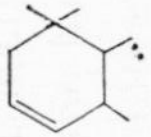 =O
Carotenes											
Phytoene	5	—	—	2	—	—	—	—	—	—	—
Phytofluene	6	2	—	2	—	—	—	—	—	—	—
ε-Carotene	9	2	1	—	—	—	—	—	—	—	—
α-Carotene	9	1	2	—	—	—	—	—	—	—	—
β-Carotene	9	1	1	1	—	—	—	—	—	—	—
α-Zeacarotene	8	1	1	—	—	—	—	—	—	—	—
β-Zeacarotene	8	—	—	2	—	—	—	—	—	—	—
ζ-Carotene	7	1	1	1	—	—	—	—	—	—	—
δ-Carotene	9	1	1	—	—	—	—	—	—	—	—
γ-Carotene	9	—	1	2	—	—	—	—	—	—	—
Neurosporene	8	—	—	2	—	—	—	—	—	—	—
Lycopene	9	—	—	2	—	—	—	—	—	—	—
Xanthophylls											
α-Carotene epoxide	9	1	1	—	—	—	1	—	—	—	—
Flavochrome	9	1	1	—	—	—	—	1	—	—	—
Citroxanthin	9	—	2	—	—	—	—	1	—	—	—

									$F_6^{6'}$
Echinenone	—	—	—	—	—	1	—	2	9
Rhodoxanthin	—	2	—	—	2	2	—	—	10
Canthaxanthin	—	—	—	—	—	2	—	2	9
Gazaniaxanthin	—	1	—	—	—	1	1	—	9
α-Cryptoxanthin (1',2'-dihydro)	1	1	—	—	—	1	1	—	9
Zeinoxanthin (3'-hydroxy)	—	—	—	—	—	1	1	—	9
Cryptoxanthin (3-hydroxy)	—	2	1	—	—	1	1	—	9
Rubixanthin	—	1	—	—	—	1	—	—	8
Chloroxanthin	—	—	1	—	—	—	—	1	9
Lycoxanthin	—	—	1	—	—	—	—	1	9
Torulene	—	—	—	—	—	1	—	1	9
Anhydrorhodovibrin	—	1	2	2	—	—	—	—	9
Spirilloxanthin	—	1	2	2	—	—	—	—	9
Rhodopin	—	—	2	2	—	—	—	—	9
Celaxanthin	—	—	—	1	—	—	—	—	9
Rubichrome	—	—	—	1	—	—	—	1	9
Lutein	—	1	—	—	—	1	1	2	9
3,4-Dehydrorhodopin	—	1	2	2	—	2	2	1	9
Zeaxanthin	2	2	—	—	—	2	2	2	9
Isolutein	—	—	—	2	—	—	2	2	9
Chrysanthemaxanthin	—	—	—	—	—	—	2	2	10
Eschscholtzxanthin	—	—	—	—	—	—	2	2	9
Lycophyll	—	—	2	2	—	—	2	—	9
Antheraxanthin	2	2	—	—	1	2	2	1	9
Mutatoxanthin	2	2	—	—	1	2	2	—	9
Violaxanthin	2	2	—	—	2	2	2	—	9
Neoxanthin (5'-hydro-6'-hydroxy)	2	2	—	(3)	1	2	2	1	9
Auroxanthin	2	2	—	2	—	2	2	2	9
Astaxanthin	2	2	—	2	—	2	2	—	9

[a] $F_6^{6'}$ signifies the number of ethylenic bonds in the polyene chain between carbons 6 and 6'.

be light petroleum, 25% diethyl ether in light petroleum and 50% ether. The characteristics of the gradient can be altered by changing the composition of the original solvents.

The adsorbent must be chosen bearing in mind the types of carotenoid to be separated. More polar adsorbents should be chosen for the carotenes and less polar ones for the xanthophylls. A list of common adsorbents is given in Table II.

The packing of the column is usually carried out using a slurry. The adsorbent is mixed into a slurry with the least polar solvent to be used and is run into the column which is blocked at its lower end by a polythene tube and spring clip. The adsorbent is retained in the wide part of the column with a plug of glass wool or non-absorbent cotton wool. The adsorbent is allowed to settle out of the slurry and then the polythene tube is removed and the adsorbent packed by allowing the solvent to percolate through it. A suitable flow rate is about 1–2 drops of eluate per sec. If the adsorbent is very fine, the flow rate may be too slow. This can be increased by including in the slurry a fairly high percentage (40–60% by weight) of a filter-aid such as celite. Flow rates can also be increased by applying pressure from an aspirator or gas cylinder (through a reducing valve) to the top of the column. The use of a pump to reduce the pressure at the column outlet is not recommended with organic solvents.

Sucrose columns, however, are packed dry (Strain, 1958). Sucrose is added to the column, fitted with a cotton-wool or glass-wool plug, to a depth of about 1 cm. This is pressed down with a suitable tamping rod rather than being compacted by vibration. Portions of sucrose are added, 1 cm depth at a time, and each pressed down, until a suitable depth is reached. The sample is then added at the top of the column and chromatography is begun by percolating a suitable solvent through the column.

Alumina columns are often used for a preliminary separation of carotenoids since they are easy to pack, and run rapidly. The diffuse nature of the bands obtained makes it unsuitable as an adsorbent for more precise separations. Alumina as supplied is normally activated, and it can be deactivated to meet individual requirements by adding the requisite amount of water as the slurry is prepared.

The usual solvents used in column chromatography are listed in Table III.

Chloroform has been omitted from this list because of the effect of traces of hydrochloric acid on certain carotenoids in chloroform solution (see p. 528). All solvents should be purified immediately before use, light petroleum by percolation through silica gel and distillation and ether by drying over sodium wire and distillation from reduced iron powder. Methanol and ethanol may be purified by distillation from a Grignard reagent.

4. *Adsorption Affinities of Carotenoids*

The strengths of adsorption of different carotenoids on a given adsorbent bear a definite relationship to their chemical structures. In the carotenoids considered in this account, hydroxyl substituents probably exert by far the greatest influence on adsorption affinities. This effect is markedly decreased if the hydroxyl group is esterified.

TABLE V

The Increasing Order of Carotenoid Adsorption Affinities on Alumina

Phytoene	Chloroxanthin
Phytofluene	Lycoxanthin
ε-Carotene	Torulene
α-Carotene	Anhydrorhodovibrin
Neo-β-carotene U	Spirilloxanthin
β-Carotene	Rhodopin
α-Zeacarotene	Celaxanthin
β-Zeacarotene	Cryptoflavin
Neo-β-carotene B	Rubichrome
ζ-Carotene	Cryptochrome
Pro-γ-carotene	Lutein
Protetrahydrolycopene	3,4-Dehydrorhodovibrin
Poly-*cis*-lycopene IV–VI	Isolutein
Prolycopene	Chrysanthemaxanthin
δ-Carotene	Flavoxanthin
γ-Carotene	Eschscholtzxanthin
Neurosporene	Lycophyll
Leprotene*	Antheraxanthin
Poly-*cis*-lycopene III–I	Taraxanthin
Tetrahydrolycopene	Violaxanthin
Neolycopene A	Neoxanthin
Lycopene	Auroxanthin
α-Carotene-5,6-epoxide	Capsanthin
Flavochrome	Capsorubin
Citroxanthin	Diatoxanthin
Echinenone	Diadinoxanthin
Rhodoxanthin	Dinoxanthin
Physoxanthin	Peridinin
Canthaxanthin	Fucoxanthin
Gazaniaxanthin	Monodemethyl spirilloxanthin
α-Cryptoxanthin	Myxoxanthophyll
Zeinoxanthin	Corynexanthin
Isocryptoxanthin	Aphanicin
Cryptoxanthin	Astaxanthin
Rubixanthin	Oscillaxanthin
Sarcinaxanthin	Astacin

* = Isorenieratene

The effectiveness of functional groups on the strength of adsorption decreases in the sequence:

Hydroxy-; Dioxo-; oxo-; 5,8,5′,8′-diepoxy; 5,8-epoxy; 5,6,5′,6′-diepoxy; 5,6-epoxy-.

An extra double bond increases the polarity of a carotenoid, but the effect of this relative to that of other functional groups is difficult to assess, as the effect varies with the situation of the double bond within the molecule. It is a general rule that of the three common forms of the

TABLE VI

The Relative Positions of Certain Carotenoids on Different Adsorbents

(Solvent: light petroleum/acetone—in order of increasing adsorption affinity. (Strain 1939, 1948))

Sucrose	Celite	Magnesium oxide
α-Carotene	α-Carotene	α-Carotene
β-Carotene	β-Carotene	β-Carotene
Lycopene	Lycopene	Cryptoxanthin
Rhodoxanthin	Cryptoxanthin	Lutein
Cryptoxanthin	Rhodoxanthin	Zeaxanthin
Lutein	Lutein	Lycopene
Zeaxanthin	Zeaxanthin	Rhodoxanthin

ionone structure, the ψ-form has the highest and the α-form the lowest polarity.

Table IV lists carotenoids of known structure in order of increasing polarity or adsorption affinity, and shows how this physical property is dependent on structure. Table V lists many carotenoids in order of increasing adsorption affinity on alumina columns. Although the order of carotenoids on a given adsorbent does not vary, changes in order can occur on different adsorbents with the more strongly adsorbed compounds. Strain (1939, 1948) examined this problem in detail, and some of his findings are summarized in Table VI.

G. CRYSTALLIZATION

Karrer and Jucker (1950) state: "The crystallization of carotenoids requires considerable practice, especially if small amounts are involved." As carotenoids in plant tissues occur in only very small amounts (c. 50–150 p.p.m. in the best sources), it is not often that experiments are carried out on a scale sufficiently large to allow the isolation of pigments in crystalline form. When absolute purity is required, as in radiochemical experiments, crystallization, usually with the addition of carrier, is essential. In most investigations, however, it is not necessary to isolate the pigments in crystalline form in order to identify them.

It is possible to describe in general terms the technique of crystallizing carotenoids (Goodwin, 1955). The carotenoid is obtained in as pure a form as possible by chromatographic methods and the solvent is removed under nitrogen. Different methods are required for carotenes and xanthophylls.

1. *Carotenes*

The residue is dissolved in the minimal amount of benzene. Methanol (3–4 vols.) is then added and the mixture is placed at $-20°$C for some hours. An alternative method uses light petroleum and ethanol.

2. *Xanthophylls*

Crystallization can usually be accomplished by dissolving the carotenoid residue in the minimal amount of methanol and cautiously adding a few drops of water and cooling.

Details for the crystallization of individual carotenoids have been described by Karrer and Jucker (1950).

III. IDENTIFICATION OF CAROTENOIDS

One of the most important characteristics of a carotenoid is its visible absorption spectrum, and the determination of this is still an important step in carotenoid identification. The structural characteristics of a carotenoid are also reflected in the adsorption affinity, a parameter that can be determined much more readily now that new rapid micro-techniques, adsorption chromatography on paper and thin layer chromatography, are available.

The technique in this case is to chromatograph samples of the unknown carotenoids under investigation side by side with authentic samples, and together as a mixture with authentic samples. The inability of a system to separate the two samples indicates that they are the same, and extra weight is lent to this identification if more than one chromatographic method is used.

A conclusive identification of a carotenoid is normally based on co-chromatography with authentic samples in at least two different systems, and on the absorption spectra in two different solvents.

Other physical properties of carotenoids are of use in their identification. Partition coefficients between light petroleum and methanol-water mixtures have been used for many years as a means of distinguishing between carotenes and xanthophylls. Infra-red and nuclear magnetic resonance spectroscopy have already proved their worth in the structural analysis of carotenoids by Weedon and his co-workers. These techniques are discussed in Chapter 3.

A. ADSORPTION CHROMATOGRAPHY ON PAPER

The types of paper used for these separations are Schleicher and Schüll No. 287, with a Kieselguhr content of about 20% (Jensen and Jensen, 1959; Davies, 1961a, b, c); an industrial filter paper containing 20% kieselguhr manufactured by the Metafiltration Co. Hounslow (Davies, 1961a) and Schleicher and Schüll No. 667 (impregnated with alumina) as used by Jensen (1960).

The procedure is best carried out on circular paper at room temperature in a Petri dish with the technique of Rutter (1948). The solvent system is light petroleum (40–60°) either alone or mixed with various proportions of acetone. The carotenoid mixture is dissolved either in acetone or in an acetone–light petroleum mixture. An aliquot containing 10–100 μg of carotenoid is applied to the centre of the paper by means of a capillary, in such a way that the diameter of the spot does not exceed 1 cm. After the application of each portion, the solvent is evaporated at room temperature in a stream of nitrogen. When the whole aliquot has been applied, a small drop of acetone is added to the paper at the centre of the carotenoid spot. This causes the carotenoids to form a narrow annular band surrounding the centre of the paper; the position of this ring is marked as the origin. A wick is inserted at the centre of the ring, and separation of the carotenoids occurs when the paper is held horizontally between two Petri dishes with the wick dipping in solvent contained in the lower dish. The whole process, with a 12·5-cm diameter paper takes 10–15 min.

For determination of R_F values, the papers are dried in a jet of nitrogen and the positions of the concentric rings marked with pencil. The position of the solvent front can be determined by its bluish fluorescence under ultra-violet light. When separating components of low R_F value, the solvent can be allowed to evaporate from the rim of the paper which extends outside the Petri dishes.

If it is required to elute the carotenoids, the drying stage is eliminated and the coloured zones containing the carotenoids are cut out immediately after separation, packed tightly into glass tubes with one end drawn out into a capillary, and eluted with ether (Davies, 1961a). The extracts are taken to dryness, made up in light petroleum and examined spectrophotometrically. Jensen and Jensen (1959) claimed that with this method, R_F values are reproducible within ± 0.01 units and recoveries of carotenoids are between 97 and 100%. The R_F values of various carotenoids in such systems are shown in Tables VII and VIII.

TABLE VII

R_F Values of Carotenes Chromatographed on Schleicher and Schüll No. 667 Paper (Alumina Impregnated) (Jensen, 1960)

Carotene	Light petroleum	20% benzene in light petroleum
α-Carotene	0·43	0·66
β-Carotene	0·38	0·62
γ-Carotene	0·05	0·15
Phytofluene	0·77	0·88
ζ-Carotene	0·36	0·60
Lycopene	0·02	0·08

TABLE VIII

R_F Values of Carotenoids in Different Solvents on Schleicher and Schüll No. 287 Paper (20% Kieselguhr)

(Jensen and Jensen, 1959; Jensen, 1962, 1963a, b; Davies, 1961a, b)

Carotenoid	Percentage of acetone in light petroleum				
	0	2	5	10	20
β-Carotene	0·95	0·98	0·98	0·98	—
γ-Carotene	0·68	—	—	—	—
Lycopene	0·53	0·68	—	—	—
Spheroidenone	—	0·66	0·86	—	—
Cryptoxanthin	0·29	0·62	0·81	0·91	—
Chloroxanthin	0·13	0·46	0·73	0·90	—
Anhydrorhodovibrin	—	0·35	0·60	—	—
Hydroxy-R	—	—	0·45	—	—
Spirilloxanthin	—	0·18	0·40	0·76	—
Hydroxylycopene	—	—	0·39	0·75	—
Rhodopin	—	—	0·39	0·75	—
Lutein	—	—	0·39	0·72	0·91
3,4-Dehydrorhodopin	—	—	—	0·70	—
Zeaxanthin	—	0·09	0·30	0·59	0·87
Astaxanthin	—	—	—	0·57	0·85
Rhodovibrin	—	—	—	0·54	—
P 518	—	—	—	0·46	—
Violaxanthin	—	—	0·18	0·44	0·83
Fucoxanthin	—	—	—	0·40	0·81
Monodemethylated spirilloxanthin	—	—	—	0·40	—
Rhodoxanthin	—	—	0·10	0·27	0·72
α-Bacterioruberin	—	—	—	0·02	0·44

Use has been made of reversed-phase paper chromatography in the separation and identification of xanthophylls (B. H. Davies and R. J. H. Williams, 1963, unpublished) with paper impregnated with liquid paraffin and a dimethylformamide–water mixture or a methanol–water mixture as solvent (Davies and Goodwin, 1959). The separation is neither as efficient nor as rapid as with reversed-phase thin-layer chromatography.

A form of two-dimensional paper chromatography has been used by Booth (1962) for the separation of carotenoids and other plant lipids. This was based on the method of Green *et al.* (1955) as described in detail by the Analytical Methods Committee (1959). If only carotenoid separations are required, a suitable adaptation would be as follows:

The filter paper (32 × 22 cm) is impregnated with zinc carbonate (by immersing in a zinc–ammine solution containing 16 g ZnO, 25 g $(NH_4)_2CO_3$, 150 ml NH_4OH and 600 ml water, and allowing to dry) and the chromatogram run in the first dimension with 30% benzene in cyclohexane. For the second dimension, the unused part of the paper, after drying, is soaked in a 3% solution of liquid paraffin in light petroleum, allowed to dry, and developed with 75% aqueous ethanol. The separation takes about 4 h, and it is questionable whether such a slow form of paper chromatography, involving an intermediate drying stage, is of any real value in carotenoid analysis.

B. THIN-LAYER CHROMATOGRAPHY OF CAROTENOIDS

Thin-layer chromatography has emerged as an invaluable technique in the qualitative analysis and identification of carotenoids, especially if it is necessary to detect carotenoids present as impurities or in trace quantities in naturally occurring mixtures of carotenoids. Its only disadvantage is that the adsorption of carotenoids on inorganic layers can give rise to artifacts by oxidation and isomerization. The xanthophylls are more susceptible to this, and Randerath (1963) has recommended that these oxygenated carotenoids be separated by a reversed-phase form of thin-layer chromatography on impregnated layers, rather than by the more common technique of adsorption chromatography.

1. *Thin-layer Adsorption Chromatography*

Although there is a tendency for carotenoids, especially xanthophylls, to be oxidized or isomerized while undergoing this form of chromatography, this can be significantly reduced if the separation is accelerated by using a suitable saturation chamber (Davies, 1963). The use of such a chamber keeps the atmosphere round the samples saturated with solvent vapour, thus stabilizing the compounds, and also facilitates the maintenance of standard conditions, which are essential to analysis by thin-layer chromatography.

The R_F value of a compound in thin-layer adsorption chromatography is not completely independent of concentration and of the presence of other substances as it is in paper chromatography. A high concentration of an individual compound causes an elongation of the zone which can either take the form of a trailing effect, or may be an elongation of the zone in the direction of the solvent front. The effect of foreign materials on thin-layer R_F values is exemplified by the separation of a carotenoid mixture which contains a large amount of neutral lipid. The effect of the fat is apparently to increase the R_F values of all the carotenoids. Thus the concept of R_F is not so meaningful in adsorption thin-layer chromatography as it is in paper chromatography, and co-chromatography with an authentic sample must be used as the primary criterion of identification, rather than comparison of the R_F of a carotenoid with published values.

Carotenoids are usually so strongly coloured that the use of special reagents for detection is unnecessary. There are, however, some important exceptions. Some of the important carotenoid precursors, such as phytoene and phytofluene and related compounds such as squalene, are colourless. While phytofluene fluoresces green in long-wave ultraviolet light, and can easily be detected in this way on thin-layer chromatograms, the other compounds do not fluoresce. Several staining methods for all the compounds are available. The most sensitive of these is the use of iodine vapour, which stains the unsaturated polyenes brown. As little as 0·05 μg of the polyene can be detected (Davies et al., 1961; Mercer et al., 1963). A slightly less sensitive reagent is antimony trichloride, applied as a spray in chloroform. After heating the polyenes show up as variously coloured spots (Davies et al., 1963a).

Rhodanine has been recommended by Winterstein and Hegedüs (1960) for the detection of the less strongly coloured carotenoid aldehydes. The chromatogram is sprayed first with alcoholic rhodanine and then with concentrated ammonium hydroxide and dried in a stream of hot air; the aldehydes are revealed as violet spots.

Several different chromatographic systems have been used for the separation of carotenoids by thin-layer adsorption chromatography. Squalene, lycopersene, phytoene and phytofluene have been separated on Silica Gel G plates with light petroleum as the developing solvent (Davies et al., 1961, 1963a; Mercer et al., 1963); the same layers, with 15% methanol in benzene as developer are satisfactory for a general separation of xanthophylls (B. H. Davies, 1962, unpublished). Alumina layers, with varying concentrations of benzene in light petroleum as the solvent have been used for the separation of carotenes, as have been mixed layers of magnesium oxide and Silica Gel G (50:50 w/w) with the same solvent (Davies et al., 1963b). The earliest reports of carotenoid separations described the use of mixed adsorbents. Typical of these was the silicic acid–rice starch layer (Demole, 1958, 1959)

TABLE IX

Behaviour of Carotenoids on Thin-layer Adsorption Chromatography

(Bolliger, 1962; Stahl et al., 1963; O. Isler and co-workers, unpublished; Davies et al., 1963a, B. H. Davies and J. Villoutreix, unpublished; Demole, 1958, 1959)

Carotenoid	Thin-layer system											
	A	B	C	D	E	F	G	H	I	J	K	L
(Squalene)*	0·41	—	—	—	—	—	—	—	—	—	—	←— 1·0 —→
Lycopersene	0·30	—	—	—	—	—	—	—	—	—	—	—
Phytoene	0·21	—	—	—	—	—	—	—	—	—	—	—
Phytofluene	0·10	—	—	—	—	—	—	—	—	—	—	—
α-Carotene	—	0·81	—	0·88	—	—	—	0·84	0·75	←— 0·97 —→	←— 1·0 —→	—
β-Carotene	—	0·75	0·96	0·84	—	—	0·82	0·69	0·75	—	—	1·0
β-Zeacarotene	—	0·62	—	—	—	—	—	—	—	—	—	—
ζ-Carotene	0·0	—	—	—	—	—	—	—	0·65	—	—	—
γ-Carotene	—	—	—	0·4–0·5	—	—	0·74	—	0·56	—	—	—
Lycopene	—	—	—	0·1–0·2	—	—	—	0·0	—	0·0	—	—
Torulene	—	—	—	—	—	—	—	—	—	—	0·98	—
Torularhodin Me ester	—	—	—	—	—	—	—	—	—	0·83	0·94	1·0
Methyl bixin	—	—	—	—	—	—	—	—	—	0·13	0·81	0·97
Canthaxanthin	—	—	0·38	—	—	—	0·0	—	—	—	0·63	0·90
Cryptoxanthin	—	—	—	—	0·43	0·74	—	—	—	—	0·54	0·75
Lutein	—	—	—	—	0·34	0·55	—	—	—	—	—	0·35
Antheraxanthin	—	—	—	—	—	—	—	—	←— 0-0·07 —→	—	—	0·32
Zeaxanthin	—	—	0·17	—	—	0·57	—	←— 0·0 —→	—	←— 0·0 —→	—	0·24
Violaxanthin	—	—	—	—	—	—	—	—	—	—	←— 0·1–0·11 —→	0·21
Capsanthin	—	—	—	—	—	—	—	—	—	—	—	0·16
Capsorubin	—	—	—	—	—	—	—	—	—	—	—	0·13
Bixin	—	—	0·51	—	—	—	—	—	—	—	—	0·05
Azafrin	—	—	—	—	—	—	—	—	—	—	—	0·02
Echinenone	—	—	—	—	0·82	—	0·10	—	—	—	—	—
Rhodoxanthin	—	—	—	—	0·16	0·94	—	—	—	—	—	—
Isozeaxanthin	—	—	0·63	—	—	—	—	—	—	—	—	—

* Added for comparison

which gave a good general separation of the carotenoids of *Rhodospirillum rubrum* when developed with 15% ethyl acetate in light petroleum (Davies, 1961a). A mixture of Silica Gel G and calcium hydroxide (1:6 w/w) has been used successfully for the separation and identification of carotenes, with 5% benzene in light petroleum as the developer (Davies, 1961a; Bolliger, 1962). Bolliger (1962) and Stahl *et al.* (1963) have studied the behaviour of thirty or so carotenoids in various systems. Their results are summarized, with those of other workers, in Table IX.

When carotenoids have been run on a thin-layer chromatogram, the adsorbent in the appropriate zones can be scraped off and eluted with ether. This solution is then available for further analysis. When thin-layer adsorption chromatography is used for a preparative purpose, the adsorbent should be pre-treated by extraction with ether before the thin layers are prepared, in order that ether-soluble contaminants are eliminated.

2. *Partition Chromatography of Carotenoids on Thin Layers*

Carotenoids are separated satisfactorily on kieselguhr layers impregnated with liquid paraffin or triglycerides (Egger, 1962; Randerath, 1963). Paraffin-impregnated layers are adequate for separating unsubstituted hydrocarbons or for carotenoids containing oxygen, not in the form of hydroxyl or carbonyl groups, while layers impregnated with polar triglycerides (vegetable oils of low acid content) are better suited for the more polar xanthophylls (Randerath, 1963).

Kieselguhr plates are prepared in the normal way and are impregnated with liquid paraffin or vegetable oil with a 7% solution in light petroleum. A narrow strip of adsorbent at the bottom of the plate is left unimpregnated. This is used for the application of the samples. The solvents used are polar mixtures containing various proportions of acetone, methanol and water (see Table X).

KEY TO TABLE IX

Adsorbent	*Solvent*
A. Silica Gel G	Light petroleum (b.p. 40–60°).
B. Silica Gel G+MgO (1+1)	10% Benzene in light petroleum.
C. Silica Gel G (with starch)	n-Hexane+ether (3+7).
D. Silica Gel G+Ca(OH)$_2$ (1+6)	2% Benzene in light petroleum.
E. Silica Gel G+Ca(OH)$_2$ (1+6)	Benzene.
F. Silica Gel G+Ca(OH)$_2$ (1+6)	2% Methanol in benzene.
G. Silica Gel G	50% Benzene in light petroleum (b.p. 90–110°).
H. Ca(OH)$_2$	5% Light petroleum in methylene chloride.
I. Silica Gel G	20% Methylene chloride in undecane.
J. Mg$_3$(PO$_4$)$_2$	Carbon tetrachloride.
K. Mg$_3$(PO$_4$)$_2$	Benzene.
L. Silica Gel G	20% Ethyl acetate in methylene chloride.

TABLE X

R_F Values of Carotenoids on Impregnated Kieselguhr
Layers

(Randerath, 1963)

Carotenoid	A	B
Capsanthin	—	0·74
Isozeaxanthin	—	0·49
Zeaxanthin	—	0·54
Isozeaxanthin dimethyl ester	0·60	—
Cryptoxanthin	0·90	0·07
Rhodoxanthin	—	0·26
Torularhodin methyl ester	0·48	—
Echinenone	0·61	—
Lutein	—	0·56
Lutein epoxide	—	0·72
Violaxanthin	—	0·84
Neoxanthin	—	0·95
β-Carotene	0·10	0·0
γ-Carotene	0·15	0·0
Lutein dipalmitate (helenien)	0·02	—

KEY

A. Kieselguhr impregnated with liquid paraffin—run in
Methanol/acetone 5:2 (Saturated with liquid paraffin).
B. Kieselguhr impregnated with vegetable oil—run in
Methanol/acetone/H_2O 20:4:3 (Saturated with veget-
able oil).

C. THE VISIBLE ABSORPTION SPECTRA OF CAROTENOIDS

The position of the long-wave absorption bands (usually three) of
carotenoids is a function of the number of conjugated double bonds in
the molecule. An increase in this number results in an increase in the
wavelength of maximal absorption. The positions of the absorption
maxima also depend on the solvent used, increasing from their lowest
value in light petroleum or hexane to their highest value in carbon
disulphide. The introduction of a hydroxyl group into the molecule has
little effect on the positions of the maxima; this is also true of the
introduction of an oxo-group which is not conjugated to the polyene
chain. Structural variations have a profound effect on the shape of the
absorption spectrum (Karrer and Jucker, 1950; Goodwin, 1955); for
instance, carotenoids with an acyclic structure have a much greater
persistence than those with a mono- or bicyclic structure, and in compounds containing two β-ionone residues, the short-wave band is reduced
to an inflexion. In the oxo-carotenoids, the typical three-banded
spectrum disappears, and is replaced by an almost completely symmetrical single band, or a single main band with weak inflexions on
either side.

The effects of structural variations on visible absorption characteristics are listed below:

1. The addition of a conjugated ethylenic bond without other changes in the structure results in a displacement of the absorption bands towards longer wavelengths.

Phytoene	3 conjugated ethylenic bonds	275	285	296 mμ
Phytofluene	5 conjugated ethylenic bonds	331	348	367 mμ
ζ-Carotene	7 conjugated ethylenic bonds	378	400	425 mμ
Neurosporene	9 conjugated ethylenic bonds	416	440	470 mμ
Lycopene	11 conjugated ethylenic bonds	446	472	505 mμ

(Spectra in light petroleum)

2. If an ethylenic bond in a 6-membered ring is moved out of conjugation to an isolated position, the maxima are displaced to shorter wavelengths.

β-Carotene	(425)	451	483 mμ
α-Carotene	422	444	475 mμ
ϵ-Carotene	418	444	475 mμ

(Spectra in light petroleum)

3. If a terminal conjugated double bond is replaced by a 5,6-epoxide group, the maxima are displaced to shorter wavelengths.

α-Carotene	420	445	475 mμ
α-Carotene-5,6-epoxide		442	471 mμ

(Spectra in light petroleum)

4. Conversion of a carotenoid 5,6-epoxide into the isomeric furanoid 5,8-epoxide results in the displacement of the absorption maxima towards shorter wavelengths.

3,3',6'-Trihydroxy-5,6-epoxy-α-carotene	473	501 mμ
3,3',6'-Trihydroxy-5,8-epoxy-α-carotene	450	479 mμ

(Spectra in CS_2)

5. When open chains undergo ring closure, there is a displacement of the absorption maxima to shorter wavelengths, with a concomitant loss of persistence.

Lycopene	446	472	505 mμ
γ-Carotene	431	462	495 mμ
β-Carotene	(425)	451	483 mμ

(Spectra in light petroleum)

TABLE XI

Visible Absorption Maxima of Carotenoids in Light Petroleum
(Spectra recorded in *n*-hexane are marked thus *)

Anhydrorhodovibrin	455	482·5	516		Jensen (1962)
Antheraxanthin	423	444	437		Davies (1961a)
Aphanicin		474	504	*	Goodwin (1955)
Aphanin		453			Goodwin (1955)
Auroxanthin	382	402	427		Williams (1963)
α-Bacterioruberin	464	494	528		Jensen (1962)
Canthaxanthin		466		*	Isler and Schudel (1963)
Capsanthin		474·5	504	*	Goodwin (1955)
Capsorubin	444	474	506		Goodwin (1955)
α-Carotene	422	444	473		Isler and Schudel (1963)
α-Carotene-5,6-epoxide		442	471	*	Goodwin (1955)
β-Carotene	(425)	451	482		Goodwin (1955)
γ-Carotene	437	462	494		Isler and Schudel (1963)
δ-Carotene	428	458	490	*	Goodwin (1955)
ε-Carotene	419	444	475		Isler and Schudel (1963)
ζ-Carotene	378	400	425		Davies (1963) unpublished
Celaxanthin	456	486·5	520	*	Goodwin (1955)
Chloroxanthin	417	440	470	*	Jensen (1963c)
Chrysanthemaxanthin		421	450	*	Goodwin (1955)
Citroxanthin		427	456	*	Goodwin (1955)
Crocetin	400	420	445	*	Karrer and Jucker (1950)
Cryptoxanthin	425	451	483	*	Goodwin (1955)
α-Cryptoxanthin	421	446	475	*	Cholnoky *et al.* (1958)
3,4-Dehydrorhodopin	455	483	517		Jensen (1962)
Echinenone		458			Davies (1963) unpublished
Eschscholtzxanthin	442	472	502	*	Karrer and Leumann (1951)
Flavochrome		422	450	*	Karrer and Jucker (1950)
Fucoxanthin	425	450	478	*	Goodwin (1955)
Gazaniaxanthin	434·5	462·5	494·5	*	Goodwin (1955)
Helenien	420	445	475	*	Cholnoky *et al.* (1958)
Hydroxy-echinenone		460		*	Krinsky and Goldsmith (1960)
Hydroxy-P 481	455	483	516	*	Jensen (1962)
Hydroxy-R	460	483	516	*	Jensen (1963b)
Hydroxy-Y	429	454	486	*	Jensen (1963c)
Isozeaxanthin		451	478	*	Isler and Schudel (1963)
Isolutein		442	471	*	Goodwin (1955)
Leprotene=Isorenieratene	425	452	484	*	Goodwin (1955)
Lutein	420	447	477	*	Goodwin (1955)
Lycopene	446	472	505	*	Isler and Schudel (1963)
Lycophyll	444	473	504		Karrer and Jucker (1950)
Lycoxanthin	444	472·5	503		Jensen (1962)
Monodemethylated spirilloxanthin	462	494	528		Jensen (1962)
Mutatochrome		427	456	*	Goodwin (1955)
Mutatoxanthin		426	456		Karrer and Jucker (1950)
Myxoxanthin		458			Goodwin (1955)
Neoxanthin	415	437	466	*	Goodwin (1955)
Neurosporene	416	440	470		Isler and Schudel (1963)
P 481	455	482·5	516		Jensen (1962)
P 518	487·5	518	555		Jensen (1963a)

TABLE XI—cont.

Physalien		452	480	*	Isler and Schudel (1963)
Physoxanthin		445	474	*	Bodea and Nicoara (1957)
Phytoene	275	285	296		Davies (1961a)
Phytofluene	331	348	367		Davies (1961a)
Phytofluenol	332	348	368	*	Goodwin (1955)
Pigment R (Spheroidenone)	(460)	482	513	*	Land (1955)
Pigment Y (Spheroidene)	429	455	486·5	*	Jensen (1963c)
Prolycopene		443·5	470		Goodwin (1955)
Rhodopin	443	470	503·5		Jensen (1962)
Rhodovibrin	455	483	516		Jensen (1962)
Rhodoxanthin	458	489	524	*	Goodwin (1955)
Rubixanthin	432	462	494	*	Goodwin (1955)
Sarcinaxanthin	415	440	462	*	Goodwin (1955)
Spheroidenone	(460)	482	513	*	Land (1955)
Spirilloxanthin	468	499	534		Jensen (1962)
Taraxanthin	417·5	442	472	*	Goodwin (1955)
Torularhodin	467	501	537		Goodwin (1955)
Torulene	460	484	518	*	Isler and Schudel (1963)
Violaxanthin		443	472	*	Goodwin (1955)
α-Zeacarotene	399	421	449	*	Petzold et al. (1959)
β-Zeacarotene	406	428	454	*	Isler and Schudel (1963)
Zeaxanthin	423	451	483	*	Goodwin (1955)
Zeinoxanthin	422	445	424		Petzold et al. (1959)

TABLE XII

Visible Absorption Maxima of Carotenoids in Carbon Disulphide

Anhydrorhodovibrin	493	521	558·5	Jensen (1962)
Antheraxanthin		478	510	Goodwin (1955)
Aphanicin		494	533	Goodwin (1955)
Aphanin		488–494		Goodwin (1955)
Astacin		500		Goodwin (1955)
Astaxanthin		502		Goodwin (1955)
Auroxanthin		423	454	Goodwin (1955)
α-Bacterioruberin	500·5	533·5	572	Jensen (1962)
Bixin	457	491	526·5	Karrer and Jucker (1950)
Canthaxanthin		500		Goodwin (1955)
Capsanthin		503	542	Karrer and Jucker (1950)
Capsorubin	470	503·5	541·5	Goodwin (1955)
α-Carotene		477	509	Goodwin (1955)
α-Carotene 5,6-epoxide		471	503	Goodwin (1955)
β-Carotene	(450)	485	520	Goodwin (1955)
γ-Carotene	463	496	533	Goodwin (1955)
δ-Carotene	457	490	526	Goodwin (1955)
Celaxanthin	487	521	562	Goodwin (1955)
Chrysanthemaxanthin		451	480·5	Goodwin (1955)
Citroxanthin		459	489·5	Goodwin (1955)
Corynexanthin	435	466	495	Goodwin (1955)
Crocetin	426	453	482	Karrer and Jucker (1950)
Cryptochrome		424	456	Karrer and Jucker (1950)
Cryptoflavin		459	490	Karrer and Jucker (1950)

TABLE XII—cont.

Cryptoxanthin	453	483	518	Goodwin (1955)
Echinenone		488–494		Goodwin (1955)
Eschscholtzxanthin	474	507	542	Karrer and Leumann (1951)
Flavochrome		451	482	Karrer and Jucker (1951)
Fucoxanthin	445	477	510	Goodwin (1955)
Gazaniaxanthin	461	494·5	531	Goodwin (1955)
Hydroxy-P 481	491	522	559	Jensen (1962)
Hydroxy-R	(490)	520	555	Jensen (1963b)
Hydroxy-Y	457	486	522	Jensen (1963c)
Isorenieratene	452	484	520	Yamaguchi (1958)
Isolutein		472	502	Goodwin (1955)
Leprotene = Isorenieratene	477	499	517	Goodwin (1955)
Lutein	445	475	508	Goodwin (1955)
Lycopene	477	507·5	548	Karrer and Jucker (1950)
Lycophyll	472	506	546	Goodwin (1955)
Lycoxanthin	473	507	547	Goodwin (1955)
Mutatochrome		459	489·5	Goodwin (1955)
Mutatoxanthin		459	488	Karrer and Jucker (1950)
Myxoxanthin		488–494		Goodwin (1955)
Myxoxanthophyll	454	484	518	Goodwin (1955)
Neoxanthin		463	493	Goodwin (1955)
Oscillaxanthin	494	528	568	Goodwin (1955)
P 481	493	521	558·5	Jensen (1962)
P 518	528	562	601	Jensen (1963a)
Peridinin	450	482	516	Goodwin (1955)
Pigment Y (Spheroidene)	457	486	522	Jensen (1963c)
Pigment R (Spheroidenone)	(495)	519·5	553	Land (1955)
Prolycopene		469·5	500·5	Goodwin (1955)
Renieratene	463	496	532	Yamaguchi (1957)
Rhodopin	476	505	544	Jensen (1962)
Rhodovibrin	491	522	559	Jensen (1962)
Rhodoxanthin	491	525	564	Goodwin (1955)
Rubichrome		472	501	Goodwin (1955)
Rubixanthin	461	494	533	Goodwin (1955)
Sarcinaxanthin		469	494	Goodwin (1955)
Spheroidenone	(495)	519·5	553	Land (1955)
Spirilloxanthin	495	532	571·5	Jensen (1962)
Sulcatoxanthin	450	482	516	Karrer and Jucker (1950)
Taraxanthin	441	469	501	Goodwin (1955)
Torularhodin	500	541	582	Goodwin (1955)
Torulene	488	522	563	Goodwin (1955)
Trollichrome		450	479	Goodwin (1955)
Trollixanthin		473	501	Goodwin (1955)
Violaxanthin	440	470	501	Goodwin (1955)
Zeaxanthin	450	483	518	Goodwin (1955)

6. Introduction of a hydroxyl group results in very little change either in the position of the absorption maxima or in the spectral shape.

β-Carotene	(425)	451	483 mμ
3-Hydroxy-β-Carotene	(425)	451	483 mμ
3,3'-Dihydroxy-β-Carotene	(425)	451	483 mμ

(Spectra in light petroleum)

TABLE XIII

Visible Absorption Maxima of Carotenoids in Chloroform

Anhydrorhodovibrin	470·5	499	533	Jensen (1962)
Antheraxanthin		460·5	490·5	Goodwin (1955)
Aphanicin		474	504	Goodwin (1955)
Aphanin		475		Goodwin (1955)
Auroxanthin	385	413	438	Williams (1963)
Azafrin		428	458	Karrer and Jucker (1950)
α-Bacterioruberin	475	506	544	Jensen (1962)
Bixin	443	475	509·5	Karrer and Jucker (1950)
Canthaxanthin		482		Goodwin (1955)
α-Carotene		454	485	Goodwin (1955)
α-Carotene 5,6-epoxide		454	483	Goodwin (1955)
β-Carotene		466	497	Goodwin (1955)
γ-Carotene	447	475	508	Goodwin (1955)
δ-Carotene	440	470	503	Goodwin (1955)
Chrysanthemaxanthin		430	459	Goodwin (1955)
Citroxanthin		435	469	Goodwin (1955)
Corynexanthin	423	447	478	Goodwin (1955)
Crocetin		434·5	463	Karrer and Jucker (1950)
Cryptoflavin		438	468	Goodwin (1955)
Cryptoxanthin	433	463	497	Goodwin (1955)
Echinenone		473		Goodwin (1955)
Eschscholtzxanthin	456	488	520	Karrer and Jucker (1950)
Flavochrome		433	461	Karrer and Jucker (1950)
Fucoxanthin		457	492	Goodwin (1955)
Hydroxy-echinenone		474–481		Krinsky and Goldsmith (1960)
Hydroxy P 481	469	498	532	Jensen (1962)
Hydroxy R		501		Jensen (1963b)
Hydroxy Y	440	465·5	500	Jensen (1963c)
Leprotene = Isorenieratene	428	460	495	Goodwin (1955)
Lutein	428	456	487	Goodwin (1955)
Lycopene	456	485	520	Goodwin (1955)
Mutatoxanthin		437	468	Karrer and Jucker (1950)
Neoxanthin	421	447	477	Williams (1963)
P 481	470·5	499	533	Jensen (1962)
Pigment R (Spheroidenone)		499		Land (1955)
Pigment Y (Spheroidene)	440	465·5	500	Jensen (1963c)
Prolycopene		453·5	484	Goodwin (1955)
Rhodopin	455	482	516	Jensen (1962)
Rhodovibrin	469	498	532	Jensen (1962)
Rhodoxanthin	482	510	546	Goodwin (1955)
Rubixanthin	439	474	509	Goodwin (1955)
Sarcinaxanthin	423	451	480	Goodwin (1955)
Spheroidenone		499		Land (1955)
Spirilloxanthin	(475)	505	543	Jensen (1962)
Torularhodin	483	515	554	Goodwin (1955)
Torulene	469	501	539	Goodwin (1955)
Trollichrome		430	458	Goodwin (1955)
Trollixanthin		455	482	Goodwin (1955)
Violaxanthin	424	451·5	482	Goodwin (1955)
Zeaxanthin	429	462	494	Goodwin (1955)

TABLE XIV

Visible Absorption Maxima of Carotenoids in Benzene

Anhydrorhodovibrin	471	500	534	Jensen (1962)
α-Bacterioruberin	481	511	549	Jensen (1962)
Canthaxanthin		485		Davies (1963) unpublished
Capsanthin		486	519	Karrer and Jucker (1950)
Capsorubin	455	486	520	Goodwin (1955)
α-Carotene 5,6-epoxide		455	484	Goodwin (1955)
β-Carotene		466		Davies (1963) unpublished
γ-Carotene	447	477	510	Goodwin (1955)
Citroxanthin		440	470	Goodwin (1955)
Cryptoflavin		439	470	Karrer and Jucker (1950)
α-Cryptoxanthin	433	457	488	Cholnoky et al. (1958)
Echinenone		475	(495)	Davies (1963) unpublished
Eschscholtzxanthin	459	486	520	Karrer and Leumann (1951)
Foliachrome		432	460	Karrer and Jucker (1950)
Foliaxanthin		448	478	Karrer and Jucker (1950)
Flavochrome		434	462	Karrer and Jucker (1950)
Flavoxanthin		432	481	Goodwin (1955)
Gazaniaxanthin	447·5	476	509	Goodwin (1955)
Hydroxy-R	(475)	501	530	Jensen (1963b)
Hydroxy-Y	439	467	501	Jensen (1963c)
Isolutein		453	482	Goodwin (1955)
Isorenieratene	440	464	472	Isler and Schudel (1963)
Lycopene	455	487	522	Goodwin (1955)
Lycophyll	456	487	521	Karrer and Jucker (1950)
Mutatochrome		440	470	Goodwin (1955)
Mutatoxanthin		439	468	Karrer and Jucker (1950)
Neoxanthin		447	477	Goodwin (1955)
P 481	471	500	534	Jensen (1962)
P 518	510	539	575	Jensen (1963a)
Pigment R (Spheroidenone)	(475)	499	513	Land (1955)
Pigment Y (Spheroidene)	440·5	467·5	501·5	Jensen (1963c)
Prolycopene		455·5	485	Goodwin (1955)
Renieratene	440	465	492	Yamaguchi (1957)
Rhodopin	456	484	519	Jensen (1962)
Rhodovibrin	473	502	535	Jensen (1962)
Rhodoxanthin	474	503·5	542	Goodwin (1955)
Sarcinaxanthin	423	451	480	Goodwin (1955)
Spheroidenone	(475)	499	513	Davies (1961a)
Spirilloxanthin	479	510	548·5	Jensen (1962)
Taraxanthin	428·5	455	485	Eugster and Karrer (1957)
Torularhodin	485	519	557	Goodwin (1955)
Trollichrome		432	458	Goodwin (1955)
Trollixanthin	427	454	482	Eugster and Karrer (1957)
Violaxanthin	428	453·5	483	Eugster and Karrer (1957)

7. Introduction of a carbonyl group in conjunction with the system of ethylenic double bonds in the polyene chain, displaces the portions of the absorption maxima to higher wavelengths and alters the shape of

TABLE XV

Visible Absorption Maxima of Carotenoids in Ethanol

Antheraxanthin	424	447	477	Davies (1961a)
Auroxanthin	381	402	427	Williams (1963)
Canthaxanthin		477		Petracek and Zechmeister (1956)
ϵ-Carotene	418	442	471	Goodwin (1955)
Chrysanthemaxanthin		421	448	Karrer and Jucker (1950)
Celaxanthin	455	488	520·5	Karrer and Jucker (1950)
Corynexanthin	415	437	367	Goodwin (1963)
Cryptoflavin		430	460	Karrer and Jucker (1950)
Cryptoxanthin	424	452	486	Karrer and Jucker (1950)
Diadinoxanthin		448	478	Goodwin (1955)
Diatoxanthin		453	481	Goodwin (1955)
Dinoxanthin		441	471	Goodwin (1955)
Echinenone		470		Krinsky and Goldsmith (1960)
Eschscholtsxanthin	446	472	503	Karrer and Jucker (1950)
Gazaniaxanthin	434·5	462	494·5	Karrer and Jucker (1950)
Hydroxy-echinenone		462		Krinsky and Goldsmith (1960)
Hydroxy-R		487		Jensen (1963b)
Lutein	420	446·5	476	Karrer and Jucker (1950)
Lutein 5,6-epoxide	418	442	471	Karrer and Jucker (1950)
Lycopene	443	472	502	Karrer and Jucker (1950)
Lycophyll	444	474	505	Karrer and Jucker (1950)
Lycoxanthin	444	474	505	Jarrer and Jucker (1950)
Mutatoxanthin	409	430	457·5	Karrer and Jucker (1950)
Myxoxanthophyll	445	471	503	Goodwin (1955)
Neoxanthin	417	438	467	Krinsky and Goldsmith (1960)
P 518		522		Jensen (1963a)
Pigment R				
(Spheroidenone)		488		Land (1955)
Pigment Y				
(Spheroidene)	429	454	486	Jensen (1963c)
Rhodopin	455	470	501	Jensen (1962)
Rhodoxanthin		496	538	Karrer and Jucker (1950)
Rubixanthin	433	463	496	Karrer and Jucker (1950)
Sarcinaxanthin	415	441	469·5	Karrer and Jucker (1950)
Siphonoxanthin		455		Strain (1958)
Spheroidenone		488		Land (1955)
Spirilloxanthin	465	491	526	Jensen (1962)
Taraxanthin	416	442	471	Thomas (1962)
Torularhodin	463	493	529	Karrer and Jucker (1950)
Torulene	456	486	520	Karrer and Jucker (1950)
Trollichrome		424	451	Karrer and Jucker (1950)
Trollixanthin		447	474	Karrer and Jucker (1950)
Violaxanthin	420	441	471	Karrer and Jucker (1950)
Zeaxanthin	423·5	451	483	Karrer and Jucker (1950)

the spectrum to such an extent that only one symmetrical band may remain.

β-Carotene	(425)	451	483 mμ
4-oxo-β-Carotene		458	mμ
4,4'-Dioxo-β-Carotene		466	mμ

(Spectra in light petroleum)

TABLE XVI

Visible Absorption Maxima of Carotenoids in Acetone

Anhydrorhodovibrin	459	487·5	522	Jensen (1962)
α-Bacterioruberin	470	500	533·5	Jensen (1962)
Lycopene	446·5	475	506	Jensen (1962)
Lycoxanthin	447·5	476	507	Jensen (1962)
Monodemethylated spirilloxanthin	467	499	533	Jensen (1962)
P 518	495	528	559	Jensen (1963a)
Rhodopin	447·5	477	508	Jensen (1962)
Rhodovibrin	460	488	522	Jensen (1962)
Spirilloxanthin	468	499	534	Jensen (1962)

8. Introduction of a carbonyl group out of conjugation with the chromophoric system produces very little change.

$$4,4'\text{-Dioxo-}\beta\text{-Carotene} \qquad 500 \text{ m}\mu$$
$$3,4,3',4'\text{-Tetraoxo-}\beta\text{-Carotene} \qquad 500 \text{ m}\mu$$

(Spectra in CS_2)

9. The *cis-trans* configuration of a carotenoid has an effect on the absorption spectrum. This is discussed in detail in Section III, D.

TABLE XVII

Visible Absorption Maxima of Carotenoids in Pyridine

Astacene		498		Isler and Schudel (1963)
Azafrin		428	458	Karrer and Jucker (1950)
Crocetin	411	436	464	Karrer and Jucker (1950)
Eschscholtzxanthin	463	489	521	Karrer and Jucker (1950)
Mutatoxanthin		443	473	Karrer and Jucker (1950)
Oscillaxanthin	483	514	552	Karrer and Jucker (1950)
Torularhodin	485	518	558	Karrer and Jucker (1950)
Torulene	475	508	545	Karrer and Jucker (1950)

10. The solvent in which the carotenoid is dissolved for spectroscopic examination has considerable influence on the positions of the absorption maxima. The most common solvent for spectrophotometric work is light petroleum (b.p. 40–60°). Conclusive identification of carotenoids should rely on the use of more than one solvent. A list of the recorded absorption spectra for various carotenoids is given in Tables XI to XVII. The solvents most frequently used are light petroleum or hexane, carbon disulphide, benzene, chloroform, ethanol, acetone, and pyridine.

D. *Cis-* AND *Trans-* ISOMERS OF CAROTENOIDS

An essential part of the identification of a carotenoid is nowadays the determination of its stereochemistry, for some carotenoids occur in nature as *cis*-isomers of the normal all-*trans* form. Mixtures of *cis*-isomers can be obtained *in vitro* from all-*trans* carotenoids by several methods:

(1) Refluxing a carotenoid in an organic solvent.
(2) Melting carotenoid crystals.
(3) Treatment with acids.
(4) Illuminating carotenoid solutions, especially in the presence of catalytic amounts of iodine (iodine insolation).

The most important of these from the practical point of view is the method of iodine insolation. The essentials of this technique have been described by Zechmeister (1960):

"One or several well-stoppered 25 or 50 ml Pyrex volumetric flasks, each containing a hexane or benzene solution of 5–25 mg of the pigment and 1–2% iodine (pigment is 100%) are exposed for 5–45 min to the light of 2 parallel fluorescent lamps (40 W, 3,500° white or yellow) at 60 cm distance."

In an earlier method, conducted in diffuse laboratory daylight, the concentration of carotenoid was about 0·1 mg/ml hexane or benzene (about 2×10^{-4} M). The weight of iodine is 1–2% that of the pigment. Stereoisomeric quasi-equilibrium is usually attained in 15–60 min.

In his authoritative review of the *cis-trans* isomerism of the carotenoids, Zechmeister (1960) indicated that the transformation products of all-*trans* carotenoids exhibit certain features:

(1) Isomerization products absorb at shorter wavelengths in the visible region of the spectrum than the all-*trans* forms. If a single isomerization product is subjected to iodine insolation, the reverse change occurs to give the same equilibrium mixture as before. When an all-*trans* compound is isomerized, a new peak usually appears (*cis*-peak) in the ultra-violet region of the spectrum. Isomerization of an all-*trans* compound also causes a loss in colour intensity of the solution.
(2) Isomerization products are more stable than the starting materials.
(3) The melting points of *cis*-isomers are lower than those of the corresponding all-*trans* forms.
(4) Isomerization products often revert to the all-*trans* form on crystallization. Others crystallize heterogeneously.
(5) If the molecule contains one or more asymmetric carbon atoms, isomerization is often accompanied by a change in the optical rotation.
(6) The strengths of adsorption (adsorption affinities) of the transformational products differ from that of the all-*trans* form.

17

Of these characteristics of the *cis* isomers of carotenoids, the most important from the analytical point of view are:

(a) the differing adsorption affinities; and

(b) the relationship between *cis-trans* isomerism and adsorption spectra.

1. *Effect of* cis-trans *Isomerization on Adsorption Affinity*

Mixtures of carotenoid isomers can be resolved by techniques of adsorption chromatography. The isomerization of an all-*trans* carotenoid may either increase or decrease the adsorption affinity with the result that in a column chromatogram some *cis-* zones appear above the all-*trans* compound while others run below (Zechmeister, 1960). In the same way, differences between *cis-* and *trans-* carotenoids are reflected in considerable variations in R_F values in adsorption chromatography on paper (Jensen, 1962) and in thin-layer chromatography. There is, as yet, no reasonable explanation of why some *cis*-isomers should have a greater and others a lesser adsorption affinity than the all-*trans* compound. *Cis*-isomers of a carotenoid, nevertheless, can be isolated and identified by chromatographic methods in the same way as these techniques are used for the parent compounds.

2. *Effect of* cis-trans *Isomerization on Absorption Spectra*

The products of isomerization of an all-*trans* carotenoid absorb at shorter wavelengths in the visible region than the all-*trans* isomer; the extinction coefficient of the *cis-* forms are less than that of the parent compound. This means that if a solution of an all-*trans* carotenoid is treated with iodine and the absorption spectrum continuously observed in a recording spectrophotometer, there will be a shift of the spectral bands towards the blue end, and a loss of extinction. If a *cis*-isomer is treated in this way, the reverse change takes place, but the final equilibrium is the same. This is, therefore, a simple method of differentiating between *cis-* and *trans*-isomers, and for determining the stereoisomeric set to which a pigment belongs.

Another characteristic of the formation of most, but not all, *cis*-isomers is the appearance of an absorption maximum in the ultra-violet region of the spectrum, between 320 and 380 mμ. The "*cis*-peak" of normal, fully unsaturated carotenoids is, in hexane, 142 ± 2 mμ below the long wave band of the visible absorption spectrum of the all-*trans* isomer (see Table XVIII). The difference in benzene is usually 145–146 mμ. This parameter is less variable than others, for example, the difference between the *cis*-peak and the wavelength of maximal absorption of the all-*trans* isomer varies between 109 and 116 mμ. The molecular extinction coefficient of the *cis*-peak is variable, but rarely exceeds the value (E_{1cm}^{Mol}) of 6×10^4.

The examination of the ultra-violet spectrum for a *cis*-peak is thus an important part of the final identification of a carotenoid. The best media for the observation of *cis*-peaks are non-polar solvents such as hexane, cyclohexane or benzene.

TABLE XVIII

The Position of the *cis*-Peak in Various Stereoisomeric Sets
(Zechmeister, 1960)

		Distance between cis-*peak and:*	
Carotenoid	Cis-*peak*	*longest wave max.* $(m\mu)$ *of all-*trans *compound*	λ_{max} $(m\mu)$ *of all-*trans *compound*
Phytofluene	260	107	88
ζ-Carotene	296	129	104
Neurosporene	332	136	118
Lycopene	362	141	111
Spirilloxanthin	384	143	109
γ-Carotene	349	143	112
4-Hydroxy-γ-Carotene	350	141	110
β-Carotene	338	142	114
Cryptoxanthin	339	141	113
Zeaxanthin	336	144	116
Physalein	338	141	113
Isozeaxanthin	337	141	114
β-Carotene monoepoxide	330	145	116
β-Carotene diepoxide	328	142	111
Antheraxanthin	331	141	115
		(In ethanol)	
α-Carotene	331	143	114·5
4-Hydroxy-α-Carotene	330	144	115
Lutein	331	143	114·5
Capsanthin	355	143	109
Dimethylcrocetin	314	134	108

Thus differentiation between *cis*- and *trans*- carotenoids is carried out largely by spectrophotometric methods such as:

(i) observation of the effect of iodine treatment on the visible absorption spectrum;

(ii) observation of the ultra-violet spectrum (320–380 $m\mu$) for "*cis*-peaks".

The final identification of a carotenoid isomer can only be carried out using these methods in conjunction with a chromatographic method. It is, as yet, impossible to assign an absolute stereochemical description of a carotenoid on the basis of simple tests. The most detailed information of this nature is given by the infra-red spectrum of a carotenoid. This has been dealt with earlier (Chapter 3).

E. PARTITION COEFFICIENTS

The distribution of carotenoids between light petroleum and a methanol–water mixture has long been used for differentiating between carotenes and xanthophylls, and has been suggested (p. 500) as a means of separating these two types of carotenoids in purification procedures.

Krinsky (1963) carried out a detailed quantitative study of the partition coefficients of twenty-five carotenoids between light petroleum and methanol–water mixtures. With these partition coefficients, a linear relationship has been established between the M_{50} values (the M_{50} value of a carotenoid is the percentage of methanol required to give a partition coefficient of 1·0) and the relative polarities of the carotenoids. The relative polarity is derived from the sum of the polarities of the individual functional groups of the molecule. The groups were assigned the following relative polarities based in a value of 1·00 for the non-allylic hydroxyl group:

Non-allylic hydroxyl	1·00
Allylic hydroxyl	0·89
Ketone	0·72
Acetyl ester	0·47
5,6-epoxide	0·24
5,8-epoxide	0·24

This method could thus be used in conjunction with other techniques for carotenoid identification and for determining the number, type and position of functional groups in the molecule. It appears to be a potentially useful technique, but as it stands is obviously limited in its application, and is at present overshadowed by the far more valuable method of thin-layer chromatography.

F. CHEMICAL REACTIONS OF CAROTENOIDS

Many colour reactions of carotenoids have been described (see, e.g., Karrer and Jucker, 1950), but few of these empirical tests are of any real value in quantitative carotenoid analysis. There are, however, two tests which have proved useful in the identification of carotenoid epoxides.

(a) Karrer (1945) showed that in the presence of a trace of hydrochloric acid, a chloroform solution of a 5,6-epoxide isomerizes to the furanoid epoxide. It is for this reason that unpurified chloroform (which often contains traces of hydrochloric acid) is not recommended as a solvent in carotenoid analysis. This conversion can also be carried out in ethanolic solution (Krinsky and Goldsmith, 1960; Williams, 1963).

A few drops of 0·1 N HCl are added to an ethanolic solution of the suspected 5,6-epoxide and the mixture allowed to stand for 3 minutes. If the carotenoid is a mono-5,6-epoxide, a spectral shift of 18–25 mμ to shorter wavelengths is observed. A shift of about 40 mμ indicates the presence of two 5,6-epoxy groups in the carotenoid molecule.

(b) Yamamoto *et al.* (1961) described a reaction of carotenoid epoxides with mercuric chloride in the solid state which results in the formation of intense blue and blue-green complexes. The crystalline pigment is mixed with dry, powdered mercuric chloride in a 1:5 (w/w) ratio, and sealed in air or *in vacuo* in a tube which is heated in a steam bath for one minute. After heating, the tube is broken and the contents extracted with acetone. The absorption maxima of the products are all in the range of 600–700 mμ. The reaction is given both by 5,6- and 5,8-epoxides.

IV. QUANTITATIVE DETERMINATION OF CAROTENOIDS

The standard method of carrying out the quantitative determination of carotenoids is by spectrophotometry. This method requires that the carotenoid should be chromatographically pure.

The $E_{1\,cm}^{1\%}$ of a carotenoid is the extinction of a 1% solution in a 1-cm light path optical cell. Values of the $E_{1\,cm}^{1\%}$ are available for most carotenoids (Table XIX). The carotenoid is dissolved in a suitable volume

TABLE XIX

$E_{1\,cm}^{1\%}$ Values for Carotenoids

Carotenoid	$E_{1\,cm}^{1\%}$	λ_{max} (mμ)	Solvent
Anhydrorhodovibrin	2,700	482·5	Light petroleum
Aphanin	2,158	458	Light petroleum
Astacin	1,690	498	Pyridine
Auroxanthin	1,850	402	Ethanol
Azafrin	2,200	409	Light petroleum
α-Bacterioruberin	2,350	494	Light petroleum
Bixin	4,200	456	Light petroleum
Canthaxanthin	2,200	466	Hexane
Capsanthin	1,790	486	Benzene
α-Carotene	2,800	445	Light petroleum
β-Carotene	2,505	451	Light petroleum
γ-Carotene	3,100	462	Light petroleum
δ-Carotene	3,210	456	Hexane
ε-Carotene	2,890	442	Light petroleum
ζ-Carotene	2,270	400	Light petroleum
Chloroxanthin	2,470	437·5	Hexane
Crocetin	4,025	424·5	Light petroleum
Cryptoxanthin	2,460	451	Hexane
α-Cryptoxanthin	2,633	446	Hexane

TABLE XIX—cont.

Carotenoid	$E_{1\,cm}^{1\%}$	λ_{max} (mμ)	Solvent
3,4-Dehydrorhodopin	3,100	483	Light petroleum
Echinenone	2,158	458	Light petroleum
Eschscholtzxanthin	2,820	472	Ethanol
Fucoxanthin	2,025	477	Carbon disulphide
Gazaniaxanthin	2,600	462·5	Hexane
Helenien	766	445	Hexane
Hydroxy-P 481	2,700	483	Light petroleum
Hydroxy-R	2,005	498	Benzene
Hydroxy-spirilloxanthin	2,350	499	Light petroleum
Hydroxy-Y	2,543	465	Benzene
Isolutein	2,780	453	Benzene
Isorenieratene	2,250	465	Benzene
Isozeaxanthin	2,400	451	Hexane
Lutein	2,160	475	Carbon disulphide
Lycopene	3,450	472·5	Hexane
Lycophyll	3,270	473	Hexane
Lycoxanthin	3,360	472·5	Light petroleum
Monodemethylated spirilloxanthin	2,350	494	Light petroleum
Myxoxanthin	2,158	458	Light petroleum
Neoxanthin	2,270	438	Ethanol
Neurosporene	2,990	440	Light petroleum
P 481	2,700	482·5	Light petroleum
Physalien	1,340	451	Hexane
Physoxanthin	2,360	445	Hexane
Phytoene	1,250	285	Light petroleum
Phytofluene	1,350	348	Light petroleum
Pigment R (Spheroidenone)	2,065	499	Benzene
Pigment Y (Spheroidene)	2,630	466	Benzene
Prolycopene	1,920	433·5	Light petroleum
Renieratene	2,250	465	Benzene
Rhodopin	3,100	470	Light petroleum
Rhodovibrin	2,700	483	Light petroleum
Rhodoviolascin	2,350	499	Light petroleum
Rhodoxanthin	1,900	489	Hexane
Spheriodenone	2,065	499	Benzene
Spirilloxanthin	2,470	510	Benzene
Taraxanthin	2,800	442	Ethanol
Torularhodin	2,040	501	Light petroleum
Torulene	3,240	484	Hexane
Trollixanthin	2,780	457	Benzene
Violaxanthin	2,216	454	Benzene
α-Zeacarotene	2,450	421	Hexane
β-Zeacarotene	2,570	428	Hexane
Zeaxanthin	2,350	451	Hexane
Zeinoxanthin	2,690	445	Light petroleum

(For references see Tables XI–XVII).

of the chosen solvent (for the greatest accuracy, the volume should be such that the extinction of the solution is between 0·5 and 0·8 for manual instruments or towards the top of the scale for automatic recorders;

the volume is accurately measured by using a volumetric flask) and the extinction accurately determined in a 1-cm cell at the wavelength of maximal absorption in that solvent. Then follows the calculation of the amount of carotenoid.

If x g of the carotenoid dissolved in y ml solution gives an extinction of E at its wavelength of maximal absorption, then

$$x = \frac{Ey}{E_{1\,cm}^{1\%} \times 100}$$

REFERENCES

Analytical Methods Committee (1959). *Analyst* **84**, 356.

A.O.A.C. (1952). *J. Ass. off. Agric. Chem. Wash.* **35**, 738.

Bodea, C., and Nicoara, E. (1957). *Ann. Chem.* **609**, 181.

Bolliger, H. R. (1962). *In* "Dünnschichtschromatographie" (E. Stahl, ed.), p. 217, Springer, Heidelberg.

Booth, V. H. (1962). *Biochem. J.* **84**, 444.

Cholnoky, L., Szablocs, I., and Nagy, E. (1958). *Ann. Chem.* **616**, 207.

Davies, B. H. (1961a). Ph.D. Thesis, University of Wales.

Davies, B. H. (1961b). *Phytochemistry* **1**, 25.

Davies, B. H. (1961c). *Biochem. J.* **80**, 48P.

Davies, B. H. (1963). *J. Chromatog.* **10**, 518.

Davies, B. H., and Goodwin, T. W. (1959). *Biochem. J.* **73**, 10P.

Davies, B. H., Goodwin, T. W., and Mercer, E. I. (1961). *Biochem. J.* **81**, 40P.

Davies, B. H., Jones, D., and Goodwin, T. W. (1963a). *Biochem. J.* **87**, 326.

Davies, B. H., Villoutreix, J., Williams, R. J. H., and Goodwin, T. W. (1963b). *Biochem. J.* **89**, 96P.

Demole, E. (1958). *J. Chromatog.* **1**, 24.

Demole, E. (1959). *Chrom. Revs.* **1**, 1.

Egger, R. (1962). *Planta* **58**, 664.

Eichenberger, W., and Grob, E. C. (1963). *Helv. chim. acta* **46**, 2411.

Eugster, C. H., and Karrer, P. (1957). *Helv. chim. acta* **40**, 69.

French, C. S., and Milner, H. W. (1955). *In* "Methods of Enzymology" (S. P. Colowick and N. O. Kaplan, eds.), vol. I, p. 64, Academic Press, New York.

Garton, G. A., Goodwin, T. W., and Lijinsky, W. (1951). *Biochem. J.* **48**, 154.

Goodwin, T. W. (1955). *In* "Modern Methods of Plant Analysis" (K. Paech and M. V. Tracey, eds.), vol. III, p. 272, Springer, Heidelberg.

Goodwin, T. W. (1958). *Biochem. J.* **68**, 503.

Green, J., Marcinkiewicz, S., and Watt, P. R. (1955). *J. Sci. Fd Agric.* **6**, 274.

Hodgkiss, W., Liston, J., Goodwin, T. W., and Jamikorn, M. (1954). *J. gen. Microbiol.* **11**, 438.

Isler, O., and Schudel, P. (1963). *In* "Carotine und Carotinoide" (Wissenschaftliche Veröffentlichungen der Deutschen Gesellschaft für Ernährung), vol. 9, p. 54. Steinkopff, Darmstadt.

Jensen, A. (1960). *Acta chem. scand.* **19**, 2051.

Jensen, A., and Jensen, S. L. (1959). *Acta chem. scand.* **13**, 1863.

Jensen, S. L. (1962). "The Constitution of Some Bacterial Carotenoids and their Bearings on Biosynthetic Problems," 199 pp., Bruns, Trondheim.

Jensen, S. L. (1963a). *Acta chem. scand.* **17**, 303.

Jensen, S. L. (1963b). *Acta chem. scand.* **17**, 500.

Jensen, S. L. (1963c). *Acta chem. scand.* **17**, 489.

Karrer, P. (1945). *Helv. chim. acta* **28**, 474.

Karrer, P., and Jucker, E. (1950). "Carotenoids," 384 pp., Elsevier, Amsterdam.

Karrer, P., and Leumann, E. (1951). *Helv. chim. acta* **34**, 445.

Krinsky, N. I. (1963). *Anal. Biochem.* **6**, 293.

Krinsky, N. I., and Goldsmith, T. H. (1960). *Arch. Biochem. Biophys.* **91**, 271.

Kuhn, R., and Lederer, E. (1931). *Ber. dtsch. Chem. Ges.* **64**, 1349.

Kuhn, R., and Winterstein, A. (1931). *Ber. dtsch. Chem. Ges.* **64**, 326.

Kuhn, R., Winterstein, A., and Lederer, E. (1931). *Hoppe Seyl. Z.* **197**, 141.

Land, D. G. (1955). Ph.D. Thesis, University of Liverpool.

Lederer, E. (1938). *Bull. Soc. Chim. biol.* **20**, 554.

Lederer, E., and Lederer, M. (1957). "Chromatography," 2nd edn., 711 pp., Elsevier, Amsterdam.

Mercer, E. I., Davies, B. H., and Goodwin, T. W. (1963). *Biochem. J.* **87**, 317.

Mrak, E. M., Phaff, H. J., and Mackinney, G. (1949). *J. Bact.* **57**, 407.

Peterson, N. J., Bell, T. A., Etchells, J. L., and Smart, W. W. G. (1954). *J. Bact.* **67**, 708.

Petracek, F. J., and Zechmeister, L. (1956). *Arch. Biochem. Biophys.* **82**, 117.

Petzold, E. N., Quackenbush, F. W., and McQuistan, M. (1959). *Arch. Biochem. Biophys.* **82**, 117.

Randerath, K. (1963). "Thin-Layer Chromatography," 250 pp., Verlag-Chemie, Weinheim; Academic Press, New York.

Rutter, L. (1948). *Nature, Lond.* **161**, 435.

Simpson, K. L., Wilson, A. W., Burton, E., Nakayama, T. O. M., and Chichester, C. O. (1963). *J. Bact.* **86**, 1126.

Simpson, K. L., Nakayama, T. O. M., and Chichester, C. O. (1964). *Biochem. J.* (in press).

Stahl, E., Bolliger, H. R., and Lehnert, L. (1963). *In* "Carotine und Carotinoide" (Wissenschaftliche Veröffentlichungen der Deutschen Gesellschaft für Ernährung), vol. 9, p. 129, Steinkopff, Darmstadt.

Strain, H. H. (1939). *J. Amer. chem. Soc.* **61**, 1292.

Strain, H. H. (1948). *J. Amer. chem. Soc.* **70**, 588.

Strain, H. H. (1958). "Chloroplast Pigments and Chromatographic Analysis," 180 pp., Pennsylvania State Univ. Press.

Thomas, D. M. (1962). M.Sc. Thesis, University of Wales.

Tswett, M. (1903). *Proc. Warsaw. Soc. Nat. Sci., Biol. Sec.* **14**, Min. 6.

Williams, B. L. (1963). M.Sc. Thesis, University of Wales.

Windaus, A. (1909). *Chem. Ber.* **42**, 238.

Winterstein, A., and Hegedüs, B. (1960). *Chimia* **14**, 18; *Hoppe Seyl. Z.* **321**, 97.

Yamaguchi, M. (1957). *Bull. chem. Soc. Japan* **30**, 979.

Yamaguchi, M. (1958). *Bull. chem. Soc. Japan* **31**, 51.

Yamamoto, H. Y., Chichester, C. O., and Nakayama, T. O. M. (1961). *Anal. Chem.* **33**, 1792.

Zechmeister, L. (1960). *Forschr. der Chem. organ. Naturstoffe* **18**, 223.

Zechmeister, L., and Cholnoky, L. V. (1943). "Principles and Practice of Chromatography," 361 pp., Chapman and Hall, London.

Chapter 19

ANALYTICAL METHODS FOR FLAVONOIDS

T. SWAIN

Low Temperature Research Station, Downing Street,
Cambridge, England

I. INTRODUCTION

Investigations on the nature of any natural product involves three separate procedures, extraction, isolation or purification, and determination of structure. Obviously the ease with which the last stage may be carried out determines to a large extent the scale of extraction and the sophistication of the isolation procedure. In recent years, analytical methods in organic chemistry, both qualitative or quantitative, are wherever possible carried out on a micro scale: that is with amounts of the order of a milligram or less. Quantitative micro-analytical procedures based on gravimetric, volumetric, colorimetric and gasometric estimations, or on the measurement of selected electro-chemical properties have of course been in use since the turn of the century, mainly to meet the requirements of biochemistry. These earlier methods were usually confined to the estimation of individual substances or groups of substances of interest in animal biochemistry. However, just over a decade ago there was a rapid change over to the use of micro-techniques in the chemistry of natural products. This followed the almost simultaneous introduction of paper and other chromatographic methods for the

533

separation of polar metabolites on the one hand, and of relatively cheap commercial spectrophotometers on the other (cf. Milton and Waters, 1949, 1955).

These two tools have been of inestimable value in flavonoid chemistry. Previously the amounts of a single flavonoid glycoside usually required for identification by the methods of classical organic chemistry were at least of the order of a few grams. In order to obtain such amounts by the tedious and relatively inefficient separation procedures used (see Seshadri, 1962; Geissman, 1955) upwards of one kilogram of plant material was needed. Furthermore such isolations were only successful when fairly large amounts of a single component were present in the plant tissues. The general methods which were used for purification, besides leading to loss of labile sugar or acyl groups, often failed to separate the individual flavonoid glycosides from their congeners or from free sugars (Harborne, 1962a). Furthermore, identifications based on melting points, elemental analysis and the preparation of derivatives also led to great losses. It is not surprising therefore that relatively few glycosides had been isolated prior to 1950 (cf. Harborne, 1963 with Karrer, 1956).

Today it is possible to separate several individual flavonoid glycosides by paper chromatography, to determine their structure, and to estimate the quantities present spectrophotometrically using only a gram or so of plant material (e.g. Harborne, 1962b). When identification of commonly occurring aglycones only is required, 100 mg of fresh tissue is often sufficient (Bate-Smith, 1962). The whole outlook of flavonoid chemistry has thus been changed by the use of these modern techniques. Undoubtedly in the future, the more powerful tools of gas chromatography and mass spectroscopy, which when used together enable analyses and structural determinations to be carried out on sub-microgram amounts of complex mixtures, will come into common use in the flavonoid field. Infra-red and, especially, nuclear magnetic resonance spectroscopy, which are presently of great value to the organic chemist in determining the structure of unknown compounds, will certainly also be developed further so that they too can be used with quantities of a similar order of magnitude.

Although, as mentioned above, most modern methods of qualitative analysis involve quantitative measurements, this is not always so. Qualitative analysis must usually be carried out on pure compounds and therefore requires their prior separation from the original extract. Quantitative analysis, on the other hand, by the use of specific procedures, can be used to determine the amount of one individual compound present in a mixture, although more often it is used to measure the concentration of cognate groups of compounds. Since all the methods of this latter type may be also used to determine the concentration of individual pure substances, it is desirable to describe first the methods used for the isolation and for the determination of the structure of flavonoid compounds.

II. EXTRACTION OF FLAVONOID COMPOUNDS

A variety of solvents have been used to extract flavonoids from plants (Seshadri, 1962). The solubility of individual flavonoid compounds varies as greatly as does their structure (see Chapter 8), but it should be remembered that, except perhaps for the flavolans (polymeric leuco-anthocyanins and related substances, Swain, 1962), the majority of compounds in living cells are normally present in the vacuole, and are therefore water-soluble. However, extraction with water or predominantly aqueous solvents suffers from three disadvantages. One, many other substances, especially those of high molecular weight are also extracted and usually either interfere with subsequent manipulations, or are difficult to separate completely from certain flavonoids. Two, unless the solution is boiled vigorously, glycosidases, phenolases and many other enzymes which act on phenolic compounds are not completely destroyed, which can lead to changes in the individual flavonoids originally present. Three, because of its relatively high boiling point and vapour pressure, water is difficult to remove rapidly and completely. Occasionally, though, aqueous solvents have to be used because the desired compound is too insoluble in organic solvents (e.g. betacyanins). In general, however, alcohols are the solvents of choice. Methanol, because of its lower boiling point, is often preferred to ethanol, propanol and higher alcohols being used only rarely. With fresh material, absolute solvents may be used, but with dried plants or predominantly woody tissue prior wetting or the use of aqueous alcohols is often an advantage. In fact, the use of absolute followed by aqueous alcoholic solvents has been used for the partial fractionation of flavolans (Goldstein and Swain, 1963). The alcohols will extract all types of flavonoid compounds; for anthocyanins however, just sufficient (c. 0·1%) hydrochloric or other volatile acid should be present to prevent their conversion to pseudo-base form (see Chapter 8). With some labile compounds, for example, aromatic esters, it is possible that alcoholysis will occur but does not appear to be experienced for the majority of flavonoid compounds.

When only one solvent is used, its choice not only depends on the compounds which are being examined, but also on the plant tissue in which they occur, and the nature of any other substances which may be present. This is why it is usual, on a large scale at least, to employ a succession of three or four solvents usually in the order petrol, benzene, ether, ethyl acetate, alcohols and finally an aqueous solvent. Even on a small scale it is often useful to remove lipids from certain tissues (e.g. seeds) with petrol before proceeding to extract the flavonoids with alcohol. Most of the flavonoid aglycones, with the exception of the anthocyanidins, are soluble to some extent in ether, and ethyl acetate, some of the more highly methylated compounds being also soluble in benzene. Flavonoid glycosides are, however, generally only extractable with ethyl acetate or with alcohols and other more polar solvents.

The original extract may sometimes be usefully partly purified, by further simple solvent extraction. For example, chlorophyll and carotenoids can be removed from ethanolic leaf extracts by light petroleum.

Whichever solvent is used for extraction or method for the isolation of the desired individual components, the next step before separation is usually one of concentration. When working on a large scale, components usually separate out in an impure form during this stage. Care should be taken not to concentrate too far, especially when acid has been used for the extraction, because of the loss of more labile components. For the same reason concentration is also best carried out at the lowest possible temperature, preferably under nitrogen or *in vacuo*.

III. ISOLATION OF FLAVONOID COMPOUNDS

A. CLASSICAL METHODS

The classical methods for obtaining pure flavonoid compounds, although of little value for detailed examination of plant extracts, are still of use in obtaining relatively large quantities of individual flavonoids. For anthocyanins, the usual method is repeated precipitation of the alcoholic acid solution with ether; for other flavonoid glycosides a variety of procedures are used including lead acetate precipitation, fractional crystallization, and re-extraction with different solvents. A number of such procedures are adequately described by Seshadri (1962) and Geissman (1955).

B. CHROMATOGRAPHIC METHODS

1. *Column Chromatography*

Although column methods had been developed for the separation of a number of different classes of compounds over the years prior to 1939 (Strain, 1942), the general use of very polar adsorbents, such as alumina, precluded their successful application to compounds like the flavonoids. Karrer and Strong (1936) did use alumina for the final purification of anthocyanidins but the method was not successful with total plant extracts. As mentioned earlier, the introduction of partition chromatography on silica gel (Martin and Synge, 1941) soon led to its application in the successful separation of flavonoid compounds, being first used for tea catechins in 1947 (Bradfield *et al.*, 1947) and for anthocyanins a short time later (Spaeth and Rosenblatt, 1950). The success of partition chromatography for the separation of polar compounds led to an increased interest in other chromatographic methods about this time, and Wender and his co-workers developed the use of the polyacrylic ion-exchange resins (Gage *et al.*, 1951) and the mild inorganic adsorbant magnesol (hydrated magnesium silicate) (Ice and Wender, 1952) for the isolation and separation of flavonol glycosides. The obvious advantage of paper chromatography in this field (Harborne, 1958a, 1959) led to the application of cellulose as a column material (Forsyth, 1952), and when properly packed this is probably the most useful for certain separations. More recently powdered nylon (polyamide) has come into increasing use because of its high loading capacity (Carelli *et al.*, 1955, Hörhammer *et al.*, 1961). The commercial samples presently available suffer from the drawback of requiring some purification before use, but purer forms are now becoming available (Egger, 1961). The column chromatography of flavonoids would probably have been developed more extensively but for the success of the methods introduced for the identification of flavonoids on a milligram scale (Nordström and Swain, 1953). Such amounts can readily be obtained in a pure state by chromatography on thick paper. This has the advantage that not only can the variations in the solvents and so on used in the separation be rapidly evaluated by trial runs beforehand, but that previous knowledge regarding the behaviour of a large number of different flavonoid compounds on paper chromatograms often enables the nature, and even the actual identity of the compound to be deduced by the behaviour of the compound during the separation procedure. Nevertheless, where larger amounts of substances are required, column chromatography on polyamide or like substances will continue to be used with advantage. It is probable also, that the greater analytical power of column chromatography will find many uses in plant biochemistry in the future. For example Hansen and Zucker (1963) quantitatively analysed ten hydroxycinnamic acid derivatives, many previously unrecognized, from the potato tuber by chromatography on silica gel.

2. *Paper Chromatography*

Paper chromatography is such a well-known technique and its use in the flavonoid field has been so well-reviewed recently (Seikel, 1962; Harborne, 1958a, 1959) that a bare outline of recommended techniques is sufficient.

The usual paper used for "large scale" separation (i.e. 1 to 100 mg) is Whatman No. 3, or its equivalent; the solution to be separated is applied as a continuous even streak or band along the start line, keeping the width as narrow as possible. Up to 10 ml can readily be streaked by successive applications. For the majority of flavonoids separation is first effected by the use of n-butanol:acetic acid:water (BAW) mixtures (e.g. 6:1:2; Nordström and Swain, 1953). After development and drying, the positions of the individual bands are located either by their fluorescence in the ultra-violet or by spraying a test strip with a suitable reagent (e.g. diazotized p-nitroaniline, Swain, 1953; ferric chloride and potassium ferricyanide, Barton et al., 1952). The bands are cut out, the compounds eluted, usually with 70% aqueous alcohol, and the solutions concentrated for re-purification in a second solvent.

The choice of second (and subsequent) solvents is usually made on the basis of a prior examination of each band by chromatography on ordinary filter paper in several solvent systems. Each band is then re-chromatographed in a suitable solvent or combination of solvents until pure, as judged by chromatographic and spectral means. The solvents usually used for subsequent purification include n-butanol-water (1:1 top phase, BW), 5% aqueous acetic acid (5HA), and n-butanol-ethanol-water (4:1:2·2 v/v, top phase, BEW), and in the case of anthocyanins n-butanol-2 N hydrochloric acid (B2H) and 15% acetic acid (15 HA) (see Harborne and Sherratt, 1961).

In BAW aglycones usually run faster than glycosides, and their R_F values decrease depending on the number of hydroxyl and sugar groups they contain. In 5HA the opposite is true, except that planar molecules such as quercetin and its -7-glycosides do not move in this solvent. The effect of substitution on R_F values and the colour reactions on paper of a large number of flavonoid compounds has been given by Harborne (1958a, 1959) and by Seikel (1962).

3. *Thin Layer Chromatography*

Thin layer chromatography of flavonoid compounds both on polyamide and on silica gel plates is now well established (Egger, 1961; Hörhammer et al., 1960). Whether it will ever be used in separating components in sufficient quantity for structural determination remains doubtful, since its resolving power for glycosides is not as good as paper (Egger, 1961). However, it will undoubtedly be used more extensively in the future as a rapid tool for the comparison of unknowns with authentic compounds. Details of the methodology and some R_F values of flavonoid glycosides are given by Randerath (1963).

IV. THE QUALITATIVE ANALYSIS OF FLAVONOID COMPOUNDS

The qualitative analysis of a flavonoid glycoside involves three distinct steps: one, the identification of the aglycone; two, the identification of the sugar; and three, the identification of the point of sugar attachment and the type of link involved.

The classical methods of identification of flavonoid aglycones have been well described elsewhere (Venkataraman, 1962) and need not be further detailed here, except to point out that one of the usual steps is treatment with alkali which splits the heterocyclic ring leading to a mixture of fragments from ring A and ring B (see Chapter 9).

In the last ten years, such methods have been superseded by the general application of paper chromatography and spectroscopy to structural problems (Nordström and Swain, 1953). With further developments (Harborne, 1958b, 1960, 1964; Harborne and Sherratt, 1961; Chandler and Harper, 1961) such methods enable the structure of the glycosides or acylated glycosides of most flavonoid compounds to be readily determined with the minimum of both material and time.

Briefly, the method involves R_F and spectral measurements on the isolated compound itself; hydrolysis and identification of the sugar or sugars by paper chromatography, and of the aglycone by a combination of paper chromatography and spectroscopy; determination of the point of attachment by either spectroscopic means, or methylation prior to hydrolysis and identification of the partly methylated aglycone, or selected oxidations; determination of the type of sugar link by the use of selective hydrolytic enzymes.

Two illustrations must suffice to show the power of the method, both taken from recent work by Harborne (1962b, 1964) with additional comments and interpolations from the author's own experience.

The first concerns the identification of the 4-glucoside-4'-glucosyl glucoside of 4,2',4'-trihydroxy chalkone (I). This compound, along with

(I) R = Glucosylglucosyl
    R' = Glucosyl
(II) R = R' = H
(IV) R = Glucosylglucosyl
    R' = H
(V) R = R' = Glucose
4,2',4'-Trihydroxychalkone and its glycosides

three other glycosides of 4,2',4'-trihydroxychalkone and five flavonol glycosides was isolated from gorse (*Ulex europaeus*) by large scale chromatography using three solvent systems (BAW, BEW, H_2O).* The ultra-violet spectrum of the compound had two bands, one of relatively

* See p. 538.

low intensity at 237 mμ and the other main band at 361 mμ. This pointed to the strong probability that the compound was a chalkone glycoside, since flavonols which have absorption bands in the same long wavelength region (see Table I) all have a second band of roughly equal intensity at 250–260 mμ (see Table II, Chapter 8, p. 217). The fluorescence of a spot of the compound on filter paper in ultra-violet light was dull dark brown and did not change on fuming the paper with ammonia; three other components which had similar spectra were also dull brown in ultra-violet light but two of these on fuming with ammonia gave an orange fluorescence, characteristic of chalkones. The R_F value of the compound was relatively low in BAW (0·36) and high in water (0·80) indicating that the compound was probably a glycoside containing two or three molecules of sugar. After careful hydrolysis of a portion of the compound with mineral acid (2 N HCl) the aglycone was extracted with ethyl acetate, and the excess acid, which otherwise interferes with chromatographic separation, was removed by treatment with a solution of di-n-octylmethylamine in chloroform (Harborne, 1958b; Harborne and Sherratt, 1961). The only sugar in the residual solution was glucose identified by chromatography in three solvent systems. The ethyl acetate solution contained, as expected from the earlier work (Nordström and Swain, 1956), two compounds, one proving by R_F values and colour reactions to be 4,2′,4′-trihydroxychalkone (II), and the other the corresponding

(III) Liquiritigenin

flavanone (III), ring closure having been effected by the hydrolysis conditions. Hydrolysis of the compound with β-glucosidase gave a product (IV) which proved to be identical with one of the other chalkone glycosides present, together with 1·16 equivalents of glycose. The glucose was estimated by a paper chromatographic method (Pridham, 1956) and the amount of "aglycone" estimated spectrophotometrically making the assumption (shown to be valid in other cases, see Table I) that sugar substitution in most cases does not greatly alter the absorptivity of flavonoid compounds. These data showed that the compound contains only one simple glucose residue attached to one hydroxyl group and that the rest of the glucose must be present as a di- or trisaccharide. The product (IV) of enzyme hydrolysis had similar R_F values to a third glycoside of 4,2′,4′-trihydroxychalkone (V) which readily

TABLE I

Spectral Properties of Flavonoid Colouring Matters[a]

Compound	Structure and Hydroxyl Substitution	EtOH or MeOH HCl[b]		Ethanolic AlCl₃
		λ_{max} (mμ)	log ϵ	λ_{max} (mμ)
Flavonols				
Kaemperol	5,7,4'	367	4·32	426
Fisetin	7,3',4'	370	4·43	430
Queretin	5,7,3',4'	371	4·33	431
Rutin	-3-rutinoside	361	4·29	420
Isoquercitrin	-3-glucoside	361	4·32	422
Myricetin	5,7,3',4',5'	378	4·29	450
Quercetagetin	5,6,7,3',4'	363	4·34	427
Patuletin	5,7,3',4',6-OMe	373	—	438
Gossypetin	5,7,8,3',4'	386	4·22	446
Gossypitrin	-7-glucoside	386	4·20	448
Chalkones				
Isoliquiritigenin	4,2',4'	372	4·42	442
Butein	3,4,2',4'	382	4·46	455
Coreopsin	-4'-glucoside	385	—	445
Okanin	3,4,2',3',4'	381	4·49	420
Aurones				
Sulphuretin	6,3',4'	399	4·55	405
Aureusidin	4,6,3',4'	399	4·44	459
Maritimetin	6,7,3',4'	415	4·48	—
Leptosidin	6,3',4'; 7-OMe	406	4·45	412
Anthocyanins				
Pelargonidin	5,7,4'	520	—	520
Callistephin	-3-glucoside	513	4·35[c]	520
Cyanidin	5,7,3',4'	535	—	553
Antirrhinin	-3-rhamnoglucoside	523	4·46[c]	541
Peonidin	5,7,4'; 3-OMe	532	—	532
Delphinidin	5,7,3',4',5	546	—	569
Myrtillin-a	-3-glucoside	534	—	557
Petunidin	5,7,4',5'; 3'-OMe	546	—	560
Malvidin	5,7,4'; 3',5'-diOMe	542	—	542

[a] Data from Jurd (1962), Harborne (1962) and Swain (unpublished). Only long wavelength band given.

[b] Anthocyanins in MeOH-HCl, rest in EtOH.

[c] Quoted values of log ϵ for anthocyanins are variable, probably owing to the use of solvents of varying pH. These figures taken from Jorgensen and Geissman (1955) refer to 1% aqueous hydrochloric acid. For callistephin in 1% methanolic hydrochloric acid, a value of log $\epsilon = 4·50$ (λ max. 516 mμ) was derived from the curve of Sondheimer and Kertesz (1948). J. B. Harborne (1964, personal communication) quotes the following values for MeOH/HCl: pelargonidin-3,5-diglucoside, λ_{max} 510 mμ, log ϵ 4·51; cyanidin-3-galactoside, λ_{max} 530 mμ, log ϵ 4·48; delphinidin-3,5-diglucoside, λ_{max} 535 mμ, log ϵ 4·37.

produced 1·99 moles of glucose and 4,2',4'-trihydroxychalkone (II) with β-glucosidase, and therefore was a dimonoside of (II). Compound IV which was not hydrolysed by the enzyme, was therefore a glucosyl-glucoside and thus the original compound (I) contained two sugar residues, glucose and glucosylglucose. The position of attachment of these two sugar residues follows from spectral data. The long wavelength band of the compound was ~ 10 mμ less than the aglycone (II) (Table I), similar to that of the 4,4'-di-O-methyl ether, and it gave a shift with aluminium chloride solution (to 410 mμ) showing that the hydroxyl group at C_2, *ortho* to the carbonyl group is free. The spectra and colour reactions of the partial hydrolysed compound IV showed that the disaccharide group in this compound was at $C_{4'}$, since with base its long wavelength band moved to 420 mμ with no change of absorptivity. The structure of the original compound is therefore as shown (I). It will be noted that in this case no methylation techniques were used to determine the position of sugar attachment. This is because when such procedures are applied to chalkones they lead to mixtures of chalkone and flavanone partial methyl ethers which are difficult to separate (cf. Nordström and Swain, 1956) and in any case were not necessary for the unequivocal identification of (I). However, methylation and hydrolysis were used to prove the structure of one of the five flavonol glycosides present in the gorse flowers, the previously unknown quercetin-3,7-diglucoside (VI), (Harborne, 1962b). Partial acid hydrolysis was also used to identify this compound which gave glucose, quercetin (VII) and the two known 7-(VIII) and 3-glucosides (IX) thus showing its identity as VI.

(VI) R = R' = Glucosyl
(VII) R = R' = H
(VIII) R = H, R' = Glucosyl
(IX) R = Glucosyl, R' = H
Quercetin and its glucosides

The second example concerns the acylated anthocyanin monardein (X) isolated from the petals of *Monarda didyma* by large-scale paper chromatography in B2H, followed by purification in BAW and 15HA. The ultra-violet spectrum of this compound in methanolic hydrochloric acid had three bands at 285, 314 and 507 mμ. The position of the long wavelength band indicates this is probably a derivative of pelargonidin since other anthocyanins absorb at higher wavelengths, and the band at 314 mμ indicates that a hydroxy cinnamic acid is probably present. The ratio of the absorptivity at 440 mμ to that at 407 mμ was 21, showing that

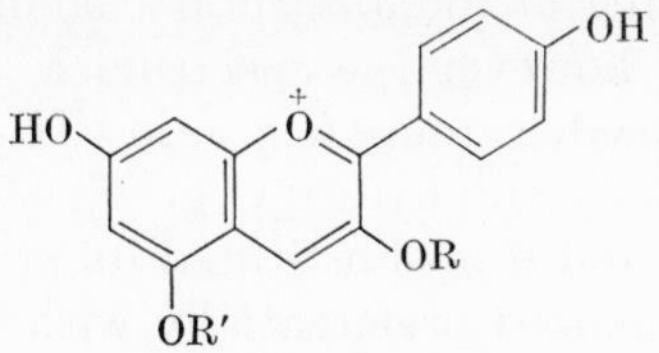

(X) R = p-Coumarylglucosyl
    R' = Glucosyl
    Monardein
(XI) R = R' = Glucosyl
(XIII) R = Glucosyl; R = H
(XIV) R = H; R' = Glucosyl
(XV) R = R' = H

the compound was a 3,5-diglycoside (3-glycosides of pelargonidin have ratios of 35 to 42, Harborne, 1958a). The ratio of the 314 mμ to 507 mμ bands was 67 showing that the one mole of hydroxy cinnamic was present (Harborne, 1958a). On alkaline hydrolysis under nitrogen it gave

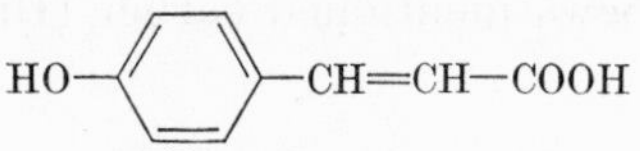

(XII) p-Coumaric acid

pelargonidin-3,5-diglucoside (XI) and p-coumaric acid (XII) and determination of the ratios of the two compounds spectrophotometrically after chromatographic separation confirmed the 1:1 ratio. Partial acid hydrolysis gave the same two products together with pelargonidin-3-glycoside (XIII), pelargonidin-5-glucoside (XIV), pelargonidin (XV) and glucose. The identification of these compounds was made by paper chromatographic comparison with pure substances in three or more solvents (Harborne, 1958b). The position of the p-coumaryl group was shown by oxidation with hydrogen peroxide (Chandler and Harper, 1961) which yields the group substituted at C_3 only and in this case gave an acylated glucose (see Chapter 8). This compound was isolated by paper chromatography in BAW, and on alkaline hydrolysis gave p-coumaric acid and glucose, but was unaffected by β-glucosidase. These data indicate that the acyl group was not attached to the reducing group of the sugar and confirm the structure of monardein as X.

Before leaving the subject a few general points on spectral methods should be made. The spectra of the various classes of phenolic compounds have been described in Chapter 8 (p. 217), and it was pointed out that the wavelength of the absorption band nearest (or in) the visible (band I) is dependent on the extent of conjugation in the molecule and therefore points to the probable structure. Certain other structural features can be easily demonstrated by observation of the changes induced in the spectrum on the addition of certain reagents. The addition of strong base for example causes shifts of the absorption bands towards the visible (bathochromically); if however the spectrum is destroyed by such a procedure, readily oxidizable groups (e.g. as in VII) are probably present. In flavones and flavonols, the hydroxyl group at C_7 is more strongly acidic than the others and if unsubstituted its presence can be readily demonstrated as it is ionized preferentially with sodium acetate. This causes a bathochromic shift of band II (at 250–270 mμ) of about 10–15 mμ. The presence of an unsubstituted ortho-dihydroxy group in flavones, flavonols, aurones and chalkones can readily be demonstrated by the change of band I of the spectrum on the addition of buffered boric acid; with anthocyanins, aluminium chloride is preferable. With the other classes, however, a change in band I on the addition of aluminium chloride indicates that the hydroxyl group ortho- or peri- to the carbonyl group is free (cf. sulphuretin and aureusidin, Table I). Further details of these methods are given by Jurd (1962).

Other examples of the use of chromatographic methods can be obtained from the reviews mentioned earlier (Harborne, 1958a, 1959, 1962a; Seikel, 1962).

V. The Quantitative Analysis of Flavonoid Compounds

A. INTRODUCTION

The quantitative analysis of phenolic compounds has been recently reviewed (Swain and Goldstein, 1964) and therefore no more than a few selected methods, all based on optical measurements will be discussed here. All the methods which have been developed for flavonoid compounds in the last few years have in fact relied on the use of spectrophotometers or like instruments. In many cases, especially with the four classes of flavonoid compounds which are of interest as plant colouring matters (Chapter 8), advantage may be taken of the high molar absorptivity shown by the compounds themselves in the near ultra-violet and the visible (Jurd, 1962) (Table I). For other substances, use may be made of the coloured derivatives formed either by reaction with substitution reagents, or by chelation with metals. One also has recourse to the susceptibility of phenolic compounds to oxidation, and by using oxidants which give coloured reduction products can determine the concentration of most phenolic compounds present in plant extracts. Many of the reagents used for substitution or the formation of chelates really measure the concentration of special groups (phenolic nuclei, King and White, 1956) present in the mixture of phenolic compounds, and can in fact be used for this purpose (Goldstein and Swain, 1963). For example, hydroxy flavans, which contain no deactivating groups, react with the relatively weak electrophiles like vanillin in the presence of strong acids to yield coloured products, and thus their concentration can be determined in the presence of other flavonoids (Swain and Hillis, 1959). Similarly it is possible to measure the concentration of o-dihydric phenols in the presence of monohydric phenols by the use of molybdates (Goldstein and Swain, 1963).

B. GENERAL METHODS OF ANALYSIS

There are no ideal methods for measuring the total concentration of flavonoid compounds in a given extract. Such methods are precluded by the variation in both the structure and the number of hydroxyl groups of these compounds (see Chapter 9), which gives rise to large differences in their spectra (Table I, see also Table II, Chapter 8, p. 217) and in their response to analytical reagents. The best methods for estimating the concentration of total phenols are those based on the use of the complex heteropoly acids such as phosphomolybdic and phosphotungstic acids

(XVI) R = H; (+)-Catechin
(XVII) R = OH; Leucocyanidin

(XVIII) 4-Ethylresorcinol   (XIX) Homocatechol

(Folin and Denis, 1915; Folin and Ciocalteau, 1927). These acids oxidize the majority of compounds containing free phenolic groups, being themselves reduced to molybdenum or tungsten blues, which can be conveniently measured spectrophotometrically (Swain and Hillis, 1959). For reproducible results careful attention must be paid to the conditions under which the oxidation is carried out, especially to the prior removal of easily oxidized non-phenolic compounds such as ascorbic acid. With any given phenol the reaction is reasonably stoicheiometric, but each compound naturally reacts differently depending on its oxidation-reduction potential (Goldstein and Swain, 1963). Even though a complex phenol, such as (+)catechin (XVI) gives a molar absorptivity with the reagent which is approximately equal to the sum of those of the separate phenolic nuclei (e.g. 4-ethylresorcinol XVIII and homocatechol XIX, see Goldstein and Swain, 1963), it is obvious that it is essential to select reference substances with the greatest of care. In general the compound selected as a standard should have a structure as close as possible to the majority of components in the mixture under examination. Unfortunately most plant extracts will contain colourless phenolic compounds such as caffeic acid (XX) derivatives, which react equally or even more strongly with the heteropoly acids, than the flavonoids responsible for colour, and it is usually not possible therefore to estimate the concentration of the latter in crude extracts by such methods.

Methods for the estimation of total flavonoids in plant extracts which make use of electrophilic substitution reagents suffer from several drawbacks (see Goldstein and Swain, 1963; Swain and Goldstein, 1964). Not only are the majority of these reagents rather unstable (diazotized amines, 4-aminophenazone, 2,6-dibromoquinone chlorimide, nitrous acid) but the reactions are carried out in alkaline solution, where many phenols are rapidly oxidized. Furthermore the presence of carbonyl groups in several flavonoids reduces their reactivity. Again, the presence of colourless phenolic compounds makes it almost impossible to use such methods for the determination of the components responsible for pigmentation in crude plant extracts.

C. SPECIAL METHODS OF ANALYSIS

The determination of the concentration of individual compounds or groups of compounds in a crude plant extract is best made spectrophotometrically at a specific wavelength, usually, but not necessarily, that of maximum absorptivity (Table I). Often it is useful to make the measurements at specific pH values with or without the addition of metals which form chelates with certain groups (see Chapter 8). The

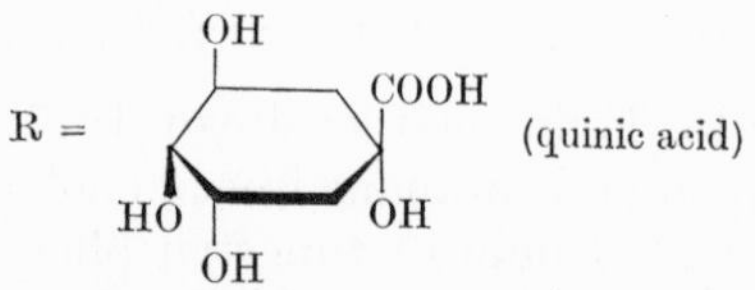

R = (quinic acid)

(XVI) Chlorogenic acid

choice of method depends not only on the compounds to be estimated but also on the nature of other components present (e.g. Jorgensen and Geissman, 1955). The flavonols, chalkones and aurones which are responsible for flower colour all absorb in the same region (360–410 mμ, cf. Table I) and if interfering substances are present, whose spectra overlaps theirs in neutral ethanol, it is often possible to select suitable conditions under which the two sets of spectra are more widely separated. For example, if an extract contains large amounts of chlorogenic acid

(XXI) and smaller amounts of isoquercitrin (VIII), it may be better to estimate the concentration of the latter after the addition of aluminium chloride (Dowd, 1959), as can be seen plainly from the curves shown in Fig. 1 (cf. Table I). Other salts might be used as in the Wilson boric acid method for flavonols (Wilson, 1939). If the mixture has been analysed qualitatively direct spectral measurements on two or more selected wavelengths are often sufficient to determine the concentration of any one component (cf. Goodwin and Morton, 1946; Roberts and Smith, 1961) since this makes it possible to eliminate interference due to other substances.

Occasionally, however, it is necessary to use different types of specific reactions. For example flavanones, unlike other classes of flavonoids, gave a red or purple colour on acidification after reduction with sodium borohydride which has been applied as a method for analysis (Eigen

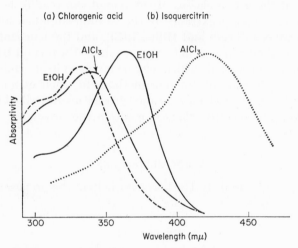

FIG. 1. Spectrum of (a) chlorogenic acid and of (b) isoquercitrin in EtOH, with and without aluminium chloride.

et al., 1957), and similar methods could perhaps be applied to other classes of flavonoids which give distinctive colour reactions with different reagents (see Seikel, 1962; Venkataraman, 1962). In the case of the anthocyanins, which have high absorptivities in the visible region (Table I), well removed from any other class of flavonoid compound there is usually no difficulty in direct spectral estimation, bearing in mind that the absorptivity is pH dependent. However, if one needs to determine their concentration in extracts from pigmented leaves, for example, chlorophyll and certain carotenoids might interfere with their direct estimation. This can be overcome in three ways: one, the difference in absorptivity between the oxonium and pseudo-base forms can be measured by determining the optical properties of say pH 1·0 and pH 5·0 (Sondheimer and Kertesz, 1948; see also Swain and Hillis, 1959); two, the anthocyanin can be destroyed by oxidation with hydrogen peroxide (Swain and Hillis, 1959); three, the anthocyanins can be extracted into aqueous HCl which leaves the chlorophyll and so on behind. In both cases the absorptivity due to chlorophyll is unchanged by the procedure. It is possible that the latter method could also be applied for the estimation of flavonols.

The flavonoid compounds (catechins XVI and leuco-anthocyanins XVII) which are the precursors of the substances responsible for the brown pigmentation of autumn leaves, and for enzymic browning of fruit and vegetables (Chapter 8, p. 242) cannot usually be easily estimated spectrophotometrically since they absorb light in general region of most other phenolic substances (λ max. c. 280 mμ, log ϵ, 3·6–3·8). The concentration of these two classes of compound can readily be estimated together in crude plant extracts by the vanillin-sulphuric acid method mentioned earlier (Swain and Hillis, 1959), and the leucoanthocyanins separately by their conversion to anthocyanins (Swain and Hillis, 1959). Other phenolic compounds which may be involved in enzymic browning require the application of different methods for their estimation. Two such methods, for chlorogenic acid and tyrosine are described by Mapson et al. (1963), reference to others is made in the review by Swain and Goldstein (1964).

ACKNOWLEDGEMENT

I wish to thank Dr. J. B. Harborne for help in the preparation of this chapter.

REFERENCES

Barton, G. M., Evans, R. S., and Gardner, J. A. F. (1952). *Nature, Lond.* **170**, 249.
Bate-Smith, E. C. (1962). *J. Linn. Soc. (Bot.)* **58**, 95.
Bradfield, A. E., Penney, M., and Wright, W. B. (1947). *J. chem. Soc.* 32.
Carelli, V., Liguori, A. M., and Mele, A. (1955). *Nature, Lond.* **176**, 70.
Chandler, B. V., and Harper, K. A. (1961). *Austral. J. Chem.* **14**, 586.
Dowd, L. E. (1959). *Anal. Chem.* **31**, 1184.
Egger, K. (1961). *Z. anal. Chem.* **182**, 161.
Eigen, E., Blitz, M., and Gunsberg, E. (1957). *Arch. Biochem. Biophys.* **68**, 501.
Folin, O., and Ciocalteau, V. (1927). *J. biol. Chem.* **73**, 627.
Folin, O., and Denis, W. (1915). *J. biol. Chem.* **22**, 305.
Forsyth, W. G. C. (1952). *Biochem. J.* **51**, 511.
Gage, T. B., Morris, Q. L., Detty, W. E., and Wender, S. H. (1951). *Science* **113**, 522.
Geissman, T. A. (1955). *In* "Modern Methods of Plant Analysis" (K. Paech and M. V. Tracey, eds.), vol. III, p. 450, Springer, Berlin.
Goldstein, J. L., and Swain, T. (1963). *Phytochemistry* **2**, 371.
Goodwin, T. W., and Morton, R. A. (1946). *Biochem. J.* **40**, 628.

Hansen, K. R., and Zucker, M. (1963). *J. biol. Chem.* **238**, 1105.

Harborne, J. B. (1958a). *J. Chromatography* **1**, 473.

Harborne, J. B. (1958b). *Biochem. J.* **70**, 22.

Harborne, J. B. (1959). *J. Chromatography* **2**, 581.

Harborne, J. B. (1960). *Biochem. J.* **74**, 262.

Harborne, J. B. (1962a). *Fortsch. Chem. org. Naturst.* **20**, 165.

Harborne, J. B. (1962b). *Phytochemistry* **1**, 203.

Harborne, J. B. (1963). *In* "Chemical Plant Taxonomy" (T. Swain, ed.), Academic Press, London.

Harborne, J. B. (1964). *Phytochemistry* **3**, 151.

Harborne, J. B., and Sherratt, H. S. A. (1961). *Biochem. J.* **78**, 298.

Hörhammer, L., Stich, L., and Wagner, H. (1961). *Arch. Pharm.* **294**, 685.

Hörhammer, L., Wagner, H., and Lay, B. (1960). *Pharmazie* **15**, 645.

Ice, C. H., and Wender, S. H. (1952). *Anal. Chem.* **24**, 1616.

Jorgensen, E. C., and Geissman, T. A. (1955). *Arch. Biochem. Biophys.* **55**, 392.

Jurd, L. (1962). *In* "The Chemistry of Flavonoid Compounds" (T. A. Geissman, ed.), Pergamon, New York.

Karrer, P., and Strong, F. M. (1936). *Helv. chim. acta* **19**, 25.

Karrer, W. (1956). "Konstitution und Vorkommen der organischen Pflanzenstoffe," Birkhäuser, Basel.

King, H. G. C., and White, T. (1956). *In* "The Chemistry of Vegetable Tannins". Soc. Leather. Trades Chemists, Croydon, England.

Mapson, L. W., Swain, T., and Tomalin, A. W. (1963). *J. Sci. Fd Agric.* **14**, 673.

Martin, A. J. P., and Synge, R. L. M. (1941). *Biochem. J.* **35**, 1358.

Milton, R. F., and Waters, W. A., Eds. (1949). "Methods of Quantitative Micro Analysis", 1st Edn., Arnold, London.

Milton, R. F., and Waters, W. A., Eds. (1955). "Methods of Quantitative Micro Analysis," 2nd Edn., Arnold, London.

Nordström, C. G., and Swain, T. (1953). *J. chem. Soc.* 2764.

Nordström, C. G., and Swain, T. (1956). *Arch. Biochem. Biophys.* **60**, 329.

Pridham, J. B. (1956). *Anal. Chem.* **28**, 1967.

Randerath, K. (1963). "Thin Layer Chromatography," Academic Press, New York.

Roberts, E. A. H., and Smith, R. F. (1961). *Analyst* **86**, 94.

Seikel, M. K, (1962). *In* "The Chemistry of Flavonoid Compounds" (T. A. Geissman, ed.), Pergamon, New York.

Seshadri, T. R. (1962). *In* "The Chemistry of Flavonoid Compounds" (T. A. Geissman, ed.), Pergamon Press, New York.

Sondheimer, E., and Kertesz, Z. I. (1948). *J. Amer. chem. Soc.* **70**, 3478.

Spaeth, E. C., and Rosenblatt, D. H. (1950). *Anal. Chem.* **22**, 1321.

Strain, H. (1942). "Chromatographic Adsorption Analysis," Interscience, New York.

Swain, T. (1953). *Biochem. J.* **53**, 200.

Swain, T. (1962). *In* "The Chemistry of Flavonoid Compounds" (T. A. Geissman, ed.), Pergamon, New York.

Swain, T., and Goldstein, J. L. (1964). *In* "Methods in Phenolic Chemistry" (J. B. Pridham, ed.), Pergamon, Oxford.

Swain, T., and Hillis, W. E. (1959). *J. Sci. Fd Agric.* **10**, 54.

Venkataraman, K. (1962). *In* "The Chemistry of Flavonoid Compounds" (T. A. Geissman, ed.), Pergamon, New York.

Wilson, C. W. (1939). *J. Amer. chem. Soc.* **61**, 2303.

AUTHOR INDEX

Numbers in italics refer to the pages on which references are listed at the end of each chapter.

A

Aasmundrud, O., 4, 20, *26*, 480, *486*
Abe, Y., 249, 250, 259, 272, 273, *277*
Acheson, R. M., 249, 256, *276*
Adams, J., 330, *331*
Agranoff, B. W., 147, 150, 151, *169*, *171*
Ahmad, R., 76, *122*
Ahrens, K., 398, *400*
Ahrue, I., 56, *74*
Ainley, A. D., 230, *242*, 249, *276*
Airth, R. L., 17, *26*, 177, 180, *195*, 472, *486*
Akermark, B., 344, *352*
Akhtar, M., 92, 114, *122*
Akulovich, N. K., 54, 55, 61, *71*
Albert, A., 223, 227, *242*
Albertson, P. Å, 191, *195*
Albrecht, A. G., 240, *243*
Alden, R. A., 314, *332*
Aldrich, R. A., 41, 46, *73*
Alexander, G. J., 335, *353*
Algar, J., 297, *305*
Allan, J., 234, 235, *242*
Allard, H. A., 406, *434*
Allen, M. B., 4, 17, *26*, 27, 57, 60, 62, *70*, 130, 132, 133, 134, 135, 136, *140*, *141*, 367, 376, *379*, 398, *400*, 474, 487
Allen, R. J. L., 451, *457*
Allport, D. C., 318, *330*
Alston, R. E., 250, *276*, 290, *305*
Altman, K. I., 50, 61, 63, *71*
Amesz, J., 179, *195*, 373, *379*
Analytical Methods Committee, 512, *531*
Anchel, M., 321, *331*
Anderson, A. F. H., 17, *26*, 478, 479, *485*
Anderson, D. G., 105, *122*, 148, 151, 152, 154, *169*
Anderson, I. C., 396, *401*
Anderson, J. M., 61, *70*, 160, *169*, 475, 478, 480, *485*

Anderson, R. F., 140, *140*, *141*, 395, *402*
Angapindu, A., 475, 479, 480, *485*
A.O.A.C., 496, *531*
Appleman, D., 57, *71*
ApSimon, J. W., 327, *330*
Archer, B. L., 164, *169*
Archibald, J. L., 23, 24, *26*
Ardao, C., 59, *70*, 444, *455*, 484, *485*
Arigoni, D., 147, *170*
Arnold, M., 140, *140*, *141*
Arnold, W., 468, *487*
Arnon, D. I., 367, 368, 371, *379*, *380*, 465, *485*
Aronoff, S., 7, *26*, 445, *455*, 463, 464, 470, 484, *486*, *488*
Asen, S., 263, *276*, 304, *305*
Aubert, C. C., 348, *353*
Ayer, W. A., 6, *28*

B

Bader, F., 110, *125*
Bader, G., 187, *196*
Bailey, G. F., 128, 137, *140*, *141*, 450, *455*, 471, *488*
Baker, W., 231, 234, *242*, 294, *305*
Bamji, M. S., 160, *169*
Banbury, G. H., 386, 387, 388, *400*
Bandurski, R. S., 166, 167, *169*
Barbatschi, F., 330, *331*
Barber, G. A., 293, *305*
Barber, M. S., 80, 87, 92, 93, 95, 96, 98, 114, 118, 120, *122*
Barker, J., 451, *457*
Barnard, D., 164, *169*
Barnett, H. L., 140, *140*, 149, *171*, 395, *400*
Barton, D. H. R., 301, *305*, 337, 339, *352*
Barton, G. M., 538, *548*
Baruah, P. B., 215, *242*, 453, *455*
Basz, W., 297, 299, *305*, *306*
Bataille, J., 149, *169*
Bates, R. B., 118, *122*

551

18*

Y

Z

SUBJECT INDEX

A

Absorption changes, light induced, in photosynthesis, 371

Absorption spectra of
bile pigments, 181
carotenoids, 87, 516
Chlorobium chlorophylls, 22
chlorophylls, 12
flavonoids, 218, 541
phycocyanins, 178
phycoerythrins, 189
phytochrome, 207

Acetyl coenzyme A, conversion into carotenoids, 145

Actinocin, 349

Action spectra, 360, 362

Adenosine triphosphate (ATP) formation, 367

Adsorption affinities of carotenoids, 504, 507

Afzelin, 216

Aglycones, 230, 236
identification of, 539

Algae, distribution of carotenoids in, 130
distribution of phycobilins in, 178
evolution of, 135
extraction of carotenoids from, 496
extraplastidic carotenoids of, 134
phototaxis of, 389

Alkannin, 329

Allomerization of chlorophylls, 8

Allylic alcohols, dehydration of, 102

Aluminium, effect on flower colour, 226

δ-Amino levulinic acid, 37

Anhydrorhodovibrin, 161, 492

Antheraxanthin, 131, 492

Anthocyanidins, 222

Anthocyanins, 221
absorption spectra of, 541
chelation of, 262
chemical reactions of, 227
chemical synthesis of, 226
effect of phytochrome on, 416
and flower colour, 225

Anthocyanins—*contd.*
formation of, 288
glycosides of, 259
hydroxylation and colour of, 251
identification of, 538
in leaves, 271
methylation of, 256
pH effects, 263
in senescence and storage, 452

Anthraquinones, 310

Antirrhinin, 541

Aphanicin, 492

Aphanin, 492

Apigenidin, 221

Apigenin, 213, 219, 255

Arabinose, 224

Aromatic carotenoids, 80

Artocarpin, 231

3-Arylcoumarins, 299

Astacin, 492, 499

Astaxanthin, 492, 499

Astragalin, 232

Atrovenetin, 339

Aureusidin, 214, 240, 269, 541

Aurones, absorption spectra of, 541
biosynthesis of, 291
chemistry of, 240
identification of, 538
and flower colour, 239, 267
structure of, 239

Auroxanthin, 492

Autoxidation of keto-carotenoids, 110

Averufin, 314

Autumn colours in leaves, 273, 448

Azafrin, 81, 492

B

Bacteriochlorophyll, biosynthesis of, 63
determination of, 468

Bacteriochlorophyll *a*, absorption spectrum of, 20
properties of, 19
structure of, 19

Bacteriochlorophyll *b*, properties of, 20

573

D

E

End-group detection in carotenoids by
  biochemical methods, 98
  chemical methods, 96
  NMR, 92
Enhancement effect in photosynthesis,
  361
Epanorin, 344
Epoxides, formation and rearrange-
  ment of, 107
  identification of, 528
  in senescence, 449
Eriodictoyl, 213
Eschscholtzxanthin, 102, 493
Esterification of xanthophylls, 448
Etiolation, control of, 424
Euglenanone, *see* Canthaxanthin
Euglenophyta, distribution of caro-
  tenoids in, 134
Euxanthic acid, 342
Excelsin, 237
Extraction of
  carotenoids, 494
  chlorophylls, 463
  flavonoids, 535

F

Fall colours of leaves, 273, 448
Farnesol, 7
Ferredoxin, role in photosynthesis, 378
Fisetin, 541
Flagellates, phototaxis of, 389
Flavanones, configuration of, 287
  formation of, 286
  rearrangement of, 298
Flavasperone, 340
Flaviolin, 317
Flavochrome, 493
Flavones, 230
  aglycones of, 230
  chemical reactions of, 235
    and flower colour, 233
  chemical synthesis of, 234
  glycosides of, 232
Flavonoids, 211
  absorption spectra of, 218, 541
  analysis of, 533
  biosynthesis of, 279
  changes in storage and senescence,
    452
  classification of, 212
  column chromatography of, 536

Flavonoids—*contd.*
  constitution of, 217
  determination of, 545
  distribution of, 249
  extraction of, 535
    and flower colour, 450
  glycosidic forms of, 223
  identification of, 538
  influence of light on formation of, 303
  isolation of, 536
  miscellaneous types of, 241
  paper chromatography of, 537
  thin layer chromatography of, 538
Flavonols, 230
  absorption spectra of, 541
  aglycones of, 230
  biosynthesis of, 288
  chemical reactions of, 235
  chemical synthesis of, 234
    and flower colour, 233
  glycosides of, 232
  identification of, 541
Flavoskyrin, 311
Flavoxanthin, 131, 493
Flavyllium anhydrobases, 228
Flowers, distribution of carotenoids in,
  137
  extraction of carotenoids from, 496
Flower colour, 225
  changes in, 265
  contribution of
    aurones, 239, 267
    carotenoids, 251, 269
    chalkones, 238, 267
    flavones and flavonols, 233, 267
    flavonoids, 250
  influence of viruses, 266
Flowering, action spectra of, 413, 414
  effect of phytochrome, 412
Fluorescence in photosynthesis studies,
  377
Fluorimetry in chlorophyll determination, 472
Foliachrome, 493
Foliaxanthin, 493
Fonsecin, 340
Formononetin, 295
Fruits, anthocyanins of, 273
  colour of, 273, 448
  distribution of carotenoids in, 136
  extraction of carotenoids from, 496
  storage of, 452

Date Due